Reference Electrodes

Theory and Practice

Reference Electrodes
Theory and Practice

Edited by
DAVID J. G. IVES
Birkbeck College, London

GEORGE J. JANZ
Rensselaer Polytechnic Institute
Troy, New York

1961

ACADEMIC **P**RESS • *New York and London*

ACADEMIC PRESS INC.
111 FIFTH AVENUE
NEW YORK 3, N. Y.

United Kingdom Edition
Published by
ACADEMIC PRESS INC. (LONDON) LTD.
17 OLD QUEEN STREET, LONDON, S. W. 1

Library of Congress Catalog Card Number: 60-16910

PRINTED IN THE UNITED STATES OF AMERICA

Contributors

ROGER G. BATES, *National Bureau of Standards, Washington, D. C.*

DONALD B. CATER, *University of Cambridge, Cambridge, England*

GRAHAM J. HILLS, *Imperial College, London, England*

DAVID J. G. IVES, *Birkbeck College, London, England*

GEORGE J. JANZ, *Rensselaer Polytechnic Institute, Troy, New York*

RICHARD W. LAITY, *Princeton University, Princeton, New Jersey*

IAN A. SILVER, *University of Cambridge, Cambridge, England*

FRANK R. SMITH, *Mullard Research Laboratories, Salfords, Redhill, Surrey, England*

Preface

While there are many excellent texts principally concerned with the exposition of electrochemical theory, there are none, as far as the authors are aware, which devote attention to experimental aspects of the subject beyond the undergraduate student level. The authors have themselves felt the need from time to time of a book which would meet this deficiency, including between the same covers critical and reasonably exhaustive accounts, with full bibliographies, of the experimental methods by which the most reliable reference electrodes may be set up. Having applied themselves to the task of meeting this need, the authors very soon realized the necessity of including an adequate theoretical treatment so as to maintain a functional balance throughout between theory and experiment. The reason for this is very clear in retrospect; it is that all reference electrodes must, for full understanding, be examined from *both* mechanistic and thermodynamic viewpoints. They must, in the limit, be regarded as working electrodes at which balanced processes maintain a dynamic equilibrium which the act of use in measurement must not significantly disturb. In nearly every case, these processes take place by special mechanisms which are themselves of great intrinsic interest and it is only by a study of these processes that progress in developing electrodes for specialized use in research and industry can conceivably be achieved.

The result is a much larger work than was originally envisaged, written at a level which it is hoped will commend the book both to honors graduate students and to research workers in specialized fields. It has been a deliberate policy to make no separation, except that which is indicated in the tables of contents, between theory and experiment, and it is hoped that the reader, understanding the reasons for this, will be patient when he finds it necessary to read a whole chapter or more to obtain the information he requires.

The definition of "reference electrode" is conceived to be largely self-explanatory, but is nevertheless elucidated in some detail in the first chapter, which provides the necessary *general* background in relation to basic theory, conventions, and applications of all the electrodes which are discussed. The second chapter deals with the hydrogen electrode, the most important and satisfactory of all reference electrodes. It includes the first attempt at a comprehensive account of its mechanism of operation, as well as full details of all the useful forms of it that have been devised and used in practice. Chapters 3 and 4 are principally concerned with electrodes reversible to halide ions, since these probably come second in order of importance of application to thermodynamic tasks. In Chapter 5 a return is made to pH-sensitive electrodes; it deals with the glass electrode which is now the most versatile and widely used electrode in this class. Chapter 6 provides perhaps the first comprehensive discussion of the application of organic redox systems to electrodes suitable for pH determination; in practice this amounts to a full discussion of the quinhydrone electrode and its congeners and it is possible that these systems have not of recent years been as fully exploited as could be desired.

In Chapter 7, in addition to a full treatment of metal–metal oxide electrodes, attention is drawn to the increasing and widespread importance of electrodes at which oxygen or its derivatives is electromotively active. Sulfide-reversible electrodes are also included in this chapter.

Sulfate ion–reversible electrodes seemed to require a section on their own, which is given in Chapter 8. The further chapters are devoted to specialized fields in which chemical research employing reversible electrodes is at present progressing rapidly. Chapter 9 deals with nonaqueous electrode systems and Chapter 10 with membrane electrodes. It very often happens that pure physical chemists remain unaware of the exploits of their colleagues in allied fields of enquiry, and it may be salutary for many to read of the developments of technique in biochemical and medical fields which are described in Chapter 11. Finally, Chapter 12 is concerned with electrodes in fused salt systems, a field in which activity is proliferating at the present time, and which introduces new problems and new concepts foreign to the older branches of the physical chemistry of solutions. It is in this field that the newer methods of irreversible thermodynamics are particularly fruitful, and it is therefore appropriate that they should be elucidated in this particular chapter with the proviso that their field of application is wider, and that they might well have found their place in more sophisticated writing in other chapters of the book.

All of the authors have, at one time or another, themselves been faced with experimental difficulties and problems, and it is hoped that their experiences, incorporated in this book, will be of use to others. They will be grateful for corrections of errors or for further useful information which readers may feel moved to supply and they wish to acknowledge the constructive suggestions and criticisms which have already been made by their colleagues.

December 1960

DAVID J. G. IVES
GEORGE J. JANZ

Contents

Chapter One

General and Theoretical Introduction

D. J. G. Ives and G. J. Janz

I. Preamble

The aim of the present work is to perform a useful service which existing electrochemical texts do not offer. It is intended to meet a demand for a critical and selective compilation of information about the reference electrodes which are widely used in many branches of pure and applied electrochemistry.

The experimenter who desires for the first time to set up an electrode system for his own purposes normally finds that books and monographs devote inadequate attention to experimental methods. Turning to the original literature, he often finds that his attention is directed to successively earlier references, until the information he ultimately tracks down is likely, he feels, to be of historical rather than of practical interest. Persevering, he may eventually accumulate a mass of diverse, or even contradictory, directions, so that he must either make an arbitrary choice of recipes, or arrive at his own by experimental trial and error. This troublesome procedure is in the interests of good experimentation and is often the way in which advances in technique are made. Even if it were feasible, it would be pretentious and undesirable to attempt to arbitrate in each case

1

upon the "best" procedure and method. Indeed, what may be best in one set of circumstances may not be so in another. All that can be done is to ease the task of the experimenter by giving a reasonably exhaustive account of what has been done before, and by making such points of comparison and criticism as may be helpful.

Attention is confined to electrodes which are commonly used as a means to an end in physicochemical problems, and some emphasis has been placed upon applications in which accuracy of measurement is of prime importance. It is, of course, pointless and misguided to strive after accuracy for its own sake, beyond sensible limits of significance in relation to the problem in hand. But in some connections, existing levels of accuracy are still inadequate and great progress could be made if only they could be improved upon. Thus, the measurement of the electromotive force (emf) of a reversible galvanic cell is the most accurate way of measuring the Gibbs free energy change of a reaction. But to determine the entropy and enthalpy changes for the same reaction, the temperature coefficient of the emf of the cell is needed in order to apply the Gibbs-Helmholtz equation; this calls for an accuracy of measurement higher by an order of magnitude. If, in turn, it is desired to evaluate the heat capacity change accompanying the reaction, the temperature coefficient of the enthalpy change is needed so that the Kirchhoff relation may be applied. This requires another considerable increment of accuracy. If, finally, interest attaches to the way in which the heat capacity change varies as a function of temperature (which is indeed the case), the demand for accuracy becomes exorbitant. Each partial differentiation with respect to temperature involves the chopping away of one or more significant figures, and this may well involve the loss of all significance on the way. This, unappreciated, can have unfortunate consequences.

A corollary to the stated objective of this work, to aid the experimenter, is that it should provide a sufficient theoretical background to enable him to deal effectively with the problems he may meet, and to promote clarity of definition and thought. A minor application of this policy may be made in considering the title of the book.

At a reversible electrode, a dynamic equilibrium is established between different material phases, one of which is a metal and another an electrolytic solution. Gaseous or solid nonmetallic phases may also be involved. The equilibrium will be a function of the chemical potentials, or partial molar Gibbs free energies, of all the material components which are concerned. But electrons are essential participants so that, aside from certain difficulties shortly to be discussed, the electrical potential difference between the metallic and electrolytic phases is an intensity factor which is uniquely determined by the equilibrium. Then, if for a given electrode in equilibrium all but one of the components are in standard states, the chemical potential of the component which is not in a standard state may be obtained by *reference* to the measured potential difference. It is in this particular sense that the word "reference" is used in the title.

II. The Concept of Electrode Potential

There is a fundamental difficulty in arriving at an unambiguous definition of electrode potential. Setting aside the minor question of sign conventions, this quantity involves the concept of the electrical potential difference between the metal of the electrode and the solution with which it is in equilibrium. These two phases are totally dissimilar. In classical electrostatics, all that is needed to determine the potential at a given point is to measure the work required to bring a unit test charge from infinity to that point. Similarly, a potential difference may be determined from the difference between two such work terms. But what, in practice, is to be used as a test charge? A metal consists of a close-packed ionic lattice which provides macro-orbitals for the accommodation of electrons in quantized energy bands, in conformity with the Pauli principle. Energy equal to the work function, ϕ, is liberated when a free electron is dropped into the highest occupied energy level. An electron dropped into an aqueous solution would certainly perform a reduction, for it is the most powerful of reducing agents. Similar considerations arise for any real charged particle when it is examined for suitability as a test charge. None of them has the property of charge alone; all of them are atomic constituents, foreign bodies, or chemical reagents. There is no test charge which can be used for the desired operation, for whenever a real charged particle is brought close to matter of any kind, powerful noncoulombic forces come into play.

The problem must therefore be approached in terms of the behavior of real charged particles: ions and electrons. For substances composed of uncharged atoms or molecules, the concept of chemical potential is of immense value because it comprehends all the factors which determine their behavior. Thus, it is a universal criterion of equilibrium within a system that the chemical potential, μ_i, of any component i shall, like pressure and temperature, have a uniform value in all parts of the system. The question arises, how can this function be adapted to deal with the electrochemical problem in hand? In the first place, it must be noted that chemical potential is essentially a thermodynamic function with the dimensions of energy per mole; it does not deal with individual atoms or molecules. If it turns out to be permissible to discuss the "chemical potential of sodium ions," for example, this must always mean a thermodynamic function relating to a particular macroscopic system which contains these ions, and must retain the dimensions of energy per mole. In the second place, it is necessary to enquire whether the definition of chemical potential

$$\mu_i = (\partial G/\partial n_i)_{T,P,n_j} \tag{1}$$

allows it to be applied to ions at all. This expression can be translated as the proportional increase in free energy of a system resulting from the addition to it of dn_i mole of component i, the number of moles of all other components, n_j, and the temperature and pressure being kept constant. It is impossible to add a single kind of ion to any system, for in natural systems no significant departure from electroneutrality is possible. Each kind of ion is partnered by its oppositely charged counterparts, so that if ions are to be added to a system, at least two kinds of ions must be added simultaneously. This does not, however, invalidate the definition because dG is a perfect differential, so that

$$\begin{aligned} dG &= (\partial G/\partial n_i)_{T,P,n_j} \cdot dn_i + (\partial G/\partial n_j)_{T,P,n_i} \cdot dn_j \\ &= \mu_i dn_i + \mu_j dn_j \end{aligned} \tag{2}$$

but it does mean that the chemical potential of a single kind of ion can never be separately determined. This is not to say that these quantities have no significance; thus the chemical potential of sodium chloride in aqueous solution is unambiguously the sum of the chemical potentials of the sodium ions and the chloride ions. Another implication is that ions cannot be regarded as *components*. "Component" is a word which, strictly, should be reserved for use, in the sense of the Gibbs phase rule, as an independent variable of composition, and it has been seen that this description cannot apply to ions. Nevertheless, the expression "charged component" is convenient, and its use cannot be regarded as very harmful provided that its status is not misunderstood.

With these restrictions in mind, it may next be considered that the behavior of charged particles must be largely, but not wholly, dependent upon the charges which they carry. Charge is the capacity factor of electrical energy and, according to the potential of the region in which the charged particles are situated, it must make a contribution to their total energy. This will have to be included in the function, akin to chemical potential, which is designed to express, in an overriding and comprehensive way, the behavior of charged particles.

This function is called the *electrochemical potential* and is defined by the equation

$$\bar{\mu}_i{}^\alpha = \mu_i{}^\alpha + z_i F \psi^\alpha \tag{3}$$

where $\bar{\mu}_i{}^\alpha$ is the electrochemical potential of the charged component i in phase α, $\mu_i{}^\alpha$ is its chemical potential in the same phase, $z_i F$ is its charge per mole with appropriate sign, F is the value of the faraday and ψ^α is the *internal* or *inner electrical potential* of the phase α. None of the three terms in this equation is separately determinable. In particular, the potential ψ^α is not determinable, and neither is the difference between the internal electrical potentials of dissimilar phases which is called the *Galvani potential difference*.

It is obvious that electrode potential, as defined above, is to be identified with the Galvani potential difference between the metallic phase of the electrode and the solution phase with which it is in contact. It is therefore not determinable. No single electrode potential, defined in this fundamental way, can ever be known. The quantities with this name which are recorded to four or five significant figures in the literature are measured on an arbitrary scale which will shortly be discussed. They must not be regarded as physically significant for any single electrode.

The importance of Eq. (3) depends upon its universal application to all charged species, including electrons, and upon the fact that the internal potential of a phase, ψ^α, can be broken down into two distinguishable contributions, one of which *is* determinable. This is done by considering the potential just *outside* the phase, at a distance, say, of 10^{-3} cm, or in a small cavity within the phase. In this way the effects of all but long-range coulombic forces are eliminated and have no effect upon any test charge used to determine the potential. The potential so determined is called the *Volta potential, outer electric potential,* or *contact potential, V^α.*

The other contribution is called the *surface potential, χ^α.* It is a function of the shorter range *electrical* forces which act between, for example, an ion and a dipole, a quadrupole, an octupole, an induced dipole, and the like. It is not determinable. Eq. (3) may therefore be rewritten

$$\bar{\mu}_i{}^\alpha = \mu_i{}^\alpha + z_i F(V^\alpha + \chi^\alpha) \tag{4}$$

Consideration must now be given to the effects of these complications and uncertainties upon ordinary electrochemical measurements. Happily, the effects are zero, because the only measurements which are normally attempted are those of the electrical potential difference between *two pieces of the same metal*. It does not matter in the least what this metal is, but usually it is copper, for copper wires are used to connect the experimental cell with the potentiometer or other instrument used to measure potential difference. These two copper wires, denoted Cu and Cu', are identical in chemical composition and the terms $\mu_{e^-}^{Cu}$ and $\mu_{e^-}^{Cu'}$ are identical, and so are χ^{Cu} and $\chi^{Cu'}$, so that

$$\bar{\mu}_{e^-}^{Cu} - \bar{\mu}_{e^-}^{Cu'} = F(\psi^{Cu'} - \psi^{Cu}) = F(V^{Cu'} - V^{Cu}) = FE \tag{5}$$

where E can be identified with the emf of the cell. The very great simplification that arises from the use of two pieces of copper wire was pointed out by Gibbs in 1899 (1).

There are, however, further difficulties to be clarified. Normally, a galvanic cell contains at least two different metallic phases, a solution phase and possibly solid, nonmetallic phases as well, all co-operating in a chain of processes involving transfers of ions or electrons. Each of these phases will have its own internal electrical potential, and across each interface there will be a Galvani potential difference. All of these are indeterminable, and it seems as if there is a most formidable problem which will defy solution in simple terms; certainly in the past it has been a stumbling block.

There is, in fact, no problem at all, and this is best demonstrated by means of a galvanic cell which derives the electrical energy which it can provide from a chemical reaction. There is no special reason for choosing any particular cell for the purpose; the one that has been chosen is intrinsically important and valuable as an example for other purposes. The cell is the hydrogen–silver chloride cell, which is usually represented as

$$\text{H}_2 \ (P \text{ atm}), \ \overset{-}{\text{Pt}} \ \Big| \ \text{aqueous HCl}(m) \ \Big| \ \text{AgCl} \ \Big| \ \overset{+}{\text{Ag}} \qquad (A)$$

and, except under certain extreme conditions, it has the polarity which is indicated. This is consistent with the fact that the natural cell reaction, attended by a loss of Gibbs free energy, is

$$\tfrac{1}{2}\text{H}_2 \ (P \text{ atm}) + \text{AgCl}(s) = \text{Ag}(s) + \text{HCl (aq, } m)$$

But this cell, and all others, should really be represented as

$$\overset{-}{\text{Cu}} \ \Big| \ \text{Pt} \ \Big| \ \begin{matrix} \text{H}_2 \ (P \text{ atm}) \\ \text{aqueous HCl}(m) \end{matrix} \ \Big| \ \text{AgCl} \ \Big| \ \text{Ag} \ \Big| \ \overset{+}{\text{Cu}'} \qquad (B)$$

and in terms of this the detailed operation of the cell may be followed through. On open circuit, the system is in equilibrium and no net reaction occurs. The reaction to be carried out must be done *reversibly*, that is, with no disturbance whatever of the equilibrium conditions. In practice, this means that it must occur infinitely slowly, or to but an infinitesimal extent. Under these conditions, the maximum electrical work is obtained and it must be equal to the loss in Gibbs free energy accompanying the reaction which provides it. The emf of the cell is the intensity factor of the maximum electrical work, and the capacity factor is nF coulombs, where n is the number of faradays which are transferred when the reaction proceeds to the extent which defines the magnitude of the Gibbs free energy loss, $-\Delta G$. It follows that

$$nFE = -\Delta G \qquad (6)$$

so that the problem is solved by overriding thermodynamic considerations and there is really no need to go any further. It is, however, desirable to study the mechanism of the cell reaction and to obtain an alternative picture of how this inflexible relationship arises.

The cell on open circuit is an equilibrium system and will therefore satisfy the criterion for equilibrium that $dG = 0$ for any infinitesimal test process conducted at constant temperature and pressure. This will be the case if the cell reaction proceeds to an infinitesimal extent, with the consumption of $\frac{1}{2}dn$ mole of hydrogen and the transfer of dn faraday of electricity from the copper wire Cu' to the copper wire Cu. Then, proportionally, per faraday, the following reversible transfers will take place.

(1) At the platinum–solution interface of the hydrogen electrode,

$$\frac{1}{2}H_2 \ (P \text{ atm}) \to H^+ \text{ (soln)} + e^- \text{(Pt)}$$

(2) At the silver–solution interface of the silver–silver chloride electrode,

$$Ag^+ \text{ (soln)} + e^-(Ag) \to Ag$$

At this electrode, however, solid silver chloride is present and the solubility equilibrium is preserved by a secondary reaction

$$AgCl(s) \to Ag^+ \text{ (soln)} + Cl^- \text{ (soln)}$$

so that the ionic product is kept equal to the activity solubility product, i.e.,

$$a_{Ag^+} \cdot a_{Cl^-} = K_s$$

This is the general mode of operation of metal – sparingly soluble metal salt electrodes, or "electrodes of the second kind." But this reaction may be split into two parts, which are

(3) $\qquad Ag^+(AgCl) \to Ag^+ \text{ (soln)}$

(4) $\qquad Cl^-(AgCl) \to Cl^- \text{ (soln)}$

The reaction is completed by essential electron transfers to and from the copper wires,

(5) $\qquad e^-(Pt) \to e^-(Cu)$

(6) $\qquad e^-(Cu') \to e^-(Ag).$

The changes in electrochemical potential for charged components, or of chemical potential for uncharged components, may be set out and added up, as follows:

(1) $\quad \bar{\mu}_{H^+}^{soln} + \boxed{\bar{\mu}_{e^-}^{Pt}} - \frac{1}{2}\mu_{H_2}$

(2) $\quad \mu^{Ag} - \boxed{\bar{\mu}_{Ag^+}^{soln}} - \boxed{\bar{\mu}_{e^-}^{Ag}}$

(3) $\quad \boxed{\bar{\mu}_{Ag^+}^{soln}} - \bar{\mu}_{Ag^+}^{AgCl}$

$$(4) \qquad \bar{\mu}_{Cl^-}^{soln} - \bar{\mu}_{Cl^-}^{AgCl}$$

$$(5) \qquad \bar{\mu}_{e^-}^{Cu} - \boxed{\bar{\mu}_{e^-}^{Pt}}$$

$$(6) \qquad \boxed{\bar{\mu}_{e^-}^{Ag}} - \bar{\mu}_{e^-}^{Cu'}$$

The indicated cancellations (enclosed in the boxes) facilitate the addition, the result of which is

$$\bar{\mu}_{H^+}^{soln} + \bar{\mu}_{Cl^-}^{soln} + \mu_{Ag} - \tfrac{1}{2}\mu_{H_2} - \bar{\mu}_{Ag^+}^{AgCl} - \bar{\mu}_{Cl^-}^{AgCl}$$
$$+ \bar{\mu}_{e^-}^{Cu} - \bar{\mu}_{e^-}^{Cu'} \tag{7}$$

and this can be equated to zero, for it includes both the free energy loss of the chemical reaction in the cell and the electrical energy which it has provided. These are clearly identifiable with the first and second rows of the sum, as set out above. The electrical energy expressed in this way is the potential energy which has been gained by raising one faraday of electrons up the potential jump which exists between Cu and Cu'. It could be continuously converted into electrical (or other) work by being passed reversibly round an external circuit and, in principle, a potentiometer is a device for doing this.

All the electrochemical potential terms in expression (7) are now split up into the chemical and electrical terms of the kind represented in Eq. (3). Thus, since z_i is ± 1,

$$\bar{\mu}_{H^+}^{soln} = \mu_{H^+}^{soln} + F\psi^{soln} \qquad\qquad \bar{\mu}_{Cl^-}^{soln} = \mu_{Cl^-}^{soln} - F\psi^{soln}$$

$$\bar{\mu}_{Ag^+}^{AgCl} = \mu_{Ag^+}^{AgCl} + F\psi^{AgCl} \qquad\qquad \bar{\mu}_{Cl^-}^{AgCl} = \mu_{Cl^-}^{AgCl} - F\psi^{AgCl}$$

$$\bar{\mu}_{e^-}^{Cu} = \mu_{e^-}^{Cu} - F\psi^{Cu} \qquad\qquad \bar{\mu}_{e^-}^{Cu'} = \mu_{e^-}^{Cu'} - F\psi^{Cu'}$$

On substituting in expression (7) and equating to zero,

$$\mu_{H^+}^{soln} + \boxed{F\psi^{soln}} + \mu_{Cl^-}^{soln} - \boxed{F\psi^{soln}} + \mu_{Ag} - \tfrac{1}{2}\mu_{H_2}$$
$$- \mu_{Ag^+}^{AgCl} - \boxed{F\psi^{AgCl}} - \mu_{Cl^-}^{AgCl} + \boxed{F\psi^{AgCl}} + \mu_{e^-}^{Cu} - F\psi^{Cu}$$
$$- \mu_{e^-}^{Cu'} + F\psi^{Cu'} = 0$$

It is seen at once that all the indeterminable internal electrical potentials of the solution and solid silver chloride phases cancel out. Further, since

$$\mu_{e^-}^{Cu} = \mu_{e^-}^{Cu'}$$

and

$$\mu_{Ag^+}^{AgCl} + \mu_{Cl^-}^{AgCl} = \mu_{AgCl}$$

$$\mu_{H^+}^{soln} + \mu_{Cl^-}^{soln} + \mu_{Ag} - \tfrac{1}{2}\mu_{H_2} - \mu_{AgCl} + F(\psi^{Cu'} - \psi^{Cu}) = 0 \tag{8}$$

or

$$\Delta G_{cell\ reaction} = -FE$$

which is in agreement with Eq. (6), originally obtained by a less laborious argument.

Nevertheless, this demonstration, the like of which could be made for any reversible cell, is valuable because it disposes of the old question: "Where, in a galvanic cell, does the emf really arise?" It also gives a mandate for using the chemical potentials of ions and for treating cell reactions by classical thermodynamic methods. This can now be done for the hydrogen–silver chloride cell, represented for the future by (A) and not by (B).

This cell is typical of a class of cells said to be "without liquid junction," because they contain, ostensibly, a single, homogeneous electrolyte. Closer inspection shows this to be untrue. Thus, in cell (A), the solution around the hydrogen electrode must be saturated with dissolved hydrogen ($m = 0.000761$ mole kg^{-1} at 25°C and 1 atm total pressure), but must contain no silver chloride. On the other hand, the solution adjacent to the silver–silver chloride electrode must be saturated with silver chloride ($m = 0.0000133$ mole kg^{-1} at 25°C) and may or may not contain hydrogen. The cell must therefore somewhere contain a junction between solutions which are not identical in composition. This is almost always the case and there are few, if any, cells strictly without liquid junction. There is usually, however, a fairly definite distinction between the cells classed as being with or without liquid junctions in terms of the main ionic constituents of the electrolytes concerned, but it is well to remember that this distinction may become tenuous when very dilute solutions are used.

If all the substances participating in the reversible operation of cell (A) at a particular temperature are in their standard states, the free energy change of the cell reaction will have its standard value, ΔG°, and the emf of the cell will be the standard emf, E°, appropriate to the temperature concerned. Unlike the solid phases silver and silver chloride, the state of hydrogen gas and of hydrochloric acid in solution can vary widely, so that it is necessary to derive a general expression for the emf of the cell which takes this into account.

The fundamental definition of the activity of a component i is contained in the relationship

$$\mu_i = \mu_i{}^\circ + RT \ln (a_i/a_i{}^\circ) \tag{9}$$

where R is the gas constant per mole, T is the absolute temperature, a_i is the activity of the component i in the state in which its chemical potential is μ_i and $a_i{}^\circ$ is its activity in the standard state in which its chemical potential has the standard value $\mu_i{}^\circ$. The value of $a_i{}^\circ$ is unity, but it should, strictly, be retained in Eq. (9) to avoid difficulties with dimensions. For solutes, the standard state is normally that of the ideal unimolal solution.

For hydrogen gas, the chemical potential varies as a function of pressure according to

$$\mu_{H_2} = \mu_{H_2}^\circ + RT \ln (P_{H_2}/P_{H_2}^\circ) \tag{10}$$

where $P_{H_2}^\circ$ is the standard pressure of 1 atm. The very small departure of hydrogen from ideal gas behavior can at present be ignored.

The free energy change for the cell reaction can be extracted from Eq. (8). With minor changes of notation it is

$$\Delta G = \mu_{H^+} + \mu_{Cl^-} + \mu_{Ag}^\circ - \tfrac{1}{2}\mu_{H_2} - \mu_{AgCl}^\circ \tag{11}$$

and this may be expanded in terms of Eq. (9) and (10) to give

$$\Delta G = \mu_{H^+}^\circ + RT \ln a_{H^+} + \mu_{Cl^-}^\circ + RT \ln a_{Cl^-} + \mu_{Ag}^\circ$$
$$ - \tfrac{1}{2}\mu_{H_2}^\circ - \tfrac{1}{2}RT \ln P_{H_2} - \mu_{AgCl}^\circ$$

so that

$$\Delta G = \Delta G^\circ + RT \ln a_{H^+} + RT \ln a_{Cl^-} - \tfrac{1}{2}RT \ln P_{H_2} \tag{12}$$

and since in this case $FE = -\Delta G$ and $FE^\circ = -\Delta G^\circ$,

$$E = E^\circ - \frac{RT}{F} \ln a_{H^+} - \frac{RT}{F} \ln a_{Cl^-} + \frac{RT}{2F} \ln P_{H_2} \tag{13}$$

which is the desired general equation for the emf of cell (A).

The question of single electrode potentials may now be raised again. Fundamentally indeterminate as they are, they will have to be expressed on some arbitrarily invented scale. It may well be asked, why is it necessary to do this at all? Would it not be better to stick to the quantities which can be measured unambiguously, namely, the emf values for complete cells? The answer is that it undoubtedly would be better and that it should be done on every possible occasion. Nevertheless, in important fields of electrochemistry, and of its applications, some degree of compromise has to be made between thermodynamic rigor and utilitarian empiricism. It is undeniably convenient to have a list of electrode potentials. Apart from anything else, n electrode potentials, taken in pairs, will give the emf values for $n(n-1)$ cells, or information about the same number of oxidation-reduction reactions.

The step will therefore be taken of dividing the emf of cell (A) into two contributory electrode potentials; one due to the hydrogen electrode, varying as a function of a_{H^+} and P_{H_2} alone; the other due to the silver–silver chloride electrode, varying as a function of a_{Cl^-} alone. The difficulty is immediately encountered that, in any cell, the metal–solution interfaces of the two electrodes are opposed to each other. They are related somewhat like an object and its mirror image, thus:

$$\text{Metal} \mid \underset{E_1}{\text{Solution}} \mid \underset{E_2}{\text{Metal}}$$

Then the cell emf must be the difference between the electrode potentials E_1 and E_2, but there is no immediate reason for selecting either of the alternatives $E = E_1 - E_2$ or $E = E_2 - E_1$ in preference to the other. It is therefore not surprising that difficulties have arisen from the adoption of alternative conventions by different authorities. This matter is discussed in Section IV of this chapter; at present it need only be indicated that guidance is available from Eq. (6), namely,

$$nFE = -\Delta G \tag{6}$$

If the cell reaction is a spontaneous one, as it must be to give any electrical energy at all, ΔG is negative, and this makes the emf, E, positive.[1] In accordance with this, noting the *observed* polarity of the hydrogen–silver chloride cell, the division of the emf may be made:

$$E = \underbrace{E^\circ_{\text{Ag,AgCl,Cl}^-} - (RT/F) \ln a_{\text{Cl}^-}}_{\substack{\text{silver–silver chloride} \\ \text{electrode potential}}}$$

$$\underbrace{- E^\circ_{\text{H}_2,\text{H}^+} - (RT/F) \ln a_{\text{H}^+} + (RT/2F) \ln P_{\text{H}_2}}_{\substack{\text{hydrogen electrode} \\ \text{potential}}} \tag{14}$$

The convention is universally accepted that $E^\circ_{\text{H}_2,\text{H}^+}$, the standard potential of the hydrogen electrode, shall be taken as zero at all temperatures, thus setting up the arbitrary hydrogen scale of electrode potentials. From Eq. (14) it is seen that the potential of the nonstandard hydrogen electrode, is on this scale,

$$E_{\text{H}_2,\text{H}^+} = \frac{RT}{F} \ln \frac{a_{\text{H}^+}}{(P_{\text{H}_2})^{1/2}} \tag{15}$$

which can be put into the concise form

$$2\mu_{\text{H}^+} - \mu_{\text{H}_2} - 2EF = 0 \tag{16}$$

In this division of an emf into electrode potentials, a nonthermodynamic assumption has been covertly made. It is that it is possible to determine the activity of a single ionic species; this is not the case, unless more significance is attributed to the Debye-Hückel calculation than is strictly justifiable. All that can be determined is a mean ion activity

$$a_{\pm} = (a_+^{\nu_+} \cdot a_-^{\nu_-})^{1/\nu} \tag{17}$$

for an electrolytic solute which provides, on dissociation, ν_+ cations and ν_- anions "per molecule," where $\nu = \nu_+ + \nu_-$. This is related to determinable molalities by

$$a_{\pm} = \gamma_{\pm} \cdot m_{\pm} \tag{18}$$

[1] Variation in sign of the *number*, n, is excluded.

where all the terms take the same form as indicated in Eq. (17), and $\gamma_\pm$ is a mean molal ionic activity coefficient which tends to unity at infinite dilution. This activity coefficient is a function of the ionic interactions which are responsible for the nonideality of the solute. These naturally occur predominantly between ions of opposite sign of charge, and in very dilute solutions they are coulombic in nature and are calculable. In stronger solutions, specific ionic properties must enter, together with such solute–solvent interactions which can no longer be regarded as independent of concentration. It is thus clear that the task of interpreting activity coefficients, let alone their dependence upon temperature, involves complex physicochemical problems, except under near-ideal conditions. It is also obviously a matter of doubt whether any real significance can be attached to a single ion activity coefficient. It has nevertheless been unavoidable, in splitting an emf into electrode potentials to make some arbitrary assumption, such that $a_+ = a_- = a_\pm$.

To summarize, it is evident that no single electrode potential can be known, nor any thermodynamic property of a single ionic species, yet such quantities are widely used in electrochemical calculations. For this to be acceptable, appropriate safeguards should always be adopted. Thus, in discussing any single electrode in such nonthermodynamic terms, the relevant precaution is to pose the question, "Can this electrode be combined with another to give a reversible cell with an emf which is thermodynamically calculable?" Or, "Can this electrochemical potential, or ionic activity, be combined with another similar term to give a physically measurable quantity?"

The electrode potentials so generally employed in everyday electrochemistry are best regarded as the emf values of cells formed by combining each of the electrodes in turn with a standard hydrogen electrode, any liquid junction potential which arises being set at zero. Thus, for each electrode, the hypothetical cell is considered as

$$\text{H}_2,\ 1\ \text{atm}\ |\ \text{H}^+\ (\text{aq},\ a_{\text{H}^+} = 1)\ ||\ \text{M}^{n+}\ (\text{aq})\ |\ \text{M} \qquad \text{(C)}$$

where the double line is used to indicate perfect elimination of liquid junction potential. If theelectrode in question is in equilibrium with a hypothetical, ideal, unimolal solution of its own ions, its potential will have the standard value, $E^\circ_{\text{M, M}^{n+}}$.[2] It will be consistent with the convention to be adopted to take the sign of the electrode potential as identical with the polarity of the electrode, with respect to the hydrogen electrode, in the cell (C), above.

[2] The value of the standard electrode potential will vary according to the concentration scale that is used (see Chapter 4).

Special comment is needed upon the convention that the standard hydrogen electrode potential is to be taken as zero *at all temperatures,* for this goes far beyond the assumption that it is to be taken as zero at one temperature. A digression dealing with the general problem of standard states appears to be necessary to clarify the position.

In thermodynamics, the large bulk of recorded free energy data are expressed on a scale of standard free energies of formation, or standard chemical potentials, of compounds at 25°C and 1 atm pressure. This scale is established by setting the chemical potentials of the constituent elements under these conditions of temperature and pressure at zero. There is a similar scale for enthalpies of formation. In effect, the liberty is taken of ignoring the specific properties of individual elements, but, because it is of the essence of G and H that they are extensive properties, this is immaterial when the only requirement is to derive values for ΔG and ΔH, i.e., the *changes* in these properties which accompany isothermal reactions. For entropy, on the other hand, the third law and statistical mechanics provide an absolute scale upon which the standard entropies, at 25°C and 1 atm pressure, of elements and compounds alike are expressed. This difference of scales causes no difficulty when it is desired to apply the fundamental relation

$$\Delta G = \Delta H - T\Delta S \qquad (19)$$

to an isothermal reaction, for every Δ term is a *difference* between the value of an extensive property for products and that of the same property for reactants.

If, however, it is desired to study how the free energy of a reaction changes with temperature, then Eq. (19) must be expanded into its most general and significant form, which is

$$\Delta G = \Delta H_0 + \int_0^T \Delta C_P \cdot dT - T \int_0^T (\Delta C_P/T) \cdot dT - T\Delta S_0 \qquad (20)$$

where ΔH_0 and ΔS_0 are the energy and entropy changes which accompany the reaction at the absolute zero of temperature and ΔC_P is the total change of heat capacity brought about by the reaction.[3] For practical calculations, a less fundamental relation is used, based upon empirical expressions for variation of heat capacity with temperature, of the form

$$C_P = \alpha + \beta T + \gamma T^2 \ldots \qquad (21)$$

It is

$$\Delta G = \Delta H_0 - \Delta\alpha T \ln T - (\Delta\beta/2)T^2 - (\Delta\gamma/6) T^3 \ldots + JT \qquad (22)$$

where both ΔH_0 and J are integration constants to be evaluated from determined values of ΔH and ΔG at a single temperature. It is clear from

---

[3] Heats of phase transitions must, of course, be appropriately included in these integrations.

either of Eqs. (21) or (22) that it is no longer possible to ignore the specific properties of individual elements when they participate in a reaction which is to be conducted over a range of temperatures. If, for example, it is decided to set the chemical potential of hydrogen at 1 atm pressure to zero at 25°C, this cannot simultaneously be done at any other temperature without a definite breach with physical reality. Thus,

$$(\partial \mu^{\circ}_{H_2}/\partial T)_P = -S^{\circ}_{H_2} \qquad (23)$$

which is not zero, but a finite, positive quantity the value of which is known with some accuracy.

Such a step is not taken if it is avoidable, but, unfortunately, this is not the case in the present state of knowledge about ions in solution. For the hydrogen electrode, Eq. (16),

$$2\mu_{H^+} - \mu_{H_2} - 2EF = 0 \qquad (16)$$

is as rigorous as it can be. If the electrode is a standard one, and E is put at zero at all temperatures,

$$\mu^{\circ}_{H^+} = \tfrac{1}{2}\mu^{\circ}_{H_2}$$

It follows that

$$(\partial \mu^{\circ}_{H^+}/\partial T)_P = \tfrac{1}{2}(\partial \mu^{\circ}_{H_2}/\partial T)_P$$

and, in turn, that $S^{\circ}_{H^+} = \tfrac{1}{2}S^{\circ}_{H_2}$, where $S^{\circ}_{H^+}$ is the partial molal entropy of hydrogen ion in ideal unimolal solution, and $S^{\circ}_{H_2}$ is the molal entropy of pure hydrogen gas at 1 atm pressure. This is seen to be a convenient fiction, necessary to achieve a uniform potential scale for other electrodes at whatever temperature. Consequently no physical significance must be attached to it any more than to the assumption from which it was derived, that the potential of the standard hydrogen electrode has zero temperature coefficient.

It is important to notice that it is *only* for the standard hydrogen electrode that the assumption of zero temperature coefficient of electrode potential is made. It is on this basis that the non-zero temperature coefficients of the other standard electrode potentials provide information about partial molal entropies for ions in relation to that of the hydrogen ion, that is to say, on the purely arbitrary basis that $\bar{S}^{\circ}_{H^+} = 0$.

It may be commented that matters of reference states and arbitrary assumptions are common sources of difficulty in the thermodynamic thought in which every worker with electrodes may sooner or later find himself engaged and it is well to remember that there is nothing fundamental about them.

III. Reversible and Irreversible Electrodes

The act of measuring the emf of a galvanic cell must cause no significant departure from equilibrium conditions. Cells and electrodes must be designed, in relation to the measuring instrument to be used, so that this condition is satisfied. But all instruments for measuring emf, or for indicating that a potentiometer is off balance, require a transfer of electricity in order to operate. Although this quantity of electricity may be vanishingly small, it follows in principle that the electrodes of a cell must be "working electrodes" to a greater or less degree and must be able to meet the demands made upon them without significant disturbance of potential. Electrodes which meet this demand with plenty to spare are good electrodes and those which fail to meet it are faulty. There are, of course, other reasons for defective electrode behavior, but this only serves to reinforce a point of general importance. It is that, whatever the experimenter's main interest may be, it is not enough for him to take a purely thermodynamic view of his electrode system. If an electrode does not *work* properly, its failure to do so presents a physicochemical problem outside the scope of thermodynamics, perhaps a difficult one, but often rewarding in its interest. It must be examined in such terms as the chemical purity and physical states of the essential phases and interfaces, whether the electrode construction is suitable to facilitate the desired electrode process, what is the mechanism of this process and what are the factors which limit its rate, what extraneous influences may be having adverse effects; the field of inquiry may be very wide. It is impracticable in this introductory section to deal faithfully with all the problems of this kind that might arise, and the present purpose is to suggest some lines of thought which may be helpful on such occasions.

It is logical first to define the kind of electrode which is most to be desired. It is the hypothetical, completely reversible, nonpolarizable electrode, the potential of which is unaffected when electric current flows across the metal–solution interface. This property would require the electrode to have zero resistance, or impedance. Since processes of chemical change and transport of matter must keep pace with the flow of electricity, and do not occur in practice either unhindered or in absence of a gradient of chemical potential, it is obvious that the ideally nonpolarizable electrode is unattainable. It may, however, be approached under favorable conditions, some of which are almost self-evident. Thus, if the potential of a given electrode is to be adequately controlled by a single, well-defined, freely-occurring process, it is clear that the essential solid phases must be present in adequate amounts, and the proper ion constituents must be contained in the solution at sufficiently high concentrations. It would be naive to expect the Nernst equation for the reversible potential of a metal–metal ion electrode, namely,

$$E_{M,M^{n+}} = E^\circ_{M,M^{n+}} + \frac{RT}{nF} \ln a_{M^{n+}} \tag{24}$$

to hold for indefinitely decreasing activity of the metal ion, $a_{M^{n+}}$. As this activity tends to zero, the potential clearly cannot attain, for a number of reasons, the inordinate values suggested by too literal application of the equation. Apart from anything else, the electrode would sooner or later become unable to provide enough electricity, at the proper potential, to work any recording instrument. In the limit, it is obvious that "potential" has no practical meaning unless it is associated with a tangible charge. An alternative statement of what happens with decreasing ionic population of the solution is that, at some stage, it will become mechanistically impossible for the ions to control the electrode potential. Then, under the usual conditions, the potential will become unstable and indefinite, not so much controlled by, as at the mercy of, dissolved oxygen and such other impurities as the solution may contain.

The departure of an electrode from ideal reversibility may be studied on a quantitative basis. In principle, every electrode at rest may be regarded as a mobile equilibrium system, in which the equilibrium state is maintained by forward and back reactions proceeding at equal rates, defined by the slowest step in the over-all electrode process. Since these processes involve the transfer of charge across the metal–solution interface, their rates may be expressed in terms of electric currents, and are sensitive to any variation in the effective potential difference across the interface. Thus, if a potential more negative than the equilibrium value is imposed upon the electrode from an external source, a finite cathodic current will pass.[4] This, however, is but an observable, net current and will be merely the difference between an increased forward reaction rate and a decreased back reaction rate.

There are good reasons for selecting the Tafel relation,

$$\eta = a + b \log i \tag{25}$$

as the equation typical of the kinetics of electrode processes; η is the over-potential, which is the difference between the potential of the electrode when it carries a current density i and the equilibrium potential, and a and b are constants. The form of this equation shows that the current is exponentially dependent upon potential; in fact, that part of the Galvani potential difference which assists a charge transfer process does so by linearly diminishing the effective activation energy of the process.

---

[4] *A cathodic process* is one in which electrons supplied to the metal phase of an electrode from an external source pass across the interface and perform a reduction: discharge of a cation; charge of an anion. Conversely, an *anodic process* is accompanied by an oxidation and involves withdrawal of electrons from the metal phase into the outer circuit. Either process can occur at negative or positive potentials over a wide range on any scale. This is consistent with Faraday's intentions when he coined the words in question, which should therefore not be related with "negative" or "positive."

It is important that the net current density be regarded as the difference between current densities determined by the finite forward and back reaction rates of a mobile equilibrium. Thus, for a cathodic process, the net current density is the difference between a larger cathodic current density and a smaller anodic one. The Tafel law applies only to these separate current densities and not to their difference. It will therefore hold for experimentally observed current densities only under conditions far enough from equilibrium for one of the opposing currents to be suppressed. If, in the vicinity of equilibrium, this is not the case, the joint effect of the Tafel laws for the opposed currents provides the relation

$$i = i_0 \eta F/RT \tag{26}$$

where i is the net current density in either direction. It is clear from this that for a given value of i, η is small when i_0 is large. For the ideal, non-polarizable electrode, η must be zero under all conditions, and this would require the impossible; for no real system could the exchange current density tend to infinity. But the practical condition for a real electrode to be "thermodynamically well-behaved" is seen to be that its exchange current must be large compared with any net current that it is required to pass in use. It is not always easy to attain this condition, and if in a particular case the exchange current should fall too low (perhaps by reason of decreasing ion activity in solutions successively diluted), not only may the electrode become polarizable, but it may no longer be able to attain its proper equilibrium potential at all. Some other process, dependent upon impurities but capable of sustaining a higher i_0 may take over. This statement may be compared with a similar one made previously in less informative terms.

Exchange current densities for various kinds of metal–solution interfaces cover a range of about 10^{-2} to 10^{-18} amp cm^{-2}, but the useful range for reference electrodes is normally much more restricted than this; it will in part depend upon the sensitivity of the measuring instrument to be used. One of the highest i_0 values is for hydrogen ion discharge at platinum, which is one reason why the hydrogen electrode is one of the most satisfactory of all.

The measurement of exchange current (discussion of which is outside the present terms of reference) is neither easy nor feasible as a normal ancillary to potentiometric work, except in one rather *ad hoc* way which may not always be easy to apply. In the close vicinity of the equilibrium potential, the net current passed by an electrode forms a linear plot against the displacement of the potential from the equilibrium value and the slope of this plot is proportional to the exchange current. Clearly, to determine such a slope (or, rather, its inverse) is no more than a common sense way of determining the polarizability of an electrode. Provided that the other electrode of the cell is known to be less polarizable, this can be done in a purely comparative way in terms of potentiometer settings and galvanometer deflections on either side of the null point. Any hysteresis effects which are observed indicate gross irreversibility. Under suitable circumstances, this procedure can give quite useful information (2, 3), and is

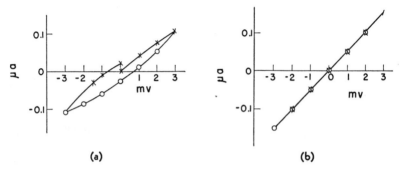

FIG. 1. Micropolarization tests for electrode reversibility.

illustrated in Fig. 1, which relates to tests applied to unsatisfactory (a) and satisfactory (b) calomel electrodes.

In attempting to understand the deterioration in electrode behavior which accompanies increasing deviation from ideal nonpolarizability, it is reasonable to inquire whether there are alternative ways in which deviations can arise, and, in the extreme case, to what sort of electrode do they ultimately lead. What happens when the exchange current decreases to zero?

The exchange current is determined by the rate of the slowest reaction step involved in the electrode process. In general, a reaction rate is equal to the product of a specific rate constant, or velocity constant, and one or more concentration terms.[5] Formally, a given reaction rate may tend to zero either because the velocity constant tends to zero, or because a concentration tends to zero. These alternatives might arise for an electrode process either by the incidence of a high potential barrier opposing the charge-transfer step, or by the reduction of an ion concentration term to vanishing point. Both of these effects occur and, separately or together, they will lead in the limiting case to the ideally polarized electrode, across the metal–solution interface of which no charged particle of any kind passes. It is worth while to give brief consideration to this kind of electrode; it is again an idealized type which may be approached in practice, but hardly attained.

―――――――――

[5] Possibly, for a heterogeneous reaction, a two-dimensional term.

Grahame (*4, 5*) was the first clearly to state that the existence of the (nearly) ideally polarized electrode does not require the postulation of a barrier to charge transfer. In fact, this electrode was defined as one for which, at equilibrium, the concentration of every charged component is finite in one phase only. The illustration needed to clarify this is provided by the electrode

$$Hg \mid KCl \text{ (aq, } m = 1)$$

maintained at the potential for which the metal–solution interfacial energy is a maximum (the electrocapillary maximum, ecm). There is no evident reason why any conceivable electrode reaction should not proceed to an equilibrium; if it is assumed that it does so, and if the equilibrium states are calculated by use of known standard potentials, the following results are obtained:

$$2Hg \text{ (metal)} \rightarrow Hg_2^{2+} \text{ (solution)} + 2e^- \text{ (metal)}$$
[equilibrium activity of Hg_2^{2+} ions $\sim 10^{-37}$ gm ion liter^{-1}]

$$K^+ \text{ (solution)} + e^- \text{ (metal)} \rightarrow K \text{ (amalgam)}$$
[equilibrium atom fraction of K in Hg $\sim 10^{-45}$]

$$2Cl^- \text{ (solution)} \rightarrow Cl_2 \text{ (gas)} + 2e^- \text{ (metal)}$$
[equilibrium pressure of Cl_2 (gas) $\sim 10^{-56}$ atm]

$$2H_3O^+ \text{ (solution)} + 2e^- \text{ (metal)} \rightarrow H_2 \text{ (gas)} + 2H_2O$$
[equilibrium pressure of H_2 gas $\sim 3 \times 10^{-5}$ atm]

The last term is not quite negligible, but there is in this case a very high barrier which opposes the discharge of hydrogen ions. Otherwise, all the equilibrium activities so calculated are vanishingly small, so that all the natural electrode reactions involving the passage of charged particles across the interface have a negligible tendency to occur. It will be seen that, in accordance with the definition given above, mercury ions and electrons are confined to the metallic phase, whilst potassium, hydrogen and chloride ions are confined to the aqueous phase. In this example, however, the potential has been treated as an independent variable and fixed. The questions arise, has not such an electrode system, adequately specified, an equilibrium potential of its own and, if not, why is it of interest in an article dealing with reference electrodes?

The first answer is that, in principle, the electrode system must have an equilibrium potential, but, since it will pass no electricity, normal methods of measuring potential do not apply. Excluding any effects of impurities (the system is very sensitive to traces of oxygen), the potential will depend upon the charge carried by the mercury phase. Since this may no longer be varied by transfers across the metal–solution boundary, it has ceased to be self-adjusting, and thus becomes part of an "adequate specification" of the electrode system. The condition of zero charge upon the mercury surface may, however, be attained by allowing a reservoir of mercury to deliver a fine stream of droplets beneath the surface of the solution. Each droplet carries away a part of any residual charge which may originally have been present. Consideration indicates that under these conditions the potential becomes measurable, and it quite rapidly comes to the potential of the ecm. This potential is known, from the fundamental Lippmann equation, to correspond with the condition of zero charge upon the mercury surface.

The second answer is that work with the polarized electrode has made a great contribution to the theory of the electrical double layer, which is essential to the description of metal–solution interfaces, and lies at the root of all electrokinetic phenomena. The theory certainly has relevance to electrodes of all kinds, and a brief account of it, to show how, is desirable.

Adjacent to a metal–solution interface, there may be a layer of ions held firmly enough to rob them of kinetic freedom; this "close layer" of ions is called the Helmholtz layer. In the simplest case, the ions are held by electrostatic forces due to a charge externally impressed upon the metal. When this charge is first established, it can be imagined that a field is set up in the solution phase, to which the ions respond, moving to such new dispositions as to annul the field and minimize potential energy. But they are opposed in this by the disorganizing effects of random thermal motions, so that complete cancellation of the field cannot occur. The weaker residual forces then set up a diffuse layer extending further into the solution phase. This is sometimes called the Gouy layer and it closely resembles the ionic atmosphere familiar from interionic attraction theory.

The conditions in the metal phase are quite different, for a metal may be regarded as a medium of infinite polarizability incapable of sustaining any field. All its charge therefore resides at the interface, opposite to the Helmholtz layer of ions.

The attraction of ions to a metal surface in this or any other way is a process of adsorption, which is accompanied by a decrease of interfacial free energy, or interfacial tension. This is easily measurable when mercury is used. If the forces which are satisfied are purely electrostatic, Volta adsorption is said to occur. If the mercury has zero charge and if the solution ions are devoid of individualistic properties, there is no ion adsorption. This is the case at the ecm, the maximum of a parabolic electrocapillary curve generated by plotting interfacial tension against externally imposed potential. If, by making this potential more negative the mercury is given a negative charge, cations are adsorbed, and the curve declines along its "cathodic branch"; positive polarization leads to anion adsorption along the "anodic branch." The ions provided by sodium fluoride and, possibly, the alkali metal hydroxides, carbonates and sulfates appear to be the characterless nonentities needed to exclude all but Volta adsorption. Such electrolytes are said to be "capillary inactive." For these, the electrocapillary curves approach an "ideal" form; the potential of the ecm, with respect to a reference electrode of fixed potential, is constant, and the electrical potentials in both parts of the ionic double layer (Helmholtz and diffuse) are of the same sign.

With other electrolytes, individual and characteristic effects appear but, strangely enough, they are largely confined to the anodic branch. They all involve a depression of interfacial tension, increasing with positive polarization. Thus, for an assortment of electrolytes, the general appearance of a family of electrocapillary curves plotted between the same axes is that of a common cathodic branch, but a drooping sheaf of anodic branches, all falling below the "ideal" curve on the interfacial tension scale. The maximum of each curve is displaced negatively on the potential scale by an amount which increases with the droop. These features are illus-

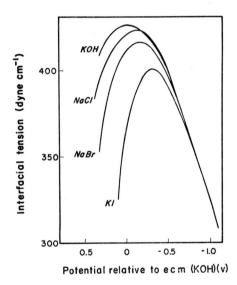

FIG. 2. Electrocapillary curves (approximate) for various aqueous solutions.

trated in Fig. 2. Why it is that, in this respect, the anions appear to be the individualists and the cations the nonentities is not yet fully understood.

If, instead of a reference electrode of fixed potential, an appropriate anion-reversible electrode is used, directly immersed in the solution phase, a thermodynamic calculation can be made to determine the "surface excesses" of the ions at the interface. It is instructive to consider the kind of result that Grahame (5) obtained in this way. The behavior of mercury in contact with 0.3 molal sodium chloride solution may be used in illustration, and discussed in terms of the purely formal diagram shown in Fig. 3, as follows.

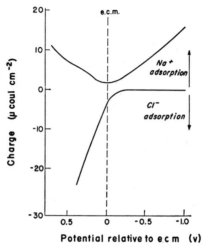

FIG. 3. Ion adsorption at mercury from 0.3 molal sodium chloride solution [approximate curves, after Grahame (5)].

Starting at potentials about 1 volt negative with respect to the ecm, i.e., at the extremity of the cathodic branch, sodium ions are adsorbed, chloride ions are not. Moving in a positive direction along the potential scale, chloride ion adsorption at first remains at zero, but Volta adsorption of sodium ions declines. But some 0.3 volt before the ecm is reached, chloride ion adsorption begins, in spite of the electrostatic field which must oppose it. It must occur in response to some other kind of force, and is called "specific adsorption." When the ecm is attained, it is no longer the case, as for capillary inactive electrolytes, that there is no adsorption. Volta adsorption is zero, but specific adsorption remains, to the extent of about 2×10^{13} chloride ions per cm^2 of surface. Since these ions are present "of their own volition," they constitute a layer of uncompensated charge, giving rise to a field which needs annulment if potential energy is to be minimized. This service is performed by sodium ions in the outer, diffuse layer, so that sodium ions are also adsorbed to an extent which satisfies the requirement of over-all electroneutrality.

Proceeding along the anodic branch, with increasingly positive imposed potentials, Volta and specific adsorption cooperate in causing the chloride ion excess to increase rapidly; so rapidly that the sodium ion excess, in the diffuse layer, also increases whereas normally it would decrease. It will be noticed that, somewhere in this traverse of the potential scale, chloride ions have replaced sodium ions as the predominant inhabitants of the Helmholtz layer, and the configuration of the ionic double layer in which the electrical potentials are of the same sign in both parts of the layer has been replaced by one in which they are different. A crude pictorial representation of the electrical double layer after this inversion has occurred is

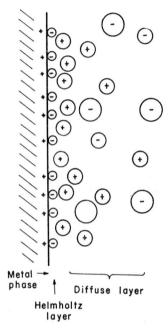

Fig. 4. Pictorial representation of electrical double layer at a positively charged mercury surface in aqueous sodium chloride solution.

shown in Fig. 4. The specifically adsorbed chloride ions in the Helmholtz layer are shown smaller than those in the solution phase because they are probably dehydrated.

It is not at all certain what is the nature of specific adsorption (whether or not, for example, it is due to a tendency to covalent binding); but it seems justifiable to distinguish it from Volta adsorption in the same way as an independent variable is distinguished from a dependent one. It is potential-determining, rather than potential-determined. Certainly, in virtue of it, chloride ion (and still more bromide and iodide in analogous systems) is predominant in controlling the behavior of the polarized electrode.

Specific adsorption of a kind is, of course, familiar in colloid science.

Silver chloride, for example, will tend to adsorb, as opportunity serves, silver ions or chloride ions because these are components of its own lattice. These will define the sign of charge on the colloid particle; oppositely charged "gegen-ions" will populate an outer, diffuse layer, preserving electroneutrality and determining the zeta-potential upon which electrokinetic effects depend.

All species participating in an electrode process must pass through the electrical double layer in their progress to or from the interface. Since the double layer is normally established very rapidly, this has no effect upon thermodynamic argument, provided that the conditions which have been laid down for satisfactory reversibility are fulfilled. All parts of the electrical double layer remain in equilibrium with the rest of the system; the electrochemical potential of each charged component is uniform throughout. If these conditions do not obtain, so that fast "equilibrium reactions" (corresponding with high exchange current) no longer fix the electrode potential as a function of the thermodynamic properties of bulk phases, then the intrusion of interfacial effects is to be expected. These may include effects due to the specific adsorption of ions (possibly impurity ions), adsorption of nonelectrolytic impurities (maximal at the potential of the ecm), electrokinetic phenomena (sensitivity of the electrode to movement of the solution), possibly photoelectric effects and, in general, effects due to any disturbing influences to which an electrode with an inadequate exchange current may be sensitive.

This section may be concluded by quoting two examples chosen to show the necessity of sometimes considering the mechanisms of electrode processes. Although treated in detail in later chapters, they will, in summarized form, admirably illustrate the present theme.

The first example is concerned with the incidence of an energy barrier opposing an essential step in an electrode reaction. The hydrogen electrode is best regarded as an oxidation-reduction electrode, required to record the potential defined by the equilibrium between hydrogen ions and molecular hydrogen, *both* in aqueous solution. But this equilibrium is not freely established in the absence of a catalyst, so the electrode is called upon to act in this capacity as well. This makes a considerable demand upon it because, at its surface, four reactions are required to proceed without significant hindrance. These are, the discharge of hydrogen ions to form adsorbed hydrogen atoms; the ionization of hydrogen atoms to form solution ions; the combination of hydrogen atoms to form molecules; the atomization of hydrogen molecules. Platinized platinum meets this demand. It adsorbs hydrogen atoms and thus forms for them a "potential well" which undermines the activation energy barriers which, for most metals, strongly oppose the discharge of ions and the atomization of molecules. But poisoning can occur and, when it is severe, the electrode becomes effectively isolated from the influence of molecular hydrogen because the atomization–recombination steps become so much hindered. The electrode may then assume a positive rest potential as high as 0.5 volt, quite well controlled by a "partial equilibrium" but not, of course, responding very well to a test for satisfactory reversibility. Before poisoning, the electrode will work as a hydrogenation catalyst because it can promote $H_2 \rightarrow 2H$, but it is rather ineffective in performing "electrochemical reductions" by means of cathodically generated hydrogen. After poisoning, however, this situation is reversed, for the reaction $2H^+ \rightarrow 2H$ is, in effect, facilitated; because the hydrogen atoms cannot readily react with each other, they are available to react with something else. Paradoxically, hydrogen electrodes can, with advancing age, suffer from "hydrogen poisoning," attributable to the burning out of catalytically active centers by the very exothermic atom recombination which they promote.

The second example relates to the calomel electrode in aqueous hydrochloric acid, i.e.,

$$Hg \mid Hg_2Cl_2 \mid HCl \text{ (aq)}$$

Its standard potential, in accordance with thermodynamic requirements, is given by

$$E^\circ_{cal} = E^\circ_{Hg,Hg_2^{2+}} + (RT/2F) \ln K_s \tag{27}$$

where K_s is the activity solubility product of calomel. But this relation cannot define how the electrode works. If it is supposed that the mechanism depends upon the charge and discharge of mercurous ions as an essential step, the difficulty is that the activity of these ions in equilibrium with the standard electrode does not exceed 10^{-18} gm ion l^{-1}, or about 600 mercurous ions per cm^3 of solution. Even if it is assumed that a mercurous ion can be discharged at a distance of 10 Å from the interface, the duty of depolarizing about 35 square meters of mercury surface devolves upon each mercurous ion. This is ridiculous, and the electrode cannot possibly work by the classical thermodynamic mechanism suggested by literal translation of Eq. (27). This view is supported by the observation that if mercury and hydrochloric acid are brought together before calomel is added, the electrode does not work properly. There are unambiguous signs of the behavior of a polarized electrode. But if the mercury and the calomel are allowed to interact together in the dry state before the addition of the aqueous phase, the electrode is capable of admirable behavior (6). The reason is believed to be that dry interaction allows a monolayer of covalently bound chlorine atoms to form on the mercury surface. This layer is thought to act as a vital intermediate in promoting a mobile electrode reaction which must, of course, fit the thermodynamic framework set by Eq. (27). Further work on the mechanism of this electrode process has lent support to this view (*7, 8*).

IV. Conventions

If there is one way more than another in which the experimenter needs help, it is in dealing with the inconsistent sign conventions which have been used in the electrochemical literature for many years. Nothing will alter the fact that the literature exists and must be consulted, so that there is no option but to meet the difficulties which are involved, with the hope that means will be found to obviate them for the future.

Under these circumstances, help is best provided by a clear and brief statement which recommends a definite policy. Such a statement has been made by the International Union of Pure and Applied Chemistry (IUPAC) (*9*) and has become known as the Stockholm Convention. It is concise, lucid and authoritative[6] and everything possible should be done to secure its universal adoption.

The essential contents of the Stockholm Convention may be summarized in three simple rules, as follows:

(1)   The emf of a cell is invariably related to the Gibbs free energy change of the cell reaction by the expression $nFE = -\Delta G$.
(2)   A cell is to be represented so that its emf is identical with the potential of the right-hand electrode measured with respect to the potential of the left-hand electrode.
(3)   The electrode potential of an electrode is equal to the emf of a cell formed from the electrode concerned on the right and a standard hydrogen electrode on the left.

These rules carry the following implications: for every spontaneous cell reaction, ΔG is negative, so that the emf of the cell is positive and the cell is represented with the positive electrode on the right.

This rule is no more specialized or exacting than the usual convention of writing a chemical equation so that the reaction is shown as proceeding from left to right, i.e., reactants on the left, products on the right. It is also no more inflexible. Thus, a chemical reaction may proceed in one direction or the other according to the way in which the activities of the substances participating are adjusted. In precisely the same way, the emf of a cell in which the activities of one or more reactants can be varied over a wide

[6] This description does not apply to a report (*10*) of the Proceedings of the 8th Meeting at Madrid in 1956 of the International Committee of Electrochemical Thermodynamics and Kinetics (CITCE). Only statements published in the Comptes rendus of IUPAC can be regarded as internationally authoritative.

enough range will somewhere change its sign; in other words, the polarity of the cell will undergo reversal. There is no need to rewrite the chemical equation for the cell reaction every time such a situation is encountered, and equally there is no need to alter the formulation of the cell in which the reaction occurs. If, for the *one* way in which the chemical equation is written changing conditions produce a change of sign of ΔG from negative to positive for the left to right reaction, then, simultaneously, the *one* way in which the cell is written will express the fact of the reversal in polarity. This may be summarized

A → B; ΔG negative; emf positive; positive electrode on right.

A → B; ΔG positive; emf negative; negative electrode on right.

To illustrate this by means of specific examples, if the reaction

$$\tfrac{1}{2}H_2 + AgCl = Ag + HCl(m)$$

is accompanied by a decrease in free energy, as is normally the case, ΔG is negative, and the hydrogen–silver chloride cell, represented by

$$H_2, Pt \mid aqueous\ HCl(m) \mid AgCl \mid Ag \qquad (A)$$

has a positive emf and the electrode on the right is positive with respect to the electrode on the left. But if the molality of the hydrochloric acid is increased above 9.1 mole kg⁻¹, the reaction goes the other way, and ΔG for the reaction, *as written*, becomes positive. The emf of the cell, *as written*, becomes negative, and the electrode on the right is negative with respect to the electrode on the left. For the analogous reaction

$$\tfrac{1}{2}H_2 + AgI = Ag + HI(m)$$

ΔG changes sign when m is around 0.1 mole kg⁻¹, so that the cell

$$H_2, Pt \mid HI(m) \mid AgI \mid Ag \qquad (D)$$

changes its polarity well within the normally accessible concentration range of the electrolyte. Hence, the cell emf is positive for $m > 0.1$ and negative for $m < 0.1$ mole kg⁻¹.

Clearly, the important thing is to write down the cell reaction on the one hand, and the representation of the cell on the other, in a self-consistent way, and rules (1) and (2) provide the means for doing so. The operation of these two rules may be further illustrated and checked by considerations of the following kind.

The reaction for which ΔG is negative occurs spontaneously in the cell when the electrodes are connected together by means of an external, resistive circuit. If the equation for the reaction is written so that its natural progress is from left to right under a given set of conditions, then the cell must be written so that, under these same conditions, electrons would flow from left to right in the external circuit. Alternatively, it is often said that "positive electricity" would flow *through the cell* from left to right. In yet another way, the same thing can be stated in the form that oxidation would take place at the left-hand electrode and reduction would take place at the right-hand electrode.

The third rule, concerned with defining electrode potential, introduces an additional element of arbitrary choice. It is that in the cell which is used for this purpose, the standard hydrogen electrode is always on the left and the hypothetical cell reaction always involves a flow of electrons from left to right in the external circuit joining the electrodes. In other words, the cell reaction is always one in which gaseous hydrogen performs a reduction. If for this reduction reaction ΔG is negative, the emf of the cell is positive and the corresponding electrode potential is positive. If, on the other hand, ΔG for the reduction is positive, the emf of the cell is negative and the corresponding electrode potential is negative. All this is entirely consistent with experimental facts, for although these hypothetical cells cannot be set up in practice, real cells which approximate to them can be, and in every case these real cells have the polarities which would be expected from the convention.

Further points to be noted about the electrode potentials defined by the Stockholm Convention in this way are:

(1)   They are all "reduction potentials."
(2)   They can each be regarded (with reservations that have already been discussed) as the potential of the metallic phase of the electrode with respect to the potential of the solution phase with which it is in contact.
(3)   They are positive for noble metals.
(4)   They are identical with the electrode potentials of the "European sign convention" and are opposite to those of the "American sign convention".

It may be useful to show how the proposals of the Stockholm Convention lend themselves to the derivation of expressions for electrode potentials as functions of the activities of ions in solution. This is very commonly carried out by applying the van't Hoff isotherm (or "reaction isotherm") to an oxidation–reduction equilibrium. It must be emphasized that this can only be done for a complete chemical reaction, or cell reaction, and not for a half-cell, or electrode reaction. Accordingly, each electrode of interest must be combined with a hydrogen electrode.

To take a specific example, the cell

$$H_2, Pt \mid H^+ \parallel Fe^{3+}, Fe^{2+} \mid Pt \qquad (E)$$

may be used to obtain a general expression for the potential of the ferric–ferrous iron oxidation–reduction potential. The reaction to be considered is

$$\tfrac{1}{2}H_2 + Fe^{3+} = H^+ + Fe^{2+}$$

If the activities of the ions in solution and the pressure of hydrogen gas have equilibrium values (denoted by superscript e) which satisfy the relationship

$$K = [a_{H^+}^e \cdot a_{Fe^{2+}}^e]/[(P_{H_2}^e)^{1/2} \cdot a_{Fe^{3+}}^e] \qquad (28)$$

where K is the equilibrium constant of the reaction, the free energy change is zero, but if they have nonequilibrium values, the free energy change is given by Eq. 29.[7]

$$\Delta G = -RT \ln K + RT \ln \{[a_{H^+} \cdot a_{Fe^{2+}}]/[(P_{H_2})^{1/2} \cdot a_{Fe^{3+}}]\} \qquad (29)$$

If the activities and the gas pressure have the standard values of unity, the free energy change has its standard value, so that

$$\Delta G^\circ = -RT \ln K \qquad (30)$$

In general, therefore,

$$\Delta G = \Delta G^\circ + RT \ln \{[a_{H^+} \cdot a_{Fe^{2+}}]/[(P_{H_2})^{1/2} \cdot a_{Fe^{3+}}]\} \qquad (31)$$

and since in general $nFE = -\Delta G$ and $nFE^\circ = -\Delta G^\circ$,

$$E = E^\circ - (RT/F) \ln [a_{H^+}/(P_{H_2})^{1/2}] + (RT/F) \ln (a_{Fe^{3+}}/a_{Fe^{2+}})$$

But in the cell which is used to define electrode potential, the hydrogen electrode is standard, with $a_{H^+} = 1$ and $P_{H_2} = 1$. Hence, the required expression for electrode potential is

$$E_{Fe^{3+},Fe^{2+}} = E^\circ_{Fe^{3+},Fe^{2+}} + (RT/F) \ln (a_{Fe^{3+}}/a_{Fe^{2+}}) \qquad (32)$$

Applied to any oxidation–reduction equilibrium, this method gives

$$E_{ox,red} = E^\circ_{ox,red} + (RT/nF) \ln (a_{ox}/a_{red}) \qquad (33)$$

where the symbols have obvious meanings and where n electrons are transferred in each elementary act of oxidation or reduction. For an electrode directly reversible to its cations, the reduced member of the "oxidation–

---

[7] This quite common way of writing the isotherm is mathematically objectionable because K and the analogous function containing nonequilibrium activities are usually not dimensionless. Strictly,

$$\Delta G = -RT \ln \{[K \cdot (P_{H_2})^{1/2} \cdot a_{Fe^{3+}}]/[a_{H^+} \cdot a_{Fe^{2+}}]\}$$

Similarly, when the nonequilibrium activities are assigned standard values of unity, the second term of the isotherm vanishes numerically, but is still significant dimensionally.

reduction" couple is the metal itself, and its activity is fixed at the standard value of unity. Then, for example,

$$E_{Zn,Zn^{2+}} = E^\circ_{Zn,Zn^{2+}} + (RT/2F) \ln a_{Zn^{2+}} \tag{34}$$

If, on the other hand, the electrode is reversible to anions, as for the hypothetically reversible chlorine electrode, it is the oxidized member of the couple which is retained at a constant activity of unity, so that

$$E_{Cl_2,Cl^-} = E^\circ_{Cl_2,Cl^-} - (RT/F) \ln a_{Cl^-} \tag{35}$$

The silver–silver chloride electrode, also reversible to chloride ions, may be regarded as a silver, silver ion electrode, for which

$$E_{Ag,Ag^+} = E^\circ_{Ag,Ag^+} + (RT/F) \ln a_{Ag^+}$$

but with the activity of silver ion controlled by the solubility equilibrium of solid silver chloride. Thus

$$a_{Ag^+} = K_s/a_{Cl^-}$$

where K_s is the activity solubility product of silver chloride. K_s is the constant which is incorporated into the standard potential of the silver–silver chloride electrode:

$$\begin{aligned} E_{Ag,AgCl,Cl^-} &= E^\circ_{Ag,Ag^+} + (RT/F) \ln K_s - (RT/F) \ln a_{Cl^-} \\ &= E^\circ_{Ag,AgCl,Cl^-} - (RT/F) \ln a_{Cl^-} \end{aligned} \tag{36}$$

which is identical in form with Eq. (35).

These formulations are entirely suited to the kind of thought which it is desirable for the experimenter to find passing through his mind in the course of his work. Thus, the experimental cell is connected by wires to the potentiometer, and it is obvious that it is the potential difference between these wires that is being determined. Which of them is positive and which negative is unambiguously observed. If one of the electrodes is a hydrogen electrode, it is useful to consider how variation in hydrogen ion activity, or in hydrogen gas pressure, may alter its potential and thus increase or decrease the emf of the cell, that is, the potential difference between the wires. If, for example, the hydrogen ion activity is increased, hydrogen ions will have an enhanced tendency to discharge, accepting electrons from the metal phase and thus making its potential more positive. Or, if the hydrogen pressure is increased, this will, by mass action effect, favor the generation of hydrogen ions. This must leave electrons behind in the metal phase, so the electrode potential must become more negative. If the other electrode of the cell is a ferric–ferrous oxidation–reduction electrode, it is useful to think that oxidizing agents accept electrons and reducing agents give them. Then, if the ratio of ferric to ferrous ion activity in the solution is increased, the potential of the unattackable metal phase will become more positive.

These considerations seem to be so simple and obvious as to be hardly worth mentioning, but the fact is that the electrode potential formulae based upon the American system of sign conventions are inconsistent with intelligent thinking of this kind. Thus, this system leads to

$$E_{H_2, H^+} = -(RT/F) \ln [a_{H^+}/(P_{H_2})^{1/2}]$$

for the potential of the nonstandard hydrogen electrode and to

$$E_{Fe^{3+}, Fe^{2+}} = E^{\circ}_{Fe^{3+}, Fe^{2+}} - (RT/F) \ln (a_{Fe^{3+}}/a_{Fe^{2+}})$$

for the ferric–ferrous electrode. These formulae appear to contradict the conclusions reached by direct observation and reasonable physical argument. This gives the student legitimate grounds for complaint and has certainly given rise to considerable confusion.

No useful purpose would be served by tracing the way in which the American convention was established. Although based in a perfectly logical way upon a foundation of pure thermodynamics, it failed to take into account the fundamental observation made by Gibbs in 1899 (1) that the only quantity which is experimentally accessible in this field of electrochemistry is the difference of electrical potential between two pieces of copper wire.

Further points to be noted about the American system of electrode potentials are: (i) they are all "oxidation potentials"; (ii) they must each be regarded as the potential of the solution phase with respect to the potential of the metallic phase with which it is in contact; (iii) they are negative for noble metals.

Many important electrochemical texts adhere to the American system, but there are promising signs for the future that it will eventually be replaced by the Stockholm Convention. It is recommended that efforts should be made to assist this desirable move towards uniformity.

V. Standard Electrode Potentials

The use of a galvanic cell to make a quantitative study of the properties of an ionic solution (or of any other homogeneous phase which may participate in a cell reaction) essentially involves a comparison between an unknown, nonstandard state of the experimental system and a known, standard state. The standard state needed for the comparison may vary according to the nature of the system being studied, but it is clear that it must be described with adequate accuracy before anything can be done. Perhaps the most fundamental preliminary work of this kind is that concerned with finding the standard emf values of cells without liquid junctions formed from a hydrogen electrode and an anion-reversible electrode. These cells are typified by the hydrogen–silver chloride cell. If the standard emf of this cell is found, it may be identified with the standard potential of the silver–silver chloride electrode.

The situation may be summarized by the statement that, if an electrode is to be used for reference purposes, its standard potential must be known. The principles of the methods used to determine standard potentials therefore fall within the scope of this work, but attention will be confined to the cases which have been described as the most fundamental.

No standard electrode can be set up experimentally because the standard states of the electrode constituents are mostly hypothetical. Strictly, the standard hydrogen electrode requires *ideal* hydrogen gas at 1 atm pressure (unit fugacity), although it is usually justifiable to ignore the nonideality of hydrogen (cf. Chapter 2, Section II, A). For electrolytic solutions, the standard state is commonly the ideal unimolal solution, which is quite different from any real solution. This is best seen in terms of the equation

$$\mu = \mu° + RT \ln m + RT \ln \gamma_{\pm} \tag{37}$$

for an ionic solute. In the standard state *both* m and $\gamma_{\pm}$ are, by definition, equal to unity. This state cannot be realized, and is quite different from the condition that $a_{\pm} = m\gamma_{\pm} = 1$, which *can* be, but only as an irrelevant numerical accident.

Since the mean ion activity coefficient, $\gamma_{\pm}$, tends to unity as the molality, m, tends to zero, the determination of a standard electrode potential involves the extrapolation to zero concentration conditions of measurements obtained with an appropriate cell. This is best illustrated in terms of the hydrogen–silver chloride cell

$$H_2 \text{ (1 atm), Pt} \mid \text{aqueous HCl}(m) \mid \text{AgCl} \mid \text{Ag} \tag{A}$$

the emf of which has been shown to be [cf. Eq. (13)]

$$E = E° - (RT/F) \ln a_{H^+} - (RT/F) \ln a_{Cl^-} \tag{38}$$

Writing a_+ for a_{H^+} and a_- for a_{Cl^-}, and remembering that $a_{\pm} = (a_+a_-)^{1/2} = m\gamma_{\pm}$ in this case,

$$E = E° - (2RT/F) \ln m - (2RT/F) \ln \gamma_{\pm} \tag{39}$$

which may be rearranged to

$$\{E + (2RT/F) \ln m\} = E° - (2RT/F) \ln \gamma_{\pm} \tag{40}$$

so that the term on the left-hand side can be directly evaluated from experimental data. This term, plotted against $\ln \gamma_{\pm}$, would give a straight line of slope $- 2RT/F$ and intercept $E°$, the desired standard potential of the silver–silver chloride electrode.

But this cell is the basis of one of the principal methods of determining activity coefficients, for which purpose $E°$ must be evaluated independently by some other extrapolation method. In other words, since $\ln \gamma_{\pm} = f(m)$, the plot must be made against some appropriate function of m. The problem is to decide what function to use, for unless it is in fact appropriate, the extrapolation may be erroneous. The difficulty is a fundamental one and must be briefly examined. It may be that the primary concern is to use a purely objective treatment, entirely devoid of any special assumptions about the nature of the function, so that the final result cannot be influenced by preconceived ideas of any kind. In this case, the experimental data may be fitted by an empirical equation, such as that used by Scatchard and Prentiss (*11*), namely,

$$E + (2RT/F) \ln m = E° - Am^{1/2} + Bm \qquad (41)$$

where A and B are adjustable coefficients.[8] If an interpolation formula like this fits the data within experimental error over an adequate concentration range, it can be supposed that it will serve for extrapolation, provided that there is no special phenomenon, entering at some inaccessibly low concentration, that might affect the extrapolation but not the interpolation. It is generally considered that such an *ad hoc* method, with no theoretical basis, is unacceptable. The alternative is to find a theoretical basis for the extrapolation. In effect, independent knowledge about $\ln \gamma_{\pm}$ must be fed into Eq. (40) in order to extract more knowledge about $\ln \gamma_{\pm}$ from it. Clearly, reliable information is needed about the physical effects which cause ionic solutes to be nonideal, at least within the range of concentrations which is significant for the extrapolation.

The meaning of the word "ideal" used in defining the standard state is restricted in sense to that of Henry's law, requiring ion–ion interactions to be zero and, implicitly, all other interactions (ion–solvent and solvent–solvent) to be precisely the same as they are at infinite dilution. Correspondingly, it would appear to be the interionic effects *alone* which need consideration, and interpretation, in terms of a theory which will be adequate for the purpose of extrapolation. However justified this assumption may turn out to be, it is unsuitable to take it entirely on trust, for to do so implies that the three quite powerful kinds of interaction which exist in electrolytic solution have no effects upon each other and can be considered in isolation. Consideration of the Gibbs-Duhem equation shows this to be thermodynamically improbable.

It is a remarkable thing that aqueous solutions have been predominantly used in pioneering work in this, and other, fields of physical chem-

---

[8] The fact that this equation turns out not to be devoid of theoretical basis is neither here nor there; it merely shows that the empirical expression was not ill-chosen.

istry, yet they are probably the most anomalous and least understood of all solutions and, except by lucky accident, least likely to meet the needs of any simplifying assumptions. In recent years, progress in revealing the complexities of aqueous solutions has been such that it is no longer satisfactory, or even quite honest, to hide them behind a screen of such assumptions, in order to make a direct approach to the single aspect of interionic actions. Since most of the electrode systems requiring understanding and mastery contain aqueous solutions, discussion of the special nature of these solutions, and of water, is very desirable in any forward-looking text upon the subject. Such a discussion accordingly follows.[9]

In water, strong intermolecular forces of *attraction* hold the molecules *apart* in an array more open than for normal liquids. This is only intelligible in terms of a theory, such as that of Bernal and Fowler (*12*), attributing to water a degree of organized, even pseudocrystalline structure, destroyed by high pressure (*13*), but rather less vulnerable to rise of temperature than could have been expected. The concept that the hydrogen bonds, which are responsible for the association of water molecules together, can, without breaking, absorb energy by bending (*14*) has gone far to resolve this difficulty, and has led to the most successful statistical mechanical calculation of the dielectric constant of water over a wide temperature range (*15*). The extent to which water has a structure may be regarded as ranging from the formation of aggregates large enough to simulate different crystalline forms (such as are needed to explain the maximum density at 4°C) to a statistical tendency towards cooperative molecular ordering, opposed by thermal motions, and perhaps declining quite rapidly over a rather narrow temperature range (*16*), without, however, significant loss of cohesion. It is not surprising that the introduction of foreign molecules has a marked effect upon this labile "order-disorder" equilibrium system. When the molecules are nonpolar (inert gas, hydrocarbon), there is an inordinate entropy loss on dissolution, which can only be explained in terms of an increase in the "ice-likeness" of water. The effect is greatest for large molecules, but in all cases decreases with rise of temperature. Frank and Evans (*17*), to whom this important observation is due, said "the water builds a microscopic iceberg around the nonpolar molecule." The "iceberg," however, is statistical rather than solid, and is perhaps better described in terms of an increase in the average life of short-range, tetrahedral aggregates adjacent to the foreign particles (*18*). Evidence for a similar stabilization of order at metal–solution interfaces (*19*) is obviously of very great interest in relation to electrodes.

Water is likely to be still more profoundly affected by ions, because the

[9] Sections of this discussion may be clarified and expanded by reference to "The Structure of Electrolytic Solutions" (W. J. Hamer, ed.). Wiley, New York, 1959.

molecules can approach them closely enough to be influenced by potential gradients of the order of 10^6 vcm^{-1}. Except for large singly-charged ions, this field "freezes" water molecules into a primary hydration shell, in which they are robbed of translational and rotational freedom. In spite of the considerable screening effect of this shell, the long-range coulombic forces emanating from an ion will exert an effect further out, causing orientation, or loss of rotational freedom, in a less well defined zone of secondary hydration. These effects are understood well enough for limits to be set to the entropy losses which accompany them, and these may be added to an "entropy of dissolution" of the ions, derived in a similar manner to that used for nonpolar solutes. On this basis, Frank and Evans (17) found that in fact ions in aqueous solution have "too much" entropy by a large margin, as opposed to the case of nonpolar solutes, which had "too little." It became necessary to suppose that this was due to a disordering effect upon the water structure, a reason for which could readily be found. In the elementary unit of the hydrogen-bonded water structure, a central water molecule may be pictured as surrounded tetrahedrally by four

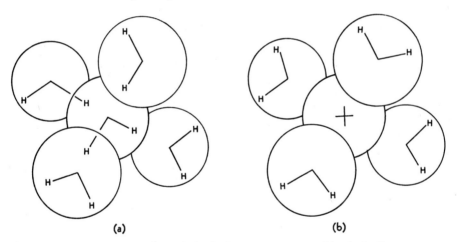

FIG. 5. Incompatible "ordering" of water structure and ion hydration.

others, as in Fig. 5a. Two of the outer molecules have hydrogen atoms directed inwards towards the oxygen lone-pair electrons of the center water molecule; the other two outer molecules have their hydrogen atoms directed outwards, away from the central water molecule. There is indeed a degree of "contra-association," involving some opposition between molecular dipoles; this is presumably why the dielectric constant of water increases when these structures are destroyed at high pressures (20). On the other hand, the water molecules under the influence of a given ion either all point inwards, or all point outwards, according to the sign of charge on the ion; the probable kind of arrangement around a cation is shown in Fig. 5b. The kind of ordering imposed by an ion is centrosymmetrical; the order of the natural water structure is not. The two kinds of ordering influence are incompatible, and where they come into conflict, the result is orientational disorder. This idea is supported by the fact that there is a quantitative correlation between the extent of this disorder, as assessed by the excess entropy, and a relative reduction in viscosity (21). Both of these effects lead to an intelligible classification of ions as "structure-breaking" (singly-charged ions larger than K^+, most anions) or "structure-making" (cations smaller, or more highly charged than K^+; OH^- and F^-) according to their net effects upon the water that surrounds them. These structural concepts for aqueous solutions are supported by many lines of experimental evidence, particularly those to do with temperature coefficients of ionic mobilities, heat capacities and dielectric relaxation times; these times are, for example, decreased by ionic solutes (structure-breaking) but increased by nonionic ones (iceberg effect) (22). These matters have been reviewed recently (23, 24).

In general, therefore, there may be four zones around a given ion: (a) primary hydration, involving dielectric saturation; (b) secondary hydration, where dielectric constant rises rapidly; (c) a zone of orientational disorder, involving enhanced fluidity; and (d) an outer zone of structurally normal water. These zones appear to vary in extent and significance in an intelligible way, according to the magnitude and sign of the charge on the ion, its size, and its average distance from neighboring ions. For very large ions (tetra-alkylammonium), or ions which carry a nonpolar residue (octanoate), there is evidence that the "nonpolar type of solvent reaction" is significant; the ions are wholly, or partly, surrounded by icebergs (18).

This is the background against which the possible effects of ion–ion interactions have to be assessed, and it is obvious that the whole problem is very complex (25). It is even uncertain that ion–ion interactions will themselves be simple. On the contrary, the Brönsted principle (26) that ions are specifically influenced by ions of opposite sign suggests that the sizes, shapes, polarizabilities, electronic configurations and relative positions of the ions concerned may be of great significance. The only hope of a simple solution to the problem would seem to lie in confining attention to solutions of very low concentration indeed. Even at 0.001 mole liter^{-1}, the average distance of a water molecule from an ion is only about 15 molecular diameters, and this might be hardly enough to preclude a significant effect, exerted by the ions, on the properties of the solvent as a whole.

It must therefore be regarded as remarkable that the interionic attraction theory of Debye and Hückel (*27*) is a resounding success, for it treats the solvent as a dielectric continuum, and assumes that the nonideality of ions is solely due to the coulombic forces between them. In other words, it is supposed that if the ions were uncharged, they would be ideal solute particles. Growth of confidence in this theory has certainly been justified by the march of its success, or that of associated theories in, for example, the field of conductance.

For a 1:1-valent electrolyte, the Debye-Hückel equation is

$$- \log \gamma_{\pm} = A'm^{1/2}/(1 + B'a_i m^{1/2}) \tag{42}$$

where A' and B' are terms, appropriate to the molality scale, calculable from fundamental constants, dielectric constant and temperature, and a_i is a distance of closest ionic approach. It is probable that the success of the Debye-Hückel treatment is due to a natural and rather well-defined division of the forces which operate between ions into short-range and long-range. Provided that solutions are very dilute and that the ions are not too small or highly charged, it appears that the long-range forces are of overriding significance, and for these conditions the treatment is adequate. Yet the denominator of the expression on the right-hand side of Eq. (42), based upon a crude "hard sphere" model, is in effect a term which begins to take account of the short-range interactions. Certainly a_i appears to have some physical significance, for it nearly always proves to be greater than the sum of the crystallographic radii of the ions concerned by a margin consistent with very limited interpenetration of hydration shells in the course of interionic encounters.[10]

If the view is taken that the theory has no business at all with any short-range effects, it still provides the so-called limiting law,

$$- \log \gamma_{\pm} = A'm^{1/2} \tag{43}$$

which is serviceable to a remarkable degree. This is specially the case in relation to conductance measurements, which remain practicable to very low ionic concentrations (*29*).

Nevertheless, because of the great experimental difficulties of dealing with extremely dilute solutions, and the near-impossibility of covering any adequate concentration *range* without trespassing outside of them, there is a compelling need for less restricted equations, both for interpolation and extrapolation.

Hückel (*30*) modified the original Debye-Hückel treatment by taking

---

[10] An alternative interpretation is that the ions do not come as close in solution as in the crystal because, in the solution, the attractive forces are weakened, but the shorter-range repulsive forces are not (*28*).

into account the probable effect of the ions in reducing the dielectric constant of the medium below that of the pure solvent, and obtained an equation of the form

$$\log \gamma_{\pm} = -[A'm^{1/2}/(1 + B'a_i m^{1/2})] + \beta m \tag{44}$$

which is capable of expressing activity coefficients, in some cases, with considerable accuracy up to molalities of around unity (*31*). But the Hückel treatment was assailable, and β can be given little more significance than that of an empirical parameter (*32*), although a possibly functional relationship between a_i and β has been observed (*33*). It is perhaps fortunate that all the short-range interactions of which the Debye-Hückel theory takes no account, ion–ion or ion–solvent, are likely to be of a type giving at least an approximately linear variation of $\log \gamma_{\pm}$ with molality, so that the Hückel equation, (44), remains the best simple equation that could be chosen. In its modified guise as a "portmanteau equation," it can be viewed in two ways. It may be regarded as an equation which contains two disposable parameters, a_i and β, to neither of which can any clear, *separate* physical significance be given. Certainly, as far as expressing $\log \gamma_{\pm}$ as a function of m is concerned, the denominator in the Debye-Hückel expression can, as a first approximation, be equated to unity if a term linear in m is added to the right-hand side of the equation. On the other hand, the significance of a distance of closest ionic approach may still be attached to a_i (perhaps rather as a pious hope) and the value of β consistent with this procedure may be examined in the light of various theories of short-range interactions.

Guggenheim (*34, 35*) has, in effect, adopted a compromise. It happens that the product $B'a_i$ in the denominator of the Debye-Hückel expression is close to unity, so that it is convenient to choose, as a standard of reference, a hypothetical electrolyte in which it *is* unity. The distance of closest ionic approach, and the difficulties associated with the concept in relation to mixed electrolyte solutions, are thus abolished. For this standard electrolyte, an equation used by Güntelberg (*36*) is adopted, namely,

$$\log \gamma_{\pm} = -A'z_{+}z_{-} [I^{1/2}/(1 + I^{1/2})] \tag{45}$$

where A' remains the fundamental Debye-Hückel coefficient, z_+ and z_- are numbers of positive and negative charges on cation and anion respectively, and I is the molal ionic strength,

$$\tfrac{1}{2} \sum m_i z_i^2$$

For a real electrolyte,

$$\log \gamma_{\pm} = -A'z_{+}z_{-} [I^{1/2}/(1 + I^{1/2})] + Bm \tag{46}$$

where B is a function of "interaction coefficients," one for each possible cation–anion combination. This treatment assumes that the mutual potential energy of two ions is the sum of two terms: a "standard" term, which is coulombic except at small distances of separation, and a "specific" term, which is zero except at small distances. Interaction coefficients derived from a variety of data have been tabulated (*35*), and the method has been shown to be of remarkably accurate and versatile application.

Stokes and Robinson (*37*), on the other hand, have retained a_i as a physically significant term, and have focused attention on the undoubted fact that the ions in aqueous, or partly aqueous, solutions are hydrated. Water molecules firmly attached to the ions, and thus forming part of the solute particles proper, discharge no function as solvent (*38*). Because of this, the activity coefficient of the hydrated solute will not be the same as the conventional activity coefficient computed with disregard of hydration. It is, however, easy to derive a relation between the two, provided that fixed "hydration numbers" can be assigned to the ions. Combination of this idea with the Debye-Hückel treatment leads, in the simplest case, to

$$\log \gamma_{\pm} = -\frac{A z_{+} z_{-} I^{\frac{1}{2}}}{1 + B a_i I^{\frac{1}{2}}} - \frac{n}{\nu} \log a_A - \log \left[1 + 0.001 \, M(\nu - n)m \right] \qquad (47)$$

where A and B are Debye-Hückel constants appropriate to molar concentrations (in terms of which the ionic strength, I, is expressed), n is the number of moles of water combined with ν moles of ions (ν_{+} moles of cations $+ \nu_{-}$ moles of anions), a_A is the activity of the solvent, of molecular weight M, and the other symbols have meanings previously defined. This equation contains two undetermined parameters, a_i and n, but with reasonable values assigned to them, very considerable success is achieved in representing activity coefficients in higher concentration ranges. It is still more notable that if account is taken of the obvious functional relation between a_i and n (for the more hydrated an ion, the larger it must be), then, by importation of independent information about apparent molal volumes and crystal radii of ions, and by assigning a constant "penetration distance" to each valency class of solute, a one-parameter equation emerges. This, requiring only a value of n to be assigned, is successful in dealing with activity coefficients to high concentrations ($m \sim 12/n$) for a number of solutes. But other effects of potential significance remain. There are "nonelectrolytic effects" which, by reason of differences in dimensions of solute and solvent particles, or of nonelectrostatic interactions, may give rise to departures from ideality of the kind normally associated with "athermal" or "regular" solutions respectively (*39*). There is also the possibility, when the mutual potential energy of a pair of ions at their distance of closest approach is commensurate with their thermal energy, of the formation of ion-pairs. This is a particular kind of incomplete dissociation (as distinct from incomplete ionization) for which Bjerrum developed a theoretical treatment (*40*). This treatment has been very adequately supported by experimental results, particularly in relation to solutes of high valency type, or to solutions in solvents of lower dielectric constant.

Gurney (*41*) has indicated a subtle effect based upon the possible consequences of the overlapping, or interpenetration, of the zones in which ions produce structural changes in the solvent. If such overlap causes an increase in free energy, there will be an effective repulsion, and vice versa. Since such structural changes can spread quite widely around the ions that cause them, it may be necessary to entertain the existence of quite long-range noncoulombic forces. This idea allowed Gurney to explain otherwise incomprehensible relationships between the activity coefficients of alkali metal halides.

It is abundantly clear that there is no single theory capable of dealing rigorously with all the effects which go to determine the properties of ionic solutions, and which can be grafted to the Debye-Hückel treatment of coulombic ion–ion interactions without importing a degree of empiricism. It is debatable whether any such grafting should be attempted, for the Debye-Hückel treatment is itself vulnerable to criticism on both mathematical and physical grounds (*42*), and may not adequately deal with coulombic forces over an extended concentration range. The alternatives are either to improve the Debye-Hückel treatment, or to discard it and make a new approach to the whole problem on a broader fundamental basis. Both of these alternatives have been put into practice.

Debye and Hückel used a Boltzmann distribution to calculate the charge density in the "atmosphere" around a reference ion, thereby obtaining it as an exponential function of the potential energy of an "atmosphere ion." For the condition that this energy was much smaller than the average thermal energy, however, all but the first two terms in the series expansion of the function were neglected, with great simplification of the calculation which followed. But, for an electrolyte of symmetrical valence type, the summation to obtain the net charge density turned out to involve the expansion of a hyperbolic sine, so that squared terms, and all other even-order terms, were zero. Hence, for this type of electrolyte alone, the Debye-Hückel approximation is a good deal closer than at first appears. Gronwall, La Mer, and Sandved (*43*) worked out the contributions of third and fifth order terms, arriving at an expression for the mean ionic mole fractional activity coefficient (rational activity coefficient), $f_{\pm}$, as follows

$$\ln f_{\pm} = -\frac{e^2 z^2}{2DkT} \cdot \frac{\kappa}{1 + \kappa a_i} + \left(\frac{e^2 z^2}{DkT a_i}\right)^3 [\tfrac{1}{2} X_3(\kappa a_i) - 2Y_3(\kappa a_i)]$$
$$+ \left(\frac{e^2 z^2}{DkT a_i}\right)^5 [\tfrac{1}{2} X_5(\kappa a_i) - 4Y_5(\kappa a_i)] \tag{48}$$

where e is the magnitude of the electronic charge, z is valency, D is dielectric constant, T is absolute temperature, κ is the reciprocal of the "radius of the ionic atmosphere" defined by

$$\kappa^2 = 4\pi e^2 \sum n_i z_i{}^2 / DkT$$

(where n_i is the average number of ions of the kind i per cm³) and the X and Y terms are complicated functions of κa_i, which the authors evaluated and tabulated. The case of unsymmetrical valency type electrolytes, which is even more complicated because none of the terms of the expansion reduce to zero, has been treated by La Mer, Gronwall, and Greiff (44). It is of interest that departures from the original Debye-Hückel theory are found to increase with the valency type of the electrolyte (i.e., in the order 1:1, 2:2, 3:3), with decreasing magnitude of a_i, and with decreasing dielectric constant. The departures are large for electrolytes of unsymmetrical, higher valency types, even in a medium with a dielectric constant as high as that of water. It is very satisfactory to find, however, that for 1:1-valent electrolytes in water, and for values of a_i greater than $e^2/2DkT$ ($= 3.57$ Å for water at 25°C), the contributions of the higher terms are very small. This condition is usually satisfied. For such electrolytes, then, the addition to Eq. (48) of a single linear term to deal with short-range forces is adequate for the representation of activity coefficients in solutions of concentration up to unimolal with "high accuracy" (45). The resulting equation for the mean molal ionic activity coefficient is

$$\log \gamma_\pm = -\frac{AC^{1/2}}{1 + Ba_i C^{1/2}} + \beta C + \text{Ext} - \log (1 + 0.03604m) \qquad (49)$$

where Ext represents the higher term contributions. It may be noted that C, the molar concentration, is identical with I, the ionic strength, for the 1:1-valent electrolyte, that the value of β will not be the same as that of the term with the same designation in the Hückel equation, and that the last term on the right of Eq. (49) deals with the relation between rational and molal activity coefficients for aqueous solutions.

Of the new approaches to the whole problem, mention can be made only of Mayer's "Cluster Sum" treatment (46), which, owing its inspiration to the cluster theory of imperfect gases (47), has been developed by Poirier (48) to the status of "an event of more than ordinary significance for electrolyte theory" (25). This treatment obtains the total potential of average coulombic force between "hard sphere" ions in a dielectric medium as a sum of pair-energies; it may be regarded as providing for ion-association of the Bjerrum type. It yields activity coefficients referring to systems at a pressure of $(\pi + 1)$ atm, where π is osmotic pressure. These, after correction to normal conditions, show fair agreement with experiment for solutes of various valency types up to moderate concentrations. It is, however, more striking that the theory predicts the very characteristic behavior associated with ion-pair formation in, for example, 2:2-valent electrolytes, and the typical shapes of $\ln \gamma_\pm - m^{1/2}$ curves for other electrolytes at higher concentrations, without recourse to any special parameter beyond a distance of closest ionic approach (49). It is admitted, however, that this *single* adjustable parameter is in part a proper "hard sphere diameter," and in part a term allowing for anything unrealistic in the model upon which the theory is based. The values of the diameters which are obtained are nearly the same as those determined by the Debye-Hückel theory, and the limiting laws for the activity coefficients are the same.

It may be recalled that, in relation to the determination of standard electrode potentials, "reliable information is needed about the physical effects which cause ionic solutes to be nonideal." The available information has been reviewed, and a background has been provided against which various extrapolation procedures may be assessed. It is clear that the Debye-Hückel limiting law shows up very well, but apart from this, nothing can be regarded as "reliable"; extensions of the law must therefore be used with a degree of caution and must be judged according to the results they give.[11]

From the theoretical angle, there is much to be said for using only the Debye-Hückel limiting law as an aid to extrapolation. Combination of this law [Eq. (43)] with the thermodynamic expression [Eq. (40)] for the emf of the hydrogen–silver chloride cell gives

$$E^{\circ\prime} = (E + 2k \log m) = E^\circ + 2kA'm^{1/2} \tag{50}$$

where $k = (RT/F) \ln 10$. Then a plot of $E^{\circ\prime}$ against $m^{1/2}$ should, as m approaches zero, tend to a straight line of slope $2kA'$ (or, since $A' \sim 0.5$ for aqueous solutions at 25°C, of slope k), giving an intercept equal to E°. This method was used by Lewis and Randall (50). It was also applied by Scatchard (51) to his own data, as well as the data of Linhart (52) and of Noyes and Ellis (53), and reasonable conformity with the limiting slope was found. But, in this method, great weight is placed upon the measurements made with very dilute solutions for which the errors become increasingly serious [as, for example, those due to the solubility of glass (54)].

Since Brönsted (55) and Scatchard (56) had found the equation

$$- \log \gamma_\pm = 0.5m^{1/2} - Bm \tag{51}$$

to apply to a number of electrolytes for values of m up to 0.1 mole kg^{-1}, Hitchcock (57) combined it with Eq. (40) and obtained

[11] Recent discussions in this field may be found in "The Structure of Electrolytic Solutions" (W. J. Hamer, ed.) Wiley, New York, 1959.

$$E^{\circ\prime} - km^{\frac{1}{2}} = E^{\circ} - 2kBm \qquad (52)$$

so that a plot of the left-hand side against m should give a straight line of slope $-2kB$ and intercept E°. It was admitted that this method cannot give a true straight line for more than a limited concentration range, but in view of the slightness of the curvature, a flexible spline could be used for extrapolating. The Hitchcock method, in the more sophisticated form

$$E^{\circ\prime} - 2ka^{\prime}m^{\frac{1}{2}} = E^{\circ} - 2kBm \qquad (53)$$

was used by Harned and Ehlers (58) for their work on the hydrogen–silver chloride cell over the temperature range from 0° to 60°C, but it remains true that, even if it is "a simple, practical extrapolation" (59), the plots are not strictly rectilinear (60).

The method of Brown and MacInnes (61) uses the full, but unextended, Debye–Hückel expression [Eq. (42)], which, combined with Eq. (40), gives

$$E^{\circ\prime} - 2kA^{\prime}m^{\frac{1}{2}} = E^{\circ} - B^{\prime}a_i m^{\frac{1}{2}} (E^{\circ\prime} - E^{\circ}) \qquad (54)$$

A plot of the left-hand side of this equation against $m^{\frac{1}{2}} (E^{\circ\prime} - E^{\circ})$ should give a straight line of slope $-B^{\prime}a_i$ and intercept E°, but a short series of successive approximations is needed until the value of E° used in computing the abscissae agrees with the value derived from the intercept. The method can be illustrated by data derived from the hydrogen–calomel cell (60),

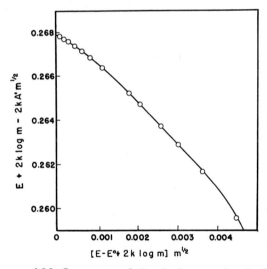

FIG. 6. Brown and MacInnes extrapolation, hydrogen–calomel cell data (60).

shown in Fig. 6, where it can be seen that the plot appears to be strictly linear for the lower range of concentrations ($m < 0.02$ mole kg^{-1}), but becomes increasingly curved with higher concentrations. Probably this method, using an equation containing only one undetermined parameter, is the most satisfactory compromise, but it still suffers from the restriction of the concentration range within which it is valid, and it needs measurements of rather high accuracy. For purposes of comparison, the Hitchcock extrapolation, applied to the same data, is shown in Fig. 7.

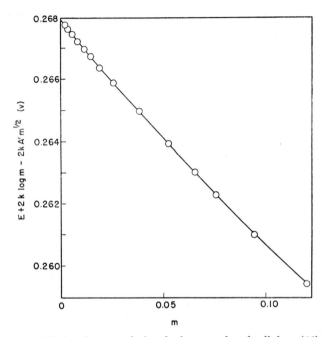

Fig. 7. Hitchcock extrapolation, hydrogen–calomel cell data (60).

Guggenheim and Prue (62) adapted Eq. (46) to obtain

$$E^{\circ\prime} - \frac{2kA'm^{\frac{1}{2}}}{1 + m^{\frac{1}{2}}} = E^{\circ} - Bm \qquad (55)$$

which, applied to the same hydrogen–calomel cell data up to $m = 0.08$ mole kg^{-1}, gave the good rectilinear plot illustrated in Fig. 8, extrapolating to the same E° values as given by the Brown and MacInnes method.

The modification of Eq. (55) suited to the Hückel equation is self-evident, and a similar linear plot is obtained. This method, *inter alia*, has been used in more recent work on this cell, on which a preliminary report has been made (63). It is clear that a "two-parameter equation" is capable of fitting the results within the present limits of experimental accuracy up to $m \sim 0.1$ mole kg^{-1}.

It appears to be the case that, for determining E°, the accuracy of the data is still of more significance than the choice of extrapolation method. But a conclusion of this kind, reached mainly by examination of data relating to a single temperature, may not be valid in the wider context of finding E° over a temperature range. Clearly, it would not be defensible to regard a function as sound for extrapolation, but unsound for interpolation,

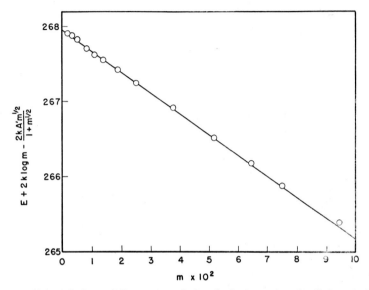

FIG. 8. Guggenheim and Prue extrapolation, hydrogen–calomel cell data (60).

when applied for both purposes over one and the same experimental concentration range. Then, if the concentration range is wide, very great care must be taken that neither E_m° or log $\gamma_\pm$ are being forced to fit some function adopted mainly for calculational convenience. This aspect becomes of enhanced significance when it is desired to study the temperature dependence of these quantities.

The method used in the most exhaustive study of the hydrogen–silver chloride cell yet accomplished, by Bates and Bower (64), was no doubt chosen with this aspect in mind. Measurements were made on 81 cells at 17 temperatures from 0° to 95°C. The extended Debye-Hückel equation (49) was combined with the thermodynamic equation (40) to give

$$E + 2k\left[\log m - \frac{A'm^{1/2}}{1 + B'a_im^{1/2}} + \text{Ext} - \log\left(1 + 0.03604m\right)\right]$$
$$= E^\circ - \beta m \quad (56)$$

with appropriate adjustments for uniform use of the molality scale. This equation was used at each temperature for solutions of concentration up to decimolal. The value of a_i was determined by conducting a least squares extrapolation for each of several assumed values of a_i, and by plotting the standard deviations of the experimental points from the least squares line against these values. In this way the value of a_i to minimize these deviations was found by interpolation. Somewhat surprisingly, it was found that a_i increased with rising temperature.

Summarizing and recalculating previous measurements on this cell, Bates and Bower showed that the main differences in the $E°$ values were attributable, in the end, to real, physical differences between the electrodes of the cell systems used. Thus, Harned and Ehler's results (58), recalculated by Swinehart (65) by the Hitchcock method, with use of revised values of the fundamental constants, gave $E°$ at 25°C = 0.22254 abs v Further recalculated in terms of Eq. (56), 0.22252 abs v was obtained, considerably higher than that derived from Bates and Bower's own measurements, namely, 0.22234 abs v. The disconcerting magnitude of this discrepancy certainly emphasizes the need for experimental advances. Fortunately, it is the quantity $(E - E°)$ which is of primary thermodynamic significance and, under one set of circumstances, may include but a small fraction of the deviations to which E and $E°$ are subject separately.

Mention must be made of variations in the direct method of determining standard electrode potentials. The first of these arises from the consideration that the essential principle is an extrapolation of measured emf's to zero ionic strength; experimentally, the required variation in ionic strength may be established by the addition of a second electrolyte. Thus, Harned and Paxton (66) used cells containing hydrochloric acid and strontium chloride in obtaining an independent value for $E°$ of the silver–silver chloride electrode.

The cell

$$\text{H}_2 \mid \text{HA}(m_1), \text{NaA}(m_2), \text{NaCl}(m_3) \mid \text{AgCl} \mid \text{Ag} \qquad \text{(F)}$$

in which HA is a weak acid and NaA is its fully ionized sodium salt, has been widely used for the determination of the thermodynamic dissociation constants of weak acids. The electrolyte is seen to be buffered, and the cell lends itself to accurate measurements at low hydrogen ion concentrations and relatively low ionic strengths. The remarkable agreement between the dissociation constant of acetic acid in aqueous solution at 25°C obtained by Harned and Ehlers (58) in this way, and that found by MacInnes and Shedlovsky (67) by the conductance method is a classic example of outstanding achievement in both these fields of electrochemical endeavor. The emf of cell (F) is given by an adaptation of Eq. (38), namely,

$$E = E^\circ - k \log K_a - k \log \frac{m_{HA}m_{Cl^-}}{m_{A^-}} - k \log \frac{\gamma_{HA}\gamma_{Cl^-}}{\gamma_{A^-}} \tag{57}$$

where K_a is the thermodynamic dissociation constant of the acid HA. The molality of the chloride ion, m_{Cl^-}, is identical with m_3, and the values of m_{HA} and m_{A^-} are obtainable from m_1 and m_2 when K_a is known, or by a short series of successive approximations when it is not. The activity coefficient quotient contained in the last term on the right is very nearly unity and varies very little as a function of total concentration; extrapolation to zero concentration is therefore peculiarly easy and accurate. Although this method has been primarily used to determine K_a when E° is known, there is no reason why it should not be reversed, and thus be used to determine E°, given an independent value of K_a. This was, in effect, done by Owen (68), who compared the cells

$$\text{H}_2 \mid \text{HBO}_2(m), \text{NaBO}_2(m), \text{NaBr}(m) \mid \text{AgBr} \mid \text{Ag} \tag{G}$$

$$\text{H}_2 \mid \text{HBO}_2(m), \text{NaBO}_2(m), \text{NaCl}(m) \mid \text{AgCl} \mid \text{Ag} \tag{H}$$

in which, it will be noted, all the molalities, m, are identical. In this case, Eq. (57) may be written for the two cells

$$\begin{aligned} E_{HBr} &= E^\circ_{HBr} - k \log K_a - k \log m - f(\gamma) \\ E_{HCl} &= E^\circ_{HCl} - k \log K_a - k \log m - f'(\gamma) \end{aligned} \tag{58}$$

Thus, K_a may be evaluated or not, for subtraction of one equation from the other gives at once

$$E^\circ_{HBr} = E^\circ_{HCl} + E_{HBr} - E_{HCl} \tag{59}$$

on the assumption that $f(\gamma) = f'(\gamma)$, which will be true to the closer approximation the more dilute the solutions used. The standard potential of the silver–silver bromide electrode is thus determined by comparison with that of the silver–silver chloride electrode. Fair agreement has been obtained, in this case, between the E° values determined by the three methods so far discussed (69).

For electrodes reversible to the same ion, a more direct comparison is available. Thus the cell

$$\text{Ag} \mid \text{AgCl} \mid \text{HCl (aq, } m) \mid \text{Hg}_2\text{Cl}_2 \mid \text{Hg} \tag{I}$$

formed by combining the silver–silver chloride and calomel electrodes has an emf equal to the difference between the standard electrode potentials, independently of the chloride ion activity in the electrolyte (70).

Basic problems associated with the determination of standard electrode potentials have now been reviewed, and it would not be appropriate to extend the discussion further. In spite of the ingenuity and care lavished upon these determinations and in spite of their importance, it is doubtful whether any standard potential can be quoted to closer than ±0.1 mv for any electrode without knowledge of its history, method of preparation, and condition of use. The hydrogen electrode alone, by a dispensation for which all electrochemists should be thankful, is subject to no such limitation.

The root of this difficulty is undoubtedly the problem of how, experimentally, to establish equilibria which involve solid components in reproducible standard states, which should be "thermodynamic ground states" of minimum energy. No such trouble arises in relation to homogeneous solution phases. This is the basis of a recent suggestion that each silver–silver chloride electrode should be standardized with respect to 0.01 molal aqueous hydrochloric acid, for which it should be agreed that the mean molal ionic activity coefficients are exactly 0.904 at 25°C and 0.908 at 0°C, until such time as a further change is shown to be necessary (*71*).

VI. Cells with Liquid Junctions

The cells so far discussed have contained one solution and two kinds of electrodes, severally reversible to cations and anions. Important as these cells are, they are limited in number and application because of the shortage of reversible electrodes. Fortunately, there is another class of cells less restricted in this way. This class contains cells with liquid junctions, in which at least two different solutions make liquid–liquid contact with each other in one or more pairs. The simplest cells of this kind are those which contain only two solutions which differ only in concentration. These are "concentration cells with transference" or "concentration cells with transport," names which arise because ions are directly transferred from one solution to the other during the operation of the cells. These cells need only one kind of electrode. Thus, the silver–silver chloride electrode will serve for the study of all chlorides in solution by this method. There is a rather widely held view that any cell with a liquid junction is less suitable for rigorous thermodynamic treatment than any cell without a liquid junction. It will shortly be seen how this impression arises, but it has already been indicated that the distinction between cells with and without liquid junctions is not as sharp as it appears at first sight, and some authorities vigorously oppose this view. Whether it is justified or not, it is certainly true that concentration cells with transport must be regarded as important instruments for obtaining accurate thermodynamic data.

With increasing difference between the two solutions which form a single junction (both ions in common, one ion in common, no ions in common), the theoretical and experimental problems concerned become less tractable. In all cases it is necessary to take into account a "liquid junction potential" which makes an essential contribution to the emf of the cell concerned. There is, however, yet another class of cell in which an attempt is made to reduce the liquid junction potential below the limits of significance. This, if successful, carries the advantage that one electrode of the cell may be invariant, becoming a constant reference electrode of fixed potential. In this case, the emf of the cell varies directly with the potential of the other electrode. Although it is clear that these suppositions are nonthermodynamic, it is a fact that for many practical purposes such cells are of wider application than any others, and occupy an important place in the general apparatus of electrochemistry. They must be used, however, with adequate safeguards, and the principal one is the realization that liquid junction potentials never can be eliminated, although they may be minimized. If they are assumed to be zero, the errors arising from this assumption must be estimated. An alternative procedure is to calibrate the reference electrode of supposedly fixed potential in a cell the other electrode of which has been characterized accurately with the minimum of nonthermodynamic assumptions. The liquid junction potential is then included in the fixed "standard potential" of the reference electrode. These considerations indicate why some attention must be given in this book to cells with liquid junctions.

Cells with liquid junctions can never be equilibrium systems because at each junction between dissimilar solutions an irreversible process of diffusion must occur, and must continue until the whole liquid phase is uniform in composition. It would therefore appear to be unsound to reason thermodynamically about such *disequilibrium* systems. But as long as the slow diffusion does not essentially alter the cell, it seems safe enough to ignore it when discussing what happens when electricity is reversibly transferred through the cell. For such a transfer to be reversible, however, the homogeneous solutions around the electrodes of the cell must meet without any discontinuity of composition. Clearly, unless this is the case, different ions will be transferred from their own milieu to a foreign one according to the direction of current flow, which will then, obviously, be irreversible. If, on the other hand, the solutions meet in a boundary zone in which the composition varies *continuously* from one extreme to the other, the composition of each elementary lamina of solution will differ but infinitesimally from those of the elementary laminae on either side of it. An infinitesimal transfer of electricity can then be made without infringing the conditions for reversibility. The requirement is easily met if the boundary zone is formed by the natural interdiffusion of the two electrode solutions. A third, or "bridge" solution may be involved as an intermediary, but it must form two "continuous junctions," one with each of the electrode solutions on either side of it.

Ideally, ions are kinetically independent entities, which participate with all the others in random thermal motions. In principle, each kind of ion has its own diffusion coefficient in a given medium at a given temperature. But this ignores the fact that every real, electrically neutral electrolyte solution contains at least two kinds of ions, which can never be regarded as independent components. If such a solution is brought into contact with pure solvent, or with a more dilute solution of the same kind, diffusion at once begins. If one kind of ion is more mobile than the other, it will tend to diffuse ahead. If it does so, it must set up an electrical double layer, involving charge separation and the establishment of an electrical field. This field will clearly be in such a direction as to retard the motion of the speedier ions, and to hasten the slower ones. A kinetic steady state is rapidly established in which both kinds of ion diffuse at the same rate, and in which there is a constant potential difference across the boundary zone within which concentration gradients are confined. Electrolytes therefore diffuse as a whole, and electroneutrality can be regarded as everywhere preserved, the extent of the charge separation concerned in the setting up of the electrical potential gradient being an infinitesimal of the second order. There can be no doubt about the reality of liquid junction potentials, nor of the basic mechanism by which they are established; whether they can be measured unambiguously, or can even be regarded as determinable quantities, is another matter.

The transfer of an infinitesimal quantity of electricity across a boundary zone formed by the interdiffusion of two homogeneous electrode solutions is to be considered. If these two solutions are identical except in concentration, cations and anions within the zone diffuse in the same direction with the same speed, under the influence of the chemical potential gradient. When electricity is passed, it is carried by cations and anions moving in opposite directions with, like as not, different speeds, under the influence of the electrical potential gradient. If the transfer is to be reversible, it must not disturb the configuration of the diffusion zone, and the potential difference imposed to accomplish it must not modify the natural potential gradient established by the diffusion process. In considering the reversible transfer of material between bulk phases, it is often said that the amounts of the phases are to be so large that they suffer no change in composition as a result of the transfer. The same principle must apply to the boundary zone, even if it does need a greater feat of the imagination; alternatively, the transfer of electricity *must* be infinitesimal in magnitude, even if the effects of it "per faraday" are calculated by proportion.

Electricity is carried across an infinitely thin element of the diffusion zone by cations and anions in proportion to their transport numbers which, within the element, are constant. There is no change in composition because incomings and outgoings exactly balance, as for the "middle compartment" of the Hittorf transport number apparatus. The electrical work expended in performing the transfer of electricity is equated to the increase in Gibbs free energy which accompanies it, i.e.,

$$-dF \cdot dE_J = dG \tag{60}$$

where dF is an infinitesimal quantity of electricity transferred and dE_J is the infinitesimal difference of electrical potential across the element. There is also, for each ion, an infinitesimal difference of chemical potential across the element, and the sum of these gives rise to dG. Arguing by proportion, then, "per faraday transferred,"

$$-F \cdot dE_J = \sum \frac{t_i}{z_i} d\mu_i \tag{61}$$

where t_i is the transport number of the ion i within the element, z_i is its valency (with appropriate sign), and the summation includes all ions. Since

$$d\mu_i = RT \, d \ln a_i \tag{62}$$

$$-dE_J = \frac{RT}{F} \sum \frac{t_i}{z_i} d \ln a_i \tag{63}$$

which is the basic differential equation for liquid junction potential. Strictly, this equation should contain a term of the kind $t_s \cdot d \ln a_s$ to deal with solvent transport. The magnitude of such a term, however, is uncertain because the amount of solvent electroconvectively transported is unknown, but it will become negligible with increasing dilution of the solutions.

Transport numbers change with concentration, so that t_i is not constant but varies from one side of the diffusion zone to the other. The zone, as a whole, does not therefore behave like a Hittorf "middle compartment," releasing on one side what enters on the other. Consequently, the total free energy effect per faraday transferred across the whole zone must be found by an integration. Hence the total liquid junction potential is given by

$$-E_J = \frac{RT}{F} \int_I^{II} \sum \frac{t_i}{z_i} d \ln a_i \tag{64}$$

where the limits of integration are set by the values of t_i and a_i relating to the homogeneous electrode solutions I and II. For the special case in which these solutions differ only in concentration, t_i and a_i are both single-valued functions of concentration. The "geometry" of the boundary is then of no significance, and the liquid junction potential turns out to be independent of the way in which the boundary is formed.

It is this fact which confers special importance to "concentration cells with transport" of the kind shown here

$$\text{Ag} \mid \text{AgCl} \mid \text{NaCl}, m_1 \vdots \text{NaCl}, m_2 \mid \text{AgCl} \mid \text{Ag} \qquad \text{(J)}$$
$$m_1 > m_2$$

where the dotted vertical line is used to indicate the liquid–liquid junction. The natural cell reaction is the transfer of sodium chloride from the higher to the lower concentration.

The electrode reactions transfer one mole of chloride ion per faraday from left to right, while chloride ions migrate from right to left, and sodium ions from left to right, across the boundary. The total free energy change is

$$\Delta G = \mu_{\text{Cl}^-}^{\text{II}} - \mu_{\text{Cl}^-}^{\text{I}} + \int_{\text{I}}^{\text{II}} (1 - t_{\text{Cl}^-}) d\mu_{\text{Na}^+} - \int_{\text{I}}^{\text{II}} t_{\text{Cl}^-} d\mu_{\text{Cl}^-} \qquad (65)$$

bearing in mind that, at all points, $t_{\text{Na}^+} + t_{\text{Cl}^-} = 1$, and that $z_{\text{Na}^+} = +1$ and $z_{\text{Cl}^-} = -1$. The first two terms on the right-hand side of Eq. (65) may be replaced by

$$\int_{\text{I}}^{\text{II}} d\mu_{\text{Cl}^-}$$

so that

$$\Delta G = \int_{\text{I}}^{\text{II}} (1 - t_{\text{Cl}^-}) d\mu_{\text{Na}^+} + \int_{\text{I}}^{\text{II}} (1 - t_{\text{Cl}^-}) d\mu_{\text{Cl}^-}$$

$$= \frac{RT}{F} \int_{\text{I}}^{\text{II}} t_{\text{Na}^+} d \ln a_{\text{Na}^+} + \frac{RT}{F} \int_{\text{I}}^{\text{II}} t_{\text{Na}^+} d \ln a_{\text{Cl}^-}$$

$$= \frac{2RT}{F} \int_{\text{I}}^{\text{II}} t_{\text{Na}^+} d \ln \gamma_\pm m$$

Hence the emf of the cell may be written

$$E = -2k \int_{m_1}^{m_2} t_{\text{Na}^+} d \ln \gamma_\pm m \qquad (66)$$

in which, it will be noticed, no "nonthermodynamic" single ion properties remain, except for determinable transport numbers.

Not only are cells of this kind well-behaved but, as already pointed out, they require electrodes reversible to only one kind of ion. Since very accurate transport number data have become available, mainly from the refined moving-boundary method of MacInnes and Longsworth (72), these cells have been exploited for accurate activity coefficient determinations. Clearly, in this, an extrapolation must also be involved in order to convert ratios of activity coefficients to the scale defined by $\gamma_{\pm} \to 1$ as $m \to 0$. Alternative procedures have been used (73). It is of interest that the Brown and MacInnes method (61) was developed in this connection and, applied to the measurements of Shedlovsky and MacInnes (74) on hydrochloric acid concentration cells, gave good agreement with the results of Harned and Ehlers (58) from cells without transport. More recent work (75, 76) has consolidated this position, and there is no doubt that cells of this kind take their place with other methods for accurate activity coefficient determinations. It is therefore clear, from the discussions in the preceding section, that they also play a part in the fixing of standard electrode potentials.

Cells in which solutions of different electrolytes meet are different in behavior, for much depends upon how the junctions are formed. Much ingenuity has been exercised in devising methods of forming junctions with reproducible properties (77). Obviously, because of this difficulty, such cells are of correspondingly less practical value, except in one important connection. This arises because of the nonthermodynamic, but compelling, desire to set up cells in which one of the electrodes can be regarded as of fixed potential. The electrode in question must clearly have all its component phases of fixed composition, so that the standard solution phase must make a liquid junction with the nonstandard electrolyte in the other part of the cell, and the problem is, what to do about the liquid junction potential which must be present. Steps may be taken to calculate and allow for it, or to minimize it until it is negligible. In either case, further insight is needed into the magnitudes of these potentials and possible methods of computing them.

To obtain this, a return is made to Eq. (63), but, for simplicity, nonideality is ignored, and molar concentrations are used, i.e.,

$$-dE_J = \frac{RT}{F} \sum \frac{t_i}{z_i} d \ln C_i \qquad (67)$$

Let the boundary solution, at every point, have a composition obtainable by mixing a fraction x of electrode solution 2 with a fraction $(1 - x)$ of electrode solution 1. Then the concentration of each ion will be given by (dropping the subscript i),

$$\begin{aligned} C &= xC_2 + (1 - x)C_1 \\ &= C_1 + (C_2 - C_1)x \end{aligned} \qquad (68)$$

Hence,

$$d \ln C = dC/C = [(C_2 - C_1)/C]dx \qquad (69)$$

The transport number of each ion is defined by

$$t = Cuz/[x \sum C_2 uz + (1 - x) \sum C_1 uz] \qquad (70)$$

where u and z represent ionic mobilities (cm^2 sec^{-1} volt^{-1}) and valencies, with appropriate signs. Combination with Eq. (69) and rearrangement gives

$$\frac{t}{z} \cdot d \ln C = \frac{u(C_2 - C_1)dx}{\sum C_1 uz + x \sum uz(C_2 - C_1)} \tag{71}$$

Substitution in Eq. (67) then leads, on integration, to

$$-E_J = \frac{RT}{F} \int_{x=0}^{x=1} \frac{\sum u(C_2 - C_1)dx}{\sum C_1 uz + x \sum uz(C_2 - C_1)} \tag{72}$$

$$E_J = \frac{RT}{F} \cdot \frac{\sum u(C_2 - C_1)}{\sum uz(C_2 - C_1)} \ln \frac{\sum uzC_1}{\sum uzC_2} \tag{73}[12]$$

which is the Henderson equation (78) for liquid junction potential. It contains nothing characteristic of the "geometry" of the junction, but does require continuity of composition.

If only univalent ions are involved, the equation becomes

$$E_J = \frac{RT}{F} \cdot \frac{(U_1 - V_1) - (U_2 - V_2)}{(U_1 + V_1) - (U_2 + V_2)} \ln \frac{(U_1 + V_1)}{(U_2 + V_2)} \tag{74}$$

where the U and V terms are $\sum C_i u_i$ for cations and anions respectively, appropriate to solutions indicated by subscripts, and the ionic mobilities, u_i, are taken as positive. If the solutions are of the same concentration and have one ion in common, the equation reduces to the Lewis and Sargent formula (79),

$$E_J = \frac{RT}{F} \ln \frac{\Lambda_1}{\Lambda_2} \tag{75}$$

where Λ_1 and Λ_2 are the equivalent conductances of the solutions concerned. Tests of this relation (80) have shown it to be surprisingly successful in a number of cases.

The present interest, however, centers upon the use of "salt bridges" in attempts to eliminate liquid junction potentials. Their effectiveness can be illustrated by data from the cell (81)

$$\text{Hg} \mid \text{Hg}_2\text{Cl}_2 \mid 0.1 \ N \ \text{HCl} \ \vdots \ xN \ \text{KCl} \ \vdots \ 0.1 \ N \ \text{KCl} \mid \text{Hg}_2\text{Cl}_2 \mid \text{Hg} \quad (\text{K})$$

When $x = 0.1 \ N$, the emf of the cell is 27.0 mv, which can be credibly identified with the liquid junction potential between 0.1 N HCl and 0.1 N KCl solutions. When x is increased, the emf falls, being 5.15 mv for $x = 1.75 \ N$ and 1.1 mv for $x = 3.5 \ N$. It is common to use saturated potassium chloride solution ($N \sim 4.2$) for this purpose. If this is "solution

[12] $\int_0^1 \frac{a dx}{b + cx} = \frac{a}{c} \ln \left(1 + \frac{c}{b}\right)$

1," enormously concentrated compared with "solution 2," it can be seen that the coefficient of the logarithmic term in Eq. (74) will approximate to

$$\frac{4.2(u_{K^+} - u_{Cl^-})}{4.2(u_{K^+} + u_{Cl^-})}$$

and since $u_{K^+} \sim u_{Cl^-}$, the entire junction potential will approach zero. Other highly soluble salts with ions as close in mobility as possible (e.g., ammonium nitrate) may be used, but in no case can complete elimination of liquid junction potential be assumed to take place. On the contrary, a residual potential, or what is worse, an uncertainty about it, around 1 to 2 mv must be faced. The assumptions made in deriving the Henderson equation — that the boundary is of the "mixture type," that ionic mobilities are independent of concentration, and that activity coefficients are unity — are all so gross that nothing better can be expected.

Various kinds of liquid junction have been classified and discussed by Guggenheim (81). Of these the simplest is the free diffusion junction formed from an initially sharp boundary; it has been widely used in accurate emf measurement and requires no special precautions except, ideally, the preservation of cylindrical symmetry. Ingenious devices have been described to satisfy this condition (82). It is doubtful whether the procedure suggested by Bjerrum (83), of making measurements with 3.5 N and 1.75 N potassium chloride bridges and subtracting the difference in emf from that obtained with the first, is valid. Similarly, his suggestion that bridge solutions should be made "equitransferent" by using appropriate salt mixtures, which has been extensively explored (84, 85), has recently been shown to have no advantage (86).

In spite of these disabilities, salt bridges are very widely used, and for many purposes in which an absolute uncertainty of 1 to 2 mv can be tolerated, are entirely satisfactory. They are also of great importance in cells of the kind almost universally used in pH determinations.

H₂ | test solution ⦙ KCl (satd) ⦙ reference electrode of fixed potential   (L)

The left-hand electrode may be any electrode responding to hydrogen ion activity in the same way as the hydrogen electrode (glass, quinhydrone, metal–metal oxide), and the reference electrode is normally a saturated calomel electrode:

$$\cdots ⦙ KCl \; (satd) \mid Hg_2Cl_2 \mid Hg \qquad (M)$$

In this case, the saturated potassium chloride solution which makes the junction may be called a "half-bridge." The use of such electrodes in this way is put upon a new basis by, in effect, combining the liquid junction potential with the agreed standard potential of the fixed reference electrode. Thus, if the test solution is replaced by a buffer solution derived from a weak acid of which the thermodynamic dissociation constant is accurately known (from conductance measurements, or from cells without liquid junctions), the reference electrode may be independently "calibrated." A practical pH scale can be set up in this way (*87*), but this matter is discussed in a chapter which follows.

Finally, mention must be made of ingenious extrapolation procedures for the complete elimination of liquid junction potentials. The cell

$$\text{Ag} \mid \text{AgCl} \left| \begin{array}{c} \text{KCl}, \, xm \\ \text{KNO}_3, \, (1 - x)m \end{array} \right. \vdots \, \text{KNO}_3, \, m \, \vdots \left. \begin{array}{c} \text{AgNO}_3, \, xm \\ \text{KNO}_3, \, (1 - x)m \end{array} \right| \text{AgCl} \mid \text{Ag}$$

$$(\text{N})$$

clearly has an emf, as x tends to zero, entirely devoid of any liquid junction potentials. Satisfactory extrapolation methods have been devised (*88*) and lead to results (in this case the solubility product of silver chloride) in very close agreement with those obtained by independent methods [such as conductometric titration (*89*)]. It is appropriate to mention that, handled in this way, the cell

$$\text{Ag} \mid \text{AgCl} \left| \begin{array}{c} \text{KCl}, \, xm \\ \text{KNO}_3, \, (1 - x)m \end{array} \right. \vdots \left. \begin{array}{c} \text{KBr}, \, xm \\ \text{KNO}_3, \, (1 - x)m \end{array} \right| \text{AgBr} \mid \text{Ag} \quad (\text{O})$$

has given a difference between $E°$ values for silver–silver chloride and silver–silver bromide electrodes in excellent agreement with the data from cells without liquid junction (*90*).

VII. Common Experimental Problems

Difficulties in making and using particular electrodes are discussed in later chapters. Since many experimental problems might go by default for the very reason that they are common to most electrode systems, or to potentiometric measurements in general, it is desirable to collect them in one place. Experimental troubles are too diverse to be accommodated in any brief, connected account, so that in the following sections, a somewhat arbitrary classification has been made, and limited terms of reference have been chosen. Thus, it would be impracticable to discuss the design and construction of measuring instruments. The experimenter is very well served by the instrument makers, and it is reasonable to limit the discussion to things for which he should himself be responsible, and to difficulties he can meet without specialized assistance.

A. Use of Instruments

1. Insulation

The importance of adequate insulation is self-evident and is normally well looked after when high impedance electronic voltmeters are used, as in commercial pH meters for use with glass electrodes. Relevant factors are the internal resistance of the experimental cell (for glass electrodes, as high as 2–5×10^9 ohms) and the grid current of the electrometer valve (which can be, but often is not, below 10^{-12} amp). Insulation difficulties are not usually expected to affect ordinary potentiometric measurements, but this again may depend upon the resistance of the cell. Troubles have in fact been encountered in using very high grade potentiometers in a special way (Section VII,B, 2) with very high resistance cells.

It is obvious that due attention must be given to the insulation of all parts of an experimental circuit. Even if standing an acid-daubed storage battery on a wooden bench is hardly mentionable, it is believed that glass cells immersed in water-filled thermostats are not infrequent offenders. If oil-filled baths are inconvenient, the device of treating the outside of the cell with a trace of silicone grease may be used with advantage.

2. Screening

It is not immediately apparent why the protection of apparatus used for essentially dc measurements from the effects of stray external fields should be important, unless the circuit contains some rectifying element. Yet this does seem to be the case, and it is common experience that the use of an "equipotential surface," supplied by an earthed, well-conducting metal sheet under the whole of the potentiometric equipment is very advantageous in eliminating erraticities in null-point indications (91). Coaxial cables, with earthed screens, are also to be recommended for connections between potentiometer and cell.

3. Calibrations

Even potentiometers of the highest grade should not be used, in accurate work, without internal calibration. This can most easily be done, by an obvious method, with the aid of two ancillary potentiometers, which can be of simple type. It is as well to keep a continuous check upon any possible "zero error."

Since all measurements of emf are based upon comparisons with the emf of a standard cell, the greatest care is necessary to keep this standard unchanged. Repeated checks against an independent standard, as well as periodical calibrations against national standards, are desirable. Cells of this kind are not normally constructed in the laboratory, and no reference will be made to the considerable literature on the subject. If it is not normally practicable to keep standard cells under permanent thermostatic temperature control, it is a satisfactory compromise to protect them from sudden temperature changes by keeping them inside a large Dewar vessel. The vessel should be fitted with a thermometer adequate to take account of the temperature dependence of the standard emf. A useful check on the calibration of a potentiometer (which cannot be assumed not to change with time) is to arrange for one or other of a pair of standard cells to be used in the "measuring circuit."

4. Galvanometers

The sensitivity of the galvanometer, used as a null-point indicator, which may be required depends upon the desired accuracy of measurement and upon the internal resistance of the cell. Usually it is found that the cell resistance is too high to achieve the advantageous condition that it is equal to that of the galvanometer, and it is, in any case, a quantity which will vary widely from cell to cell. Clearly, a high resistance galvanometer must be used ($> 10^3$ ohms); it should be equipped with a sensitivity control, and should be critically damped. A round figure for sensitivity adequate for readings, under normal conditions, to the nearest 10 μv is 400 mm μa^{-1}. It is perfectly practicable, with a suitable galvanometer and a potentiometer lacking a slide wire (slide wires are not favored), to obtain the last significant figure by a "method of swings" (6).

5. Spurious Potentials

Potentiometers, like other mechanical devices, require periodical attention and service. Grossly erratic behavior will, of course, arise from fouling of current-carrying contacts in the circuit which provides the standard potential gradients. The other contacts, which divide these gradients suitably, carry no current at the null point, and do not immediately provide such unambiguous danger signals when they become dirty. But supposedly "homogeneous" metal–metal contacts which are really contaminated with foreign material are always possible sources of spurious potential differences and of rectifying actions. Troubles of this nature may be indicated by "double deflection" of the galvanometer, i.e., initial and final deflections in opposite directions.

Thermoelectric effects are not normally encountered unless considerable temperature differences exist between various parts of the circuit. If this is the case, all "unlike" metal–metal contacts should be matched in pairs, each member of the pair being kept at the same temperature, and temperature gradients should as far as possible be confined to homogeneous conductors.

B. Electrode and Cell Construction

1. General Considerations

If measured emf values are to be of absolute thermodynamic significance, they should be determined by the properties of pure bulk phases alone, and should not depend upon the way in which the cells and electrodes are constructed. It is desirable to provide experimental evidence that this condition has been satisfied by obtaining identically the same results with electrodes that vary widely in design and history. Sometimes this is easy, and sometimes it is difficult or (at present) impossible. If it should be impossible, the clearest and most complete account should be given of the preparation of the electrodes, including evidence of their reproducibility in behavior and of steps which may have been taken to cancel out the "nonthermodynamic" factors which partially control their potentials. The provision of a cell with multiple electrodes, each of a kind prepared in the same way, is a desirable insurance against sporadic fluctuations in properties, but it is of no value in dealing with the more fundamental difficulty.

General features of cell design and use cannot be laid down without reference to the objectives of the work in hand. There must be some matching between means and ends and, preferably, an intention to take a little more trouble than may prove to be necessary. At one end of the scale of experimental elaboration, it may be that electrodes carried in bungs, closing two-ounce pots for electrode vessels, contact tubes plugged with cotton wool to hinder diffusion, and the like, will be perfectly satisfactory. Further along the scale, all-glass apparatus with greased joints and taps, and arrangements for excluding oxygen, may be adequate for highly reversible electrode systems not very sensitive to contamination. At the other extreme, precautions to exclude grease and to ensure rigorous freedom from surface-active impurities may be vitally necessary. All that can be done is to direct attention to the circumstances in which one or another precaution may become necessary.

2. Cell Impedance

All steps should be taken, consistent with other requirements, to reduce the ohmic resistance of a cell to a minimum, in order to make the best use of the sensitivity of recording instruments. In the case that a high impedance input electronic voltmeter is used, these aspects are not usually significant, but it remains true that the most accurate measurements are carried out by means of classical potentiometers, when they are important. The low conductance of dilute solutions, particularly in nonaqueous media, is a standing difficulty, calling for a cell design in which the conducting paths are as short and wide as possible. But it may be necessary, even in a cell "without liquid junction," to prevent interdiffusion of the electrode solutions, and it may be tempting to use capillary connections to achieve this. This is often found to result in an intolerable loss of sensitivity. The conflict of interests may sometimes be resolved by inserting a wide-bore tap, opened only when measurement is to be made, between the electrode vessels. Unobserved gas bubbles, trapped in "solution circuits" are sometimes responsible for inordinately high cell resistance.

The exchange current of an electrode, discussed in Section III, is also relevant under this heading, for if it is inadequate, the cell impedance will be correspondingly high, and the cell will be polarizable. This may lead to a game which might be called "chasing the null point," as well as to the extraneous influences that were previously indicated. The general comment is that, given satisfactory electrode preparation (reasonable homogeneity of surface, freedom from "bald patches," etc.), it may still be advantageous to make the electrodes as large as circumstances allow. Apart from increased exchange current, reduced sensitivity to surface contamination and the like, the larger the electrode–solution interface, the better the chance that it will be "representative," with local abnormalities "integrated out."

On occasions, it may be necessary to use cells with an extremely high internal resistance (as with glass electrode cells), and this usually involves discarding the potentiometer in favor of the valve voltmeter. But attention may be drawn to the device of using the out-of-balance voltage between the cell and the potentiometer to charge a high insulation-resistance condenser; at the null point there is zero ballistic deflection when the condenser is connected independently to a galvanometer (*92*).

3. Connections to Electrodes

These connections often involve glass–metal seals which are a perennial source of trouble. Platinum–soft glass seals are satisfactory and may be adopted, with or without graded seals, if soft glass–solution contacts can be tolerated. Otherwise, use may be made of platinum–Pyrex pinch seals. The simplest form is the Housekeeper seal (*92a*), in which the edges of the flattened 0.05 mm diam platinum wire are filed to a sharp V-shape before being pinched into a Pyrex capillary. Seals based on thin platinum foil are described in relation to hydrogen electrodes in Chapter 2, Section II,B,1, and can be made vacuum-tight (*93*). In these, a platinum strip, 1–2 cm × 0.05 cm × 0.001 cm is "pinched" into a thin walled Pyrex tube, mechanical strength being supplied either by suitable struts, or, better, by subsequent building up of the seal to a robust thickness by means of molten glass. It has been found that such seals are less stable if formed at the very end of a contact tube; they should be somewhat displaced, so that the end of the tube forms a small "bell" of unchanged diameter. For permanent use of such contact tubes, steps should be taken to obviate the rather rapid destruction of very thin platinum foil by amalgamation. Seals of this kind are not strain-free, and are best kept out of the solution phase, since strain effects at metal–glass–solution junctions are capable of giving rise to spurious potentials (94). Reference may be made to an admirable publication on these, and associated, topics. (94a).

Platinum tube seals (95) through Pyrex are vacuum-tight, but always develop "collar cracks" which are said to be harmless. A very interesting further alternative is to use thin Pyrex rods which have been platinized by use of a "platinum paint" (96).

Leaky metal–glass seals are obviously to be excluded, together with dirty or wet mercury contact tubes, in which unsuspected "secondary cells" can so easily be set up. The use of mercury in contact tubes is vigorously opposed by certain authorities. Wood's metal, m. p. 65.5°C, is a satisfactory alternative.

C. Solid Phases and Surfaces

1. The Nonrepresentative Nature of Surfaces

Although the intention is to establish equilibria between bulk phases, the fact remains that the surfaces of solids are seldom, if ever, in equilibrium with the phases they enclose. Because of rigidity, there is no means by which strains can be relieved at ordinary temperatures, and no mechanism by which continuous equilibrium could be maintained. Yet it is obviously these surfaces which are directly concerned in setting up "equilibria" between adjacent phases. This is a standing difficulty which can only partially be met by ensuring that the solid phases are formed under conditions in which departures from equilibrium states are likely to be minimized. Thus, metal phases should be free from thermal and mechanical strains, and this is why it is the normal electrochemical practice to prepare them by electrodeposition. It would be unreasonable to expect the Beilby layers of rolled or polished metals to have no energy in excess of the "interior metal" and, if massive metals are to be used for electrodes, careful annealing would seem to be an essential prerequisite. The removal of atypical surface layers by electropolishing does not seem, as yet, to have been exploited.

Beyond drawing attention to these key difficulties and emphasizing their cardinal importance in relation to all solid phases, there seems little to be done at present in offering advice about how best to deal with them.

2. Adsorption

The ready occurrence of adsorption at solid surfaces is but a reflection of the atypical, "unsaturated" nature of the surfaces. Whilst it is sufficiently obvious that bulk phases must be pure enough to show their standard thermodynamic properties, it is less apparent that quite minor impurities may, by concentrating at functional interfaces, exert an overriding control over the behavior of the entire system.

3. Photoelectric Effects

Such effects are not normally encountered, but this may be due to the fact that they are seldom suspected or looked for. There is correspondingly little to be said about them, except that it is clearly unsafe to assume that electron-transfer processes at metal–solution interfaces can be entirely indifferent to the incidence of radiation on the metal. While evidence exists in support of this contention (97), it is true that such effects are likely to be significant in relation to electrode kinetics rather than equilibria.

D. SOLUTION PHASES

1. Impurities

Remarks already made about the critical effects of impurities in certain cases apply with redoubled force to the solution phase because of the ready transport of surface active material to the metal–solution interface of an electrode. If all the impurity contained in only 1 cm³ of solution is collected into a surface zone 1 cm² in area and 1 Å thick, there is a "concentration factor" of 10^8. Thus, 0.1 mg of impurity per liter of solution could very easily provide a complete monolayer of impurity at a functional interface. In this connection, the use of deionized water for the preparation of solutions may be considered. While ion exchange resins are being continuously improved and may in many cases be used with impunity, the fact remains that low conductance is not itself an adequate criterion of purity. Surface active impurities, likely to be specifically adsorbed, are clearly to be sedulously avoided. It seems to be advisable to use conductance water prepared by a distillation method. The still described by Stuart and Wormwell (98) has been found, over many years, to provide water with a conductance little greater than that due to self-ionization.

Oxygen as an impurity is frequently objectionable for specific reasons that are discussed in later chapters. It is often desirable, in any case, to arrange for a cell solution to be swept out by an inert gas (usually hydrogen or nitrogen, deoxygenated over copper at 500°C) for purposes of stirring. It is then useful to provide an alternative path for the gas over the surface of the solution.

The solubility of glass, or ion exchange between glass and acid solutions, presents a standing problem when extremely dilute solutions are to be used. For this silica, or possibly Teflon, apparatus would seem to be the only satisfactory cure.

2. Concentration of Solution

When calls are swept with gas streams, the provision of presaturators is desirable, otherwise serious changes in concentration may occur by evaporation. It may also be emphasized that the very low concentrations in solution of substances mainly present in other phases (as hydrogen in the hydrogen electrode) require to be standardized and guarded from change as carefully as any others.

VIII. Units and Numerical Constants

In relation to numerical calculations, a problem of some concern is the continued shift in the values of the fundamental physical constants. Cohen (99), in 1959 remarked: "It is unfortunate that a final and complete list of the values of the physical constants cannot be written down, but it is a reflection of the vitality of physics that this is so; it is only for a dead science that the final answers can be given." Whether this is to make a virtue out of necessity or not, it is certainly true that change continues and constant vigilance is necessary.

The majority of the existing data in the electrochemical literature are referred to one or other of three tabulations of fundamental constants, namely, the values recommended by the International Critical Tables in 1930 (100), by Birge in 1941 (101), or by the Subcommittee on Fundamental Constants of the National Research Council, Washington, in 1952 (102). The last of these has been generally adopted for present numerical calculations.

Unfortunately, further changes have since occurred. The Tenth General Conference on Weights and Measures (103, 104) decreed, with international agreement, that the triple point of water should be assigned a temperature of 273.16°K exactly. It follows that the normal freezing point of water is 273.15°K, and this is 0° on the Celsius scale ["sometimes loosely called the Centigrade scale" (105)]. This change has not been adopted in two monographs on electrolytic solutions published since 1958 (23, 31).

Less fundamental, but important to interionic attraction theory, is the dielectric constant of water, which was redetermined by Malmberg and Maryott (106) in 1956. Their results, together with the earlier values of

Wyman and Ingalls (*107*), based on the measurements of Wyman (*108*), are shown in Table I, which also includes the densities of water. The

TABLE I

DENSITY d AND DIELECTRIC CONSTANT D FOR WATER
AS A FUNCTION OF TEMPERATUREt^a

$t(°C)$	0	5	10	15	18	20	25	30
d(gm/ml)	0.99987	0.99999	0.99973	0.99913	0.99862	0.99823	0.99707	0.99568
D	87.74_0	85.76_3	83.83_2	81.94_5	80.83_5	80.10_3	78.30_3	76.54_6
	(88.15)	(86.12)	(84.15)	(82.23)	(81.10)	(80.36)	(78.54)	(76.77)

t	35	40	45	50	55	60	65	70
d(gm/ml)	0.99406	0.9922_4	0.9902_4	0.9880_7	0.9857_3	0.9832_4	0.9805_9	0.9778_1
D	74.82_3	73.15_1	71.51_1	69.91_0	68.34_4	66.81_2	65.31_9	63.85_5
	(75.04)	(73.35)	(71.70)	(70.10)	(68.53)	(67.00)	(65.51)	(64.05)

t	75	80	85	90	95	100		
d(gm/ml)	0.9748_9	0.9718_3	0.9686_5	0.9653_4	0.9619_4	0.9583_8		
D	62.42_5	61.02_7	59.65_7	58.31_7	57.00_5	55.72_0		
	(62.62)	(61.22)	(59.85)	(58.51)	(57.19)	(55.90)		

[a] Values in brackets are from Wyman and Ingalls (*107*).

majority of published results in which the dielectric.constant of water is significant are based on the earlier work (*108*), but the change presents an additional problem for anyone engaged on calculations based on interionic attraction theory and wishing to compare older with newly reported measurements. Robinson and Stokes (*23*) have embraced this change, but Harned and Owen (*31*) have continued to use the Wyman and Ingalls dielectric constants for consistency with the bulk of their source material, suggesting that the difference between the two sets of values can be regarded for the present as a measure of the uncertainty of existing knowledge about this property of water. Appropriate values of the Debye-Hückel constants for water between 0° and 100°C are to be found in the two monographs concerned. Parsons (*109*) provides values adjusted to the new dielectric constants and the revised ice-point. For values of dielectric constants of pure liquids other than water, the tables of Maryott and Smith (*110*) are to be noted.

Two further embarrassments to those engaged in electrochemical calculations must be noted. The first is the abandonment of the international system of electrical units in favor of absolute units, which took place officially in 1948. Table II supplies the necessary conversion factors. In the

TABLE II

CONVERSION FACTORS FOR ELECTRICAL UNITS

Unit	int^a/abs	abs/int^a
Volt	0.999670	1.000330
Ampere	1.000165	0.999835
Ohm	0.999505	1.000495
Coulomb	1.000165	0.999835
Joule	0.999835	1.000165

^{a} U.S. International units (see reference *99*, p. 34).

electrochemical literature at large, it is seldom unequivocally stated whether recorded emf values are quoted in international or in absolute volts. The writers have done their best to cope with this difficulty. The best guidance that can be given is that, if no statement is made, or if the publication concerned preceded the early months of 1948, there is tolerable certainty that the authors have used international volts.

The second embarrassment is encountered by the unwary reader in consulting recent physical texts. He may be puzzled to find that the values of Avogadro's number, the gas constant, and the faraday have undergone marked increase. This is because the physicists refer these quantities to the physical mole, which is equal to 1.000375 chemical mole.

This unsatisfactory situation is likely to be abolished in the future. Thus, it is anticipated that the 1961 meeting of the International Union of Pure and Applied Chemistry (IUPAC) will confirm a recommendation to chemists to adopt a new scale of atomic weight of the dominant natural isotope of carbon, carbon-12, in replacement of the currently used scale based on the whole number 16 as the atomic weight of natural oxygen. A concise account of the historical events leading up to this projected change has been given (*111*). It will lead to a reduction of all the atomic weights of the old chemical scale by a factor of 0.999957 (or division by 1.000043), and a similar reduction of Avogadro's number. Thus, the value due to Dumond and Cohen (*112*), based on $O = 16$, namely 6.02322×10^{23} will be changed to $C^{12} = 12$, 6.02296×10^{23}. This is about one and a half times the estimated uncertainty, $\pm 0.00017 \times 10^{23}$, and less than one-third of the changes that have been advocated in the last nine years for other reasons. Similar changes, involving division by 1.000043, will have to be

TABLE III

VALUES OF CERTAIN FUNDAMENTAL CONSTANTS[a]

Constants	Symbols	Units	I.C.T. 1930 (100)	Birge 1941 (101)	N.R.C. 1952 (102)	Cohen 1959 (99)	Parsons 1959 (109)	Probable error[b]
Faraday	F	coulomb (gm equiv)$^{-1}$	96,500	96,487	96,493.1	96,495.1	96,493	±2
Avogadro's number	N	molecules (mole)$^{-1}$ × 10^{-23}	6.061	6.0228	6.02380	6.02334	6.0230	±0.0002
Gas constant	R	joule degree^{-1} mole^{-1}	8.315	8.31436	8.31439	8.31467	8.3147	±0.0003
Gas constant	R	cal degree^{-1} mole^{-1}	1.9869	1.9869	1.98719	1.97827	1.9872	±0.00007
Boltzmann constant	k	erg degree^{-1} molecule^{-1} × 10^6	1.372	1.38047	1.380257	1.38041	1.38049	±0.00005
Electronic charge		esu × 10^{10}	4.774	4.8025	4.80223	4.802734	4.80294	±0.00009
Ice-point		°K	273.1	273.16	273.16	273.150[c]	273.150[c]	—
Ideal gas molar volume (0°C, 1 atm)		cm^3 mole^{-1}	22,411.5	22,414.6	22,414.6	22,414.5	22,414.5	±0.1
Velocity of light	c	cm sec^{-1} × 10^{-10}	2.9986	2.99776	2.997902	2.997925	2.997928	±0.000004
Planck constant	h	erg sec	6.554	6.6242	6.62377	6.62492	6.6254	±0.0002
Mechanical equivalent of heat	j	joule cal^{-1}	4.185	4.1855	4.1840[c]	4.1840[c]	4.1840[c]	—

[a] All units are absolute and, where appropriate, are referred to the chemical mole.
[b] From references 99 and 109, whichever is the greater.
[c] Defined.

made in the gas constant and the faraday, but these will very seldom be of significance until the accuracy of electrochemical measurements is appreciably increased. Thus, $(RT/F) \ln 1.000043$ is of the order of 1 μv.

It is evident that any dedicated person attempting comprehensive recalculation of recorded work on the basis of the most recent values of the physical constants would have an endless and repetitive task, and it seems doubtful if anyone would have the fortitude to attempt it. Each worker must make his own decision about what to do in relation to his own problems; fortunately, except for work of the highest accuracy, many of the changes in the quantities he must use are not significant. If they are, it is obviously best for him to calculate his own derived functions, such as the Debye-Hückel constants. For this reason, no extensive tabulations are included in this book.

Table III provides a summary of the values of fundamental constants recommended by various authorities, and Table IV shows the values of the quantity $2.30258(RT/F)$, since this is so frequently required in potentiometric calculations.

TABLE IV

VALUES OF $k = 2.30258(RT/F)$ (ABSOLUTE VOLTS)

Temp., °C	k (references 102, 23); ice-point = 273.16	k (reference 109); ice-point = 273.150
0	0.054197	0.054195
5	0.055189	0.055187
10	0.056182	0.056179
15	0.057173	0.057171
18	0.057768	0.057766
20	0.058165	0.058163
25	0.059158	0.059155
30	0.060149	0.060147
35	0.061141	0.061139
40	0.062133	0.062131
45	0.063126	0.063123
50	0.064117	0.064115
55	0.065109	0.065107
60	0.066102	0.066099

REFERENCES

1. Gibbs, J. W., "Collected Works," Vol. 1. Longmans, New York, 1899.
2. Hammett, L. P., and Lorch, A. E., *J. Am. Chem. Soc.* **55**, 70 (1933).
3. Cousens, R. H., Ives, D. J. G., and Pittman, R. W., *J. Chem. Soc.* 3972 (1953).
4. Grahame, D. C., and Whitney, R. B., *J. Am. Chem. Soc.* **64**, 1548 (1942).
5. Grahame, D. C., *Chem. Revs.* **41**, 441 (1947).
6. Hills, G. J., and Ives, D. J. G., *J. Chem. Soc.* 311 (1951).

7. Cousens, R. H., Ives, D. J. G., and Pittman, R. W., *J. Chem. Soc.* 3980, 3988 (1953).

8. Dibbs, H. P., Ives, D. J. G., and Pittman, R. W., *J. Chem. Soc.* 3370 (1957).

9. Christiansen, J. A., and Pourbaix, M., *Comp̧t. rend. conf. union intern. chim. pure et appl., 17th Conf. Stockholm* p. 83 (1953).

10. Bockris, J. O'M., Darmois, E., Defay, R., Lange, E., Milazzo. G., Valensi, G., and Van Rysselberghe, P., *Intern. Comm. Electrochem. Thermodynam. and Kinet.* (*CITCE*), *Proc. 8th Meeting, Madrid, 1956* (1958). Butterworths, London, 1958.

11. Scatchard, G., and Prentiss, S. S., *Chem. Revs.* **13**, 139 (1933).

12. Bernal, J. D., and Fowler, R. H., *J. Chem. Phys.* **1**, 515 (1933).

13. Bridgman, P. W., "The Physics of High Pressures," p. 346. Bell, London, 1949.

14. Pople, J. A., *Proc. Roy. Soc.* **A205**, 163 (1951).

15. Harris, F. E., and Alder, B. J., *J. Chem. Phys.* **21**, 1031 (1953).

16. Feates, F. S., and Ives, D. J. G., *J. Chem. Soc.* 2798 (1956).

17. Frank, H. S., and Evans, M. W., *J. Chem. Phys.* **13**, 507 (1945).

18. Frank, H. S., and Wen, Wen-Yang, *Discussions Faraday Soc.* **24**, 133 (1957).

19. Grahame, D. C., *J. Chem. Phys.* **23**, 1725 (1955).

20. Dorsey, N. E., "The Properties of Ordinary Water Substance," American Chemical Society Monograph No. 81, p. 367. Reinhold, New York, 1940.

21. Gurney, R. W., "Ionic Processes in Solution," Chapters 9 and 10. McGraw-Hill, New York, 1953.

22. Haggis, G. H., Hasted, J. B., and Buchanan, T. J., *J. Chem. Phys.* **20**, 1452 (1952).

23. Robinson, R. A., and Stokes, R. H., "Electrolyte Solutions," 2nd ed., Chapter 1. Academic Press, New York, 1959.

24. "Interactions in Ionic Solutions," *Discussions Faraday Soc.* **24** (1957).

25. Frank, H. S., and Tsao, M.-S., *Ann. Rev. Phys. Chem.* **5**, 43 (1954).

26. Brönsted, J. N., *J. Am. Chem. Soc.* **44**, 877 (1922); **45**, 2898 (1923).

27. Debye, P., and Hückel, E., *Physik. Z.* **24**, 185 (1923).

28. Gurney, R. W., "Ionic Processes in Solution," p. 255. McGraw-Hill, New York, 1953.

29. Fuoss, R. M., and Kraus, C. A., *J. Am. Chem. Soc.* **55**, 476 (1933); Ives, D. J. G., *J. Chem. Soc.* 731 (1933); Ives, D. J. G., and Pryor, J. H., *J. Chem. Soc.* 2104 (1955).

30. Hückel, E., *Physik. Z.* **26**, 93 (1925).

31. Harned, H. S., and Owen, B. B., "The Physical Chemistry of Electrolytic Solutions," p. 509. Reinhold, New York, 1958.

32. Guggenheim, E. A., "Thermodynamics," 3rd ed., p. 356. North-Holland Publ., Amsterdam, 1957.

33. Harned, H. S., and Owen, B. B., "The Physical Chemistry of Electrolytic Solutions," p. 511. Reinhold, New York, 1958.

34. Guggenheim, E. A., *Phil. Mag.* [7] **19**, 588 (1935); **22**, 322 (1936).

35. Guggenheim, E. A., and Turgeon, J. C., *Trans. Faraday Soc.* **51**, 747 (1955).

36. Güntelberg, E., *Z. physik. Chem.* **123**, 199 (1926).

37. Stokes, R. H. and Robinson, R. A., *J. Am. Chem. Soc.* **70**, 1870 (1948); Robinson, R. A., and Stokes, R. H., "Electrolyte Solutions," 2nd ed., p. 239. Academic Press, New York, 1959.

38. Bjerrum, N. K., *Z. anorg. u. allgem. Chem.* **109**, 275 (1920); *Medd. Kgl. Vetenskapsavdel. Akad. Nobelinst.* **5** (16), 1 (1919).

39. Hildebrand, J. H., and Scott, R. L., "The Solubility of Non-electrolytes." Reinhold, New York, 1950.

40. Bjerrum, N. K., *Kgl. Danske Videnskab. Selskab.* **7**, No. 9 (1926); "Selected Papers," p. 108. Munksgaard, Copenhagen, 1949.

41. Gurney, R. W., "Ionic Processes in Solution," Chapter 16. McGraw-Hill, New York, 1953.
42. Fuoss, R. M., and Fuoss, A. S., *Ann. Rev. Phys. Chem.* **3**, 51 (1952).
43. Gronwall, T. H., La Mer, V. K., and Sandved, K., *Physik. Z.*, **29**, 358 (1928).
44. La Mer, V. K., Gronwall, T. H., and Greiff, L. J., *J. Phys. Chem.* **35**, 2245 (1931).
45. Harned, H. S., Owen, B. B., "The Physical Chemistry of Electrolytic Solutions," p. 467. Reinhold, New York, 1958.
46. Mayer, J. E., *J. Chem. Phys.* **18**, 1426 (1950).
47. Mayer, J. E., and Mayer, G. M., "Statistical Mechanics," Chapter 13. Wiley, New York, 1940.
48. Poirier, J. C., *J. Chem. Phys.* **21**, 965, 972 (1953).
49. Harned, H. S., and Owen, B. B., "The Physical Chemistry of Electrolytic Solutions," p. 542. Reinhold, New York, 1958.
50. Lewis, G. N., and Randall, M., "Thermodynamics," p. 334. McGraw-Hill, New York, 1923.
51. Scatchard, G., *J. Am. Chem. Soc.* **47**, 641 (1925).
52. Linhart, G. A., *J. Am. Chem. Soc.* **41**, 1175 (1919).
53. Noyes, A. A., and Ellis, J. H., *J. Am. Chem. Soc.* **39**, 2532 (1917).
54. Randall, M., and Young, L. E., *J. Am. Chem. Soc.* **50**, 989 (1928).
55. Brönsted, J. N., *J. Am. Chem. Soc.* **45**, 2898 (1923).
56. Scatchard, G., *J. Am. Chem. Soc.* **47**, 648 (1925).
57. Hitchcock, D. I., *J. Am. Chem. Soc.* **50**, 2076 (1928).
58. Harned, H. S., and Ehlers, R. W., *J. Am. Chem. Soc.* **54**, 1350 (1932); **55**, 652, 2179 (1933).
59. Harned, H. S., and Owen, B. B., "The Physical Chemistry of Electrolytic Solutions," p. 431. Reinhold, New York, 1958.
60. Hills, G. J., and Ives, D. J. G., *J. Chem. Soc.* 319 (1951).
61. Brown, A. S., and MacInnes, D. A., *J. Am. Chem. Soc.* **57**, 1356 (1935).
62. Guggenheim, E. A., and Prue, J. E., *Trans. Faraday Soc.* **50**, 231 (1954).
63. Gupta, S., Hills, G. J., and Ives, D. J. G., *Discussions Faraday Soc.* **24**, 147 (1957).
64. Bates, R. G., and Bower, V. E., *J. Research Natl. Bur. Standards* **53**, 283 (1954).
65. Swinehart, D. F., *J. Am. Chem. Soc.* **74**, 1100 (1952).
66. Harned, H. S., and Paxton, T. R., *J. Phys. Chem.* **57**, 531 (1953).
67. MacInnes, D. A., and Shedlovsky, T., *J. Am. Chem. Soc.* **54**, 1429 (1932).
68. Owen, B. B., *J. Am. Chem. Soc.* **57**, 1526 (1935).
69. Harned, H. S., and Owen, B. B., "The Physical Chemistry of Electrolytic Solutions," p. 495. Reinhold, New York, 1958.
70. Gerke, R. H., *J. Am. Chem. Soc.* **44**, 1684 (1922).
71. Bates, R. G., Guggenheim, E. A., Harned, H. S., Ives, D. J. G., Janz, G. J., Monk, C. B., Prue, J. E., Robinson, R. A., Stokes, R. H., and Wynne-Jones, W. F. K., *J. Chem. Phys.* **25**, 361 (1956); **26**, 222 (1957).
72. MacInnes, D. A., and Longsworth, L. G., *Chem. Revs.* **11**, 171 (1932).
73. MacInnes, D. A., "The Principles of Electrochemistry," p. 160. Reinhold, New York, 1939; Robinson, R. A., and Stokes, R. H., "Electrolyte Solutions," 2nd ed., p. 200. Academic Press, New York, 1959.
74. Shedlovsky, T., and MacInnes, D. A., *J. Am. Chem. Soc.* **58**, 1970 (1936).
75. Hornibrook, W. J., Janz, G. J., and Gordon, A. R., *J. Am. Chem. Soc.* **64**, 513 (1942).
76. Janz, G. J., and Gordon, A. R., *J. Am. Chem. Soc.* **65**, 218 (1943).
77. MacInnes, D. A., "The Principles of Electrochemistry," p. 226. Reinhold, New York, 1939.

78. Henderson, P., Z. physik. Chem. 59, 118 (1907); 63, 325 (1908).
79. Lewis, G. N., and Sargent, L. W., J. Am. Chem. Soc., 31, 363 (1909).
80. MacInnes, D. A., and Yeh, Y. L., J. Am. Chem. Soc. 43, 2563 (1921).
81. Guggenheim, E. A., J. Am. Chem. Soc. 52, 1315 (1930).
82. Smith, N., and Speakman, J. C., Trans. Faraday Soc. 44, 1031 (1948); Smith, G. S., Trans. Faraday Soc. 45, 752 (1949).
83. Bjerrum, N., Z. Elektrochem. 17, 389 (1911).
84. Manov, G. G., De Lollis, N. J., and Acree, S. F., J. Research Natl. Bur. Standards 33, 273 (1944).
85. Grove-Rasmussen, K. V., Acta Chem. Scand. 2, 937 (1948); 3, 445 (1949); 5, 422 (1951).
86. Finkelstein, N. P., and Verdier, E. T., Trans. Faraday Soc. 53, 1618 (1957).
87. MacInnes, D. A., Belcher, D., and Shedlovsky, T., J. Am. Chem. Soc. 60, 1094 (1938).
88. Owen, B. B., and Brinkley, S. R., J. Am. Chem. Soc. 64, 2171 (1942).
89. Gledhill, J. A., and Malan, G. McP., Trans. Faraday Soc. 48, 258 (1952); cf. Guggenheim, E. A., and Prue, J. E., ibid. 50, 231 (1954).
90. Owen, B. B., and King, E. J., J. Am. Chem. Soc. 63, 1711 (1941).
91. White, W. P., J. Am. Chem. Soc. 36, 2011 (1914).
92. Carasso, J. I., and Pittman, R. W., J. Chem. Soc. 1084 (1956).
92a. Housekeeper, W. G., J. Chem. Inst. Elect. Eng. 42, 954 (1933).
93. Campbell, W. B., J. Am. Chem. Soc. 51, 2419 (1929).
94. Garrett, A. B., Hogge, E., and Heiks, R., Science 92, 18 (1940).
94a. Robertson, A. J. B., Fabian, D. J., Crocker, A. J., and Dewing, J., "Laboratory Glass-Working." Butterworths, London, 1957.
95. Wichers, E., and Saylot, C. P., Rev. Sci. Instr. 10, 245 (1939).
96. Coffin, C. C., Can. J. Research B18, 318 (1940).
97. Hillson, P. J., and Rideal, E. K., Proc. Roy. Soc. A199, 295 (1949).
98. Stuart, J. M., and Wormwell, F., J. Chem. Soc. 85 (1930).
99. Cohen, E. R., in "Methods of Experimental Physics," (I. Estermann, ed.) Vol. I, Chapter 2. Academic Press, New York, 1959.
100. "International Critical Tables," Vol. I, p. 17. McGraw-Hill, New York, 1930.
101. Birge, R. T., Revs. Modern Phys. 13, 233 (1941).
102. Rossini, F. D., Gucker, F. T., Johnson, H. L., Pauling, L., and Vinal, G. W., J. Am. Chem. Soc. 74, 2699 (1952).
103. Comptes rendus des Séances de la Dixième Conférence Générale des Poids et Mesures, Gauthier-Villars, Paris, 1954.
104. Crittenden, E. C., Science 120, 1007 (1954).
105. Guggenheim, E. A., "Thermodynamics," 3rd ed., p. 19. North-Holland Publ., Amsterdam, 1957.
106. Malmberg, C. G., and Maryott, A. A., J. Research Natl. Bur. Standards 56, 1 (1956).
107. Wyman, J., Jr., and Ingalls, E. N., J. Am. Chem. Soc. 60, 1182 (1938).
108. Wyman, J., Jr., Phys. Rev. 35, 623 (1930).
109. Parsons, R., "Handbook of Electrochemical Constants." Butterworths, London, 1959.
110. Maryott, A. A., and Smith, E. R., Table of Dielectric Constants of Pure Liquids. Natl. Bur. Standards Circ. No, 514 (1951).
111. Whiffen, D. H., Proc. Chem. Soc., p. 97 (1960).
112. Dumond, J. W. M., and Cohen, E. R., "Handbook of Physics," pp. 7–143. McGraw-Hill, New York, 1958.

Chapter Two

The Hydrogen Electrode

G. J. Hills and D. J. G. Ives

I. Introduction and Theory

A. THE STATUS OF THE HYDROGEN ELECTRODE

The hydrogen electrode is universally adopted as the primary standard with which all other electrodes are compared. It is a fortunate circumstance that it is the best electrode of all, capable of the highest degree of reproducibility and, contrary to statements frequently made, it is comparatively easy to prepare and use. Its virtues may be associated with the fact that, provided certain conditions are satisfied, its potential is determined solely by the properties of homogeneous phases which are easy to reproduce.

B. BASIC THEORY

The hydrogen electrode is best regarded as an oxidation-reduction electrode at which equilibrium is established between electrons in a noble metal, hydrogen ions in solution, and dissolved molecular hydrogen. The activity of the dissolved hydrogen is normally an independent variable, fixed by maintaining equilibrium with a known partial pressure of hydrogen in the gas phase. If the electrode is viewed in this way, an expression for its potential can be directly written down, by analogy with any other electrode controlled by a homogeneous oxidation-reduction system. Thus,

$$E = E° + \frac{RT}{2F} \ln \frac{(a_{H^+})^2}{P_{H_2}} \tag{1}$$

but, by universal convention, $E°$ (defined by appropriate standard states) is set at zero at all temperatures, thus establishing the hydrogen scale of electrode potentials (cf. Chapter 1, Section II).[1]

There is, however, an important difference between the hydrogen electrode and other reversible oxidation-reduction electrodes. It is that the exchange equilibrium

$$H_2 \text{ (aq. soln.)} \rightleftharpoons 2H^+ \text{ (aq. soln.)} + 2e^-$$

is not established in the solution phase. In other words, the rate constants of the homogeneous exchange reactions are negligibly small. This is hardly surprising, since the forward reaction must have an activation energy commensurate with the heat of dissociation of the hydrogen molecule (103.2 kcal mole^{-1}). If, then, an inert metal electrode is placed in a solution containing hydrogen molecules and hydrogen ions, it will *not* assume a potential defined by this equilibrium, for the equilibrium does not exist. Something more is required of the metal than to give or receive electrons; it must catalyze the equilibrium. It is generally agreed that the metal must be able to adsorb hydrogen atoms in order to perform this task, so the hydrogen electrode reaction may be represented

$$H_2 \text{ (aq. soln.)} \rightleftharpoons 2H \text{ (adsorbed on metal)} \rightleftharpoons 2H^+ \text{ (aq. soln.)} + 2e^-$$

It is seen that this equilibrium involves four processes, all of which must take place sufficiently freely for the electrode to work properly. But only two of the processes involve electron transfer (discharge of hydrogen ions, ionization of hydrogen atoms) so that, in this case, the exchange current (Chap. I, Section III) is not a sufficient criterion of the reversibility of the whole electrode reaction. On the other hand, the properties of a metal which enable it to facilitate the electron transfer equilibrium have much in common with those involved in catalysis of the atomization–combination equilibrium, so that it is rare for an electrode with an adequate exchange current to be unsatisfactory.

---

[1] Insofar as the hydrogen ion in aqueous solution is hydrated, Eq. (1) should include a term to deal with the activity of water. This term will tend to zero at zero concentration and is in any case inappreciable under most circumstances; it is therefore omitted for simplicity, at the present stage.

C. The Metal Phase

Metals likely to act as active substrates for the hydrogen electrode equilibrium are those which readily adsorb hydrogen atoms, but not too readily, for the atoms must act as active intermediates in promoting the mobility of the electrode reaction. Clearly, they will be unable to do this if they are locked away in a stable hydride phase. Suitable metals are to be looked for in the transitional series, for the transition metals are generally noted for their catalytic activity. This activity is due to the same structural feature as needed to promote hydrogen atom adsorption; the incomplete occupation of d orbitals by electrons in the isolated atoms, and the existence of incompletely filled d bands in the massive metals. In the case of palladium, hydrogen will enter the metal and exist in the form of protons in interstitial positions in the crystal lattice, the electrons having been accepted into the band system of the metal. But, for the reversible hydrogen electrode, it is not desirable that hydrogen atoms should so readily penetrate into the metal phase. If they do so, they become inaccessible to the solution phase with which they are required to remain in equilibrium. It is for this reason that massive palladium is not normally suited to form a satisfactory hydrogen electrode. Platinum, although slightly permeable to hydrogen by a similar mechanism, is very much less intimate in its association with hydrogen and is, under most circumstances, ideally suited for making hydrogen electrodes.

The discussion, however, is greatly widened by the consideration that the desired equilibrium must be established at a metal–solution interface, so that the properties of a metal which are significant are *surface* properties. It is evident that, at the surface of any solid, there is an abrupt discontinuity of structure, where abnormalities are to be expected because of unsaturation of the fields of force which, in the bulk of the phase, are satisfied. Catalytic activity and power to adsorb foreign atoms or molecules may naturally follow, and the field of search for effective metals is correspondingly expanded. The normal characteristics of metal surfaces are heterogeneity and variability in properties. According to the way in which it has been prepared or treated, the surface of a given metal may show as wide a variation in properties as the surfaces of different metals. No uniformity of catalytic power is to be expected for any normally prepared metal surface. The existence of active centers has long been proven; the corners and edges of crystal grains, intergranular boundaries, growth-steps and lattice dislocations are all likely to be of higher activity than perfect crystal planes. The reason is clear that, at such sites of structural irregularity, the residual, unsatisfied fields of force are strongest; the atoms there are in energy states higher than normal and seek to gain stability by any means available to them. This is exploited in allowing them to engage in an adsorption process that will facilitate a desired reaction. But there are other ways in which the active centers can reach stability. They may preferentially adsorb an impurity and thus become "poisoned," or they may be "burned out" in the act of catalyzing such an intensely exothermic reaction as the combination of hydrogen atoms.

These considerations indicate the difficulty in specifying what will be the ideal substrate for the hydrogen electrode reaction. It may, in any case, vary according to circumstances and certainly the development of satisfactory electrodes has been largely empirical. Nevertheless, some general principles may be stated, as follows.

(1)   The metal must be noble and must not itself dissolve or react with the solution.

(2)   Catalytic activity, associated with crystal imperfection, is enhanced by fine subdivision. It is therefore a normal, but not invariable, practice to electrodeposit the active metal in finely-divided form upon a massive metal substrate.

(3)   The greater the surface area, the greater the number of centers active for catalysis that are, by chance, produced. This again suggests the desirability of using finely-divided deposits with high ratios of real to geometric surface areas.

(4)   Heavy deposits of active metal, however, may be objectionable because hydrogen atoms which penetrate into their recesses cannot remain in mobile equilibrium with the solution phase. Solution may also penetrate, but, held in the pores of a "micro-sponge," may differ significantly in physical state from the bulk phase with which it cannot freely interchange. Sluggish response to changing conditions is to be expected of such overloaded electrodes, as well as undue capacity to adsorb essential solution constituents.

(5)   Consideration of the four processes concerned in the hydrogen electrode equilibrium raises the question of whether all four will be equally facilitated by the same kind of catalytic site. If not, deliberate differentiation of the electrode surface to provide local areas of diverse properties may be advantageous. This is a feature of some recommendations for the preparation of hydrogen electrodes.

(6)   In certain nonaqueous or partly aqueous media, or in solutions containing reducible organic constituents, the catalytic surface of the electrode may promote undesired, nonelectrochemical, hydrogenation reactions. It then becomes necessary to design electrodes of suitably limited catalytic activity.

Many of these points will be elucidated in sections which follow.

D. THE MECHANISM OF THE REVERSIBLE HYDROGEN ELECTRODE

There is no agreed and complete theory of how the reversible hydrogen electrode works. Much of the discussion which follows is debatable but serves to correlate experimental facts and to provide a basis for thought about the problems concerned. Attention must first be given to that section of the hydrogen electrode equilibrium to which the main research effort has been devoted.

Interest in the electrodeposition of hydrogen has been renewed within the last decade, and has played its part in establishing present views about the kinetics of electrode processes. Progress has been slow because of inherent experimental difficulties, mainly associated with variability in properties of metal surfaces and extreme sensitivity of experimental systems to adventitious impurities. Reviews have appeared from time to time (1–4), and trends of development may be illustrated by reference to papers dealing with theoretical (5) and experimental (6) approaches. Concordance of opinion has not been reached upon all aspects of this somewhat intractable subject, commonly referred to as "hydrogen overpotential," but an outline of the salient facts and views must be presented.

Evolution of hydrogen at a cathode is opposed by one kind of activation energy barrier or another. The rate at which it occurs, defined by current density, is an exponential function of overpotential, which is the difference between the potential of the working cathode and that of a reversible hydrogen electrode in the same solution. This is consistent with the classical Tafel law (see Chapter 1, Section III),

$$\eta = a + b \log i \tag{2}$$

where η is the overpotential at current density i, a is a constant (related to the exchange current density) characteristic of the metal of which the cathode is made and of its surface state, and b is the "Tafel slope," which is one of the parameters indicative of reaction mechanism. Rectilinear Tafel plots are not always obtained, perhaps because of inhomogeneity of electrode surfaces, or changes in their properties with time or with the progress of the reaction (7), or because reaction mechanism changes with reaction rate. Nevertheless, the Tafel relation remains the basic equation of electrode kinetics. The higher the activation energy barrier which opposes an electrode process, the greater will be the overpotential needed to maintain the process. The general problem is to find what is the reaction path, how and where in this path the barrier arises, and thus to identify the rate-determining step.

For the hydrogen evolution reaction, only three reaction steps are generally envisaged, any one of which may be rate-determining. The first is the act of ion discharge, in which electron transfer occurs. Rate-limitation by this step, giving rise to the "slow discharge theory," was suggested by Erdey-Grúz and Volmer (8), discussed in quantum-mechanical terms by Gurney (9), and modified by Horiuti and Polanyi (10), who showed the significance of the adsorption on the cathode of hydrogen atoms. Further modified by Frumkin (11) in terms of the Stern theory of the electrical double layer (12), the theory coped with the observed nondependence of overpotential on pH, and the effects of added salts. Careful measurements with mercury electrodes (13–16) have supported rate-limitation by slow discharge at high overpotential metals (17); it is characterized by a Tafel slope of 0.118 volt at 25°C. There is some doubt about how the reaction is completed in these cases. Thus the surface of the mercury cathode remains bare of hydrogen atoms (18), which must therefore leave it by some quite easy path, although mercury is unable to catalyze their combination to form molecules.

The second step is the combination of hydrogen atoms upon the cathode surface. If it is rate-limiting, this gives rise to the "slow combination theory." Historically the earliest, it was proposed by Tafel (19) and was supported by Bonhoeffer's observation (20) that metals arranged in order of increasing hydrogen overpotential fell in order of decreasing power to catalyze hydrogen atom combination in the gas phase. But the theory requires the Tafel slope to have a value of 0.029 volt at 25°C, and since this is not generally observed, the theory cannot be generally valid. Evidence (21) that atom combination may occur differently at metal–gas and metal–solution interfaces was used to discount (22) the "Tafel-Bonhöffer relationship," but it has been strongly reinforced (23), and it is now seen that if overpotential and catalytic power are not directly related together, they are both functionally connected with hydrogen atom adsorption.

The Tafel slope of 0.029 volt at 25°C is sometimes observed for low overpotential metals such as platinum. If this is taken to indicate rate-limitation by slow combination, a somewhat paradoxical situation is created, for these metals are the best catalysts for the combination. Then, it would appear, at platinum electrodes atom combination is very fast but is rate-limiting, while at mercury it is very slow but is not rate-limiting. This is a difficult, if not inconceivable conclusion. Moreover, with these active metals under suitable circumstances, the same Tafel slope can be obtained for quite a different reason (24), so that although this slope does sometimes indicate slow combination (25), it is an interpretation which requires caution. A further complication is that, apparently, combination rate-limited by surface diffusion may give rise to a slope of 0.058 volt at 25°C (26).

The third step, alternative to the second, is the "electrochemical desorption" of hydrogen atoms. This is a reaction between a hydrogen ion, an adsorbed atom, and an electron, in which discharge, combination and release of a hydrogen molecule occur in one co-operative act. Although suggested earlier (27, 28), this step is usually associated with Horiuti (29). If it takes control of the reaction rate, a Tafel slope of 0.118 volt at 25°C is to be expected, or, under special circumstances, 0.038 volt (30). Evidence from Tafel slopes therefore requires more supplementation in this case than the others, and recourse is sometimes made to Horiuti's "stoichiometric number" (31). This is defined as the number of acts of the rate-determining step accompanying one act of the over-all reaction. Formally, it is determinable from the overpotential–current density slope at zero overpotential, and has values of 2, 1, and 1 for discharge, combination, and electrochemical desorption as rate-limiting steps. It is, however, difficult to determine with certainty, and it has been said that it is an inadequate criterion of mechanism (32). Better evidence is now available from potentiostatic techniques which are capable of showing how the population of the cathode surface with hydrogen atoms changes in time from the instant at which a constant overpotential is established. In this way Gerischer (18) has found that, in all probability, electrochemical desorption is rate-limiting at copper, but not at silver, electrodes, but this is at variance with previous conclusions from other evidence (33, 34).

To summarize: much of the earlier work, although it included monumental contributions which are still of interest (35), was deficient experimentally. It is still not quite clear whether this may not be the case for more recent and elaborate work, but it appears that drastic revisions of older techniques (36–38), may well give more reproducible and intelligible results, and much is to be expected of new ones more sensitive to conditions and events at metal–solution interfaces (39). There is now less tendency to attach a particular mechanism to each individual metal (40), and increased attention is paid to the influence of the heat of adsorption of hydrogen atoms in directing reaction path (41, 42). Doubts have been expressed, however, whether the three main reaction steps are adequate to accommodate all the experimental facts (43).

Incomplete and unbalanced as this outline may be, it correctly shows that the hydrogen evolution reaction is not free from complexities and uncertainties, in spite of the work devoted to it. Less attention has been given to the reverse reaction, and still less to concerted studies of all four simultaneous processes which sustain the hydrogen electrode equilibrium. In these circumstances, any theory of how the hydrogen electrode works must be judged by its usefulness. Butler's theory (44) has the merit of simplicity and will be used in the discussion which follows.

The theory considers the discharge of a hydrogen ion from aqueous solution at the surface of a metal in terms of the energy-distance diagram shown in Fig. 1. The zero of the energy scale is at the top, and relates to a

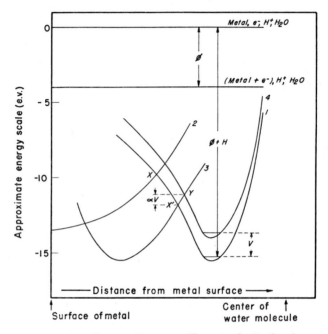

FIG. 1. Energy–distance diagram to illustrate the Butler theory.

hypothetical reference system consisting of the metal, a free electron, a free proton, and a water molecule (one, for simplicity), all without interaction upon each other, i.e.,

$$\text{Metal, } e^-, \text{ H}^+, \text{ H}_2\text{O}$$

Operations are conducted upon this system so as to give, in the first place, the situation which immediately precedes ion discharge. The electron is first allowed to fall into the highest occupied energy level in the metal. Energy is liberated equal in magnitude to the work function, ϕ, of the metal, and the system

$$(\text{Metal} + e^-), \text{ H}^+, \text{ H}_2\text{O}$$

is shown at an appropriate lower energy level in the diagram. Next, the proton is allowed to form a hydronium ion, H_3O^+, by interaction with the water molecule, which is brought to a distance from the metal surface suitable for the act of discharge which is about to take place. The hydration energy, H, will be liberated (ca. 12 ev), provided that the proton is at the equilibrium distance from the center of the water molecule. If it is not, the energy will vary as a function of the distance, so that the energy of the system represented by

$$\text{(Metal + e}^-), \ (\text{H}^+ + \text{H}_2\text{O} \rightleftharpoons \text{H}_3\text{O}^+) \qquad \text{(A)}$$

will follow a curve such as that labelled 1 in Fig. 1.

A return is now made to the original reference system of noninteracting components, and alternative operations are carried out which will lead to the situation immediately following ion discharge. The electron is allowed to combine with the proton, forming a hydrogen atom with liberation of energy, 13.5 ev., numerically equal to the ionization potential of a hydrogen atom. The hydrogen atom and the water molecule are supposed to repel each other to an extent which is a function of the distance between them. Accordingly, the energy of the system

$$\text{Metal, } (\text{H} + \text{H}_2\text{O} \rightleftharpoons \text{H}_3\text{O}) \qquad \text{(B)}$$

is represented by curve 2 in the diagram. This curve makes an intersection with curve 1 at the point X, where systems A and B are identical in energy and configuration. At this point, transitions between the two systems are favored. To the left of point X in the diagram, it is clear that system A lies at a higher energy level than system B, but this does not stimulate the discharge process because the electron transfer involves a quantum-mechanical leakage across a high potential barrier at the surface of the metal, which can only take place between levels identical, or nearly identical, in energy. Under such circumstances, the transition A → B would require an electron in a high energy level in the metal and a hydronium ion in a high vibrational energy level. Such levels are sparsely populated and the corresponding transitions are improbable. It is evident that, for discharge to occur, the hydronium ion must be close enough to the metal surface.

The argument to this point is the same as Gurney's (9) and does not indicate how a reversible discharge-ionization process, of low activation energy in either direction, may arise. But if there is an interaction between the hydrogen atom and the metal, varying with distance and similar in magnitude to the adsorption energy of hydrogen atoms on platinum (about 50 kcal gm atom^{-1}, or 2 ev), curve 2 in Fig. 1 will be replaced by curve 3, which represents the system

$$\text{(Metal } \cdots \cdot \text{ H } \cdots \cdot \text{ H}_2\text{O}) \qquad \text{(C)}$$

in which the hydrogen atom is under the joint influence of the metal surface and the neighboring water molecule. Curve 3 intersects curve 1 at the lower level X', showing how adsorption reduces the height of the effective barrier to discharge. If now a potential difference, V, is applied so as to make the metal negative with respect to the solution, the work required to remove an electron from the metal will be reduced to $(\phi - V)$ ev. Curve 1 is therefore raised bodily a distance V to the new position indicated by curve 4, and the point of intersection with curve 3 is shifted to Y. The vertical distance between Y and X' is less than V; it is equal to αV, where α is a "transfer coefficient," less than unity, which has the value 0.5 if the intersecting curves are equally inclined to the vertical, i.e., if the barrier is symmetrical. It is seen that negative polarization of the metal has reduced the height of the barrier to discharge in a manner consistent with the Tafel law. It can also be seen that, within a certain range of potentials, the energy minima corresponding with states immediately preceding and following discharge are not widely separated on the energy scale. They are separated from each other by a barrier (rounded and lowered by resonance) low enough to allow discharge and ionization processes to occur at comparable and appreciable rates. This is the situation required for the operation of the reversible hydrogen electrode.

This picture, developed from the slow discharge theory in its simplest form, does not clearly show how thermodynamic and kinetic requirements are to be reconciled. Before approaching this problem, particular attention must be paid to the adsorbed atomic hydrogen. The equilibrium constant for the gas phase reaction

$$\tfrac{1}{2}H_2 \rightleftharpoons H$$

is $10^{-35.6}$ atm$^{1/2}$ at 25°C (45), so that the partial pressure of atomic hydrogen in equilibrium with molecular hydrogen gas at 1 atm pressure is vanishingly small. Nevertheless, there must be equality of chemical potential, so that for a common standard state of 1 atm pressure,

$$\tfrac{1}{2}\mu_{H_2} = \tfrac{1}{2}\mu^{\circ}_{H_2} + \tfrac{1}{2}RT \ln P_{H_2} = \mu_H = \mu_H{}^{\circ} + RT \ln P_H \qquad (3)$$

in the usual notation. P_H is extremely small compared with P_{H_2} because $\mu_H{}^{\circ}$ is extremely large compared with $\tfrac{1}{2}\mu^{\circ}_{H_2}$. If now the hydrogen atoms become adsorbed upon a metal, they do so because the adsorption process is accompanied by a fall of Gibbs free energy, and this kind of disparity is greatly reduced. Adoption of a more suitable standard state for the adsorbed atomic hydrogen leads to

$$\mu_{H_{ad}} = \mu^{\circ}_{H_{ad}} + RT \ln n_H \qquad (4)$$

where n_H is the number of moles of atomic hydrogen per cm^2 of surface. That this expression involves the gross approximation that the adsorbed atoms behave like the particles of a two-dimensional ideal gas does not obscure the fact that, at equilibrium,

$$\tfrac{1}{2}\mu_{H_2(gas)} = \mu_{H(gas)} = \mu_{H_{ad}} \tag{5}$$

but, because $\mu^{\circ}_{H_{ad}}$ is no longer excessively large in value, n_H is no longer a vanishingly small quantity. It may, indeed, be large enough to promote a reaction of significant rate, which P_H certainly is not.

These considerations clearly reveal the properties required of a metal which is to act as a satisfactory substrate for the hydrogen electrode equilibrium (cf. Section I, C). Its power to adsorb hydrogen atoms must fall between certain limits to suit kinetic requirements. If adsorption is very weak, $\mu^{\circ}_{H_{ad}}$ is high and n_H, which determines the population of the surface with hydrogen atoms, is inadequate to maintain any reaction of appreciable rate. If adsorption is very strong, $\mu^{\circ}_{H_{ad}}$ is low, and n_H may reach its upper limit, corresponding with a complete monolayer of atoms, without the chemical potential $\mu_{H_{ad}}$ [cf. Eq. (4)] attaining the value necessary to come into equilibrium with molecular hydrogen at 1 atm pressure. Secondary adsorption on top of such a monolayer (which is akin to an over-stable surface hydride) would again be weak.

Similar considerations may be reached by considering, for example, that the adsorption energy must be great enough to reduce the activation energy for the atomization of molecular hydrogen to a reasonable magnitude, but not so great as to make it too difficult to dislodge a hydrogen atom from its adsorbed state.

The problem of correlating thermodynamic and kinetic factors involved in the hydrogen electrode equilibrium may now be approached. An electrode system is considered, in equilibrium with a fixed pressure of hydrogen and a fixed concentration of hydrogen ions. The electrode potential has precisely the value required by thermodynamics, and the rates of the discharge and ionization processes are equal. This is the case for a variety of different pieces of metal used for the electrode, with surface properties varying over a wide range, and there is difficulty in seeing how this can be so. The significant quantities, and the relationships between them, are displayed, in a self-explanatory way, in Fig. 2.

Suppose that the adsorption energy is increased by an amount ΔX, by replacing one piece of metal by another, more active piece. This is equivalent to dropping curve 3, in Fig. 1, by this distance on the energy scale. The activation energy for discharge will be decreased by $\alpha\Delta X$, where α is a transfer coefficient having the value 0.5 if the barrier is symmetrical. On the other hand, the activation energy for ionization will be increased by $(1 - \alpha)\Delta X$. Correspondingly, the rate constants for discharge and ionization will be multiplied by the factors $e^{\alpha\Delta X/RT}$ and $e^{-(1-\alpha)\Delta X/RT}$. The rate of discharge, for unit area of electrode surface, will also be increased in the ratio $e^{\alpha \Delta X/RT}$, since the concentration of hydrogen ions is fixed. But to calculate the new rate of ionization, account must be taken of the change in the surface concentration of adsorbed atoms. According to the Boltzmann law, this will have been increased in the ratio $e^{\Delta X/RT}$. Hence the rate of ionization per unit area of electrode surface will be increased by the factor $e^{\alpha \Delta X/RT}$ and is again equal to the rate of discharge. There has been no disturbance of the electrode potential to compensate for the change in adsorption energy. But it must also be shown that the chemical potential of the adsorbed atoms has not been disturbed, for equilibrium with a fixed pressure of hydrogen gas must be preserved. If the adsorption energy is identified with $\mu^{\circ}_{H_{ad}}$ in Eq. (4), it is seen that this condition is satisfied.

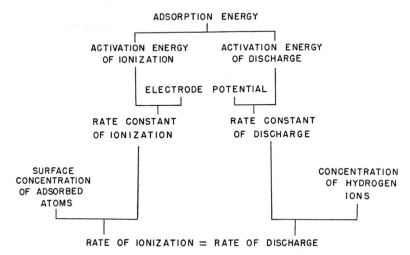

Fig. 2. Relations between quantities significant in the kinetics of the hydrogen electrode reaction.

Satisfying in some respects, the theory is incomplete and retains difficulties. The adsorbed atoms occupy a key position at the center of the equilibrium which it is desired to interpret in kinetic-molecular terms. One-half of the picture has been crudely sketched, and no less adequate a representation of the other half is needed. This involves the atomization and combination reactions, which, under the same thermodynamic restrictions, must also come to equality in rate for all significant values of the adsorption energy. Alternative mechanisms have been proposed for these reactions, and they must follow quite different kinetic laws from those relating to ionization and discharge. The activation energy for atomization is likely to depend on geometrical and electronic factors which vary from one crystal face of a metal to another; that of combination may depend upon the activated migration of the adsorbed atoms over the metal surface. These questions may be considered (46) in the light of the Lennard-Jones theory (47) of the adsorption of gases on solids, and in the context of chemisorption studies (48, 49). No simple conclusions emerge upon which to build a general theory of the hydrogen electrode.

Suppose that, for a given electrode, the state of the surface is uniquely determined by a single-valued adsorption energy, or, more realistically, by a single adsorption isotherm, and by a fractional coverage of the surface with hydrogen atoms. The latter is the only variable parameter which, by suitable self-adjustment, can meet all the requirements. Two pairs of reaction rates must automatically be equalized, and two pairs of rate constants must come to thermodynamically determined ratios. This must happen for a wide range of values of each of two independent variables; hydrogen gas pressure (0.01 to 600 atm), hydrogen ion activity (at least between values appropriate to 3 M sodium hydroxide and 8 M sulfuric acid solutions), over a wide range of temperatures (0° to 250° C) for every one of a multitude of electrodes which differ from each other in surface state, crystal structure, or position in the periodic table of the metals from which they are made. The fact is that such diversified electrodes do record the same thermodynamic potential with great precision, and there seems to be an acute need of a simplifying principle to explain why.

It was this need which prompted a suggestion (50)[2] that an essential property of a metal to be used as a hydrogen electrode is to have a heterogeneous surface, bearing sites which cover a wide range of adsorption energies. Precedence was available in Audubert's idea (51) that cathodic and anodic processes generally occur at the local areas upon an electrode surface which are best suited to them. Thus, at the hydrogen electrode, it was supposed that discharge of hydrogen ions takes place preferentially at "deeper" sites of greater adsorption energy, whilst ionization occurs more easily from "shallower" sites, sufficiently free migration of adsorbed atoms over the metal surface providing the necessary redistribution. It may be noted that these suggestions might have been made on the basis of an adaptation of Dole's theory of the glass electrode (52). They lead to a reaction scheme of the kind shown in Fig. 3, where, for simplicity, only two kinds of site are represented.

Continuous arrows show the predominant paths of the various "partial processes." It will be noted that the deep sites are cathodic and the shallow ones anodic, electrons flowing from one to the other within the metal phase in a manner precisely analogous to the flow of current between the "local elements" of accepted corrosion theory (53).

[2] Made at the time on somewhat mistaken grounds.

This proposal introduces the additional degree of freedom which seems to be needed to explain the versatility of the hydrogen electrode. But it has been pointed out (54) that a "triangular" reaction scheme, such as that represented in Fig. 3, is expressly forbidden by the Onsager principle

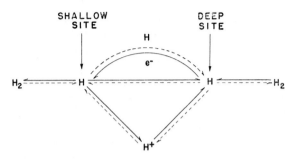

Fig. 3. Formal scheme for the hydrogen electrode reaction at a metal carrying two kinds of adsorption site.

of microscopical reversibility (55) for a system which is truly in equilibrium. The rejoinder is that real hydrogen electrodes are not in equilibrium; while catalyzing the rapid establishment of an equilibrium in which the metal phase is not thermodynamically concerned, they are undergoing irreversible changes which ultimately terminate their useful working life. They all have heterogeneous surfaces in which abnormally energetic metal atoms act as active sites, and these participate in processes which must promote the attainment of uniformity in surface properties. When this state is reached the electrodes go out of commission and cease to record the correct reversible potential. The "differentiated site theory" of the hydrogen electrode thus necessarily involves the assumption that no hydrogen electrode can continue to operate indefinitely, and this is believed to be in accord with experimental facts. If the theory is debatable, it has the merit that the attempt to support it by appeal to experimental observations is not unsuccessful and brings certain matters of importance and interest to light.

In an outstanding contribution to the study of the hydrogen electrode reaction, Hammett (56) used single-sided, horizontally-disposed, bright platinum electrodes, in both acid and alkaline solutions. The solutions were strongly stirred and were kept in equilibrium with hydrogen gas. For electrodes of varying activity, he obtained "polarization curves" of the kind shown in Fig. 4; the curves are numbered in order of decreasing activity, and increasing age, of the electrodes concerned. That all the electrodes were capable of reversible behavior is shown by the fact that the curves pass through the origin, but it is particularly noteworthy that they do so without any inflection. Thus, on the "cathodic side," it is seen that the shapes of the curves are generally consistent with an exponential dependence of current upon overpotential. On the anodic side, however, this is not the case, and there is clear evidence that the anodic process (the

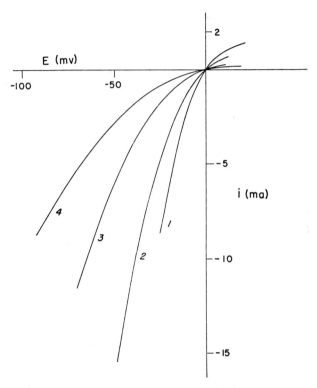

FIG. 4. Examples of Hammett's polarization curves.

generation of hydrogen ions from molecular hydrogen) is not in this case occurring at a rate determined by the electrode potential in the usual way. Hammett (57) reached this conclusion, showing by a straightforward kinetic analysis that the steady state of these electrodes at each polarization must be controlled by all four of the reactions involved in the hydrogen electrode equilibrium. An alternative analysis (50) was based upon the tendency of these results to conform with a Tafel law of slope 0.118 volt as increasingly negative polarization suppressed the ionization, in relation to the discharge, process. The data shown in Fig. 4 are replotted in Fig. 5 to illustrate this. If, on this basis, it can be assumed that the cathodic reaction is governed throughout by the same Tafel relationship, the Tafel lines can be used to calculate discharge currents; the ionization currents are then derived from the observed currents by difference. The results of such an exploratory calculation are shown in Fig. 6, which merits detailed comment.

The most striking feature is that the ionization current is greater at negative than at positive polarizations, and is quite different from the discharge current in the way it depends upon electrode potential. If the curves are traced along from the negative end of the potential scale, it is seen that

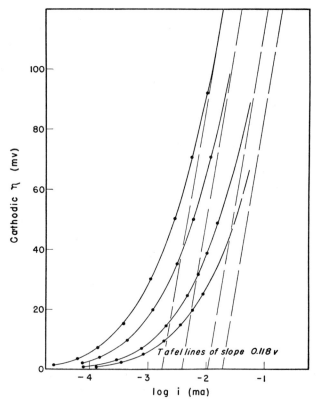

Fig. 5. Relation of Hammett's results with Tafel lines of slope 0.118 volt.

the discharge current falls, steeply at first, along an exponential curve. This is determined by the primary assumption that was made. The ionization current at first rises, but not exponentially, then passes through a flat maximum and thereafter decreases steadily, even when anodic polarization supervenes. This must be due to the onset of rate-limitation by the provision of hydrogen atoms. As the ionization increases in facility, a major supply of hydrogen atoms, the discharge process, dwindles until eventually ionization can occur only at a rate controlled by the atomization of molecular hydrogen. A situation is then reached in which, at a given electrode potential, discharge is limited in rate by its own effective activation energy barrier; the reverse process of ionization, however, is not. This carries the implications that ionization is intrinsically the easier process; indeed, if it were not, it would surely be confined to the anodic range of polarizations. It is particularly striking to notice that at equally unfavorable polariza-

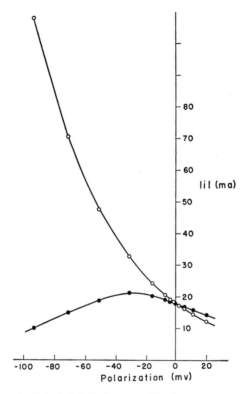

Fig. 6. Calculated discharge and ionization currents.

tions of, say, 25 mv, ionization occurs at about twice the rate of discharge. This conclusion is consistent with the fact that when a hydrogen electrode fails, its potential always deviates from the equilibrium value in the positive direction. It is also consistent with the reaction scheme of Fig. 3, and therefore gives circumstantial support to the differentiated site theory. Hammett's electrodes may not have been free from the effects of poisons (58) and were certainly not typical of ordinary hydrogen electrodes, but this does not detract from the value of his work in showing that the state of every hydrogen electrode, whether in equilibrium or not, must be determined by four simultaneous processes, and it is a matter of interest to sort them out and to find which of them may be intrinsically the slowest.

It has long been known that inactive, bright platinum electrodes assume positive rest potentials in hydrogen-saturated, acid solutions (*59*). This behavior has been attributed to the presence of poisons (*60*), but this is not consistent with the results of experiments made by Beans and Hammett (*61*). They found that the potential difference between bright and platinized platinum electrodes, in hydrogen-saturated hydrochloric acid persisted for months and survived shorting of the electrodes together. Their experimental cell was a closed system which should have been "self-cleaning." This work is believed to be important, and has been repeated (*62*) with results that merit brief description.

Two electrodes of platinized platinum, one of bright platinum and one of gold were enclosed together in a totally sealed, vacuum-tight cell containing aqueous hydrochloric acid and hydrogen. The initial rest potentials, with respect to the platinized electrodes, of the bright platinum and gold electrodes were $+340$ and $+420$ mv, and were persistently recorded after the disturbing effects of shorting all the electrodes together, performing gentle cathodizations or anodizations, or heating the whole cell to 90°C had died away. Connection of either of these electrodes to one of the platinized electrodes in the cell showed, on a microammeter, an initial current flow of about 10 μa, falling rapidly to about 0.5 μa, which persisted indefinitely, and was greatly increased by shaking the cell. With rise of temperature, the potential of the bright platinum electrode fell to zero at 70°C; that of the gold electrode decreased steadily by about 2 mv per degree, both of these changes being reversible. With passage of time, both rest potentials declined at the same rate, and, in two months, had fallen by about 330 mv. The identical decay of the apparent positive potentials of the dissimilar electrodes indicated that the change had really taken place in the reference electrodes within the cell by a process of slow deactivation. This is certainly more probable than a slow activation of the inactive electrodes. This cell may be regarded as a model, in terms of which the differentiated site theory of the hydrogen electrode may be examined. But reference to Fig. 3 will show that if, in the model, the bright and platinized platinum electrodes are taken to typify shallow and deep adsorption sites, there is the important difference that they are now separated from each other and transfer of hydrogen atoms between them is impossible. The behavior of the cell is interpreted in the following way.

Although it is supposed that the bright platinum electrode carries mainly shallow adsorption sites, hydrogen ion discharge can occur upon it with some facility, if less readily than at the platinized electrode. Thus, it has been shown (*62*) that in nitrogen-swept, strongly acid solution, anodic polarization exceeding 500 mv is required to suppress discharge at bright platinum. Ionization of hydrogen atoms, on the other hand, is believed to take place more readily at a bright platinum surface than at a platinized one. But in the model cell, the supply of hydrogen atoms to the bright electrode is restricted, for it is not an active catalyst for the atomization of molecular hydrogen (63). The electrode therefore acquires little atomic hydrogen from this source, and none from any migration process. In these circumstances, the main supply of hydrogen atoms at the bright electrode must come from the discharge process. Thus, although intrinsically easier, ionization at this electrode must wait upon discharge, and the electrode will assume such a positive rest potential as to bring the rates of these two opposing processes to equality. This is considered to be the source of the positive rest potential of the bright platinum electrode, which therefore carries a surface concentration of hydrogen atoms not in equilibrium with the gas phase. This is known to be the case (64). This view is supported by the effect of increasing the temperature, for as the hindrance to atomization is overcome, the electrode eventually becomes reversible, and its rest potential falls to zero. There is no doubt that poisons promote and increase positive rest potentials of this kind (64), but they do so by inhibiting the atomization–combination equilibrium, thus isolating the electrode from the gas phase. That this is so is clearly shown by the opposite effects of poisons upon the catalytic activity of a metal in relation to hydrogenation (which is suppressed) and upon its "electrocatalytic activity" in performing cathodic reductions (which is enhanced) (65).

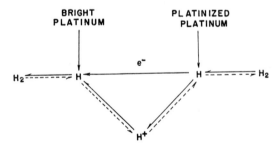

Fig. 7. Formal scheme for the bright platinum–platinized platinum cell.

If the electrodes of the model cell are connected together, electrons flow from the platinized electrode to the bright electrode. The discharge process at the bright electrode is increased in rate, and so is the ionization process at the platinized electrode. The two, shorted together, operate at the equilibrium hydrogen electrode potential (61), providing an example of extreme "site differentiation." But the equilibrium scheme, represented in Fig. 7, differs from that in Fig. 3 because the hydrogen atom transfer is completely missing.

It is seen that the functions of the two kinds of site have been reversed, but this is because the bright electrode (or shallow site) is comparatively starved of hydrogen atoms. It has been demonstrated (66) that the high, positive rest potential of an electrode capable of ionizing hydrogen atoms is largely displaced to a negative value when preformed atomic hydrogen is supplied to it from the gas phase. If the shallow site were adequately supplied with atoms from deeper sites in close proximity to it, on the same piece of metal, no doubt the same would apply. The model cell has therefore supported the differentiated site theory in principle.

The theory, it has been mentioned, appears to infringe the Onsager principle (54, 55). Equally, the model cell appears to infringe the second law of thermodynamics, for the cell reaction, if it is merely the transfer of hydrogen from one electrode to the other across zero pressure difference, would not yield electrical energy. The behavior of the cell, however, is an experimental fact amenable to repeated checking and confirmation, and in both cases the infringements are avoidable by recognizing that the platinum, intimately concerned as it is in the electrode processes, is itself undergoing change. It is known that hydrogen electrodes are subject to fatigue and become inactive with increasing age at a rate which increases with the removal of the last traces of oxygen from the solution. Hammett and Lorch (67) have shown that platinum black slowly loses activity when it is kept in hydrogen, and many allusions can be found in the literature to "hydrogen poisoning" (35, 68–71) resulting from long continued cathodization or exposure to hydrogen. Bright platinum electrodes of limited activity produced by anodic treatment or by exposure to oxidizing agents decay in activity, on resting in hydrogen-saturated solutions, in a matter of hours (56). In all cases, the changes are in the direction of increasing uniformity of electrode surface, or of transformation of active metal to a more stable, inactive form. Finely divided platinum is high in energy content; it may even be explosive. The dissipation of the excess energy is a natural process accompanied by a decrease in free energy. Since, in the model cell, for example, this natural process cannot take place by means of anodic dissolution and cathodic redeposition of the metal itself, an alternative mechanism operates in which hydrogen acts as the intermediary. It has been suggested (72) that each exo-energetic act, such as atom combination or, to a less extent, adsorption, knocks the metal atom at which it occurs into the next state of lower energy available to it. When all the atoms reach a low enough energy state, they can no longer promote the reactions concerned.

No such detailed discussion of the reversible hydrogen electrode has previously been given. Too often this electrode is treated as a thermodynamic instrument to be taken for granted. In the literature dealing with the hydrogen evolution reaction, there has been a tendency to exclude important phenomena from consideration because "poisoning" has provided an easy way of dismissing them. Yet these are the very phenomena of greatest practical interest, which need to be included in a useful working theory. Tentative as it may be, the theory which has been proposed answers this description.

II. Construction and Use

Many satisfactory hydrogen electrodes have been described, made of various materials and designed in various ways. Most of them involve the same essentials; a metal electrode with an active surface is immersed in a solution which is supplied with hydrogen. There are, accordingly, many common requirements, and these will be discussed in the first of the sections which follow. As far as possible the other sections will be arranged in order of increasing specialization of construction, materials and conditions of use.

A. COMMON REQUIREMENTS

1. Hydrogen

The gas supplied to a hydrogen electrode must be of adequate purity. Inert impurities, such as nitrogen, do not impair the working of the electrode but are objectionable because, by reducing the partial pressure of hydrogen, they will change the electrode potential. This effect is unlikely to be encountered, and it is more important to guard against impurities which have specifically deleterious effects. Of these, oxygen is outstanding because it is reduced at the electrode and withdraws electrons from it. The effect was studied by Lorch (73) and is illustrated in Fig. 8, in which the current flowing at a hydrogen electrode is plotted as a function of polarization (cf. Fig. 4). There is a displacement, ΔE, of electrode potential in a positive direction, dependent upon the amount of oxygen deliberately added to the hydrogen supplied to the electrode. This can be nullified by a small cathodic current, the magnitude of which measures the rate of oxygen reduction. It was shown, in this way, that this rate was controlled by the diffusion of oxygen to the electrode surface, in agreement with previous findings (74). The potential displacement is less for active (newly or heavily platinized) than for rather inactive (lightly platinized or fatigued) electrodes. It is of interest to note that these facts indicate that the unequally displaced potentials of two hydrogen electrodes of different activity, immersed in the same oxygen containing solution, should be brought to precisely the true hydrogen electrode potential by the same cathodic current. This provides an ingenious, if not convenient, method for using hydrogen electrodes in oxidizing solutions (75).

In normal practice, it is clear that complete removal of traces of oxygen from the hydrogen is to be recommended, although, for reasons already discussed, it may have the effect of shortening the working life of a hydrogen electrode. It is conceivable that a limiting trace of residual oxygen might be beneficial in avoiding this (certainly, a fatigued electrode may sometimes be revived by momentary exposure to air), but the matter has not been systematically studied.

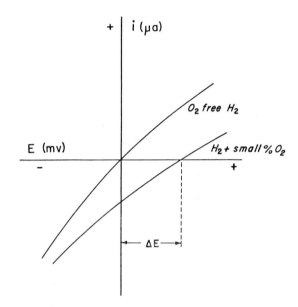

FIG. 8. Effects of traces of oxygen on the hydrogen electrode.

Other impurities to be avoided are carbon dioxide (for its effect on pH) and substances able to act as catalyst poisons, such as arsenic and sulfur compounds and carbon monoxide. These might be derived, unwittingly, from devices intended to purify hydrogen unlikely to contain them: arsenic from heated borosilicate glass, sulfur from rubber, carbon monoxide from deoxygenating liquors containing pyrogallol.

Although local electrolytic generators for hydrogen have the advantage of remaining under the direct control of the experimenter, and of not "running out," their use is attended by difficulties and is usually impracticable or even, on balance, undesirable. This is because an alkaline electrolyte must be used, which undergoes carbonation and cannot be kept oxygen-free. The gas provided is moist and spray-laden and this is objectionable for reasons which will shortly become clear. The electrolytic hydrogen commercially available in cylinders is entirely satisfactory, but, even if it can occasionally be used directly, this leaves no margin of safety and it is always desirable to use a "purification train," incorporating one, several, or all of the following items, according to circumstances.

(1)   Commercial deoxygenating cartridges, containing platinum catalysts which are active at room temperature, are available for direct attachment to cylinder heads; they are claimed to leave less than one part in 10^6 of oxygen behind, and this would certainly not disturb any reasonably active hydrogen electrode. Complete reliance on this, however, involves faith in things beyond the experimenter's own control, and is unsuitable for work which requires the greatest care. These cartridges are recommended as a first line of defence.

(2)   A three-way tap, to allow the apparatus to be isolated, and to permit the flushing out of air when a cylinder is changed.

(3)   A dust-filter to remove gas-borne particles from every source.

(4)   An absorption tube for carbon dioxide, packed with potassium hydroxide pellets, which are more suitable than "dusty" absorbents. This tube comes suitably after the preliminary deoxygenation device, because traces of moisture are essential for full activity.

(5)   The main deoxygenation device, of which many alternative forms are satisfactory. One of them is represented in Fig. 9. It consists of a

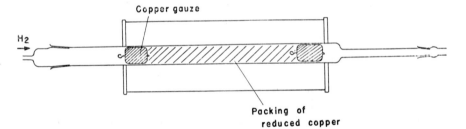

Fig. 9. Deoxygenating furnace tube.

clear, vitreous silica tube, 30×2 cm, equipped at each end with silica-glass ground joints, a well-lagged furnace winding, and packed with reduced copper. This may take the form of turnings, or reduced "wire form" oxide, enclosed between copper gauze plugs. Various working temperatures from 450 to 700°C have been recommended (76), but are not critical. Palladized, or platinized asbestos at 200°C can be used as an adjunct or an alternative. Heated uranium is probably the most efficient reagent of all, but will not normally be convenient.

(6)   A final dust filter, in the form of a sintered glass disk.

Under no circumstances should liquid reagents through which the gas is bubbled be used because of the extreme difficulty of removing microdroplets injected into the gas when bubbles burst, and because of premature saturation of the gas with water vapor. This not only condenses elsewhere uncontrollably, but adversely affects the operation of any final "hot tube" catalytic deoxygenating unit. The latter is much to be preferred and can be fully efficient on its own.

It is convenient to use flexible connections in setting up the hydrogen supply system, but there is no doubt that such connections are, in principle, undesirable. There is lack of agreement about the extent of compromise which is permissible, and it will, of course, vary according to the care which is needed by the work in hand. If it is desirable to make all-glass connection between the last purification unit and the experimental cell (which can be facilitated by use of ground joints and flexible glass spirals), it may still be reasonable to join the gas cylinder to the system by a rubber or plastic tube. It has been claimed that no deleterious effects have been observed by use of PVC (polyvinyl chloride) connections (77), but there is no doubt about the permeability of this material, and of other plastics, to hydrogen, increasing with age and the "sweating out" of plasticizers. Rubber pressure tubing, conditioned by boiling in caustic soda solution, thorough washing, and aging for 24 hrs. in hydrogen (78) may be preferred. Clearly, each experimenter may have his own views, but there will be general agreement that the problem is not unimportant, that long flexible gas leads are to be avoided as far as possible, and that there is little harm in well-found glass-to-glass joints made good with plastic or rubber sleeves.

The gas phase within the electrode compartment of the experimental cell is saturated with the vapor of the solution. If this saturation takes place in the cell itself, significant amounts of solvent will be removed by the continued passage of gas. This must be obviated by the use of a presaturator closely associated with, and kept at the same temperature as, the cell. It should be filled with the cell solution, but, if this is dilute, it may be filled with the pure solvent. In this case, however, it should be remembered that the removal of "bubbling spray" is impracticable, and the effect of it must be tolerated.

The basic requirement is that the partial pressure of the hydrogen gas with which the cell solution is brought into equilibrium must be known with adequate accuracy, so that the observed emf can be corrected to the value appropriate to the standard state of 1 atm pressure of (ideal) hydrogen gas. Knowledge is therefore needed of the vapor pressure of the solution and the total pressure within the cell, which (in absence of pressure gradients in the hydrogen outlet) can be identified with the barometric pressure. For an accuracy of emf measurement of 0.01 mv, the pressure must be known within 0.5 mm, and it may first be indicated that this is beyond the powers of many venerable laboratory barometers. Absolute calibration of the barometer is desirable, and correction of the observed height of the mercury column to the standard temperature of 0°C is essential. Correction also to standard gravitational acceleration at sea level and 45° latitude N may also be significant. It must also be remembered that any absolute measurement of atmospheric pressure obtained in this way or otherwise (perhaps from a local meteorological authority) may need correction for the difference in altitude between the experimental cell and the place to which the pressure measurement applies.

For most aqueous solutions (not exceeding 0.5 molality at 25°C, or 0.05 at 75°C), the vapor pressure can be identified with that of pure water at the same temperature. A simultaneous correction for barometric pressure, P_{bar}, and for the vapor pressure, P_{soln}, can be made by means of

$$\Delta E = \frac{RT}{2F} \ln \frac{P_{bar} - P_{soln}}{760} \qquad (6)$$

where all the pressures are measured in mm and ΔE is the *correction* to be added to the hydrogen electrode potential. If the hydrogen electrode is the positive terminal of the experimental cell, this quantity must be added to the observed emf, but, if the hydrogen electrode is the negative terminal, it must be subtracted. It may be pointed out that the matter of sign conventions of electrode potentials assumes importance here (Chapter I, Section IV), and reiteration of a previous statement is permissible. It is desirable to think about what is happening in terms of physical realities. Thus, if the hydrogen pressure is increased above the standard value, the generation of hydrogen ions will be enhanced, leaving more electrons behind in the metal phase and causing it to become more negative in potential with respect to the solution. Hence, to correct for this displacement in a negative direction, a positive correction must be applied. Values of ΔE are provided in Table I.

These corrections are, in principle, falsified by the fact that the solution seldom is in equilibrium with the gas phase over it. In most hydrogen electrode vessels, gas bubbles enter the solution at a distance below the surface. The pressure in the gas bubbles is therefore greater, according to the hydrostatic head of solution above them, than that of the gas phase above the solution. With respect to this phase, therefore, the solution becomes supersaturated with dissolved hydrogen. This partly depends on the enormously greater rate of exchange of hydrogen between the phases across the surface of a rising bubble than across the comparatively tranquil upper solution–gas interface. Supersaturation achieved by bubbling is not rapidly dispersed and is maintained in still solution for many hours.

TABLE I

JOINT BAROMETRIC AND AQUEOUS VAPOR PRESSURE CORRECTIONS
FOR THE HYDROGEN ELECTRODE (ΔE IN μv)

Temperature (°C)	Barometric pressure (mm)[a]				
	740	750	760	770	780
0	−387	−228	−71	+83	+236
5	−425	−263	−103	+55	+211
10	−478	−312	−149	+13	+172
15	−548	−378	−211	−46	+117
20	−639	−465	−294	−125	+42
25	−762	−584	−409	−235	−64
30	−922	−739	−558	−380	−204
35	−1134	−945	−759	−575	−394
40	−1408	−1212	−1019	−829	−642
45	−1767	−1563	−1362	−1165	−970
50	−2230	−2017	−1807	−1600	−1396
55	−2835	−2610	−2388	−2169	−1954
60	−3620	−3379	−3141	−2908	−2679

[a] Linear interpolation over a pressure range of 10 mm causes negligible error.

It follows that the hydrogen electrode potential is a function of bubbler depth, and it has been shown empirically that for aqueous solutions the effective pressure which determines the potential must be represented as

$$P_{\text{bar}} - P_{\text{soln}} + (0.4\, h/13.6) \tag{7}$$

where h is depth of immersion of the bubbler in mm (79). The corrections, which are not large, are shown in Table II; they are significant in accurate measurements (80).

TABLE II

BUBBLER DEPTH CORRECTIONS FOR THE HYDROGEN ELECTRODE

Bubbler depth (cm)	2	4	6	8	10
Supersaturation potential (μv)	14	23	33	42	52

Attention has already been drawn to the fact that the thermodynamic standard state for gases is the ideal state at 1 atm pressure (Chap. I, Section V), in which the fugacity is unity. Although the nonideality of hydrogen at 1 atm pressure is commonly ignored in relation to the hydrogen electrode, the matter becomes very significant in high pressure systems (see below) and there seems to be no reason why it should not be given general consideration, if only for the sake of completeness.

The behavior of hydrogen to pressures exceeding 100 atm is accurately expressed by the equation

$$V_m = (RT/P) + B \tag{8}$$

where V_m is the molar volume and B is the second virial coefficient, which is a function of temperature (81). The fugacity, p^*, is defined by

$$\mu = \mu° + RT \ln \frac{p^*}{P°} \tag{9}$$

so that when the fugacity is equal to the standard pressure $P°$ (1 atm), the chemical potential has the standard value $\mu°$. Since

$$(\partial\mu/\partial P)_T = V_m$$

integration in terms of Eq. (8) yields

$$\mu_{P=P} = \mu_{P=P°} + RT \ln \frac{P}{P°} + BP - BP° \tag{10}$$

where $\mu_{P=P°}$ is not the standard chemical potential.

Comparison of Eq. (9) and (10) indicates that

$$\mu° = \mu_{P=P°} - BP°$$

and

$$RT \ln \frac{P}{P°} + BP = RT \ln (p^*/P°)$$

It follows that

$$\ln p^* = \ln P + (BP/RT)$$

or

$$p^* = Pe^{BP/RT} \tag{11}$$

Values for the second virial coefficient for hydrogen are given by the equation (82)

$$B = 17.42 - 314.7\ T^{-1} - 211100\ T^{-2}\ \text{cm}^3\ \text{mole}^{-1} \tag{12}[3]$$

so that fugacities may be calculated. At 1 atm pressure, the values at temperatures from 0° to 100°C exceed unity, so that the correction to the hydrogen electrode potential to allow for nonideality will be

$$\Delta E = (RT/2F) \ln p^* \tag{13}$$

The corrections are shown in Table III, and will clearly not normally be significant.

[3] In the original paper, this equation is quoted with errors of sign.

TABLE III

CORRECTIONS FOR NONIDEALITY OF HYDROGEN

t (°C)	B (cm³ mole⁻¹)	p^* ($P = 1$ atm)	ΔE (μv)
0	13.44	1.00060	7.1
25	13.99	1.00057	7.3
50	14.43	1.00054	7.6
100	15.06	1.00049	7.9

2. Half-cell Design

The basic requirements are to maintain in the hydrogen electrode vessel precisely the concentration of dissolved hydrogen defined by the external pressure, to prevent the entry of oxygen or other impurities, and to arrange, as far as possible, for routine testing for equilibrium and satisfactory reversibility of operation. Hydrogen gas is usually continuously supplied, at a rate which need not exceed 2–3 bubbles per second, and it is useful to be able to bypass the flow, at will, over the surface of the solution. When equilibrium has been established, this should have no effect upon the electrode potential, which should also be insensitive to rate of bubbling. Outlet bubblers are deplored because the fluctuating increment of pressure which they must cause will adversely affect the electrode and promote pulsative mixing of the two half-cell solutions. An open exit tube, ending in a downward-pointing capillary, not less than 1 mm in diameter, is satisfactory.

The solution path between the half-cells cannot be restricted without increasing the internal resistance of the cell, and design to avoid this involves the danger of over-free interdiffusion of the half-cell solutions. This may lead to dilution of the "standard solution of molecular hydrogen" in the hydrogen electrode vessel, and may also allow a reducible solute to enter it. This may be countered by including a wide-bore tap in the tube joining the half-cells, and keeping it closed except during the act of measuring the emf of the cell. Fortunately, experimental precautions needed to combat the disturbing effects of surface-active impurities are far less rigorous for highly reversible than for polarized electrodes and high vacuum grease can be used with impunity for the lubrication of such a tap, and in other circumstances in which a high resistance to electrical and solution leakages is essential. Another satisfactory device is to intercalate, between the "measuring" hydrogen electrode and the rest of the cell, a "buffer compartment," containing a large hydrogen electrode with its own, independent, hydrogen supply. This forms a most effective barrier against both kinds of undesired diffusion process.

Precautions against the entry of oxygen to the hydrogen electrode are too self-evident to need special comment. It must, however, be pointed out that although the Hildebrand electrode (*83*) is "classical" and did much to popularize the hydrogen electrode, it is quite unsuited to accurate measurements because it cannot prevent access of oxygen to the electrode surface. It is shown in Fig. 10a; Figs. 10b (*84*) and 10c (*85*) illustrate

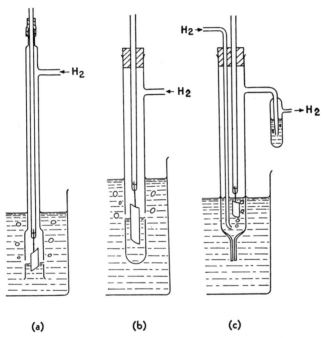

Fig. 10. Simple forms of dipping hydrogen electrode.

modifications which, in this order, are less unsatisfactory in this respect. All three are "dipping half-cell" types, often surprisingly satisfactory within their limitations.

It is desirable, particularly when a high degree of accuracy is required, to use two hydrogen electrodes, which, by their agreement, will engender confidence that both are recording an "electrode-independent" equilibrium potential. If the electrodes are identical in construction, age and situation, however, this confidence may be illusory, for both may be "nonthermodynamic" to the same degree. They should therefore be deliberately differentiated (*61*). Thus, if the two are placed in separate electrode compartments, and the emf between them is zero when hydrogen is bubbled through one, but bypassed over the surface of the solution in the other, this is a most favorable circumstance. Failing this, two electrodes in the same compartment can be differently made, or differently prepared; one may be normally and uniformly platinized while the other may be rather more heavily platinized over only part of its surface (*86*), and so on.

Numerous hydrogen electrode half-cells have been designed, many of them unnecessarily complicated (*87–89*). No attempt can be made to review them, and attention will be confined to types which have the merit of simplicity and which are suited to special working conditions.

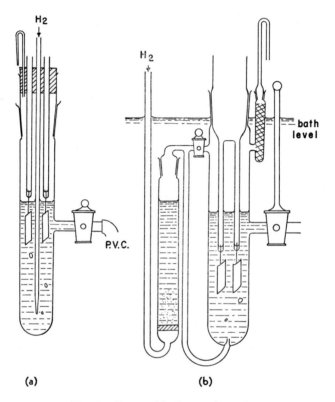

FIG. 11. Forms of hydrogen electrode.

A simple electrode system is illustrated in Fig. 11a, adequate for advanced students' laboratory work. It contains two platinized platinum electrodes mounted in a rubber bung, and incorporates a flexible connection to the second half-cell. Neither of these "compromise features" has been found to have significantly deleterious effects (*90*). A more refined design of similar type is shown in Fig. 11b, and occasion has been taken to illustrate the special difficulties which are encountered when cells are to be used at elevated temperatures. Complete immersion is the best way of obviating condensation on, and refluxing from, upper parts of the cell, but close attention must be paid to preventing leakages and defects of electrical insulation (Chapter I, Section VII,A). The half-cell illustrated is equipped with a presaturator and a hydrogen bypass.

Modifications are needed when the hydrogen electrode is to be used in a cell with a liquid junction, and reference may be made to the cell used by Bates *et al.* (*91*) in studying the effects of liquid junction potentials on

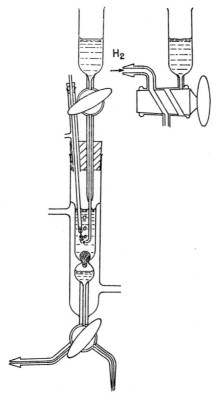

Fig. 12. Hydrogen electrode of Hitchcock and Taylor.

apparent pH values. Hitchcock and Taylor's half-cell (*92*), illustrated in Fig. 12, requires but a small volume of solution and is fitted with a water jacket for temperature control. The electrode is a platinized platinum wire spiral, and the glass bead fitting the top of the bulb in which the liquid junction is formed minimizes disturbance of the boundary by the bubbling of hydrogen. Frediani (*93*) has described an electrode constructed in a capillary stopcock, requiring only 5 to 60 mm³ of solution; a salt bridge junction is made by means of a thread saturated with potassium chloride solution.

It is sometimes undesirable to pass a continuous stream of hydrogen through the hydrogen electrode compartment, as when the solution con-

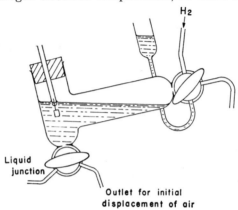

FIG. 13. The Clark rocking half-cell.

tains a very volatile component. The Clark "rocking cell" (*88*), shown in Fig. 13, has a particular advantage in avoiding this necessity. It can also make do with a single charge of hydrogen which has not been thoroughly deoxygenated, for it will itself "clean up" residual oxygen. It also involves no supersaturation errors. Conservation of gas is necessary in using the deuterium electrode (*94*), and noncontaminating, circulating gas pumps can be used with advantage (*95–97*). That used by Curry and Hugus (*97*) is illustrated in Fig. 14.

Some interest attaches to electrodes in which the catalyst is not attached to the surface of a metal substrate, but is dispersed in the hydrogen-saturated solution. Thus Biilmann and Klit (*98*) found that a bright platinum electrode came to the hydrogen electrode potential within 0.02 mv if a little colloidal palladium was added to the solution. Such additions, containing albinic acid as a stabilizer, would not normally be desirable. It is interesting to consider whether such an electrode functionally resembles a "homogeneous oxidation-reduction electrode." Hills and Ives exploited this idea in their "catalyst electrode" (*50*), in which a few mg of platinum black, added to the solution, settled upon, but was continually redispersed from, a bright platinum cone sweated to the bottom of the electrode vessel. This cone came to a potential in very precise coincidence (0.01 mv) with that of a normal platinized platinum electrode mounted in the same compartment. This not only admirably satisfied the "electrode-independence" test **for** thermodynamic equilibrium, but also gave some support to theoretical views (this chapter, Section I,D) that suggested the advantages of "site differentiation" at the hydrogen electrode. This electrode system is illustrated in Fig. 15.

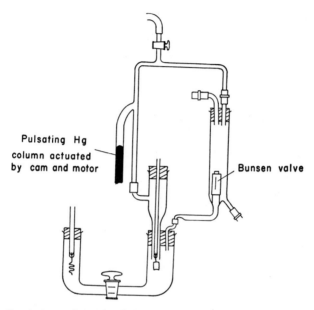

Pulsating Hg column actuated by cam and motor

Bunsen valve

Fig. 14. Simple form of gas-circulating pump applied to the hydrogen electrode.

B. Platinum–Hydrogen Electrodes

It will be clear from the preceding section that platinum forms the basis of the majority of hydrogen electrodes. Two pieces of this versatile metal, visually identical, may differ radically in their activity towards the hydrogen electrode reaction; one may be quite inert and the other highly active, according to the treatment they have received. Activity is normally assured by the electrodeposition of platinum black upon a bright metal substrate.

1. Construction of the Substrate

Platinum foil, wire or gauze may be used; the physical form seems to have no significance. It is, however, desirable to make electrodes sufficiently large (Chap. I, Section VII,B) for sensitive measurements and to reduce the demands made upon them, but not so large, in relation to the rest of the system, as to increase the possibility of errors due to solute adsorption. Usually, electrodes are made from hardened platinum foil, of thickness around 0.004 cm or more, and 1 cm² in size. The same surface area, however, is provided by a piece 2 × 0.5 cm, which is a more convenient shape for inserting into electrode vessels. The foil is welded to a platinum wire, which, sealed into a glass mounting tube, serves for physical support and electrical contact.

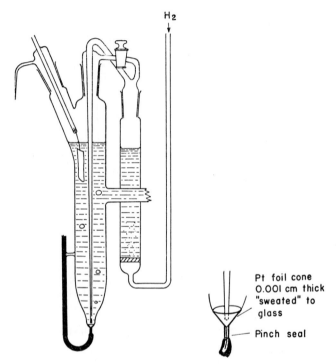

Pt foil cone
0.001 cm thick
"sweated" to
glass

Pinch seal

FIG. 15. The "catalyst electrode."

The welding may easily be done by a method illustrated in Fig. 16. The foil is held by a pair of platinum-tipped crucible tongs which are held, not by hand, but in a retort stand clamp. With care and patience, the end of the foil at which the weld is to be made is adjusted so that it is just above, but not touching, the surface of a small anvil, of a kind which is frequently part of a small workshop vise. The wire, of diameter about 0.03 cm, already mounted in its glass tube, is arranged to lie about 1 mm above the foil, in the manner shown. From a glass-working torch held in the left hand, a fine oxy-coal gas flame is cautiously brought up to the end of the wire and the foil beneath it. When the end of the wire is at a bright yellow heat, and the foil beneath bright red, the weld is made by means of a single, light blow from a jeweler's hammer. Both anvil and hammer should be scrupulously clean. Spot welding is a simpler and more precise method, but freshly cleaned copper electrodes must be used if sticking, and tearing of the foil, are to be avoided.

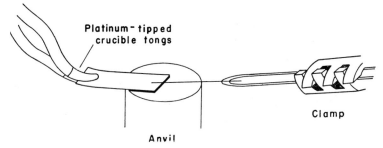

Fɪɢ. 16. Simple platinum welding technique.

It will be seen that a "stalk" of wire 2–3 cm long is envisaged, so that the foil is well separated from the glass-to-metal seal. This is desirable, since glass–metal junctions are best kept out of the solution phase in case they are strained and give rise to spurious potentials (*99*). At least one electrode design, however, from an authoritative source (*100*), involves the incorporation of the weld into the metal–glass seal, as in Fig. 17a.

For the seal, the easiest procedure is to use soft glass tubing to mount the wire, for after careful annealing, the seal is stable and vacuum-tight. If the main cell is made of borosilicate glass, electrode fitting by means of rubber or PVC bungs or sleeves is frequently unobjectionable. In other circumstances, the two kinds of glass may conveniently meet at a ground joint; alternatively, a graded seal may be used. Platinum-to-Pyrex seals have already been discussed (Chapter I, Section VII,B). They are not strain-free, and independent mechanical support is needed for the electrode, as shown in Fig. 17b. This rather clumsy and inconvenient construction has been used with advantage in cells required to maintain high vacua and to meet exceptional standards of freedom from contamination (*101*). Attention is drawn to the use of platinized glass as a substrate for the hydrogen electrode first suggested by Newbery (*102a*) and recommended by Coffin (*102b*). Platinization is carried out by means of a "platinum paint" formed by combination of dry platinic chloride with essential oils (*103*). This material decomposes on glass at a moderately high temperature to leave a bright, adherent deposit of platinum. Such preparations are commercially available. Connection to the platinum laid down in this way can be made by means of seals using a similarly platinized Pyrex rod, to which wires may be soldered. An active surface for the hydrogen electrode would be provided by the ordinary electrolytic deposition methods. The use of mercury in contact tubes is considered to be highly objectionable by many authorities, and its replacement by junctions made by welding, soldering or use of Wood's metal is recommended. Very thin platinum foil is, in any case, rather rapidly destroyed by amalgamation.

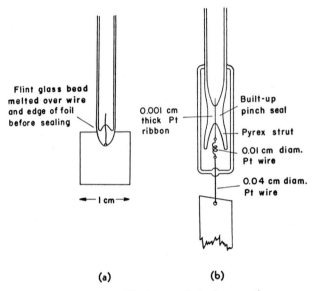

(a)　　　　　　　　　**(b)**

Fig. 17. Forms of hydrogen electrode mounting.

2. Platinization

The substrate must be clean. Treatment with warm, concentrated nitric acid and washing is satisfactory, but brief immersion in a cleaning mixture made from three volumes of 12 N hydrochloric acid, one volume of 16 N nitric acid and four volumes of water has been recommended (*100*). This mixture can be used repeatedly and also serves to strip the platinization from old electrodes. If, however, this dilute aqua regia is used, it must be followed by treatment in concentrated nitric acid and washing before proceeding to platinization. The view is held (*104*) that cathodic cleaning should always be carried out immediately before platinization in order to ensure that the surface of the platinum substrate is not oxidized. The cleaning consists of a cathodic electrolysis in very dilute sulfuric acid for ten minutes. Hydrogen should be evolved in small bubbles from the whole surface—if it is not, the surface is not clean enough. After this treatment, the electrode is washed in distilled water and platinized without delay.

It is sometimes stated that the substrate should be smooth, and should be "ironed" if necessary between a glass rod and a flat surface (*87*); this may indeed be beneficial (see below), but is not essential. Etched surfaces have been found to be quite satisfactory, and so have the matte surfaces left by the sintering of old platinization in an alcohol flame.

Directions given in the literature for platinizing electrodes vary somewhat, but there is now general agreement that the deposit should not be too heavy. Ellis (*105*) coated his electrodes so thickly with platinum black that some of it fell off when they were shaken, but it is certain that such thick deposits are inadvisable, leading to sluggish and erratic behavior as well as an inordinate capacity to adsorb wanted solutes (Section I,C above). Apart from extremes of this nature, there are two schools of thought which differ on the advisability of adding a base metal salt to the platinizing solution. The addition of about 0.02% of lead acetate certainly has a dramatic effect in promoting the deposition, very evenly, of very finely divided platinum black, in which the expansion of the normal lattice constants (*106*) may be responsible for enhanced activity. The objection to lead additions is that this metal is not thermodynamically stable in acid solutions and might furnish an undesirable impurity in the solution (*107*), but the weight to be given to it will depend upon circumstances. For highly reversible electrode systems it is probably trivial, and the method is widely used with authoritative precedence (*108, 109*). It is suitable to reproduce the directions given by Bates (*100*) for the preparation of the hydrogen electrodes used at the National Bureau of Standards.

Platinum scrap (1 to 1.5 gm), cleaned in hot, concentrated nitric acid, washed and ignited, is dissolved by digestion in warm aqua regia (3:1 by volume of concentrated hydrochloric and nitric acids). The solution is taken repeatedly to dryness on the steam bath, with intervening additions of 20 ml portions of concentrated hydrochloric acid. The residue of chloroplatinic acid hexahydrate remaining after the fourth evaporation dissolves to a clear solution in 100 ml of water, to which 80 mg of lead acetate trihydrate is added. The electrode to be platinized is used as a cathode in this solution (platinum anode), at a current density of 100–200 ma cm^{-2}, for 1 to 3 minutes. It then carries an even, very black deposit, free from streaking.

The other school of thought advocates the use of chloroplatinic acid solutions free from lead. Hills and Ives (*50*) used a 2% solution of commercial platinic chloride in 2 N hydrochloric acid, electrolyzing for 10 to 20 minutes at a current density of 10 to 20 ma cm^{-2}. Under these conditions, the current efficiency of platinum deposition is probably reduced, for the deposit is a hardly visible gray or golden film which barely reduces the sheen of a polished substrate. Electrodes so prepared are very active, as quick to reach equilibrium as any, and have an effective life to be measured in weeks. They may have the advantages associated with minimal platinization (reduced powers of adsorption, ease of conditioning for use), and are suited for use in systems sensitive to traces of impurities.

Older recommendations, such as periodic current reversals during platinization, or subsequent cathodization in sodium hydroxide or sulfuric acid solutions, have not survived the tests of experience. Much attention has been paid to the conditioning of electrodes for use in dilute, unbuffered solutions (61, 110, 111), for difficulties have been encountered with drifting electrode potentials, and have been ascribed to sorption and desorption of cations from platinum black (111, 112). It is probable that these troubles are mainly due to over-platinization; certainly they are greatly aggravated by it. Additional difficulty may be experienced in relation to dilute neutral salt solutions, due in part to the sensitivity of these solutions to traces of alkali dissolved from glass, and the entry of traces of carbon dioxide, but also to the propensity of electrodes, previously platinized in an acid medium, slowly to release acid for a very long time afterwards. This matter is discussed in some detail, together with special procedures for dealing with it, by Beans and Hammett (61). Normally, however, all that is necessary is to wash the electrodes after platinization and store them for a minimum time in water. They may be dried in vacuum (109, 113, 114) or in air before use, but prolonged exposure to air destroys activity (115). Dry electrodes must never be transferred directly from air to hydrogen; even if there is no explosion, they will be completely deactivated (116).

The electrodeposition of platinum presents some curious features of interest. It has been stated that no satisfactory deposit can be obtained from very pure chloroplatinic acid solutions (56, 117), but careful investigation has shown (67) that if the solution contains chloroplatinous acid, H_2PtCl_4, possibly as a result of overheating the platinic compound during its preparation, there is a tendency for bright platinum deposits to be obtained. This is also observed if the solution contains an excess of hydrochloric acid (118), and bright plating may be deliberately achieved by using chloroplatinous acid, or alkaline chloroplatinate solutions (61). Such bright-plated electrodes are initially active, but decay in activity rather rapidly, particularly when kept in hydrogen gas, or in hydrogen-saturated solutions. Except in special circumstances, they are not suitable for use as hydrogen electrodes.

3. Foreign Substrates

In an extensive study of the hydrogen electrode, Popoff and associates (117) recommended the electrodeposition of the active platinum catalyst upon a gold substrate, and there has been some support for this (87, 119).

Unlike massive platinum, gold does not normally absorb hydrogen, and this may confer the ability to attain equilibrium more rapidly, and ease the difficulty of using hydrogen electrodes in the presence of reducible solutes (120). Platinum black is said to adhere more firmly to gold than to platinum, but to be more easily stripped from it by anodic treatment in concentrated hydrochloric acid. The argument that gold is better than platinum because it is generally purer (116) is not weighty.

Whilst no ruling can be given, it can be said that the use of gold is not always advantageous (100), but it has its adherents and may be beneficial under special conditions. Thus, platinum bright-plated on gold from alkaline sodium chloroplatinate solution is specifically recommended for use in neutral solutions (61). The gold–platinum electrode is but one of a number of "bimetallic electrodes" that have been commended. Since the active deposit is almost invariably thin, finely divided and porous, it does not "close away" the substrate, so that such electrodes present two widely differing kinds of surface to the solution. There may be some virtue in this (this chapter, Sections C and D).

If gold foil is used, it must be welded to a supporting platinum wire which can be sealed into a glass connecting and mounting tube; whilst this is not very difficult, it is often preferred to plate a platinum foil with gold. This can be done (117) by the following procedure.

Sodium chloroaurate (1 gm) in solution in water (50 ml) is treated with dilute aqueous ammonia, avoiding excess. The precipitated oxide is filtered and washed, and immediately dissolved in a solution containing 1.5 gm of potassium cyanide in 100 ml of water. The solution is boiled to remove all traces of ammonia, and cooled. Plating from this solution is carried out at a current density of 2 ma cm^{-2} for two hours, and is unaffected (unlike the case of silver) by excess of free cyanide. Thorough washing, and soaking in distilled water is advisable before platinization, the conditions for which are not critical.

Graphite has been used as a substrate. An electrode described by Knobel (120) consisted of a small graphite rod, bored out to form a tube with a closed end. This was attached, mechanically and electrically, to a copper tube by which hydrogen was supplied from the inside, escaping into the solution through the pores in the graphite. After platinization in the ordinary way, this electrode was claimed to reach equilibrium very rapidly and to require but a small supply of hydrogen. A similar device was described by Hovorka and Evans (121) who also used the alternative platinization method of thermal decomposition of platinic chloride deposited in the graphite by soaking the tube in platinizing solution. This electrode responded correctly to changing pH, but its potential was somewhat nega-

tive to that of an orthodox hydrogen electrode. Of intrinsic interest, and
with merits of robustness and simplicity, these electrodes are unlikely to
be suitable for accurate work.

4. Unplatinized Platinum Electrodes

Hydrogen electrodes of maximum activity can bring about unwanted
hydrogenation reactions (this chapter, Section I,C). This not only alters
the system the properties of which it is desired to study, but causes deviations of the electrode potential from the proper equilibrium value. This is
because the diffusion zone of solution immediately adjacent to the electrode
surface is depleted of dissolved hydrogen, and the potential is accordingly
displaced in a positive sense. Serious trouble of this kind is associated with
the use of platinized electrodes in phthalate buffer solutions, for extensive
reduction to hexahydrophthalate can occur (122), and this is always
accompanied by drifting electrode potentials which vary with the rate of
hydrogen supply (123). In this particular case, the difficulty was minimized
by using less active platinum (124), but the best solution was found in
discarding platinum in favor of palladium (125). The problem is a general
one which seems to be encountered quite often when mixed aqueous-
organic solvents are used (126, 127) and presents a challenge: How can the
activity of an electrode be "tailored," so that it will perform its proper
electrochemical function and no other? To meet this, interest must be
taken in other methods of activating electrode surfaces.

It has long been known that the surface of bright platinum may be
activated by anodic treatment, particularly when this is alternated with
cathodization (128). This is true for the other platinum metals as well,
and for gold, and has been extensively investigated (56, 129–132). It is,
in general terms, due to the formation, and subsequent reduction, of surface oxide films, sometimes well marked by typical arrests in polarization
curves. Disordered surface arrays of metal atoms, displaced from their
normal, stable lattice sites are thereby produced, and are catalytically
active. Chemical treatment with strongly oxidizing reagents, such as
chromic acid or aqua regia, followed by cathodization, or immersion in a
hydrogen-saturated solution, can have a similar effect (56, 133). These
methods, however, usually produce evanescent activity, rather rapidly
dissipated in the presence of hydrogen, and therefore do not lend themselves to the production of serviceable electrodes. Their operation can be
seen in the reviving effect of exposure to air, or of treatment with warm,
concentrated nitric acid, on "fatigued" platinized electrodes.

Quite a different kind of procedure has been successful in producing an
active layer on the surface of bright platinum (127, 134). The essential
operation is to polish the platinum foil, supported on a glass plate, with

the rounded end of a glass rod. This alone will confer activity, bringing an otherwise positive rest potential to zero. Better results are obtained by treating the polished electrode with warm 50% aqua regia (3 volumes to 1 of concentrated hydrochloric and nitric acids, diluted with an equal volume of water) until the polish is just destroyed. Washing, warming in concentrated nitric acid for half a minute, and washing again, then provides an electrode which retains its activity for a period of hours. It can be dried in air without harm, but its activity is destroyed by cathodic treatment in dilute sulfuric acid, or by transfer from hydrogen to air. This kind of electrode was used with success in aqueous-ketonic solvents which were reduced by the normal kinds of hydrogen electrodes. It is of considerable interest that no such trouble due to reduction was found in the case of an anhydrous ketonic solvent (135).

It is probable that the operation of this "custom-built" electrode depends upon the formation of a Beilby layer during the polishing process. This layer, resting on a partially broken up and distorted crystalline substrate, is about 50Å thick and resembles a supercooled liquid. It is very susceptible to oxidation (136), and it is no doubt the subsequent reduction of the oxide so formed which promotes activity (137).

C. PALLADIUM–HYDROGEN ELECTRODES

1. Palladized Electrodes

It is interesting that Böttger (138) who, in 1897, was the first to carry out electrometric titrations with the hydrogen electrode, rejected platinized platinum in favor of palladized gold. Yet there is little doubt that a palladium catalyst is normally a poor substitute for platinum (139). Bright electrodeposits perhaps make the best basis for comparison, and for these it has been found that the activity of palladium is inferior to, and faster to decay, than that of platinum (116). To counteract this unfavorable feature, it is probable that the large real surface area of a very finely divided *black* deposit of palladium is needed to form a serviceable electrode. Certainly the enormously greater power of palladium to absorb hydrogen has no relation to catalytic activity and is a positive disadvantage. It not only promotes sluggishness of response to changing conditions, but effectively excludes the use of massive palladium as a substrate. Nevertheless, palladized platinum or gold is a satisfactory alternative to other forms of the hydrogen electrode (125, 140–142), with the particular advantage that it can be used in solutions containing some reducible substances (see above).

For the deposition of palladium black, Hamer and Acree (125) recommend a solution containing about 5% of palladium, as chloropalladous acid, and about one-tenth molar with respect to hydrochloric acid. Britton

(87) used 1–2% of palladous chloride in *N* hydrochloric acid. Bates *(139)* prepares the plating solution by electrolytic corrosion of palladium foil in 12 *N* hydrochloric acid. A current of about 500 ma is passed, with frequent reversals, between two strips of the foil dipping into about 50 ml of the acid. When about 0.5 gm of the metal has dissolved, the strips are removed, and the solution is reduced to a volume of 2–5 ml on the steam bath. Fifty ml of water and 40 mg of lead acetate trihydrate are added. Conditions for electrodeposition are not critical, and are similar to those recorded above for platinum. A palladium anode must be used. Palladized glass hydrogen electrodes have been described by Newbery *(102a)*.

It may be highly significant that all the palladized electrodes which have been used with success are *bimetallic*. Considerable interest attaches to electrodes in which palladium (or, a *homogeneous* alloy of palladium) is the only metal presented to the solution phase.

2. Pure Palladium Electrodes

Detailed studies of hydrogen-producing reactions at palladium by Schuldiner *(94, 143, 144)* have redirected attention to a different kind of hydrogen electrode of use in solutions containing no dissolved hydrogen. It is well known that palladium takes up hydrogen spontaneously from the gas phase *(145)*, at first retaining its own face-centered cubic lattice with but little expansion. After absorption of some thirty volumes of hydrogen, however, the lattice becomes unstable, and the original α-phase is converted into a considerably expanded β-phase. This transformation, during which both phases coexist, is complete when the atomic ratio of hydrogen to palladium reaches 0.6; at a ratio of 0.69, the palladium–hydrogen system is in equilibrium with hydrogen gas at 1 atm pressure. Transferred to a hydrogen-saturated solution, this "gas-charged alloy" comes to the same potential as a platinized platinum electrode. It responds to pH in the same way, and also to changes in hydrogen gas pressure, but very sluggishly *(146)*; there can be no doubt that the usual hydrogen electrode equilibrium is operative.

Palladium will absorb hydrogen from an aqueous solution through which hydrogen gas is bubbled. The process may be followed (in discontinuous experiments) by vacuum out-gassing, by reaction of the hydrogen-palladium alloy formed with ceric sulfate solution, or (in continuous experiments) in terms of the ratio of the resistivity of the palladium to its resistivity in the hydrogen-free state, R/R_0 *(147, 148)*. The latter method is complicated both by the nonlinearity of the relation between R/R_0 and the atomic ratio, H/Pd, in the alloy and by co-conduction of the bridge current (involved in the resistance measurements) through the solution in which the palladium is immersed. This takes place by proton-transfers between the metal and the solution phases, occurring predominantly in opposite directions at the two ends of the palladium wire which is normally used in such experimental work (148a). Additional difficulties, due to critical dependence of the behavior of the metal upon the pretreatment of its surface, upon traces of poisons in solution (especially when sulfuric acid solutions are used) and, perhaps, upon the entry of traces of oxygen to the apparatus, are probably responsible for disagreements in the literature which are at present in process of resolution.

Hoare and Schuldiner (147) found that the spontaneous absorption of hydrogen from solution led to a steady state with a constant H/Pd ratio of 0.03, equal to the independently determined limit for solid solution of hydrogen in the α-phase (149). At the same time, a steady electrode potential (with respect to a platinum-hydrogen electrode in the same solution) of 0.0495 ± 0.0005 volt was recorded. Further charging of the metal with hydrogen was not observed to occur spontaneously, but could be accomplished by cathodization, when the electrode potential could be brought to zero. On open circuit, however, the same positive electrode potential was subsequently recovered; it was argued that the second phase produced in the solution-charging process (designated β') differed from the normal β-phase and reasons were advanced (150) why a $\beta' \rightarrow \beta$ phase transition should not occur. It was also thought that the characteristic potential of 0.0495 volt was determined exclusively by the hydrogen-saturated α-phase.

Although it is these experiments which are the main source of disagreement, there is no doubt at all about the existence of a palladium-hydrogen electrode with an $E°$ value at 25°C of about 50 mv, whether the name "α-phase hydrogen-saturated electrode" given to it by Hoare and Schuldiner is justified or not. Formed by placing a clean, active palladium electrode (activated by anodization or palladization) in a solution saturated with hydrogen at 1 atm pressure, it is a potentially valuable hydrogen electrode. Once formed, it is quite insensitive to hydrogen pressure, can be used in hydrogen-free solutions (151) and is not at once depolarized by oxygen (152). It can be used, in conjunction with a platinum-hydrogen electrode, to determine the partial pressure of hydrogen in a solution (153).

The existence of such an electrode, with a constant difference of potential of about 0.05 volt from the ordinary hydrogen electrode was previously known (154, 155), but appears to merit further exploitation. Thus, the electrode can be very small and can be inserted directly into a narrow glass tube serving as a Luggin capillary (152). It might often form a more accurate and convenient alternative to the glass or quinhydrone electrodes. It would be suitable for use in cells with liquid junctions where ordinary hydrogen electrodes involve the nuisance of the pulsing action of gas bubbling, and has recently been advocated for use in electrophoresis cells

(*155a*). Similar electrodes can be formed for the deuterium system ($E° = 0.029$ volt)(*156*), and by gold–, silver–, nickel– (*157, 158*) and platinum–palladium alloys (*159*), each with its own reversible potential ($E°$), depending upon the foreign metal–palladium ratio.

It is at first sight disconcerting to find that other workers (e.g., see references *160, 161*) have succeeded in achieving a perfectly steady uptake of hydrogen from solution by metallic palladium up to the H/Pd ratio of 0.69, characteristic of equilibrium with hydrogen gas at 1 atm pressure. This appears to be more easily accomplished for palladium activated by

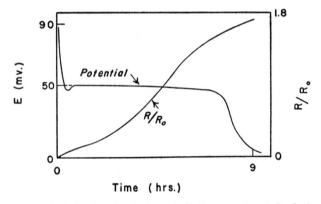

Fɪɢ. 18. The behavior of palladium in hydrogen-saturated solution.

anodization or palladization in hydrochloric acid rather than in sulfuric acid solutions. There is, however, a tendency for an arrest in hydrogen absorption to occur, whether due to inadequate activation of the metal surface, traces of poisons, special mechanisms of hydrogen uptake, or lag in nucleation of a β-phase; whether it occurs or not depends upon experimental conditions which must be exceptionally clean if it is to be avoided. Figure 18 gives an approximate representation of the course of hydrogen absorption from 2 N hydrochloric acid solution under conditions where no arrest takes place (*162*). The R/R_0 values have been corrected for proton-transfer effects (*162a*) and, as a function of time, give a plot which shows no horizontal section such as that to be found in the corresponding figure in Hoare and Schuldiner's paper (*147*). There is, nevertheless, a very well marked plateau potential, constant over a wide range of H/Pd ratios, of the same value as that previously reported. Within this region, therefore, the palladium–hydrogen system does still provide a serviceable reference electrode, and the disagreements, if they still exist, are concerned solely with the mechanism by which the constant potential is maintained.

Flanagan and Lewis support the older view (*163, 164*) that it depends upon the coexistence of two solid phases during the transformation

$$\alpha_{max} + \tfrac{1}{2} H_2 \rightarrow \beta_{min},$$

where the subscripts refer to the concentration of hydrogen in the respective solid phases. Over the plateau of constant potential there is a constant H/Pd ratio in the *surface* of the metal equal to 0.59 (β_{min}) and it is this which is potential-determining (*162*).

While no final ruling can be given on this problem, it is clear that if palladium is accessible to hydrogen gas at 1 atm pressure, the same final equilibrium state must be reached, whether a solution phase is present or not, and it is obvious that the plateau region represents an intermediate state in which equilibrium has not been reached. It is, however, a useful and long-lived steady state, and its characteristic potential is known to better than ±0.05 mv [Ratchford and Castellan (*160*) give 0.05042 ± 0.0006 volt], and this is the main fact of present interest. Outstanding questions are concerned with possible differences between β-phases generated in different ways and with the identification of the rate-limiting step in hydrogen absorption. Flanagan and Lewis (*162*) find no thermodynamic difference between solution-charged and gas-charged β-phases, but Hoare (*165*) has recently produced evidence that the *cathodically-charged* β-phase is distorted and metastable, and will spontaneously lose hydrogen on open circuit. This could account very well for the observation by Hoare and Schuldiner (*147*) of spontaneous recovery of a positive rest-potential, the validity of which has been in dispute. It seems likely that the rate-limiting step may vary according to conditions, and certainly the attainment of surface equilibria is sometimes hindered (*165a*). Quite complex mechanisms may be involved (*150, 165*), but for very active systems it appears that rate limitation is solely due to diffusion of molecular hydrogen in solution (*165b*).

It is very interesting that bimetallic electrodes including palladium as one of the metals (palladized platinum, palladium in contact with a platinum mounting) do not show positive equilibrium potentials, although this does not apply to homogeneous palladium–platinum alloys (*159*). This is attributed (*148*) to "local cell action," in which the platinum charges the palladium with hydrogen atoms until there is zero potential difference between them. This critical dependence of electrode behavior on what might be called extreme "site differentiation" is illustrated in Fig. 19 (*148*), which shows open-circuit potential–time relationships for platinum, palladized platinum and palladized palladium electrodes in hydrogen-stirred 2 N sulfuric acid, following anodic treatment. This phenomenon is clearly of interest in the context of the general theory of the hydrogen electrode (this chapter, Section I,D).

Some ingenious devices have been used to supply palladium continuously with the hydrogen it needs by electrolytic generation *in situ*. Thus, Schwing and Rogers (*166*) developed a palladium membrane electrode,

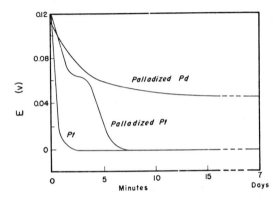

FIG. 19. Potential–time relations following anodic treatment.

coated on both sides with palladium black. One side of it was exposed to the test solution, whilst the other side was continuously supplied with cathodically deposited hydrogen. This idea has been further developed (*167*) in a number of ways. It is not yet known whether these electrodes are likely to be competitive.

D. Hydrogen Electrodes based on other Metals

Gold, rhodium, iridium, and ruthenium, activated by methods already indicated, all come to the same potential as a platinized platinum electrode in the same hydrogen-saturated solution (*46, 133, 157*), although it is probable that different steps of the hydrogen evolution reaction are rate-controlling in the various cases (*168*). Iridium black was long ago recommended as a basis for the hydrogen electrode by Lewis and co-workers (*169*). It has been shown (*67, 116*) that bright-plated iridium is rather less active than platinum and, exposed to hydrogen, loses its activity faster. Iridium deposited at low current densities appears to be more active than that deposited at high current density, and thick deposits are preferred because their activity is better retained. Chloroiridous acid is better than chloroiridic for electrodeposition. Iridium plating methods have been described by Perley and Godshalk (*170*) and by Ovenden (*171*). These platinum metals do not seem to have been exploited as hydrogen electrode catalysts to any appreciable extent.

At pH values greater than 4, nickel is sufficiently noble to be used. It was plated as an active deposit on palladium (172) to give an effective bimetallic electrode. Some attention has been given to nickel–hydrogen electrodes (173), particularly by Forresti (174), who used freshly nickel-plated nickel rods with moderate success within the pH range 4–12. It is interesting to notice that the activity of the electrodes was destroyed by heating, and that the most successful method of activating, or reactivating, them was by polishing with alumina. Raney nickel, held in a platinum basket, has been successfully used (175).

More recently, Berezina et al. (176) have studied pure nickel hydrogen electrodes for the specific purpose of measuring pH in nickel electrodeposition baths. They find that smooth nickel, which is itself useless, may be coated with a nearly black deposit of finely divided nickel by cathodization at a current density of 0.1 amp cm^{-2}, at 20°C and pH 6.6, from a bath containing 33 gm of nickel ammonium sulfate and 14 gm of Rochelle salt per liter, using a nickel anode. This electrode agrees with an ordinary hydrogen electrode over the pH range 3 to 13 in a normal series of buffer solutions, with an accuracy of about 0.1 pH unit. It is suitable for potentiometric titrations and for the measurement of pH values greater than 6.

Turning to quite a different kind of system, it is of interest to note that an illuminated film of red selenium upon a gold substrate will, after cathodic prepolarization and in absence of hydrogen gas, behave like a hydrogen electrode with an $E°$ value of 0.524 ± 0.005 volt at about 20°C (177). Although of little practical application, this is noteworthy because it may be used to illustrate the cardinal importance of hydrogen atom adsorption in promoting the hydrogen electrode function. In this case, the power to adsorb hydrogen atoms depends upon the photochemical generation of excited Se_8 entities, which are odd molecules. In the dark, this facility vanishes and the electrode ceases to operate reversibly.

III. Applications and Limitations

A. pH, Pressure and Temperature

The hydrogen electrode can be used in aqueous solutions over extremely wide ranges of pH (91). It has been used in alkali hydroxide solutions to molalities of 4 mole kg^{-1} (178) and in sulfuric acid solutions up to molalities of 17.5 mole kg^{-1} (179).

There is an impression, which stems from the authority of Nernst (61), that hydrogen electrodes fail in neutral solutions. In the absence of buffers, such solutions are, of course, extremely susceptible to disturbance of pH by adventitious effects which would be negligible in reasonably acid, alkaline, or well-buffered solutions. Difficulties which may be encountered are therefore not necessarily associated with the operation of the electrode itself, but rather with the failure to maintain an invariant solution phase. But the zone of solution which is effective in controlling the potential of the electrode is that which lies within the electrical double layer, and this may be readily disturbed by the electrode itself if there is the smallest departure from equilibrium. Thus, if with a normal potentiometric technique, 10^{-14} faraday is needed to be passed in order to get a significant galvanometer deflection, this is enough to change the pH by one unit (pH7 to pH8) in 10^{-4} cm^3 of solution, or in a layer 10^{-4} cm thick subtending an electrode of 1 cm^2 superficial area. It is also to be remembered that, somewhere within the pH range, the predominant mechanism of the electrode must change from the discharge of protons from hydronium ions to their discharge from water molecules. This is emphasized by Nagel and Wendler (*180*), who call the electrode "eine zweifache Electrode" and have made a detailed study of the practical implications of this in relation to feebly acid and feebly alkaline solutions (*181*).

The hydrogen electrode can also be used over a very wide range of pressures of hydrogen. The classical work on pressure dependence of the hydrogen electrode potential was carried out by Hainsworth, Rowley, and MacInnes (*182, 183*), who employed pressures up to 1000 atm and more. Under such conditions, the deviations of hydrogen gas from ideality become highly significant. At very high pressures, the compressibilities of all the cell components may have to be taken into account, and this may be done in terms of the thermodynamic relationship

$$(\partial E/\partial P)_T = -(\Delta V/nF) \tag{14}$$

where E is the emf of the cell and ΔV is the volume change accompanying the cell reaction. It can be seen that the pressure effect will be considerable for any reaction which involves a gas, and this must be the case for any cell which includes a hydrogen electrode. For the hydrogen–calomel cell at 25°C, ΔV is almost entirely attributable to the consumption of half a mole of hydrogen per faraday, the other terms being small and partially self-cancelling. For hydrogen, Hainsworth, Rowley and MacInnes used the equation of state

$$PV = RT(1 + 0.000537P + 3.5 \times 10^{-8}P^2) \tag{15}$$

leading to

$$E_P = E_{1\,atm} + (RT/2F) \ln P + 0.000537(P - 1) + 1.7 \times 10^{-8}(P^2 - 1) \tag{16}$$

the terms in which are self-explanatory. The experimental results agreed accurately with the predictions of this equation up to a pressure of 600 atm, but above this deviations occurred, attributable to the effect of the increasing solubility of hydrogen upon the partial molal volume of the hydrochloric acid used as electrolyte. Measurements involving the hydrogen electrode have been taken to still higher pressures (184) and also to temperatures up to 250°C (185). A very ingenious electrode for use under such conditions has been described by Greeley (185a). It consists of a silica float which keeps a platinized platinum wire just at the surface of the solution enclosed in the autoclave vessel. Electrical connection is maintained by means of a very fine platinum wire spiral. At the other extreme, the electrode operates perfectly well at very low pressures of hydrogen, certainly to 0.01 atm (186, 187).

B. USE IN PARTLY AQUEOUS SYSTEMS

The use of hydrogen electrodes in anhydrous systems is discussed in Chapter 10, but they have also been widely used in two-component solvent systems in which one component is water. The difficulties that may be encountered in such applications of the electrode do not stem from any defect in reversibility, but rather to undue chemical reactivity. The steps that may have to be taken to avoid hydrogenation of certain nonaqueous components have already been indicated (this chapter, Section II,B,4).

TABLE IV

USE OF THE HYDROGEN ELECTRODE
IN PARTLY AQUEOUS SYSTEMS

Nonaqueous component	References
Methanol	189–197
Ethanol	198–202
n-Propanol	203
Isopropanol	198, 202, 205, 126
Ethylene glycol	205–208
Propylene glycol	206
2,3-Butylene glycol	206
Glycerol	209–211
D-Glucose	212
D-Fructose	213
1,4-Dioxane	188
Acetone	127
Methyl ethyl ketone	127

The organic solvents to be used in such work must be purified with great care; even if the solvent itself has no deleterious effect on the hydrogen electrode, this may not be so for a common impurity in the solvent. Thus, Harned and his co-workers (188), studying dioxane-water systems, found it to be essential to rid the dioxane of its oxidation products, to prevent reoxidation by storing it, and its solutions, under hydrogen, and to use a vacuum technique for cell filling. It may also be noted that the high volatility of many organic solvents makes careful presaturation of the gas stream very important, and also increases the magnitude of the vapor pressure correction.

A representative list of works of this kind is presented in Table IV.

C. Poisoning and Decay

The influence of poisons on the hydrogen electrode has been mentioned in preceding sections, but it may be useful to collect and summarize this information. If poisons are defined as substances which, in traces, will hinder the proper functioning of the electrode and cause it to record a "false" potential, they may be divided into three categories. The first includes oxidizing agents, which, reduced at the electrode surface, are not deposited, but seriously deplete the concentration of molecular hydrogen in solution close to the electrode, so that its potential is displaced positively. Gaseous oxygen, and ions which can be reduced to a lower valency state (CrO_4^{2-}, Fe^{3+}, etc.) fall under this head. The second includes substances which can be reduced and deposit a solid upon the electrode. Cations of metals, such as silver, mercury, copper, lead, cadmium, and thallium answer this description. The third is comprised of substances which are preferentially adsorbed upon the active centers and paralyze catalytic action; cyanide, arsenic compounds, hydrogen sulfide, other sulfur compounds, alkaloids, colloidal impurities, and the rather indefinite materials frequently found in biological systems.

In some cases, it is probable that more than one of these deleterious effects is exercised. In others, an effect may vary with conditions; thus, nitrate ion is reduced in strongly acid solutions, but not in dilute solutions of weak acids (*214, 215*). Nitrophenols, benzoic acid, and other aromatic compounds may be reduced, particularly in warm solutions, but this may sometimes be obviated by moderating the activity of the catalyst (*123, 216*).

In general, a good hydrogen electrode should tolerate a degree of poisoning, certainly to the extent that very rigid and elaborate purifications of experimental systems are not required. With increasing poisoning, there should at first be no effect upon the equilibrium potential, but the exchange current is likely to fall; if there is a margin of safety, this will be immaterial. At a further stage, however, it is likely that the atomization–combination process will become increasingly hindered. The electrode will then become more and more isolated from the gas phase, and the potential will sooner or later become positive with respect to the equilibrium hydrogen potential. Errors as large as 0.5 volt can arise in this way.

Criteria of good electrodes, and of satisfactory operation, may be listed.

(1)   Lifetime in hydrogen-saturated media should be long.

(2)   There should be reasonable toleration to traces of oxygen in solution without potential shift.

(3)   Equilibrium potentials should be quickly reached, and should be quite insensitive to rate of hydrogen bubbling.

(4)   The slope of the current–potential line passing through the equilibrium potential should be high.

Attention may finally be redirected to the paradox that every hydrogen electrode ultimately "poisons itself" by the burning out of active centers. Attempts to revive an old electrode by exposing it to air may be successful, or it may have the opposite effect. Treatment with warm, concentrated nitric acid may also be effective, but usually it is expedient to ignite the electrode in an alcohol flame and replatinize.

REFERENCES

1. Agar, J. N., *Ann. Repts. on Progr. Chem. (Chem. Soc. London)* 54, 5 (1947).
2. Bockris, J. O'M., *Chem. Revs.* 43, 525 (1948).
3. Hickling, A., *Quart. Revs. (London)* 3, 95 (1949).
4. Bockris, J. O'M., "Modern Aspects of Electrochemistry." Academic Press, New York, 1954.
5. Parsons, R., *Trans. Faraday Soc.* 47, 1332 (1951).
6. Bockris, J. O'M., and Potter, E. C., *J. Chem. Phys.* 20, 614 (1952).
7. Busing, W. R., and Kauzmann, W., *J. Chem. Phys.* 20, 1129 (1952).
8. Erdey-Grúz, T., and Volmer, M., *Z. physik. Chem.* A150, 203 (1930).
9. Gurney, R. W., *Proc. Roy. Soc.* A134, 137 (1931).
10. Horiuti, J., and Polanyi, M., *Acta Physicochim. U.R.S.S.* 2, 505 (1935).
11. Frumkin, A., *Z. physik. Chem.* A164, 121 (1933).
12. Stern, O., *Z. Elektrochem.* 30, 508 (1924).
13. Levina, S., and Zarinskii, V., *Acta Physicochim. U.R.S.S.* 6, 491 (1937).
14. Jofa, Z. A., *Acta Physicochim. U.R.S.S.* 10, 473, 910 (1939).
15. Bockris, J. O'M., and Parsons, R., *Trans. Faraday Soc.* 45, 916 (1949).
16. Post, B., and Hiskey, C. F., *J. Am. Chem. Soc.* 72, 4203 (1950).
17. Frumkin, A., *Discussions Faraday Soc.* 1, 57 (1947).
18. Gerischer, H., and Mehl, W., *Z. Elektrochem.* 59, 1049 (1955).
19. Tafel, J., *Z. physik. Chem.* 50, 641 (1905).
20. Bonhoeffer, K. F., *Z. physik. Chem.* A113, 199 (1924); *Naturwissenschaften* 6, 219 (1927).
21. Schechter, A., *Acta Physicochim. U.R.S.S.* 10, 329 (1939).
22. Bockris, J. O'M., *J. Electrochem. Soc.* 99, 366C (1952).
23. Knorr, C. A., and Schwartz, E., *Z. Elektrochem.* 40, 38 (1934); *Z. physik. Chem.* A176, 161 (1936).
24. Kandler, L., Knorr, C. A., and Schwitzer, C., *Z. physik. Chem.* A180, 281 (1937).
25. Knorr, C. A., *Z. Elektrochem.* 59, 647 (1955).
26. Bockris, J. O'M., Ammar, I. A., and Huq, A. K. M. S., *J. Phys. Chem.* 61, 879 (1957).

27. Heyrovsky, J., *Rec. trav. chim.* **44**, 499 (1925).

28. Kobosew, N. I., and Nekrassow, N., *Z. Elektrochem.* **36**, 529 (1930).

29. Horiuti, J., and Okamoto, G., *Sci. Papers Inst. Phys. Chem. Research (Tokyo)* **28**, 231 (1936).

30. Frumkin, A., *Acta Physicochim. U.R.S.S.* **7**, 475 (1937).

31. Horiuti, J., *J. Research Inst. Catalysis Hokkaido Univ.* **1**, 8 (1948).

32. Vetter, K. J., *Z. Elektrochem.* **59**, 439 (1955).

33. Pentland, N., Bockris, J. O'M., and Sheldon, E., *J. Electrochem. Soc.* **104**, 182 (1957).

34. Bockris, J. O'M., and Conway, B. E., *Trans. Faraday Soc.* **48**, 724 (1952).

35. Baars, E., *Ber. Ges. Beförd Naturw. Marburg* **63**, 213 (1928).

36. Schuldiner, S., *J. Electrochem. Soc.* **99**, 488 (1952); **101**, 426 (1954).

37. Schuldiner, S., and Hoare, J. P., *J. Electrochem. Soc.* **103**, 178 (1956).

38. Piontelli, R., *Chem. & Ind. (London)* 1304 (1957).

39. Delahay, P., "New Instrumental Methods in Electrochemistry." Interscience, New York, 1954.

40. Parsons, R., *J. chim. phys.* (Paris) **49**, C82 (1952).

41. Gerischer, H., *Z. physik. Chem. (Frankfurt)* **8**, 137 (1956).

42. Parsons, R., *Trans. Faraday Soc.* **54**, 1053 (1958).

43. Ives, D. J. G., *Can. J. Chem.* **37**, 213 (1958).

44. Butler, J. A. V., *Proc. Roy. Soc.* **A157**, 423 (1936).

45. Rossini, F. D., Wagman, D. D., Evans, W. H., Levine, S., and Jaffe, I., "Selected Values of Chemical-Thermodynamic Properties." *Natl. Bur. Standards Circ.* **500** (1952).

46. Ives, D. J. G., and Swaroopa, S., *J. Chem. Soc.* 3489 (1955).

47. Lennard-Jones, J. E., *Trans. Faraday Soc.* **28**, 333 (1932).

48. Garner, W. E., "Chemisorption." Butterworths, London, 1957.

49. Trapnell, B. M. W., "Chemisorption." Butterworths, London, 1955.

50. Hills, G. J., and Ives, D. J. G., *J. Chem. Soc.* 305, (1951).

51. Audubert, R., *Discussions Faraday Soc.* **1**, 72 (1947).

52. Dole, M., *J. Chem. Phys.* **2**, 862 (1934).

53. Evans, U. R., "Metallic Corrosion, Passivity and Protection." Arnold, London, 1946.

54. Young, L., private communication, 1958.

55. Onsager, L., *Phys. Rev.* **37**, 405 (1931); **38**, 2265 (1931).

56. Hammett, L. P., *J. Am. Chem. Soc.* **46**, 7 (1924).

57. Hammett, L. P., *Trans. Faraday Soc.* **29**, 770 (1933).

58. Dolin, P., Ershler, B. V., and Frumkin, A., *Acta Physicochim. U.R.S.S.* **13**, 779 (1940).

59. Plzák, F., *Z. anorg. Chem.* **32**, 385 (1902).

60. Aten, A. H. W., and Zieren, M., *Rec. trav. chim.* **48**, 944 (1929).

61. Beans, H. T., and Hammett, L. P., *J. Am. Chem. Soc.* **47**, 1215 (1925).

62. Cousens, R. H., Ives, D. J. G., and Swaroopa, S., *J. Chem. Soc.* 3482 (1955).

63. Butler, J. A. V., and Armstrong, G., *J. Chem. Soc.* 734 (1934).

64. Gutt, W., and Ives, D. J. G., *Proc. Chem. Soc.* 344 (1957).

65. Kobosew, N. I., *Zhur. Fiz. Khim.* **26**, 112 (1952).

66. Levina, S. D., and Kalish, T. V., *Doklady Akad. Nauk S.S.S.R.* **109**, 971 (1956).

67. Hammett, L. P., and Lorch, A. E., *J. Am. Chem. Soc.* **55**, 70 (1933).

68. Butler, J. A. V., and Armstrong, G., *J. Chem. Soc.* 746 (1934).

69. Bowden, F. P., *Proc. Roy. Soc.* **A126**, 107 (1929).

70. Masing, G., and Laue, G., Z. physik. Chem. **A178**, 1 (1936).

71. Bodenstein, M., Ann. **440**, 177 (1924).

72. Feakins, D., private communication, 1958.

73. Lorch, A. E., Trans. Electrochem. Soc. **70**, 401 (1936).

74. Knorr, C. A., Z. physik. Chem. **A157**, 143 (1931).

75. Lorch, A. E., Trans. Electrochem. Soc. **74**, 587 (1938).

76. MacInnes, D. A., and Cowperthwaite, I. A., J. Am. Chem. Soc. **53**, 555 (1931).

77. Hills, G. J., unpublished, 1958.

78. Feakins, D., private communication, 1958.

79. Hills, G. J., and Ives, D. J. G., Nature **163**, 997 (1949).

80. Hills, G. J., and Ives, D. J. G., J. Chem. Soc. 318 (1951).

81. Guggenheim, E. A., "Thermodynamics," 3rd ed., p. 107. North-Holland Publ., Amsterdam, 1957.

82. Deming, W. E., and Shupe, L. E., Phys. Rev. **40**, 848 (1932).

83. Hildebrand, J. H., J. Am. Chem. Soc. **35**, 847 (1913).

84. Wilson, J. A., and Kern, E. J., Ind. Eng. Chem. Anal. Ed. **17**, 74 (1925).

85. Pittman, R. W., unpublished, 1959.

86. Das, S. N., private communication, 1959.

87. Britton, H. T. S., "Hydrogen Ions," 4th ed. Chapman and Hall, London, 1955.

88. Clark, W. M., "The Determination of Hydrogen Ions," 3rd ed. Ballière Tindall-Cox, London, 1928.

89. Jörgensen, H., "Wasserstoffionen Konzentration." Steinkopf, Dresden, 1935.

90. Hills, G. J., unpublished, 1959.

91. Bates, R. G., Pinching, G. D., and Smith, E. R., J. Research Natl. Bur. Stand. **45**, 418 (1950).

92. Hitchcock, D. I., and Taylor, A. C., J. Am. Chem. Soc. **59**, 1812 (1937).

93. Frediani, H. A., Ind. Eng. Chem. Anal. Ed. **11**, 53 (1939).

94. Schuldiner, S., and Hoare, J. P., J. Electrochem. Soc. **105**, 278 (1958).

95. Bollen, W. B., Ind. Eng. Chem. Anal. Ed. **3**, 203 (1931).

96. Harned, H. S., and Scholes, S. R., J. Am. Chem. Soc. **63**, 1706 (1941).

97. Curry, J., and Hugus, Z. Z., Ind. Eng. Chem. Anal. Ed. **16**, 585 (1944).

98. Biilmann, E., and Klit, A., Z. physik. Chem. **130**, 566 (1927).

99. Garrett, A. B., Hogge, E., and Heiks, R., Science **92**, 18 (1940).

100. Bates, R. G., "Electrometric pH Determinations," p. 166. Wiley, New York, 1954.

101. Dibbs, H. P., Ives, D. J. G., and Pittman, R. W., J. Chem. Soc. 3370 (1957).

102a. Newbery, E., Trans. Electrochem. Soc. **64**, 209 (1933).

102b. Coffin, C. C., Can. J. Research **B18**, 318 (1940).

103. Taylor, G. F., J. Opt. Soc. Am. **18**, 138 (1929).

104. Mattock, G., private communication, 1959.

105. Ellis, J. H., J. Am. Chem. Soc. **38**, 737 (1916).

106. Bianchi, G., Ann. chim. (Rome) **40**, 222 (1950).

107. Potter, E. C., "Electrochemistry," p. 102. Cleaver-Hume Press, London, 1956.

108. Bates, R. G., and Bower, V. E., J. Research Natl. Bur. Standards **53**, 283 (1954).

109. Harned, H. S., J. Am. Chem. Soc. **48**, 326 (1926).

110. Denham, H. G., and Morris, N. A., Trans. Faraday Soc. **26**, 510 (1928).

111. Kolthoff, I. M., and Kameda, T., J. Am. Chem. Soc. **51**, 2888 (1929).

112. Frumkin, A., and Donde, A., Ber. deut. chem. Ges. **60**, 1816 (1927).

113. Hamer, W. J., and Acree, S. F., J. Research Natl. Bur. Standards **23**, 647 (1939).

114. Bates, R. G., and Acree, S. F., J. Research Natl. Bur. Standards **30**, 129 (1943).

115. Myers, C. N., and Acree, S. F., Am. Chem. J. **50**, 396 (1913).

116. Lorch, A. E., *Ind. Eng. Chem. Anal. Ed.* **6**, 164 (1934).

117. Popoff, S., Kunz, A. H., and Snow, R. D., *J. Phys. Chem.* **32**, 1056 (1928).

118. Atkinson, R. H., *Trans. Inst. Metal Finishing* **36**, 7 (1958).

119. Weisberg, L., and Graham, A. K., "Modern Electroplating" (A. G. Gray, ed.), p. 252. Wiley, New York, 1953.

120. Knobel, M., *J. Am. Chem. Soc.* **45**, 1723 (1923).

121. Hovorka, F., and Evans, R. D., *Trans. Electrochem. Soc.* **80**, 193 (1941).

122. Draves, G. Z., and Tartar, H. V., *J. Am. Chem. Soc.* **47**, 1226 (1925).

123. MacInnes, D. A., Belcher, D., and Shedlovsky, T., *J. Am. Chem. Soc.* **60**, 1094 (1938).

124. Wilcher, F. J., and Briscoe, H. T., *Proc. Indiana Acad. Sci.* **43**, 142 (1934).

125. Hamer, W. J., and Acree, S. F., *J. Research Natl. Bur. Standards* **33**, 87 (1944).

126. Moore, R. L., and Felsing, W. A., *J. Am. Chem. Soc.* **69**, 1076 (1947).

127. Feakins, D., and French, C. M., *J. Chem. Soc.* 3168 (1956); 2284 (1957).

128. Bowden, F. P., *Proc. Roy. Soc.* **A125**, 446 (1925).

129. Butler, J. A. V., and Armstrong, G., *Proc. Roy. Soc.* **A137**, 604 (1932).

130. Armstrong, G., Himsworth, F. R., and Butler, J. A. V., *Proc. Roy. Soc.* **A143**, 89 (1934).

131. Butler, J. A. V., and Drever, G., *Trans. Faraday Soc.* **32**, 427 (1936).

132. Hickling, A., *Trans. Faraday Soc.* **41**, 333 (1945).

133. Volmer, M., and Wick, H., *Z. physik. Chem.* **A172**, 429 (1935).

134. Feakins, D., and French, C. M., *Chem. & Ind. (London)* p. 1107 (1954).

135. Everett, D. H., and Rasmussen, S. E., *J. Chem. Soc.* 2812 (1954).

136. Dobinski, S., *Phil. Mag.* [7] **23**, 397 (1937).

137. Anson, F. C., and Lingane, J. J., *J. Am. Chem. Soc.* **79**, 49 (1957).

138. Böttger, W., *Z. physik. Chem.* **24**, 253 (1897).

139. Bates, R. G., "Electrometric pH Determinations," p. 168. Wiley, New York, 1954.

140. Nylen, P., *Z. Elektrochem.* **43**, 915, 921 (1937).

141. Aten, A. H. W., and Zieren, M., *J. Electrochem. Soc.* **58**, 153 (1930).

142. Frumkin, A., and Aladjalova, N., *Acta Physicochim. U.R.S.S.* **19**, 1 (1944).

143. Hoare, J. P., and Schuldiner, S., *J. Electrochem. Soc.* **102**, 485 (1955); **103**, 237 (1956); **104**, 564 (1957).

144. Schuldiner, S., and Hoare, J. P., *J. Electrochem. Soc.* **103**, 178 (1956).

145. Smith, D. P., "Hydrogen in Metals." Univ. of Chicago Press, Chicago, 1948.

146. Hoare, J. P., Schuldiner, S., and Castellan, G. W., *J. Chem. Phys.* **28**, 22 (1958).

147. Hoare, J. P., and Schuldiner, S., *J. Phys. Chem.* **61**, 399 (1957).

148. Schuldiner, S., Castellan, G. W., and Hoare, J. P., *J. Chem. Phys.* **28**, 16 (1958).

148a. Carson, A. W., Flanagan, T. B., and Lewis, F. A., *Naturwissenschaften* **46**, 374 (1959).

149. Gillespie, L. J., and Galstaun, L. S., *J. Am. Chem. Soc.* **58**, 2565 (1936).

150. Castellan, G. W., Hoare, J. P., and Schuldiner, S., *J. Chem. Phys.* **28**, 20 (1958).

151. Schuldiner, S., and Hoare, J. P., *Can. J. Chem.* **37**, 228 (1959).

152. Fleischmann, M., and Thirsk, H. R., *Trans. Faraday Soc.* **51**, 71 (1955).

153. Schuldiner, S., private communication, 1960.

154. Stout, H. P., *Discussions Faraday Soc.* **1**, 107 (1947).

155. Hitzler, N., and Knorr, C. A., *Z. Elektrochem.* **53**, 233 (1949).

155a. Neihof, R., and Schuldiner, S., *Nature* **185**, 526 (1960).

156. Schuldiner, S., and Hoare, J. P., *J. Electrochem. Soc.* **105**, 278 (1958).

157. Hoare, J. P., Castellan, G. W., and Schuldiner, S., *J. Phys. Chem.* **62**, 1141 (1958).

158. Hoare, J. P., and Schuldiner, S., *J. Phys. Chem.* **62**, 229 (1958).

159. Carson, A. W., Flanagan, T. B., and Lewis, F. A., *Nature* **183**, 39, 150 (1959).

160. Ratchford, R. J., and Castellan, G. W., *J. Chem. Phys.* **62**, 1123 (1958).

161. Flanagan, B., and Lewis, F. A., *J. Chem. Phys.* **29**, 1417 (1958).

162. Flanagan, B., and Lewis, F. A., *Trans. Faraday Soc.* **55**, 1400, 1409 (1959).

162a. Lewis, F. A., private communication, 1960.

163. Frumkin, A., *Discussions Faraday Soc.* **1**, 137 (1947).

164. Von Stackelberg, M., and Bischoff, H., *Z. Elektrochem.* **59**, 467 (1955).

165. Hoare, J. P., *J. Electrochem. Soc.* **107**, 635 (1960).

165a. Carson, A. W., Flanagan, T. B., and Lewis, F. A., *Trans. Faraday Soc.* **56**, 363, 371 (1960).

165b. Fallon, R. J., and Castellan, G. W., *J. Phys. Chem.* **64**, 4 (1960).

166. Schwing, J. P., and Rogers, L. B., *Anal. Chim. Acta* **15**, 379 (1956).

167. Stock, J. T., Purdy, W. C., and Williams, T. R., *Anal. Chim. Acta* **20**, 73 (1959).

168. Hoare, J. P., and Schuldiner, S., *J. Chem. Phys.* **25**, 786 (1956).

169. Lewis, G. N., Brighton, T. B., and Sebastian, R. L., *J. Am. Chem. Soc.* **39**, 2245 (1917).

170. Perley, G. A., and Godshalk, J. B., U.S.P. No. 2,416,949, June, 1942.

171. Ovenden, P. J., *Nature* **179**, 39 (1957).

172. Haring, M. M., and Vanden Bosch, E. G., *J. Phys. Chem.* **33**, 161 (1929).

173. Colombier, L., *Compt. rend.* **199**, 273, 408 (1934).

174. Forresti, B., *Gazz. chim. ital.* **67**, 399 (1937); *Atti X congr. intern. chim.*, *Roma* **II**, 226 (1938); *Gazz. chim. ital.* **70**, 349 (1940).

175. Travers, A., and Aubrey, J., *Atti X congr. intern. chim.*, *Roma* **II**, 546 (1938).

176. Berezina, S. N., Vozdvizhensky, G. S., and Desideryev, G. P., Zhur. Priklad. Khim. **25**, 994 (1952); *J. Appl. Chem. U.S.S.R.* (*English Translation*) **25**, 1057 (1952).

177. Pittman, R. W., *J. Chem. Soc.* 855 (1953).

178. Harned, H. S., and Owen, B. B., "The Physical Chemistry of Electrolytic Solutions," p. 499. Reinhold, New York, 1958.

179. Harned, H. S. and Owen, B. B., "The Physical Chemistry of Electrolytic Solution," p. 574. Reinhold, New York, 1958.

180. Nagel, K., and Wendler, F., *Z. Elektrochem.* **60**, 1064 (1956).

181. Nagel, K., and Wendler, F., *Z. Elektrochem.* **63**, 213 (1959).

182. Hainsworth, W. R., Rowley, H. J., and MacInnes, D. A., *J. Am. Chem. Soc.* **46**, 1437 (1924).

183. MacInnes, D. A., "Principles of Electrochemistry," pp. 114–118. Reinhold, New York, 1939.

184. Tammann, G., and Jenckel, E., *Z. anorg. u. allgem. Chem.* **137**, 337 (1928).

185. Roychoudhury, R. N., and Bonilla, C. F., *J. Electrochem. Soc.* **103**, 241 (1956).

185a. Greeley, R. S., Smith, W. T., Stoughton, R. W., and Lietzke, M. H., *J. Phys. Chem.* **64**, 652 (1960).

186. Kitchener, J. A., and Ignatowicz, S., *Trans. Faraday Soc.* **47**, 1278 (1951).

187. Parela, T. O., *Suomen Kemistilehti* **30B**, 240 (1957).

188. Harned, H. S., and co-workers, *J. Am. Chem. Soc.* **58**, 1908 (1936); **60**, 334, 336, 339, 2128, 2130, 2133 (1938); **61**, 44, 48, 49 (1939); **61**, 2374, 2377 (1939); **65**, 54, 1117(1943).

189. Kobayashi, Y., Akai N., and Furukawa, S., *J. Sci. Hiroshima Univ.* **5**, 57 (1934).

190. Harned, H. S., and Thomas, H. C., *J. Am. Chem. Soc.* **58**, 761 (1936).

191. Parton, H. N., and Nicholson, A. J. C., *Trans. Faraday Soc.* **35**, 546 (1939).

192. Kanning, E. W., and Campbell, A. W., *J. Am. Chem. Soc.* **64**, 517 (1942).

193. Parton, H. N., and Rogers, J., *Trans. Faraday Soc.* **38**, 238 (1942).

194. Kanning, E. W., and Bowman, M. G., *J. Am. Chem. Soc.* **68**, 2042 (1946).

195. Oiwa, I. T., *J. Phys. Chem.* **60**, 754 (1956).

196. Koskikallio, J., *Suomen Kemistilehti* **30B**, 38, 43 (1957).

197. Schwabe, K., and Ziegenbalg, S., *Z. Elektrochem.* **62**, 172 (1958).

198. Harned, H. S., and Calmon, C., *J. Amer. Chem. Soc.* **61**, 1491 (1939).

199. Butler, J. A. V., and Robertson, C. M., *Proc. Roy. Soc.* **A125**, 649 (1929).

200. Patterson, A., and Felsing, W. A., *J. Am. Chem. Soc.* **64**, 1478 (1942).

201. Crockford, H. D., and Wideman, S. A., *J. Phys. Chem.* **50**, 418 (1946).

202. Harned, H. S., and Allen, D. S., *J. Phys. Chem.* **58**, 191 (1954).

203. Claussen, B. H., and French, C. M., *Trans. Faraday Soc.* **51**, 708 (1955).

204. Land, J. E., and Crockford, H. D., *J. Am. Chem. Soc.* **72**, 1895 (1950).

205. Knight, S. B., Masi, J. F., and Roesel, D., *J. Am. Chem. Soc.* **68**, 661 (1946).

206. Crockford, H. D., Knight, S. B., and Staton, H. A., *J. Am. Chem. Soc.* **72**, 2164 (1950).

207. Claussen, B. H., and French, C. M., *Trans. Faraday Soc.* **51**, 1124 (1955).

208. French, C. M., and Hussain, C. F., *J. Chem. Soc.* 2211 (1955).

209. Lucasse, W. W., *Z. physik. Chem.* **121**, 254 (1926).

210. Knight, S. B., Crockford, H. D., and James, J., *J. Phys. Chem.* **57**, 463 (1953).

211. Harned, H. S., and Nestler, F. H. M., *J. Am. Chem. Soc.* **68**, 665, 966 (1946).

212. Williams, J. P., Knight, S. B., and Crockford, H. D., *J. Am. Chem. Soc.* **72**, 1277 (1950).

213. Crockford, H. D., and Sahnovsky, A. A., *J. Am. Chem. Soc.* **73**, 4177 (1951).

214. Bates, R. G., Siegel, G. L., and Acree, S. F., *J. Research Natl. Bur. Standards* **30**, 347 (1943).

215. Bates, R. G., Diamond, P. T., Eden, M., and Acree, S. F., *J. Research Natl. Bur. Standards* **37**, 251 (1946).

216. Kolthoff, I. M., and Laitinen, H. A., "pH and Electro-Titrations," Chap. 6. Wiley, New York, 1941.

Chapter Three

The Calomel Electrode and Other Mercury–Mercurous Salt Electrodes

G. J. Hills and D. J. G. Ives

I. Introduction

The electrodes discussed in this chapter are all electrodes of the second kind, formed from mercury and an excess of a sparingly soluble mercurous salt. They are therefore reversible to the anions of the salt concerned and assume equilibrium potentials defined by the activities of these ions in solution.[1] Mercury has properties which are desirable for setting up well-behaved electrode systems. It is a noble, liquid metal, easy to purify, and therefore easy to obtain in a standard state with properties quite independent of its chemical, mechanical or thermal history. This is a considerable advantage over any solid metal, even a soft one such as lead. It also forms a large number of stoichiometric mercurous compounds, suitably well-crystallized and of low solubility in water, with properties that fit

---

[1] With the usual reservations discussed in Chapter 1, Section II.

them to act as the second invariant phase of electrodes of the second kind. These advantages, however, are offset by the fact that mercury has two valency states and, in any fully reversible electrode system, must clearly be in equilibrium with both of them. This may be stated in a specially significant way; all mercurous salts participate in a disproportionation equilibrium involving zero-valent and bivalent mercury. This may or may not have serious consequences, depending on circumstances, but it must be considered in conjunction with another disadvantageous feature. This may arise because mercury, in the *aufbau* of the elements, comes after the lanthanide contraction. With an atomic number of 80, it provides a doubly-charged mercuric ion of noninert gas structure and radius only 1.10 Å. This is associated with a marked tendency to form covalent bonds which is evident throughout the chemistry of mercury; in the present connection this is significant because the mercuric ions formed by the disproportionation of the mercurous ions interact with many species of anion to form covalent, complex molecules or ions. This action will displace the disproportionation equilibrium and lead to a total solubility of mercury compounds far in excess of what is to be expected or desired. The operation of these effects will be seen in sections which follow.

The mercury–mercurous chloride, or calomel, and mercury–mercurous sulfate electrodes are the most important and widely used of the electrodes of this type. The second of these is discussed in a separate chapter, so that a primary concern of the present writing will be the calomel electrode. It may be reiterated (cf. Chapter 1, Section VI) that these electrodes (and others) are used in different ways, according to whether the solution phase with which they are in contact is variable, or invariant in composition. In the latter case, the electrodes become reference electrodes of fixed potential, normally used in conjunction with a salt bridge. Calomel electrodes are predominantly used in this way, but then become of secondary interest in the context of this book, and are briefly discussed in a separate section.

II. The Calomel Electrode of Variable Potential

A. EARLIER WORK

The calomel electrode, introduced by Ostwald in 1890 (*1*) has had a long and checkered career, by no means yet concluded, and has outstanding interest from the historical, practical, and theoretical viewpoints. As a reference electrode of fixed potential, in equilibrium with aqueous potassium chloride solution (as in the familiar saturated calomel electrode), it was a success from the start and has been in continuous and expanding use ever since. As an electrode of variable potential, for use in thermodynamic cells, it was a dismal failure, and was universally rejected for a period of twenty years. It was then rescued from the scrap heap and now gives some promise of coming into its own as an electrode capable of providing measurements as accurate as any. It is of interest to trace the sequence of events, which depended in no small way on the classical method of preparing the electrode. This consisted of grinding mercury and calomel with successive portions of cell solution until a thick paste was obtained. This paste was added to a pool of mercury, and the cell solution was poured on top. This procedure was adequate for the one kind of electrode (e.g., saturated calomel) but not the other, as will be shown in due course.

The electrode was extensively used in thermodynamic studies of cells without liquid junction until 1920 but in the following decade, as the limitations of existing forms became apparent, it gradually fell into disrepute as an instrument of precision.

Lewis and Sargent (2) found that the potential of the electrode depended on the method of preparation and advocated rigid adherence to a given procedure. Acree and co-workers (3) prepared a large number of calomel half-cells, using potassium chloride and hydrochloric acid solutions in cells with and without liquid junction, but found large deviations in potential from electrode to electrode; only by connecting the electrodes in parallel for long periods could they obtain an ostensibly reproducible potential. Their electrodes varied in sensitivity to mechanical disturbance. Ellis (4) used with advantage electrolytically prepared calomel and adopted insensitivity to movement as a criterion of reliability. He obtained a reproducibility of ± 0.05 mv, but his electrodes became highly erratic in hydrochloric acid solutions more dilute than 0.03 N. Ming Chow (5) confirmed Ellis's work. Loomis and Meacham (6) studied the hydrogen–calomel cell, standardizing each measurement by reference to an aged calomel half-cell, but the reproducibility of the measurements was poor. Little improvement was shown in further work of the same school. (7). Similarly unsatisfactory results were recorded by Lewis, Brighton, and Sebastian (8), Linhart (9), MacInnes and Parker (10) and Harned (11), and it was these workers who instituted the silver–silver chloride electrode as a more satisfactory, alternative, chloride-reversible electrode.

All of this work was carried out with solutions containing dissolved air; although the reaction

$$2Hg + 2HCl + \tfrac{1}{2}O_2 = Hg_2Cl_2 + H_2O$$

was known, it was thought to be of significant effect only at low concentrations (4, 5). However, not only did it preclude any determination of the standard emf of the hydrogen–calomel cell, but it also affected nearly all the measurements made with the calomel electrode prior to 1922. In that year, Gerke (12) carried out the first reliable measurements with the calomel electrode. He noted that the above oxidation reaction was not restricted to very dilute hydrochloric acid; on the contrary, even potassium chloride solutions, in the presence of air, will dissolve mercury on long standing [see also (15)]. He made measurements on cells of the type

$$\text{Ag} \mid \text{AgCl} \mid \text{aqueous chloride solution} \mid \text{Hg}_2\text{Cl}_2 \mid \text{Hg}$$

containing thoroughly deoxygenated hydrochloric or acid potassium chloride solutions. The emf values he obtained were independent of the electrolyte concentration, but not of the method of calomel preparation. By combining his results with the known standard potential of the silver–silver chloride electrode, he achieved the first reliable measurement of the standard potential of the calomel electrode, i.e., 0.2679 volt[2] at 25°C.

Further experiments were reported, however, underlining the unsatisfactory performance of calomel electrodes prepared in the conventional manner (11, 13–16) and, largely on the recommendations of Randall and Young (15) and of Mukherjee and Kumar (13), the calomel electrode was abandoned in favor of the silver–silver chloride electrode.

In 1942, Mueller and Reuther (17) prepared calomel electrodes and mercury–mercurous sulfate electrodes in the classical manner, taking especial care to prepare and equilibrate their cells anaerobically. They measured the emf of the cell

$$\text{Pt, H}_2 \mid 0.1 \ m \ \text{HCl} \vdots 0.1 \ m \ \text{HCl} \mid \text{Hg}_2\text{Cl}_2 \mid \text{Hg}$$

at 5° intervals between 20° and 50°C and found it to be reproducible to a tenth of a millivolt. From the published activity coefficient data for aqueous hydrochloric acid, they calculated the standard potential of the calomel electrode to be 0.2679 volt at 25°C, in precise agreement with Gerke's earlier result.

B. The Improved Electrode

1. Factors Contributing to Irreversibility

In 1950, Hills and Ives (18, 19), impressed by the virtues of mercury as a substrate for an electrode desired to show high reproducibility, undertook a re-evaluation of the calomel electrode in direct contact with dilute hydro-

---

[2] There is often no means of deciding from published records whether data are expressed in international or absolute volts, and there is no alternative to leaving the question unanswered. The international scale is almost certainly used in older work (thus, Gerke's data are referred to "a cadmium cell of 1.0181 volt") and it is seldom that the difference between the scales (ca. 0.03%) is significantly greater than experimental error.

chloric acid solutions. They identified, but did not fully explain or under-stand, five factors which contribute to unsatisfactory performance of this system. These factors are as follows.

(a) *Dissolved Oxygen.* There seem to be two effects, one of which be-comes apparent when oxygen is introduced into an electrode system ini-tially free from it. It consists of an immediate displacement of potential in a positive direction, but it is reversible, provided that the period of oxygen-ation is short. An experiment illustrating this effect is recorded in Fig. 1.

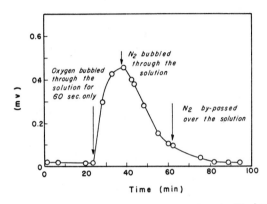

FIG. 1. The effect of dissolved oxygen on the potential of the Hg | Hg$_2$Cl$_2$ | HCl (aq) electrode.

It is unlikely that this short term effect is connected with the second, which is the very slow oxidation reaction, leading to depletion of solute, already mentioned.

(b) *Excess of Solid Phase.* If a mercury-calomel-solution paste is lib-erally heaped upon a mercury surface, the resultant electrode is never sat-isfactory. The segregation of the mercury-solution interface from the bulk of the solution cannot but be undesirable (20). It magnifies the results of any residual disequilibrium in the system and it makes for an untidy elec-trode, the potential of which is sensitive to movement and is generally irreproducible. A very thin layer of calomel is all that is required and when used, effects an immediate improvement in electrode performance.

(c) *The Wedge Effect.* Any aqueous solution over a mercury pool con-tained in a glass vessel will penetrate, by capillary action, between the mercury and the walls of the vessel. It has been descriptively called the wedge effect (21). This creates an annular liquid film in a condition which certainly cannot be typical of the bulk of the solution above the mercury. The area of the interface which this film makes with the mercury often exceeds the area of the exposed surface of the mercury, and may therefore have a predominant effect in determining the potential. It is believed that this undesirable feature may have an influence on the behavior of all mercury pool electrodes. In the present case, it is likely that a quantity of solution, isolated in a cranny about 5 cm from the nearest solid calomel, will not remain in equilibrium with it. This penetration of solution was prevented by rendering the electrode vessel hydrophobic, by a method described below, and there was a dramatic improvement in electrode behavior in consequence.

(d) *The Calomel.* It was found that commercial preparations of calomel, coarsely crystalline, were unsatisfactory, giving rise to positive deviations of potential, slow to decay, and to general erraticity. These defects were not remedied by exhaustive equilibration of the calomel with mercury and cell solution under oxygen-free conditions, and it became clear that particle size was a critical factor. Calomel prepared by chemical precipitation, or by an electrolytic method, very finely divided (0.1–5μ) and intimately mixed with a dispersion of mercury globules, was found to be satisfactory. Electrolytic calomel, however, was found to deteriorate, particularly if kept under moist conditions, and gave rise to positive deviations of potential. This was attributed to the slow generation of the basic compound Hg_2O, Hg_2Cl_2, which was identified in old calomel by X-ray powder photographs. It had the same structure as the bright yellow mineral Eglestonite, and can be looked for in calomel by grinding a small portion between the cone and socket of a ground joint. Any basic salt, which is formed in discrete crystals, shows up as a yellow streak. Chemically precipitated calomel is less susceptible to this change, which in any case is thought not to occur if the calomel is stored in the dark, with exclusion of moisture and air.

(e) *The Calomel–Mercury Interaction.* One of the most remarkable findings was that the order in which the components of the electrode system were brought together is of singular importance. Calomel, of any kind, added to mercury already covered with solution, did not give an electrode of satisfactory reversibility. But if the calomel and mercury were allowed to interact together in the dry state before meeting the solution, an electrode of admirable behavior resulted. That this effect is real enough is shown by the obvious affinity of dry, very finely divided calomel for mercury; it spreads very rapidly, almost violently, over the whole of the surface available to it, and the resulting pearly skin is preserved after the solution is added. No such skin is formed when the components of the electrode are assembled in any other order. Without undue discussion at this stage, it must be pointed out that there is strong evidence here for an intimate and specialized interaction between calomel and mercury, of a kind which is necessary to confer full reversibility upon the calomel electrode. It is now known that the required relationship can be established in other ways, one of which is aerial oxidation. It thus happened that the classical "grinding together in a mortar" technique was not without benefit, for although objectionable in other ways, it did effect this oxidative interaction.

These five factors, once identified, led to methods of preparing and using the calomel electrode which have been widely adopted. These are outlined in the following section. Theoretical aspects are kept to a later stage.

2. *Preparation of Materials*

(*a*) *Mercury*. Although the purification of mercury has been reviewed on a number of occasions (for recent examples, see references *22–24*) this matter is sufficiently important to merit brief discussion. The normal impurities can be divided into three classes: (*i*) filterable scum; (*ii*) dissolved base metals which tarnish the mercury, coating it with oxide and causing it to "tail"; (*iii*) dissolved noble metals which are not readily detected or removed, and which are often not serious contaminants. The usual methods of purification aim at removing these impurities in turn. The mercury is filtered through perforated filter papers and is then treated with acidified mercurous nitrate solution by agitating it under dilute nitric acid (as in Fig. 2) by means of a stream of air drawn through it by a water

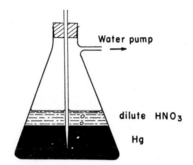

Fig. 2. First stage of mercury purification.

pump, preferably overnight. It is then convenient to pass the mercury from a funnel, with a fine jet pointing at an angle to the vertical, down a column of dilute nitric acid in a vertical tube some 60×2 cm, which terminates at its lower end in a very thick walled capillary U-tube, bent over again to form a delivery jet. The lower part of this apparatus, filled with mercury, sustains the column of dilute acid but is separated from it by an intervening layer of carbon tetrachloride, to prevent undue corrosion of the mercury and clogging of the tube with mercurous nitrate. Such a unit lasts for a long time and has the advantage that it delivers the mercury in a dry state. It can be used with confidence in cleaning mercury known to be free from gross impurities, as when it is being recovered from one experiment for use in the next. The mercury is then suitable for distillation.

Distillation procedures (*24*) are of two kinds. Foreign metals dissolved in mercury are very susceptible to oxidation. Distillation under moderately reduced pressure, with delivery of an air stream below the surface of the mercury by means of a fine capillary, is therefore extremely effective and was recommended by Hulett (*25, 26*). The distillate, even from mercury thought to be pure, is often grossly filthy in appearance; it is then passed to the nitric acid column as a preliminary to vacuum distillation, which should in any case always be the final stage. It may be remarked that commercial laboratory mercury stills, installed as permanent equipment, should, in the writers' experience, be avoided. They become, in course of time, reservoirs of impurity, and it is much better for each experimenter to have his own still. This need not be an apparatus of more than barometric height. The design illustrated in Fig. 3 has been found convenient

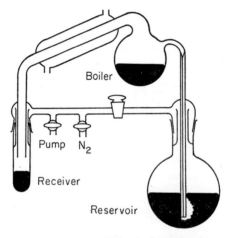

Fig. 3. Mercury still for final purification.

and effective; before use, it is pumped out and filled with nitrogen before final evacuation. This is because electrostatic effects during distillation are believed to generate ozone from residual oxygen. Distillation can easily be carried out in this apparatus by surface evaporation; avoidance of boiling is desirable. Transfers of mercury after this stage should be made, with due precautions, by means of pipettes, and not by pouring.

The appearance of mercury is extremely sensitive to minute traces of base metals as impurities; tarnishing in air is caused by 9 parts of copper in 10^8 of mercury (*24*), and even the purest mercury will, on long standing, leave a ring on a glass container. The reason for this is not known, and the mercury should be purified immediately before use.

(b) *Calomel.* The electrolytic preparation of calomel first described by Hulett (*25, 26*; see also *27*) and used by Ellis (*4*) is carried out in a manner identical with that for mercurous sulfate, which is described in Chapter 8, Section IV, but reasons have been given for preferring chemical precipitation. This may be carried out in the following way.

Five grams of reagent grade mercurous nitrate are moistened with 1 ml of concentrated nitric acid and dissolved in 100 ml of water. This solution is then added dropwise to ∼500 ml of 0.1 N hydrochloric acid contained in a covered beaker and mechanically stirred by means of a glass paddle. The addition is completed within 10 minutes and the suspension is stirred for a further hour. The precipitate is then allowed to settle, after which the supernatant solution is decanted and replaced by a further 500 ml of 0.1 N hydrochloric acid. It is then stirred for a further 24 hr, during which period the hydrochloric acid solution is replaced twice again. The precipitated calomel is finally filtered on to a sintered glass crucible, rinsed quickly with four portions of cold distilled water, and transferred to a vacuum desiccator.

It should be noted that the hydrochloric acid used must be rigorously freed from traces of bromide or iodide (*28, 29*); it is preferable to generate it from potassium chloride purified by the method (*29*) described in Chapter 4, Section III,A,7.

(c) *Hydrochloric Acid.* This should be prepared with similar precautions (cf. Chapter 4, Section III,A,6). It is conveniently stored as the azeotrope in a protected silica flask. It may be noted that, in relation to emf measurements of optimum accuracy, relevant independent variables, such as temperature and concentrations of solutions must be defined within appropriate limits. This is, however, beyond the scope of this discussion.

3. Design and Preparation of Electrodes

There are no very special features of half-cell design, other than the general ones mentioned in Chapter 1, Section VII,B, with two possible exceptions. One is that the cell mounting should be as rigid and free from vibration as possible, to avoid disturbance of the mercury. The other is that the necessity to treat the vessel with silicone preparations to render it hydrophobic requires the removal of any platinum–glass seals, for these are adversely affected. This is readily done by arranging for the mercury to form its own connection by filling a long capillary-bore tube; a removable platinum wire contact can then be used at the remote end of this tube, e.g. as in Fig. 4.

Before treating the electrode vessel with silicone preparations, it should be prepared by the normal cleaning methods and dried. Several procedures are available to render the vessel hydrophobic. By the original method (*19*) the vessel, heated to a temperature of ~100°C, is filled with a 1% solution in redistilled carbon tetrachloride of Dow-Corning Silicone fluid No. 200.

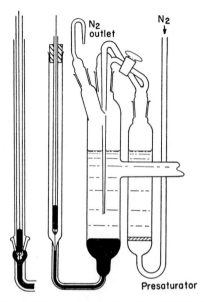

Fɪɢ. 4. Various designs for calomel half-cell.

It is then emptied, drained and baked at ~160°C for 2 hr. After cooling, the cell is thoroughly extracted with freshly distilled carbon tetrachloride to remove any unbonded silicone. More recent recommendations (*30*) suggest baking at 300°C. In either case, steaming, washing, and drying of the vessel before use is to be recommended. An alternative treatment involves exposure of the glass surfaces to the vapor of "Siloxane," $Si(OCH_3)_2Cl_2$ (*30*). It may be noted that silicone films may be removed when necessary by alternating treatments with nitric-chromic acid cleaning mixture (or concentrated nitric acid) and strong sodium hydroxide (or alcoholic potash) solution.

The clean, dry cell, so prepared, is mounted in position, and mercury is introduced. A further small quantity (2 ml) of mercury is placed in a dry, glass-stoppered vessel together with about 100 mg of calomel, prepared as already described, and perfectly dry. Vigorous shaking for 2–4 min produces a ball of mercury covered with an adherent skin of calomel. A little of this skin, transferred by means of a glass spatula to the main mercury pool, spreads at once over the whole of its surface. The quantity of calomel used is very small and it is necessary to increase it somewhat if the experimental conditions are to involve temperatures over 40°C, or solutions more concentrated than decimolal. Air is displaced from the half-cell by nitrogen or hydrogen, after which the cell solution, already saturated with the same gas, may be introduced. This should be done with the minimum of disturbance to the mercury; an apparatus for this purpose is illustrated in Fig. 5. The emf of a cell so prepared (completed with a hydrogen elec-

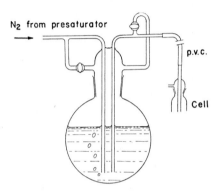

FIG. 5. Storage vessel for cell filling.

trode) reaches a steady value in about two hours, and interagreement between the duplicate electrodes built into the same cell may be within 10 μv (*19, 31, 32*); see, however, following sections.

4. The Standard Electrode Potential

Hills and Ives (*33*), using a pair of calomel electrodes combined with two or more hydrogen electrodes in a cell without liquid junction (Fig. 4), made a series of measurements with dilute hydrochloric acid solutions ranging from 0.002 to 0.1 *m*. Using the Brown and MacInnes method [Chapter 1, Section V, Eq. (54)], they extrapolated their results to infinite dilution to obtain

$$E_m° = 0.26796 \text{ abs volt at } 25°C$$

and, by an independent extrapolation,

$$E_c° = 0.26781 \text{ abs volt at } 25°C.$$

These results were later confirmed by an application of Guggenheim and Prue's method [Chapter 1, Section V, Eq. (55)] to the same data (*34*), by a further experimental study by Hills (unpublished), and by the independent study of Schwabe and Ziegenbalg (*32*).

TABLE I

STANDARD MOLAL POTENTIALS OF THE CALOMEL ELECTRODE (ABSOLUTE VOLTS)

Authors, date, and reference

Temperature (°C)	Hills and Ives 1950 (33)	Hills 1952 (35)	Pouradier and Chateau 1953 (39)	Grzybowski 1956 (36)	Gupta, Hills, and Ives 1957 (38)		Schwabe and Ziegenbalg 1958 (32)
0	—	—	—	0.27406	—	—	—
5	—	0.27286	0.27283	0.27321	0.27290	0.27289	—
10	—	0.27189	0.27187	0.27218	0.27194	0.27191	—
15	—	0.27075	0.27078	0.27099	0.27087	0.27082	—
20	—	0.26943	0.26949	0.26962	0.26962	0.26955	—
25	0.26796	0.26797	0.26804	0.26812	0.26823	0.26816	0.26796
30	—	0.26639	0.26642	0.26648	0.26661	0.26659	—
35	—	0.26466	0.26466	0.26468	0.26490	0.26485	—
40	—	0.26278	0.26273	0.26276	0.26306	0.26303	—
45	—	0.26079	0.26063	0.26068	0.26104	0.26103	—
50	—	—	0.25839	0.25841	—	—	—
55	—	—	0.25598	0.25613	—	—	—
60	—	—	0.25347	0.25376	—	—	—
65	—	—	0.25088	—	—	—	—
70	—	—	0.24767	—	—	—	—
Fundamental consts.	Birge (40)	Birge	Birge	Dumond and Cohen (41)	Birge	Birge	Birge
Type of extrapolation[a]	Brown and MacInnes	Hückel	Based on E°$_{AgCl}$, Harned and Ehlers (42), recalculated by Swinehart (43)	Brown and MacInnes	Hückel	Extended Debye-Hückel	Brown and MacInnes

[a] For types of extrapolation, see Chapter 1, Section V.

These first determinations, which had an internal consistency of 10 μv, were of an accuracy "unprecedented except for measurements by Güntelberg" [to quote Guggenheim and Prue (*34*)], have, unfortunately, not entirely lived up to expectations. Since 1951, there have been four attempts to extend the determination of $E^\circ_{calomel}$ to temperatures other than 25°C. Thus, Hills (*35*), Grzybowski (*36*) and Gupta (*37*, *38*) made measurements on the hydrogen–calomel cell over the temperature range 0–60°C, while Pouradier and Chateau (*39*) made a further study of the cell

$$\text{Ag} \mid \text{AgCl} \mid \text{KCl (aq)} \mid \text{Hg}_2\text{Cl}_2 \mid \text{Hg}$$

from 5° to 70°C. The results of these researches are set out in Table I.

The agreement between them is not good and it may be noted that the two most extensive determinations (columns 5 and 6, 7) give, for example, values of E° at 25°C considerably higher than that obtained by Hills and Ives.

The measurements of Grzybowski were made using a different type of cell (Fig. 6) and were restricted to the narrow concentration range 0.005–

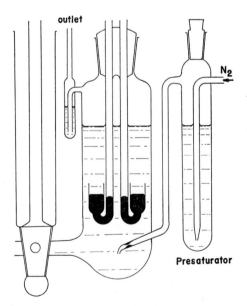

FIG. 6. Grzybowski's calomel half-cell (*36*).

0.02 m. Those of Hills, of Gupta, and of Schwabe and Ziegenbalg were performed using apparatus similar to that used in the original measurements. In all of them, the calomel electrode was prepared by the procedure recommended above, whereas the measurements of Pouradier and Chateau were made on electrodes prepared in the classical manner.

It is clear from Table I that, whatever the internal consistency within each set of measurements, the interagreement between them is disappointing to the highest degree. The differences lie outside any possible variations due to different choices of fundamental constants or extrapolation equations. Nevertheless, this does not create an impossible situation, disappointing though it may be, since for many purposes it is the quantity $(E - E°)$ which is of primary physicochemical significance (Chapter 1, Section V). The absolute values of $E°_{Hg,Hg_2Cl_2,Cl^-}$, however, cannot yet be regarded as fixed beyond debate, and it is therefore not yet appropriate to base fundamental calculations upon them. It is, however, clear that there is a physical reason for the discrepancies. This has been identified and is briefly discussed under the next heading.

5. Complex Reactions at the Calomel Electrode

The original work of Hills and Ives (*33*) was carried out at 25°C, and included an observation which was misunderstood. Thus, to quote from their original paper: "Readings were continued at intervals for a few hours and the cell was left overnight with the gases bypassing the solutions. Slight changes of emf sometimes occurred overnight, due to imperfection in the gas presaturation arrangements, but these were rectified by refilling the cell, and a further set of measurements was carried out. Agreement of results obtained on different days was almost invariably excellent." Thus, a cell-refilling technique became a standard procedure and was carried through by Hills in the first attempt to extend the measurements to a wider temperature range, but not with a designed regularity of routine. A similar procedure was used by Schwabe and Ziegenbalg (*32*). They also observed an apparently constant emf for their hydrogen–calomel cell after 3–4 hr, and their results were not only excellently reproducible, but gave a $E°_{calomel}$ value identical with that obtained earlier.

It became clear, however, with further work [Gupta (*38, 39*)] that the slow change in emf of the hydrogen–calomel cell, observable by overnight standing at 25°C, was not adventitious. Assumed originally to be a drift away from equilibrium, it is now known to be a very slow progress from a metastable equilibrium towards a final, stable one and is due to the disproportionation of calomel. This conclusion is supported by the following experimental facts.

(1) The $Hg \mid Hg_2Cl_2 \mid HCl$ (aq) electrode, after being set up, shows a behavior similar to, or better than, other well-behaved electrodes; thermal and other local equilibria (diffusion, adsorption, etc.) are established at a normal rate, and the emf of the cell concerned levels off to a value which

is constant to within 10 μv over several hours. But the plateau of emf so attained is not quite horizontal; it is part of another curve which rises in the course of 24–48 hr to a slightly higher level. This is illustrated in Fig. 7. The effect increases markedly in significance as the temperature and concentration of hydrochloric acid increase.

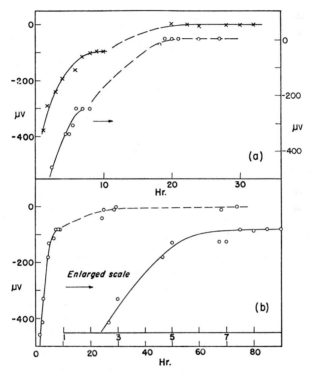

Fig. 7. The emf of the cell H_2, Pt $\mid$ HCl (aq) $\mid$ Hg_2Cl_2 $\mid$ Hg as a function of time.

(2) If an electrode, equilibrated by long standing at 25°C, is raised in temperature to 40°C, it is no longer in equilibrium when temperature gradients have fallen to zero. Left undisturbed, its potential slowly rises. If the solution above the electrode is mixed by brief stirring with nitrogen, however, the potential falls to a lower level, but creeps up again on further standing. This operation, often repeated, clearly shows the existence of two levels, the lower of which gradually rises, in the course of a day, until it coincides with the upper. It is clear that this behavior could be caused by the establishment of a concentration of soluble disproportionation products of calomel, first in the diffusion zone close to the electrode surface, and finally in the whole of the solution in the half-cell. If the electrode,

after this experiment, is returned to 25°C, it is found again not to be in equilibrium, as might be expected. In other words, the electrode shows a temperature-hysteresis effect. The existence of two levels of potential has been shown in another way. If the cell solution is circulated over highly-purified, active charcoal, disproportionation products are continuously removed and the potential does not rise. If, on the other hand, the solution is circulated over a mixture of calomel and mercury, the potential tends to a considerably higher level. These devices, however, are still under investigation; they do not necessarily lend themselves to the establishment of highly reproducible potentials of thermodynamic significance (44).

(3) With use of higher acid concentrations (>1 m) and higher temperatures (>45°C), the calomel film is visibly changed by the disproportionation reaction, and will ultimately become white in appearance and break, forming fissures which expose bare mercury to the solution. The electrode then deteriorates in behavior, becoming erratic and untrustworthy. Clearly, the special requirements for maximum reversibility of operation have been destroyed. It might be said that, in the approach of the electrode to final equilibrium under such conditions, there is a conflict between thermodynamic and mechanistic requirements.

To summarize at this stage, the calomel electrode suffers from a disability arising from the two valency states of mercury and the tendency of mercuric ions to form complexes. This severely limits the convenience of the electrode for purposes of making precise measurements. Yet two types of calomel electrode may be distinguished with their own $E°$ values differing, at 25°C, by as much as 0.24 mv. The first, which could be called the "metastable calomel electrode," is free from mercuric mercury in solution. It is satisfactory for isothermal measurements, not extending over a long interval of time, applied to the lower ranges of concentration and temperature ($\not> 0.1$ m, $\not> 25°C$). The second, the "stable calomel electrode" is that in which complete equilibrium is established between mercury, calomel and mercuric entities in solution. It is probably the most sluggish electrode on record, but its use is obligatory in the higher ranges of concentration and temperature, in which, however, its useful life is limited.

The second and sixth columns of Table I are believed to be the best figures at present available for these distinguishable types of calomel electrode. The results of the other workers, who did not suspect the existence of this complication any more than Hills and Ives did, may be affected by it to an extent impossible to assess. Errors of a systematic nature (to which extrapolation procedures are sensitive) may be caused in this way, and, of course, a hysteresis effect may be responsible for error of either sign in individual measurements, according to which side of the "loop" was involved.

6. The Calomel Electrode Under Extreme Conditions

It is noteworthy that Lietzke and Vaughan (45) have succeeded in making a study of the cell

$$\text{Ag} \mid \text{AgCl} \mid \text{HCl (aq)} \mid \text{Hg}_2\text{Cl}_2 \mid \text{Hg}$$

with hydrochloric acid as strong as unimolar up to temperatures of 250°C. Their electrode was prepared by the "paste method" and the fact that it was usable at all under such conditions shows it to be much more resistant

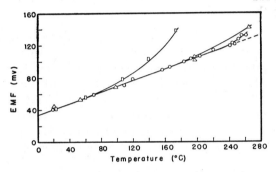

Fig. 8. The emf of the cell Ag | AgCl | HCl (aq) | Hg$_2$Cl$_2$ | Hg at high temperatures (45); (○, 1.0 M; △, 0.5 M; □, 0.1 M HCl).

than what may be called the "film electrodes" which have been discussed; there is much more reserve of material. Even so, loss of calomel was very rapid above 200°C, by disproportionation and hydrolysis to various basic mercuric salts. The data obtained are illustrated in Fig. 8.

7. The Calomel Electrode in Aqueous-Alcoholic and Other Media

Apart from some earlier measurements of low precision (46–48) and a few very recent and accurate investigations, the calomel electrode has not been used in alcoholic and aqueous-alcoholic media. The extensive studies of such systems by the schools of Hartley and of Harned and by Feakins and French were all made after the establishment of the silver–silver chloride electrode as the pre-eminent, anion-reversible electrode, and all used it (cf. Chapter 4, Sections II,B and II,C).

Recently, however, Schwabe and his co-workers have begun a similar series of investigations using the improved form of the calomel electrode. They have, so far, extended its use to solutions of hydrogen chloride in aqueous methanol (32), aqueous dioxane (49) and aqueous glycol (50) of various compositions. Their apparatus and preparative procedure were very similar to those advocated by Hills and Ives and the reproducibility of the results varied from ±10 to ±20 μv, in the more aqueous solvent mixtures, to ±50 μv in the nearly anhydrous media. The generally satisfactory nature of the measurements was considered by these authors to compare favorably with those made using the silver–silver chloride electrode in similar solutions.

The corresponding standard electrode potentials were obtained in one of two ways. In the first, the complete expression for the cell emf in dilute solutions was written as

$$E = E_m° - 2k \log m_{HCl} + 2k \left[\frac{A'm^{1/2}}{1 + B'a_i m^{1/2}} + \log \left(1 + \frac{m\,M_{xy}}{1000} \right) \right] \quad (1)$$

where $k = (RT/F) \ln 10$, M_{xy} is the mean molecular weight of the solvent and the other terms have their usual significance. This equation is rearranged as in the Brown-MacInnes method [Chapter 1, Section V, Eq. (54)] to give a linear extrapolation of slope equal to $B'a_i$. In the second way, a further, linear term, Cm, (but not the extended terms) was added to the Debye-Hückel expression and the equation for the cell emf was then rearranged in the usual way to give, provided that the appropriate value of a_i is known, a linear extrapolation of slope C; the values obtained are given in Table II.

TABLE II

Standard Molal Potentials of the Calomel Electrode (32, 49, 50)

Solvent system	Percentage (w/w) of organic solvent	$E_m°$ (abs volts, 25°C)
Methanol-water	20.22	0.2545
	43.12	0.2415
	68.33	0.2173
	99.29	0.1027
Dioxane-water	20	0.2501
	45	0.2104
	70	0.1126
	82	−0.0014
Ethylene glycol-water	19.25	0.2570
	50	0.2364
	77.91	0.20125

The attempted extension of the calomel electrode to certain aqueous solutions of physiological interest, e.g., containing glycerophosphates, was less successful and this almost certainly reflects the slow attainment of the complex electrode equilibria in this system (*51*).

C. Theory of the Calomel Electrode

The study of the calomel electrode raises many interesting points; appreciation of some of them at an earlier stage would have saved a good deal of trouble. It is a reflection of this kind which is the main theme of this book, and it is therefore suitable to discuss certain theoretical aspects at some length, beginning with those that should have been foreseen. Although this discussion will be of no direct help to the experimenter in his immediate objectives, it may be suggested that it illustrates the wealth of interest which attaches to but one type of electrode. Similar explorations with others may be equally fruitful in the future.

1. Solution Equilibria

It has already been emphasized (Chapter 1, Section III), and brief illustrations have been provided, that the conformity of an electrode system with thermodynamic requirements gives no information whatever about its mechanism of operation, nor about any other equilibria in which it may be involved aside from the "official" one. Full understanding of the system requires it to be examined from all angles, and for mercury-based electrodes one of the most important of these is concerned with all the equilibria in which mercury may be involved. These primary equilibria may be represented as follows:

$$\left.\begin{array}{l} \text{Hg (liquid)} \\[1.2em] \text{Hg}^\circ \text{ (in solution)} \end{array}\right\} \overset{\text{(i)}}{\underset{\text{(ii)}}{\rightleftharpoons}} \begin{array}{c} \text{Hg}_2^{2+} \text{ (aq)} \\[1.2em] 2\text{Hg}^{2+} \text{ (aq)} \end{array} \overset{\text{(iv)}}{\underset{\text{(iii)}}{\rightleftharpoons}} 2\text{Hg}^+ \text{ (aq)}$$

It is seen that the species which may exist in homogeneous solution are Hg°, Hg^+, Hg_2^{2+}, Hg^{2+} and all may come into equilibrium with the bulk mercury phase, Hg (liquid). Of these, Hg°, Hg_2^{2+} and Hg^{2+} can all be studied at finite concentrations, and it is probable that the individual rate constants of the equilibrium reactions (i), (ii), and (iii), at least, are all high. The rates of the homogeneous exchange reaction between aqueous mercuric and aqueous mercurous ions, and of the heterogeneous exchange reaction between solid calomel and aqueous mercurous ions, have been studied using Hg^{205} and Hg^{203}, and were found to be immeasurably fast at room temperature (*52–54*). The homogeneous disproportionation reaction

$$Hg_2^{2+} \rightleftharpoons Hg^\circ \text{ (aq)} + Hg^{2+} \text{ (aq)}$$

is also very fast, with a half-life of certainly not more than a few milliseconds and probably not more than a microsecond (*55*).

The heterogeneous exchange reaction (i), which is of particular relevance, is also too fast to be studied quantitatively by tracer techniques, but its exchange current can be evaluated from measurements of the impedance or faradaic admittance (56) of the electrode system

$$\text{Hg (liq)} \mid \text{Hg}_2(\text{ClO}_4)_2 \text{ (aq)} \ \dots.$$

or from its faradaic rectification properties (57). At room temperature, the specific first order rate constant[3] (k) lies between 2×10^{-3} and 8×10^{-8} cm sec^{-1}.

The homogeneous disproportionation reaction and the homogeneous ion exchange equilibrium (iii) are not so easily studied quantitatively. The equilibrium constant,

$$K = a_{\text{Hg}^{2+}} \cdot a_{\text{Hg}^\circ} / a_{\text{Hg}_2^{2+}} \tag{2}$$

can be calculated from the determined ratio $a_{\text{Hg}^{2+}}/a_{\text{Hg}_2^{2+}}$ in the presence of liquid mercury and from the solubility of mercury in water. That mercury has a finite solubility in water has been well established (58, 59) and the most recent value (60) is $3.0 \pm 0.1 \times 10^{-7}$ mole liter^{-1} at 25°C. This, coupled with the value of 0.0120 for the ratio $a_{\text{Hg}^{2+}}/a_{\text{Hg}_2^{2+}}$ (61), leads to a value for K of 3.16×10^{-9} mole liter^{-1}. The same disproportionation equilibrium constant can be determined directly by radiotracer experiments and these have led to a value of 5.5×10^{-9} (60).

The cause of this discrepancy is not known; it is not serious, and it is not due to a corresponding error in the ratio $a_{\text{Hg}^{2+}}/a_{\text{Hg}_2^{2+}}$ obtaining in the presence of excess liquid mercury. This important ratio underlies the evaluation of many other equilibrium constants of complex ion formation in mercury-ion-containing solutions in contact with the mercury electrode. It may be found from an analytical study of the equilibrium

$$\text{Hg}_2^{2+} \text{ (aq)} \rightleftharpoons \text{Hg (liquid)} + \text{Hg}^{2+} \text{ (aq)}$$

in nitrate or perchlorate solutions (62–65) or, much more accurately, from the difference between the standard redox potential of the mercurous-mercuric redox couple (61, 66, 67), i.e.

$$a_{\text{Hg}^{2+}}/a_{\text{Hg}_2^{2+}} = \exp\left[(2F/RT)\,(E^\circ_{\text{Hg},\text{Hg}_2^{2+}} - E^\circ_{\text{Hg}_2^{2+},\text{Hg}^{2+}})\right] \tag{3}$$

The cell

$$\text{Pt, H}_2 \mid \text{HClO}_4 \text{ (aq)} \ \vdots \ \text{HClO}_4 \text{ (aq), Hg}_2(\text{ClO}_4)_2 \text{ (aq)} \mid \text{Hg}$$

was first studied by Linhart (68). His results, corrected first by Lewis and

---

[3] Since k is defined by the equation:

$$\text{rate (mole sec}^{-1}) = k \text{ cm}^2 \text{ mole liter}^{-1}$$

Randall (69), then by Bray and Hershey (70) and finally by Bonner and Unietis (71), led to the values 0.798_6, 0.797_5 and 0.798_6 int volt respectively for $E^{\circ}_{Hg,Hg_2^{2+}}$. The last authors also redetermined this quantity using the cell

$$\text{Ag} \mid \text{AgCl} \mid \text{HCl (aq)} \vdots \text{HNO}_3 \text{ (aq)}, \text{Hg}_2(\text{NO}_3)_2 \text{ (aq)} \mid \text{Hg}$$

and obtained the value $E^{\circ}_{Hg,Hg_2^{2+}} = 0.7961$ abs volt (0.7958 int volt). Another experimental investigation of the Linhart cell was made by El Wakkad and Salem (72). They found their measurements to be sensitive to the presence of air, and *without* deaeration of their cell and solutions (as with Linhart), they obtained 0.7988 abs volt (0.7985 int volt) i.e., almost the same value as Linhart. In the absence of air, they obtained 0.7971 abs volt, which is probably the closest approach as yet to the true value.

The agreement between the various determinations of the standard mercuric-mercurous oxidation-reduction potential is not so good (61, 66, 67, 73–75). The most recent values, 0.9075 (66, 67) and 0.9097 (61) abs volt are both higher than the value of 0.9050 abs volt found by Popoff et al. (74, 75) which for long was the accepted value. The later results both lead to values of 0.012 for the ratio $a_{Hg^{2+}}/a_{Hg_2^{2+}}$.

The dissociation equilibrium (iv), $\text{Hg}_2^{2+} \rightleftharpoons 2\text{Hg}^+$ has been referred to on several occasions (76–79), but none of the evidence for a finite concentration of monomeric mercurous ions has been substantiated and the equilibrium constant for the reaction is certainly a very small quantity (60, 80). Nevertheless, this kind of fission is to be expected and may turn out to be significant under certain circumstances (81).

In the presence of an excess of a solid mercurous salt, such as calomel, the mercurous ion activity bears a fixed relationship to the corresponding anion activity. This is required by the constancy of the activity solubility product of the solid salt, i.e.,

$$a_{Hg_2^{2+}} \cdot a_{Cl^-}^2 = K_S \tag{4}$$

The electrode potential of the mercury is thus also related to the anion activity and the normal equation for this potential

$$E = E^{\circ}_{Hg,Hg_2^{2+}} + \frac{RT}{2F} \ln a_{Hg_2^{2+}} \tag{5}$$

can be rewritten

$$E = \underbrace{E^{\circ}_{Hg,Hg_2^{2+}} + \frac{RT}{2F} \ln K_S}_{E^{\circ}_{Hg_2Cl_2}} - \frac{RT}{F} \ln a_{Cl^-} \tag{6}$$

$E^{\circ}_{Hg_2Cl_2}$, and the standard potentials of the other mercury electrodes functioning as electrodes of the second kind, can be obtained with a high degree of precision and it is these values with which we are concerned. They are alternatively the source of accurate values of K_S, to be preferred to those determined directly from solubility and conductance measurements.

Thus, adopting the values $E°_{Hg,Hg_2^{2+}} = 0.7971$ abs volt (71) and $E°_{Hg_2Cl_2} = 0.2682$ abs volt (38) at $25°$, and using the molality scale, we find that for Hg_2Cl_2,

$$K_S = 1.32 \times 10^{-18}$$

which compares with the value of 3.67×10^{-18} from solubility data $(82, 83)$. Somewhat poor agreement is to be expected in this case. This indicates that in decimolal hydrochloric acid, for example, the activity of mercurous ion is $\sim 10^{-17}$, and its concentration will be of the same order. This amounts to about 6×10^6 individual ions per liter of solution, which is totally inadequate to sustain a reaction of finite rate. Since the calomel electrode is highly reversible, and has a high exchange current, it cannot operate by a mechanism in which charge and discharge of mercurous ions is the rate-limiting step. It has already been made plain, however, that in chloride-containing solutions very much more mercury may be present in other forms, and the equilibria concerned must be examined. The mercurous chloride-water system has been studied by a very elegant conductance method by Dry and Gledhill (84). Using data from Sillén's work $(65, 85, 86)$ they tabulate the equilibrium constants shown in Table III (see also references $87, 88$). The corresponding concentrations of the various species present in a "saturated solution of mercurous chloride" are shown in Table IV.

TABLE III

Equilibria and Equilibrium Constants in the System at $25°C$

$$Hg \mid Hg_2Cl_2 \mid Cl^- \text{ (aq)}$$

Equilibria	$\log K$
$Hg_2Cl_2 \text{ (solid)} \rightleftharpoons Hg_2^{2+} + 2Cl^-$	-17.877 ± 0.003
$Hg^{2+} + Hg \text{ (liquid)} \rightleftharpoons Hg_2^{2+}$	1.945 ± 0.017^a
$Hg^{2+} + H_2O \rightleftharpoons HgOH^+ + H^+$	-3.09 ± 0.20
$Hg^{2+} + 2H_2O \rightleftharpoons Hg(OH)_2 + 2H^+$	-5.65 ± 0.12
$Hg_2^{2+} + H_2O \rightleftharpoons Hg_2(OH)^+ + H^+$	-4.4 ± 0.4
$Hg^{2+} + Cl^- \rightleftharpoons HgCl^+$	7.34 ± 0.27
$Hg^{2+} + 2Cl^- \rightleftharpoons HgCl_2$	14.26 ± 0.09
$Hg^{2+} + 3Cl^- \rightleftharpoons HgCl_3^-$	14.07 ± 0.15^b
$Hg^{2+} + 4Cl^- \rightleftharpoons HgCl_4^{2-}$	15.07 ± 0.06^b

[a] This value differs from that given originally which was later shown to be in error (61).

[b] These constants are "nonthermodynamic" and refer to solutions with an ionic strength of 0.5.

TABLE IV

THE COMPOSITION OF SATURATED AQUEOUS MERCUROUS CHLORIDE SOLUTION AT 25°C $(84)^a$

Species	Concentration (mole or gm ion liter^{-1})
H^+	$(8.17 \pm 0.08) \times 10^{-6}$
Cl^-	$(8.40 \pm 0.14) \times 10^{-6}$
$Hg(OH)_2$	$(4.03 \pm 0.10) \times 10^{-6}$
$HgCl_2$	$(3.30 \pm 0.4) \pm 10^{-6}$
Hg_2OH^+	10×10^{-8} (limits 4 to 25)
$HgCl^+$	2.7×10^{-8} (limits 1.3 to 5.5)
Hg_2^{2+}	$1.9 \pm 0.01 \times 10^{-8}$
$Hg(OH)^+$	1.4×10^{-8} (limits 0.8 to 2.5)
Hg^{2+}	$(1.46 \pm 0.11) \times 10^{-10}$

^{a} Some of these data are subject to a small correction arising out of the recent change in the equilibrium mercurous-mercuric ion activity ratio.

With increasing chloride ion concentration, the role of the complex mercuric ions becomes still more significant and the total concentration of mercury-containing solutes rises steadily. The results of studies in this field ($65, 85, 86$) are summarized in Fig. 9, which relates, however, to the

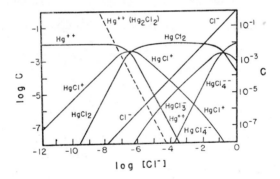

FIG. 9. Equilibrium concentrations of mercury-containing species in aqueous chloride solutions at 25°C ($65, 85, 86$).

special conditions of constant ionic strength 0.5 and an approximately constant total mercury concentration of 0.01 gm ion liter^{-1}. The diagram indicates, for example, that in decinormal hydrochloric acid in equilibrium with solid calomel and mercury, the concentration of mercurous ions is exceeded by many powers by the concentrations of mercuric species.

It is obvious that a number of electrode processes may be envisaged, all with their own specific rate constants and eaxchnge currents, but it cannot be seen that any of them is likely to account for the high degree of reversibility that is observed.

2. Phenomena at the Mercury–Solution Interface

Hills and Ives (*18, 19*), impressed by the evidence for a remarkable interaction between finely-divided, dry calomel and mercury, and by the dramatic effect of this upon electrode reversibility, suggested that a highly reactive intermediate must be formed. They supposed that this consisted of a monolayer of chlorine atoms covalently bound to the surface of the mercury. This might act as a two-dimensional vapor of calomel, very mobile on the mercury surface, and able to sustain fast exchange equilibria. This suggestion, purely imaginative at the time, has been supported by evidence of various kinds.

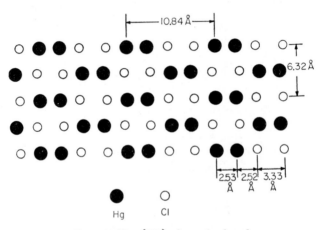

Fɪɢ. 10. The {110} plane of calomel.

The first evidence arises from the work of Thirsk (*89*), appreciation of which requires knowledge of the structure of calomel. This had been thoroughly investigated (*90–92*); it has a tetragonal unit cell, space group D_{4h}^{17} with $a_0 = 4.47$ Å and $c_0 = 10.89$ Å. It has the special property that it cleaves readily in the {110} plane (*93*). Thirsk showed that the calomel films grown anodically on mercury in hydrochloric acid solutions, whether in the form of extensive single crystals, or as a polycrystalline sheet, *all had this {110} plane parallel to the mercury surface*. This particular film with its preferred orientation has a skinlike coherence and has, according to Thirsk, the structure shown in Fig. 10.

This anodic film is similar in appearance to that formed by mechanical interaction between finely divided calomel and mercury in the dry state, and in this film also there may be this preferred orientation.

Further evidence has come from electrochemical studies of the anodization of mercury in hydrochloric acid. It has been shown that when this is carried out at an extremely low current density (e.g. 0.25 μa cm^{-2}) no calomel is at first formed, but a faradaic process proceeds which causes mercuric entities to accumulate in the solution. Prolonged electrolysis of this kind in decinormal hydrochloric acid will raise the electrode potential above the appropriate calomel potential, where it will remain for some hours. Eventually, however, calomel does appear on the mercury surface and the potential falls to the calomel value, but the electrode never attains a satisfactory degree of reversibility (94). If, however, the current density of the electrolysis is progressively increased, there is a remarkable change in the behavior of the electrode. This is accompanied by the development of a very typical potential–time curve, recorded oscillographically under constant current conditions. It shows highly reproducible features, of the kind to be seen in the reproduction of an oscillogram in Fig. 11a. It is always the case that when this kind of behavior is shown, the electrode is immediately transformed from a highly polarized state to a completely depolarized one. Measurements with ac polarization imposed upon dc show a sudden collapse of electrode impedance to take place as the transient potential peak, evident in Fig. 11a, is traversed. The situation then arises that, for example, 100,000 μcoulomb of electricity per cm^2 passed at a current density of 0.25 μa cm^{-2} will not produce a reversible calomel electrode, but 200 μcoulomb cm^{-2} passed at a current density of 100 μa cm^{-2} will do so. The evidence for a switch in electrode process is therefore very strong, and the view has been expressed that it is essentially a transition from a reaction in which mercuric ion charging predominates to one in which chloride ion discharge predominates. These alternative paths were represented as:

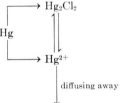

The first product of discharge is thought to be the "chloromercury" layer postulated by Hills and Ives, and this undergoes firstly two-dimensional crystallization, and then leads to the three-dimensional growth of an uniquely-orientated calomel film, the various transients in the galvanostatic potential–time records marking stages in this progress. Thus,

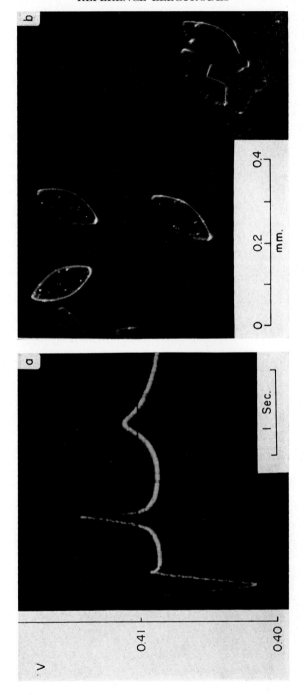

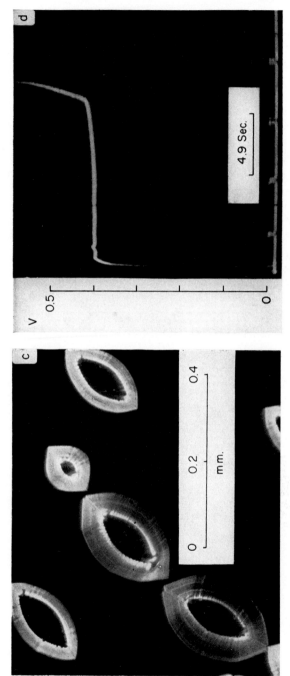

Fig. 11. The anodic production of a calomel film on mercury in 0.1 N hydrochloric acid. (a) Oscillographic record of potential against time at constant current density (100 μa cm^{-2}); (b) primary stage of calomel growth; (c) secondary stage of calomel growth; (d) oscillographic record of potential against time at constant current density (100 μa cm^{-2}) for the whole course of the passivation process.

there is no doubt at all that the main peak marks the appearance of calomel as a fully potential-determining phase. Interruption of the current and tracing of the decay of potential with time allows the progress of the loss of calomel by disproportionation to be followed (*95*). The sequence of events consequent upon low current density anodizations of this kind has also been followed by microscopical examination with reflected polarized light (*96*). The extremely high birefringence of calomel promotes the visibility of very thin films under these conditions. The photomicrographs reproduced in Fig. 11b, and c show successive stages in the growth of a calomel film towards the passivated state which finally ensues. An oscillographic record of the passivation process is shown in Fig. 11d. No doubt can remain about the unique orientation of such films, and there is little doubt that this is connected with the requirements for reversibility.

III. Calomel Electrodes of Fixed Potential

It has been indicated that, in the form of a standard half-cell of fixed potential, the calomel electrode has enjoyed the widest possible use since its inception. Two general points may first be made. Such electrodes are always made up with neutral potassium chloride solutions, never with hydrochloric acid. There is quite a fundamental difference between these two systems for reasons which are far from fully understood. The rate of disproportionation of calomel is less, and the rate of the oxidation reaction

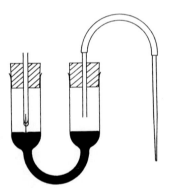

Fig. 12. Calomel half-cell.

is less, for the electrodes made up with potassium chloride. The second point is that comparatively strong solutions are used in such half-cells and, when equilibrium is established, it is likely that exchange currents are higher, although no systematic study of this has yet been made. There is, however, naturally less sensitivity to disturbing factors, and at the same time more tolerance for them, for it is very seldom that fixed potential half-cells are required to show a reproducibility better than 0.1 mv. If they are, then calibration methods are adopted.

Calomel electrodes of this kind can be prepared as compact, robust stable electrodes (cf. Fig. 12), the potentials of which are constant, and known to a millivolt or so, over the temperature range of 0° to 100°C.

Several not very radical variations in design have been reported (97–113) and some are shown in Fig. 13. These have few special features

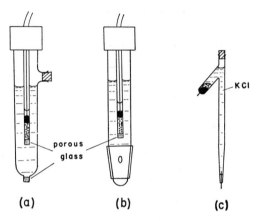

(a) **(b)** **(c)**

FIG. 13. Examples of different designs of calomel half-cells. The liquid junctions are contained: (a) in the porous glass plug; (b) in the annular space between the cone and its sleeve; and (c) in the asbestos thread which is lightly sealed into the glass.

which are not obvious on inspection, and it need only be pointed out that, whatever the design of the electrode, it is important that the liquid junction should be made in a reproducible manner but not in such a free-flowing way that serious contamination of the other electrode system with potassium chloride, or other electrolytes from the salt bridge, occurs.

In the special case of potentiometric measurements on systems at high temperatures or pressures, some elaboration of design is required. An electrode developed for this purpose by Ingruber (114) is shown in Fig. 14. It is of the normal, inverted type used in conjunction with commercial pH meters. It has, however, a cooling jacket for controlling the temperature of the electrode proper, and a pressure-tight O-ring gland around the platinum wire contact tube. Convective flow into and out of the reference electrode is minimized by the capillary outlet and also by small glass beads and potassium chloride crystals packed into the stem which serves as the salt bridge. The glass beads also minimize convective streaming of hot potassium chloride solution up into the main electrode chamber. The lower temperature coefficient of solubility of sodium chloride would make

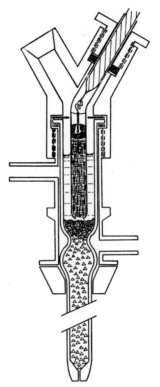

Fig. 14. Ingruber's calomel electrode system (*114*).

it a preferable component for this type of electrode and the author was apparently unaware of the successful replacement of the potassium by the sodium salt by Lauchlan and Page (*115*).

Three main forms of the calomel electrode are usually employed,

$$\text{Hg} \mid \text{Hg}_2\text{Cl}_2 \mid \text{KCl, saturated} \ldots\ldots$$
$$\text{Hg} \mid \text{Hg}_2\text{Cl}_2 \mid \text{KCl, 1 } N \text{ solution} \ldots\ldots$$
$$\text{Hg} \mid \text{Hg}_2\text{Cl}_2 \mid \text{KCl, 0.1 } N \text{ solution} \ldots\ldots$$

although other varieties have also been studied, such as

$$\text{Hg} \mid \text{Hg}_2\text{Cl}_2 \mid \text{KCl, 0.1 } m \ldots\ldots$$
$$\text{Hg} \mid \text{Hg}_2\text{Cl}_2 \mid \text{KCl, 3.5 } N \ldots\ldots$$

It may be pointed out that the saturated calomel electrode forms its own salt bridge; such an arrangement has been called a "half-bridge" (cf. Chapter 1, Section VI).

All these electrodes are normally prepared in the classical manner, i.e., from mercury in a clean glass tube to which a wet paste of mercury, calomel, and potassium chloride solution is added. In the past, only rarely was air excluded from the preparation and there was little need for such a precaution in these neutral systems, and it might even be harmful. It is, indeed, unlikely that the special techniques developed for the "dilute acid electrodes" will be suitable for direct application to the neutral ones, which are required to be robust and reasonably stable over long periods. The use of hydrophobic vessels, and of calomel of small particle size (in larger quantities) can, however, hardly be anything but beneficial (116–118). The data given below apply to electrodes prepared in the conventional way.

The principal difficulty in utilizing any form of the standard calomel half-cell is in knowing what potential on the hydrogen scale to ascribe to it. There is a fundamental difficulty (cf. Chapter 1, Section VI; Chapter 5, Section III,B) involved in the indeterminacy of single ion activities and in the evaluation of liquid junction potentials. There are two ways of attempting to deal with this. For the typical electrode system

$$\text{Hg} \;\Big|\; \text{Hg}_2\text{Cl}_2 \;\Big|\; \text{KCl } (m) \;\vdots\; \begin{array}{l}\text{liquid junction}\\ \text{or salt-bridge}\end{array} \;\vdots\; \begin{array}{l}\text{test}\\ \text{solution}\end{array} \;\Big|\; \begin{array}{l}\text{test}\\ \text{electrode}\end{array}$$

$$\underbrace{\phantom{\text{Hg}\;\Big|\;\text{Hg}_2\text{Cl}_2\;\Big|}}_{E' = E_{\text{calomel}}}$$

$$\underbrace{\phantom{\text{Hg}\;\Big|\;\text{Hg}_2\text{Cl}_2\;\Big|\;\text{KCl}\;(m)\;\vdots\;\text{liquid junction}\;\vdots}}_{E'' = E_{\text{calomel}} + E_{\text{liquid junction}}}$$

the potential E' may be calculated from the known value of $E°_{\text{calomel}}$ by using the equation

$$\left.\begin{aligned}E' = E_{\text{calomel}} &= E°_{\text{calomel}} - (RT/F)\ln a_{\text{Cl}^-}\\ &= E°_{\text{calomel}} - (RT/F)\ln m_{\text{Cl}^-}\gamma_{\text{Cl}^-}\end{aligned}\right\} \tag{7}$$

The unknown term γ_{Cl^-} may be approximately found by equating it to the corresponding value of $\gamma_{\pm}$ for the particular potassium chloride solution concerned. The value of E'' may be then found by adding to E' the calculated liquid junction potential appropriate to the system, provided all the parameters for the particular calculation are known or can be assumed (cf. Chapter 1, Section VI).

Alternatively, the same calomel half-cell can be combined directly with a hydrogen electrode or with a silver–silver chloride electrode as, for example in the cells

$$\text{Pt, H}_2 \mid \text{HCl} \vdots \text{junction or bridge} \vdots \text{KCl } (m) \mid \text{Hg}_2\text{Cl}_2 \mid \text{Hg}$$

$$\text{Pt, H}_2 \mid \text{buffer solution} \vdots \text{junction or bridge} \vdots \text{KCl } (m) \mid \text{Hg}_2\text{Cl}_2 \mid \text{Hg}$$

$$\text{Ag} \mid \text{AgCl} \left| \begin{array}{l} \text{aq chloride} \\ \text{solution} \end{array} \right. \vdots \begin{array}{l} \text{junction} \\ \text{or bridge} \end{array} \vdots \text{KCl } (m) \left| \text{Hg}_2\text{Cl}_2 \right| \text{Hg}$$

E'' is then given by the difference between the total observed emf and that due to the hydrogen (or silver–silver chloride) electrode, calculated from

$$E_\text{H} = \frac{RT}{F} \ln a_\text{H} = \frac{RT}{F} \ln m_{\text{H}^+} \gamma_{\text{H}^+} \tag{8}$$

where some arbitrary assumption must be made, such as $\gamma_{\text{H}^+} = \gamma_\pm$.

E' and E'' are normally required in alternative circumstances. When the test solution is not dilute, when it differs significantly from those used in the initial calibrations, or when the liquid junction potential is, for some reason, thought to be considerable, then E' is the better basis for the measurements. When, however, a salt bridge is used to eliminate the liquid junction potential, E'' is the quantity most conveniently used. E'' is probably not quite independent of the nature and concentration of the test solution and this difficulty can be met by choosing values which were derived from experiments as similar as possible to those under consideration (e.g. from Table VI). However, best of all is the procedure which initially calibrates the electrode system in terms of a parameter similar to that sought in the test solution and using solutions as similar as possible in nature and concentration (cf. Chapter 5, Section III,B). In this way, most of the uncertainties are eliminated from the final measurements by the self-consistency of the complete study. Precise measurements with little nonthermodynamic character can be obtained in this way.

Because of the number of different ways of evaluating the potentials of these standard half-cells, of preparing the calomel electrodes, of setting up the salt bridge, etc., there is great disparity between the values for the potentials of these electrodes quoted in the literature (cf. Table V).

Some of the discrepancies occur between E' and E'' values. This type of discrepancy should not arise with the saturated calomel electrode nor for those half-cells where the junction is made by means of a salt bridge which reduces the liquid junction potential to a very low value, so that $E' \sim E''$. The fact that it nevertheless does arise is indicative of the errors which stem from the assumptions that $\gamma_{\text{Cl}^-} = \gamma_\pm$ in saturated potassium chloride solution, and that the potential difference across the junction

$$\ldots \text{KCl } (m) \mid \text{KCl (saturated)} \mid \text{test solution} \ldots$$

is not always zero.

TABLE V

SOME PREVIOUS VALUES OF THE POTENTIALS OF THE COMMONER
REFERENCE CALOMEL HALF-CELLS AT 25°C

Saturated KCl[a]	N KCl[a]	0.1 N KCl[a]	Year, authors, and reference	Comments
—	0.2822	—	1916, Harned (119)	Direct determination; E''
—	—	0.3351	1917, Lewis et al. (8)	Direct determination; E''
0.2467	0.2847	—	1920, Fales and Mudge (20)	Direct determination; E''
0.2446	—	—	1925, Ewing (120)	Comparison between satd. and N-electrode; E''
—	0.2882	—	1925, Ewing (120)	Recalculation of Fales and Mudge's data; E''
0.2454	—	0.3353	1925, Scatchard (16)	Direct determination, excellent technique; E''
—	—	0.3341	1928, Randall and Young (15)	Direct determination; E''
—	—	0.3335	1932, Spencer (121)	Calculated from $E°$ and $\gamma_\pm$; E'
—	—	0.3337	1934, Guggenheim and Schindler (122)	Direct determination, flowing junctions, E_J evaluated; E'
0.2415	0.2800	0.3338	1937, Hamer (123)	Calculated from $E°$ and $\gamma_\pm$; E'
0.2440	—	0.3355	1937, Hamer (123)	Inferred from related studies of weak acids; E''
0.2441	—	—	1937, Hitchcock and Taylor (124, 125)	Directly determined; E''
—	0.2850	—	1937, Britton and Welford (126)	Combination of determination and calculation; E''
—	0.2816	—	1937, Glasstone (127)	Textbook value; E' (?)
0.2446	—	—	1938, MacInnes et al. (128)	Directly determined; E''
0.2443	—	0.3355	1941, Dole (129)	Textbook value; E''
0.2434	—	—	1946, Manov et al. (130)	Direct determination; E''
0.2444[b]	—	0.3356[b]	1954, Bates (131)	Textbook value; E''
0.244	0.283	0.336	1954, Kitchener (132)	Textbook value; E''
0.2412[b]	0.2801[b]	0.3337[b]	1954, Chateau (133)	Calculated from E'' and $\gamma_\pm$; E'
0.2441	0.2829	0.3353	1955, Britton (134)	Textbook value; E''
0.2420	0.2810	0.3335	1956, Potter (135)	Textbook value; E' (?)

[a] In international volts unless otherwise stated.
[b] Absolute volts.

There is no doubt in the present authors' minds that the experimentally determined half-cell potentials are to be preferred to all others and selected values for 25°C from the literature are shown in Table VI.

TABLE VI

RECOMMENDED VALUES FOR THE POTENTIALS
OF THE STANDARD CALOMEL HALF-CELLS

Half-cell	Potential (abs volts, 25°C)	
	E'	E''
Hg|Hg₂Cl₂|KCl (saturated)|buffer solution ⎫	0.2412 ± 0.0002	⎰ 0.2445 ± 0.0001
Hg|Hg₂Cl₂|KCl (saturated)|acid solution ⎭		⎱ 0.2450 ± 0.0001
Hg|Hg₂Cl₂|KCl (1 N at 25°C)	0.2801 ± 0.0002	—
Hg|Hg₂Cl₂|KCl (1 N at 25°C)|salt bridge	—	0.283 ± 0.001
Hg|Hg₂Cl₂|KCl (0.1 N at 25°C)	0.3337 ± 0.0002	—
Hg|Hg₂Cl₂|KCl (0.1 N at 25°C)|salt bridge|buffer solution	—	0.3356 ± 0.0001
Hg|Hg₂Cl₂|KCl (0.1 N at 25°C)|salt bridge|acid solution	—	0.3362 (limits not known)
Hg|Hg₂Cl₂|KCl (1 molal)	0.2810 ± 0.0002	—

It is less easy to select the corresponding values for other temperatures, but assuming that the uncertainties of the particular calibration method do not vary with temperature, reliance has been placed on Chateau's calculation of dE/dT from published $dE°/dT$ and $d \ln \gamma/dT$ data for the normal and decinormal potassium chloride–calomel electrodes (*133*), on Wingfield and Acree's measurements for the saturated electrode (*136*), and on the recent measurements of Strafelda and Polej (*116–118*) for the 3.5 N KCl electrode over the temperature range from 40° to 90°C. These data are given in Table VII.

The problem of which value to assign to the particular half-cell being used is essentially that of standardization of the pH scale (*124, 125, 128*). Rather than attempt the standardization or calibration of separate parts of a cell, it is preferable to write, for example,

$$pH = \frac{E - E° - E_J}{(RT/F) \ln 10} \tag{9}$$

where E is the observed emf, $E°$ the algebraic sum of the various constant or standard potentials and E_J is the (constant) sum of any reproducible liquid junction potentials. Irrespective of the values of $E°$ and E_J, the cell can be standardized with known *concentrations* (or activities defined in terms of stated assumptions) of (in this case) hydrogen ions and an accurate *interpolation* of the unknown values in various test solutions can then be made. Only if the range of the measurements is encompassed by the

TABLE VII

STANDARD HALF-CELL POTENTIALS AS A FUNCTION OF TEMPERATURE, IN ABSOLUTE VOLTS

Temperature (°C)	Saturated[a]	3.5 N[b] (at 25°C)	1 N[c,e] (at 25°C)	0.1 N[d,e] (at 25°C)
0	0.2602	—	0.2854	0.3338
10	0.2541	—	0.2839	0.3343
15	0.2509	—	—	—
20	0.2477	—	0.2815	0.3340
25	0.2444	—	0.2801	0.3337
30	0.2411	—	0.2786	0.3332
35	0.2377	—	—	—
38	0.2357	—	—	—
40	0.2343	0.2466	0.2753	0.3316
50	0.2272	0.2428	0.2716	0.3296
60	0.2199	0.2377	0.2673	0.3229
70	0.2124	0.2331	0.2622	0.3236(?)
80	0.2047	0.2277[f]	—	—
90	0.1967	0.2237[g]	—	—
100	0.1885	—	—	—

[a] At room temperatures, the variation with temperature is represented approximately by the equation $E'' = 0.2444 - 0.0025(t - 25)$ where t is temperature in °C; at higher temperatures, the form of the variation differs from that predicted by the more accurate equation for E', i.e.,

$$E' = 0.2412 - 6.61 \times 10^{-4}(t - 25) - 1.75 \times 10^{-6}(t - 25)^2 - 9.0 \times 10^{-10}(t - 25)^3$$

[b] Directly determined, i.e., E'' value [see also ref. (137)].

[c] Expressed by $E'_{1N} = 0.2801 - 2.75 \times 10^{-4}(t - 25) - 2.50 \times 10^{-6}(t - 25)^2 - 4 \times 10^{-9}(t - 25)^3$.

[d] Expressed by $E'_{0.1N} = 0.3337 - 8.75 \times 10^{-5}(t - 25) - 3 \times 10^{-6}(t - 25)^2$.

[e] Both sets are E' values and where a salt bridge is used, the corresponding E'' value may be approximately found by adding the quantity $(E'' - E')$ at 25° (cf. Table VI).

[f] At 79.9.

[g] At 89.9°C.

standardization, in terms of E, ionic strength, and solution composition, can reliable use be made of standard half-cells.

The data in Table VII refer to isothermal and isobaric systems. The apparatus and experiments of Ingruber (114), whilst they may maintain the reference electrode at a conveniently low temperature, introduce new factors. These have been further considered by Leonard in a recent symposium on pH measurements (138), but both papers are more concerned with technical aspects, such as electrode durability at high temperatures and pressures, than with the significance of the measurements on cells in a temperature gradient. Numerous isobaric measurements on thermocells have been made specifically for this purpose and one of the most recent has used the improved form of the calomel electrode (*139*). Their interpretation is outside the scope of this book and reference may be made to recent monographs dealing with nonisothermal cells and other steady state systems (*140*).

IV. Other Mercury–Mercurous Halide Electrodes

A. GENERAL CONSIDERATIONS

Mercurous fluoride, mercurous bromide, and mercurous iodide are all well characterized solids which can be used as the basis of electrodes of the second kind, reversible to the corresponding halide species. They are all isomorphous with calomel (*141, 142*) and it is likely that the special interaction between solid calomel and dry mercury (see Section II,C,2) is common to all the mercurous halides.

The use of the fluoride electrode is, however, severely limited by the fact that mercurous fluoride is rapidly and completely hydrolyzed in aqueous solutions (*143*). The successful use of the electrode in liquid hydrogen fluoride has been described (*144*) and will be considered elsewhere in this volume (Chapter 10), but in this chapter, which is concerned with electrodes which operate in aqueous solutions, only the mercurous bromide and mercurous iodide electrodes will be considered further.

Mercurous bromide and mercurous iodide are both stable in aqueous solution, and both have been used as the basis of electrodes for the study

TABLE VIII

SOLUBILITY PRODUCTS AND COMPLEX FORMATION CONSTANTS IN AQUEOUS SOLUTIONS OF MERCURY HALIDES AT 25°C (*85, 145*)

Equilibrium	log K		
	X = Cl	X = Br	X = I
Hg_2X_2 (solid) $\rightleftharpoons Hg_2^{2+} + 2X^-$	−17.88	−22.3	−28.3
$Hg^{2+} + X^- \rightleftharpoons HgX^+$	6.74	9.05[a]	12.87
$Hg^{2+} + 2X^- \rightleftharpoons HgX_2$	13.22	17.33[a]	23.82
$Hg^{2+} + 3X^- \rightleftharpoons HgX_3^-$	14.07	19.74[a]	27.60
$Hg^{2+} + 4X^- \rightleftharpoons HgX_4^{2-}$	15.07	21.10[a]	29.83

[a] These data differ slightly from those since recorded in two other investigations [Marcus (*146*) and Scaife and Tyrrell (*147*)]. The discrepancies are not large and do not affect the present discussion. The data of Sillén et al. (*148*) are included here for the sake of consistency with columns 2 and 4.

of aqueous halide solutions. They differ from calomel in two respects. Firstly, they are more photosensitive and, both in their preparation and use, they must be protected from uv radiation. Secondly, whilst the solubility products decrease markedly in the order, chloride to bromide to iodide, the formation constants of the corresponding complex mercuric halides increase rapidly in the same order, and progressively restrict the range of halide concentrations in which emf measurements can usefully be made, cf. Table VIII.

Both electrodes have a history similar to that of the calomel electrode and their apparent disabilities similarly retarded their development. Both, however, are probably susceptible to the type of improvement shown by the calomel electrode, and with the mercurous bromide electrode this has recently been shown to be the case. The iodide electrode has remained in the doldrums and it is possible, in view of the large complex formation constants, listed in column 4 of Table VIII, and of the ease of oxidation of iodide ions and aqueous hydriodic acid, that more precise studies with this electrode may not be possible. The present status of both electrodes is described in the following sections.

B. The Mercury–Mercurous Bromide Electrode

1. Previous Work

Apart from two pioneering studies of Goodwin (149) and Bugarsky (150) in the 1890's, the data on this electrode were, until recently, derived

TABLE IX

Summary of Previous Work on the Mercury–Mercurous Bromide Electrode
in Aqueous Bromide Solutions

Date	Authors	Electrode system	$E^\circ_{Hg_2Br_2}$ (at 25°C)
1927	Gerke and Geddes (151)	Pt, H_2 | HBr, 0.1002 m | Hg_2Br_2 | Hg	0.1392
1930	Ishikawa and Ueda (152, 153)	Pt, H_2 | HBr, 0.1012 m | Hg_2Br_2 | Hg	0.1395[a]
1935	Murata (48)	Na, Hg | NaBr (aq) | Hg_2Br_2 | Hg	—
1940	Larson (154)	Ag | AgBr | KBr (aq) | Hg_2Br_2 | Hg	0.1397[a]
1940	Dakin and Ewing (155)	Ag | AgBr | KBr (aq) | Hg_2Br_2 | Hg	0.1392₅
1942	Crowell, Mertes, and Burke (156)	Pt, H_2 | HBr, 0.1002 m | Hg_2Br_2 | Hg	$\begin{cases} 0.1391 \\ 0.1396^a \end{cases}$

[a] In these, air was not excluded from the cell and solution.

from the brief accounts of six independent but limited investigations, almost wholly confined to 25°C, which are summarized in Table IX.

In each case the electrodes were prepared in the classical manner from mercury and a wet paste of mercury, mercurous bromide, and the solution in question, and all were protected from light. Their potentials were, in general, reproducible to ±0.1 mv. The various measurements differed only in that in some cases air was excluded, whilst in others it was not. This is reflected systematically in the derived standard electrode potentials shown in Table IX, column 4. Crowell et al. (156) were able to reproduce at will either the lower or the higher value simply by excluding or allowing access of air, respectively.

The standard potentials were obtained either from the equation

$$E^\circ = E + \frac{2RT}{F} \ln m_{\text{HBr}} \, \gamma_{\pm\text{HBr}} \tag{10}$$

or from

$$E^\circ = E + E^\circ_{\text{AgBr}} \tag{11}$$

depending on which other reference electrode was used. The most recent values of the required quantities $\gamma_{\pm\text{HBr}}$ or E°_{AgBr} both stem from the same study (157) of the cell

$$\text{Pt, H}_2 \mid \text{HBr (aq)} \mid \text{Hg}_2\text{Br}_2 \mid \text{Hg}$$

and have been used to recalculate (where necessary) the original values, the most acceptable result at 25° being 0.1391 ± 0.0001 volt.

2. The Improved Electrode

In 1956, Gupta (37, 38) undertook a re-examination of the mercurous bromide electrode along the lines followed in the development of the calomel electrode. From a few simple experiments, two facts quickly emerged. (i) Dry interaction between mercury and precipitated mercurous bromide of small crystal size produced an adherent gray skin, identical in appearance with the "chloromercury" skin. (ii) Provided the technique was adopted of adding a small quantity of this skin to a dry mercury surface in a hydrophobic cell, followed by addition of deoxygenated solution, the reproducibility of electrode potential, as, for example, in the cell

$$\text{Pt, H}_2 \mid \text{HBr (aq)} \mid \text{Hg}_2\text{Br}_2 \mid \text{Hg}$$

was at once better than 10–20 μv.

The time required for final equilibrium to be reached was even longer with this electrode than with the calomel electrode, at least 24, and sometimes 48, hours being allowed before measurements on the above cell were made. This longer equilibration time is in accord with the greater degree of complex formation, and the increase of solubility of Hg_2Br_2 as the bromide concentration and the temperature were increased. It led to unsatisfactory measurements at HBr molalities > 0.3 mole kg^{-1} and temperatures $> 40°$. Often, under these conditions, the coherent, continuous film of mercurous bromide suddenly broke into fissures, to leave bald streaks or patches on the electrode surface, the potential immediately becoming unsteady.

Below these limits of bromide concentration and of temperature, satisfactory, if very protracted, measurements were readily made. The electrode was prepared in the same way as recommended for the calomel electrode (this chapter, Section II,B,3). The mercurous bromide can be prepared in two ways: by precipitation from dilute acidified mercurous nitrate solution with dilute hydrobromic acid, or by the Hulett method of anodizing a pool of mercury in dilute hydrobromic acid and continuously sweeping off the gray skin so formed. Both preparations should be carried out in red light or in apparatus shielded by a dark cloth. The product should be thoroughly equilibrated in dilute hydrogen bromide solution, and should be finally washed well before being dried in a blacked-out vacuum desiccator. The hydrogen bromide solution is best prepared by the method of Booth (*158*).

3. The Standard Electrode Potential

A series of measurements on the hydrogen–mercurous bromide cell were made using hydrogen bromide solutions of 0.005 to 0.2 molal over the temperature range from 5° to 45°C. The observed emf's, suitably corrected to standard conditions, were inserted into the extrapolation equation (44), Chapter 1, Section V, and the standard electrode potentials were obtained with a precision of ± 0.04 mv. They are shown in Table X, and refer to electrodes at final equilibrium. The value at 25° is in good agreement with that of earlier studies.

TABLE X

STANDARD MOLAL POTENTIALS OF THE MERCUROUS BROMIDE ELECTRODE (*37, 38*)

Temp (°C)	$E^{\circ}_{Hg_2Br_2}$ (abs volts)	Temp (°C)	$E^{\circ}_{Hg_2Br_2}$ (abs volts)
5	0.14095	30	0.13836
10	0.14078	35	0.13726
15	0.14041	40	0.13627
20	0.13985	45	0.13503
25	0.13917	—	—

C. The Mercury–Mercurous Iodide Electrode

1. Previous Work

Some of the limitations of the mercury–mercurous iodide electrode are clear from Table VIII, and these, coupled with the fact that solid mercurous iodide is so readily photochemically decomposed, may be sufficient to restrict its usefulness as a reference electrode to the levels of precision already obtaining. Different samples vary widely in color, depending on the quantity of free mercury present, and there is evidence that the electrode potential is appreciably sensitive to the form of solid mercurous iodide used.

The electrode was initially used in an extensive series of measurements of thermodynamic properties of aqueous metal iodide solutions, e.g. with cells of the type

$$\text{M, Hg} \mid \text{MI}_2 \text{ (aq)} \vdots \text{MI}_2 \text{ (aq)} \mid \text{Hg}_2\text{I}_2 \mid \text{Hg}$$

where M = Cd, Zn or Pb (*150, 159–164*). The electrode was made in the classical manner and its potential was reproducible to between 0.1 and 0.2 mv. These investigations were reviewed first by Gerke (*165*) and then by Vosburgh (*164, 166*), and both concluded that the standard potential, by comparison with other electrodes, was −0.0404 int volt at 25°C.

There followed an attempt by Vosburgh (*166*) to improve on the existing data by systematically investigating the effects of varying the preparations of mercurous iodide. His preparation number 7, which is described below, was the most satisfactory. He also advocated use of deaerated solutions for preparing and equilibrating the mercurous iodide and for use in the cell. A decade later, Bates and Vosburgh (*167*) used this electrode again for similar thermodynamic studies, but, more important, they also made the only recorded study of the hydrogen–mercurous iodide cell and determined its standard potential from an independent extrapolation.

2. The Standard Potential

(a) *Cell and Materials.* The measurements of Bates and Vosburgh were made on two types of cell:

$$\text{Pt, H}_2 \mid \text{KI, HCl (aq)} \vdots \text{KI, HCl (aq)} \mid \text{Hg}_2\text{I}_2 \mid \text{Hg}$$

and

$$\text{Pt, H}_2 \mid \text{KI, HOAc, NaOAc (aq)} \vdots \text{KI, HOAc, NaOAc (aq)} \mid \text{Hg}_2\text{I}_2 \mid \text{Hg}$$

where OAc represents the acetate group.

The mercurous iodide was prepared by adding, with rapid stirring, dilute acidified mercurous nitrate solution to dilute potassium iodide solution. The preparation was carried out in red light. The product was washed by decantation and digested under distilled water for three days on a steam bath in the dark. It was then equilibrated with the particular iodide solution to be used, and finally added, as a slurry, to the mercury pool electrode. Both of the solutions used in the above cells were susceptible to oxidation and were freshly prepared for each measurement, from standard solutions of hydrochloric and acetic acids and of potassium iodide.

(b) *Emf Measurements.* Both types of cell gave, after a lengthy equilibration period ($\ll 10$ hr), satisfactorily reproducible emf values, in the first case to ± 0.09 mv and in the second to ± 0.03 mv. The greater reproducibility of the cell containing the buffer solutions was offset by the less direct extrapolation involved. The measurements from the first cell were expressed by the simple equation

$$E = E^\circ_{\text{Hg}_2\text{I}_2} - (RT/F) \ln m_{\text{HCl}} \cdot m_{\text{KI}} \, \gamma_\pm^2 \tag{12}$$

The mean molal activity coefficient of HI was written as

$$\log \gamma_\pm = -A' \cdot I^{\frac{1}{2}} + C \cdot I \tag{13}$$

$$E^{\circ\prime} = E + \frac{RT}{F} \ln m_{\text{HCl}} \cdot m_{\text{KI}} - \frac{2RT}{F} \cdot A' \cdot I^{\frac{1}{2}} = E^\circ_{\text{Hg}_2\text{I}_2} - C \cdot I \tag{14}$$

A plot of $E^{\circ\prime}$ against ionic strength was linear and gave the value $E^\circ_{\text{Hg}_2\text{I}_2} = -0.0405$ volt at 25°C. The same result was obtained from the measurements with the other cell.

In spite of the apparently satisfactory nature of these experiments, the authors evidently retained some reservations regarding this electrode. Following on the successful determinations of E°_{AgI} by Owen (168), they investigated the cell (167)

$$\text{Ag} \mid \text{AgI} \mid \text{aq iodide solutions} \mid \text{Hg}_2\text{I}_2 \mid \text{Hg}$$

but had much less success than with the previous measurements. The reproducibility of the cell became worse in dilute solutions, and, amongst other things, it was noted that the cell emf, i.e., the potential of the mercurous iodide electrode, varied with the quantity of solid salt present. It is not clear to what degree the irreproducibility arose from chemical reaction between the two half-cells, but this would be minimized in the most dilute solutions. There is the clearest implication that the fault lay mainly with the mercurous iodide electrode (169), and Bates (170) later made it plain that he preferred the silver iodide electrode. From what is now known about the calomel electrode, all this is not surprising and a more complete evaluation of the mercurous iodide electrode must wait upon a radical alteration of its method of preparation, perhaps in line with those of mercurous bromide and chloride.

V. Mercury–Mercurous Salt Electrodes, other than Halides

A. GENERAL CONSIDERATIONS

Any stoichiometric, sparingly soluble mercurous salt of an inorganic or organic acid will, in principle at least, function as the basis of an electrode of the second kind. Provided only that the anion and the parent acid are compatible with the system, it can be prepared by the simple combination of mercury, mercurous salt and solution, and such an electrode is likely to give rise to a potential reproducible to 0.1 to 0.2 mv. Whether, in any given case, it would respond to further refinement would seem to depend on whether some special mechanism is required for its reversible operation, and whether this can be easily achieved. The performance of the electrode may also be modified by the extent to which soluble complexes of mercurous and mercuric ions are formed. However, no attempt at such a refinement has yet been made, although there are several recorded instances of the successful use in this connection of insoluble salts of mercury other than the halides. These are briefly described below and offer encouragement to wider exploration and application of this type of electrode.

B. PHOSPHATE

In two researches (*171, 172*) it was found that when aqueous mercurous nitrate is added to aqueous phosphoric acid, a white crystalline precipitate of Hg_2HPO_4 is formed. This stoichiometric solid in contact with mercury and phosphate solutions gives rise to a satisfactory phosphate, or hydrogen phosphate, electrode.

Attempts to prepare the same salt from solutions of Na_2HPO_4 or NaH_2PO_4 resulted only in the formation of yellow mercurous orthophosphate $(Hg_2)_3(PO_4)_2$, which was found to be quite unsuitable as the basis of a phosphate ion electrode.

Both investigations involved measurements of the emf of the cell

$$\text{Pt, H}_2 \mid \text{H}_3\text{PO}_4 \text{ (aq)} \mid \text{Hg}_2\text{HPO}_4 \mid \text{Hg}$$

at 25°C. Larson (*165*) made no attempt to exclude air from his solutions and states specifically that its presence had no effect. De Vries and Cohen (*171*) almost certainly used deaerated solutions. In both cases, steady emf values were quickly obtained which were reproducible to ±0.1 mv over a wide range of concentrations of phosphoric acid.

The standard electrode potential is not directly obtainable from an independent extrapolation. Phosphoric acid is a weak acid and knowledge of the appropriate concentrations of hydrogen and dihydrogen phosphate ions is obtainable only from *a priori* knowledge of the first dissociation constant of phosphoric acid, K_1, and the activities, a_u, or activity coefficients, γ_u, of the undissociated phosphoric acid. Thus,

$$E = E^{\circ}_{\text{Hg}_2\text{HPO}_4} - \frac{RT}{2F} \ln a_{\text{H}} \cdot a_{\text{H}_2\text{PO}_4^-} \tag{15}$$

$$= E^{\circ}_{\text{Hg}_2\text{HPO}_4} - \frac{RT}{2F} \ln K_1 \cdot a_u \tag{16}$$

$$= E^{\circ}_{\text{Hg}_2\text{PHO}_4} - \frac{RT}{2F} \ln K_1 \cdot m(1 - \alpha)\, \gamma_u \tag{17}$$

where m = total molality of phosphoric acid, and α = degree of dissociation.[4] The various uncertainties in the application of these equations would normally be resolved by extrapolation to infinite dilution, but this is not possible with the present system because the solubility of the mercurous salt is relatively high. The solubility product of Hg_2HPO_4 is 4×10^{-3} *(145)*

[4] The treatment of Larson and of De Vries and Cohen does not fully reveal the confusion which can occur in dealing with electrodes of the second kind reversible to ions of polybasic acids because of the various ways in which an E° can be defined. The differences arise from alternative choices of standard states and the choice which is made should be clearly represented in the symbolization which is used. In the present case it is clear that if $K_s = a_{\text{Hg}_2^{2+}} \cdot a_{\text{HPO}_4^{2-}}$ is the solubility product of mercurous monohydrogen phosphate, the electrode potential may be represented

$$E = \underbrace{E^{\circ}_{\text{Hg},\text{Hg}_2^{2+}} + \frac{RT}{2F} \ln K_s}_{E^{\circ}_{\text{Hg},\text{Hg}_2\text{HPO}_4,\text{HPO}_4^{2-}}} - \frac{RT}{2F} \ln a_{\text{HPO}_4^{2-}}$$

$$= \underbrace{E^{\circ}_{\text{Hg},\text{Hg}_2^{2+}} + \frac{RT}{2F} \ln K_s - \frac{RT}{2F} \ln \frac{K_2}{a_{\text{H}^+}}}_{E^{\circ}_{\text{Hg},\text{Hg}_2\text{HPO}_4,\text{H}_2\text{PO}_4^-}} - \frac{RT}{2F} \ln a_{\text{H}_2\text{PO}_4^-}$$

$$= \underbrace{E^{\circ}_{\text{Hg},\text{Hg}_2^{2+}} + \frac{RT}{2F} \ln K_s - \frac{RT}{2F} \ln \frac{K_2}{(a_{\text{H}^+})^2}}_{E^{\circ}_{\text{Hg},\text{Hg}_2\text{HPO}_4,\text{H}^+,\text{H}_2\text{PO}_4^-}} - \frac{RT}{2F} \ln a_{\text{H}^+} \cdot a_{\text{H}_2\text{PO}_4^-}$$

$$= \underbrace{E^{\circ}_{\text{Hg},\text{Hg}_2^{2+}} + \frac{RT}{2F} \ln K_s - \frac{RT}{2F} \ln \frac{K_2}{(a_{\text{H}^+})^2} - \frac{RT}{2F} \ln K_1}_{E^{\circ}_{\text{Hg},\text{Hg}_2\text{PO}_4,\text{H}_3\text{PO}_4}} - \frac{RT}{2F} \ln a_{\text{H}_3\text{PO}_4}$$

In Eqs. (15–17), it is clear that $E^{\circ}_{\text{Hg}_2\text{HPO}_4}$ has been identified with the third of these alternatives, i.e., the standard state has been chosen as unit product of the activities of hydrogen ions and of dihydrogen phosphate ions. It is evident that attention must be paid to the ways in which various authors define their E° values.

and the results in dilute solution ($m < 0.02$) all show systematic deviations resulting from the enhanced concentration of $H_2PO_4^-$ ions.

Fortunately, there is much additional data available for aqueous phosphoric acid solutions, and this makes possible use of two alternative evaluations of $E°$ from measurements on concentrated solutions in which the solubility of Hg_2HPO_4 is negligible. The first is based on Eq. (15) in which the product of a_{H^+} and $a_{H_2PO_4^-}$ is equated to $\alpha^2 m^2 \gamma_\pm^2$ and where α can be derived from accurate conductance data (173) and $\gamma_\pm$ from the Debye-Hückel equation. The second evaluation of $E°$ is based on Eq. (16), i.e. on the K_1 value determined by Bates (174) and a_u data taken from vapor pressure measurements on aqueous phosphoric acid (175). Both methods give substantially the same result and the final values of Larson recalculated in terms of the most recent value of K_1, $E°_{Hg_2HPO_4} = 0.6359$ int volt, and of De Vries and Cohen, $E° = 0.638 \pm 0.002$ int volt, can be considered to give a reliable figure for the potential of this electrode at 25°C.

C. Iodate

Mercurous iodate is another example of a stable, stoichiometric mercurous salt which can be used as the basis of a reversible electrode. Its solubility product at 25°C is 2×10^{-14}. Solutions of iodic acid oxidatively attack mercury, and all the uses of this electrode are therefore to be found in neutral or only feebly acidic solutions. Mercurous iodate is prepared by the usual precipitation reaction between dilute (0.05 N) acidified mercurous nitrate solution and 0.05 N potassium iodate solution. The only recorded preparation for use in electrodes (176, 177), suggests washing the precipitate with very dilute potassium iodate solution and storing it wet. It is also recommended that a large excess of either reactant during the precipitation should be avoided and the mercurous iodate should be well equilibrated for not less than 24 hr with the cell solution before being used.

The electrode cannot be combined directly with the hydrogen electrode, because of the oxidizing nature of iodate solutions, and Haring and his co-workers (176, 177) rejected the obvious alternative cell

$$Ag \mid AgIO_3 \mid KIO_3 \text{ (aq)} \vdots Hg_2(IO_3)_2 \mid Hg$$

because of the uncertainties attending the silver iodate electrode. They used instead the cell

$$Hg \mid Hg_2Cl_2 \mid KCl \ (m) \vdots KIO_3 \ (m) \mid Hg_2(IO_3)_2 \mid Hg$$

and evaluated $E°_{Hg_2(IO_3)_2}$ from the cell emf, the liquid junction potential between the equimolal solutions, given by the Lewis and Sargent formula, and the individual activity coefficients of the iodate ion calculated on the assumption that

$$\gamma_{IO_3^-} = (\gamma_{\pm}^2)_{KIO_3(m)}/\gamma_{K^+(m)} \tag{18}$$

and that

$$\gamma_{K^+} = (\gamma_{\pm})_{KCl(m)} \tag{19}$$

i,e.,

$$E = E^\circ - E^\circ_{calomel} + E_J + \frac{RT}{F} \ln (\gamma_{IO_3^-}/\gamma_{Cl^-}) \tag{20}$$

The emf of the cell was reproducible to only ±0.5 mv and this reproducibility deteriorated further in dilute solutions of potassium iodate (<0.05 m) and at temperatures greater than 25°C. Within these limitations, concordant values of the standard potential were obtainable, i.e. 0.3939 ± 0.004 int volt.

This figure, however, was based on a value of 0.2676 volt for $E^\circ_{calomel}$; in terms of the recent value of 0.26804 ± 0.00010 (cf. Table I), a more probable value for $E^\circ_{Hg_2(IO_3)_2}$ is 0.3944 ± 0.0004 abs volt. This figure is in good agreement with that reported from a later investigation (178), full details of which are not available. Takaćs confirms the reproducibility of the electrode to be good and, using a pair of them in cells with transport, he obtained activity coefficient data for potassium iodate in solution in excellent agreement with corresponding freezing point data. He also quotes an E° figure of 0.3942 volt but it is not known how this was obtained.

D. ACETATE

Fairly extensive use of this electrode has been made in solutions of electrolytes in glacial acetic acid (Chapter 10, Section III,B,1), but only a few studies of its behavior in aqueous solutions are recorded. Apart from the very early work of Bugarsky (150), our knowledge of this electrode stems entirely from the investigations of Larson and co-workers (179, 180), all of which refer to a single temperature, 25°C. They prepared (179) pure mercurous acetate from dilute solutions of mercurous nitrate and acetic acid; the precipitate was washed thoroughly with water and dried. The mercurous acetate electrode consisted of a pool of mercury and a paste of mercury and mercurous acetate. Its potential was reproducible to at least 0.1 mv and was apparently insensitive to the presence of air, which was therefore not excluded.

This electrode was initially combined with the quinhydrone electrode, in the cell

$$\text{Pt} \mid \text{quinhydrone, HOAc } (m) \vdots \text{ HOAc } (m) \mid \text{Hg}_2(\text{OAc})_2 \mid \text{Hg}$$

but later, this was replaced by the hydrogen electrode. The emf of the hydrogen–mercurous acetate cell was expressed as

$$E = E^\circ_{Hg_2(OAc)_2} - \frac{RT}{F} \ln K \cdot m(1 - \alpha) \, \gamma_u \qquad (21)$$

where, as before, K represents the thermodynamic dissociation constant of acetic acid; γ_u the activity coefficient of the undissociated acid, was taken as unity, and α, the degree of dissociation, equated to $(K/m)^{1/2}$. The results for acid concentrations greater than 0.3 m led to concordant values for the standard electrode potential, i.e., $E^\circ_{Hg_2(OAc)_2} = 0.5117 \pm 0.0002$ int volt at 25°C on the *molal* scale and 0.5109 int volt on the *molar* scale (*178*).

The emf values in dilute acetic acid solution showed the expected deviations, from the values predicted by Eq. (21), arising from the solubility of mercurous acetate (K_S at 25°C = 2.3×10^{-10}).

E. Oxalate

This electrode also was carefully investigated by Larson and Tomsicek (*181*) and was found to give reproducible potentials, at least in oxalic acid solutions. The electrode was prepared in the classical manner, i.e., in the same way as the mercurous acetate electrode. The mercurous oxalate was precipitated by adding 0.1 N mercurous nitrate solution to an excess of 0.1 N sodium oxalate solution. It was washed by decantation and dried in a desiccator. Mercurous oxalate is extremely light-sensitive and throughout its preparation, storage, and use in the electrode, it was protected from light.

The emf of the cell

$$\text{Pt, H}_2 \mid \text{H}_2\text{C}_2\text{O}_4 \text{ (aq)} \mid \text{Hg}_2\text{C}_2\text{O}_4 \mid \text{Hg}$$

was measured at 25°C for oxalic acid concentrations ranging from 0.05 to 0.6 N. Provided that the oxalic acid solution had been equilibrated with mercury and solid mercurous oxalate for 24 hr before use, the cell rapidly came to equilibrium and attained its final, constant emf in about 30 min. The emf may be expressed as

$$E = E^\circ_{Hg_2Ox} + \frac{RT}{2F} \ln a^2_{H^+} \cdot a_{Ox^{2-}} \qquad (22)$$

where Ox^{2-} represents the oxalate ion. The product of these activities may then be found from the first (K_1) and second (K_2) dissociation constants of oxalic acid (*182, 182a*), since

$$a^2_{H^+} \cdot a_{Ox^{2-}} = K_1 K_2 \cdot a_{H_2C_2O_4} \qquad (23)$$

If $f_{H_2C_2O_4}$ is taken as unity (a volume concentration scale was used), then,

$$a_{H_2C_2O_4} = C_{H_2C_2O_4} = (1 - \alpha)C \tag{24}$$

where C is the total concentration of oxalic acid and α is the degree of dissociation, also to be found from K_1 and K_2. The cell emf is therefore given by

$$E = E^{\circ}_{Hg_2Ox} - \frac{RT}{2F} \ln K_1 K_2 \left\{ 1 - \frac{-K_1 + \sqrt{K_1^2 - 4K_1C}}{2C} \right\} \tag{25}$$

and it was from this, that $E^{\circ}_{Hg_2Ox}$ was evaluated for each concentration used. It was found to be constant to within 0.1 mv over the whole concentration range, i.e.

$$E^{\circ}_{Hg_2Ox} = 0.4166 \pm 0.0001 \text{ int volt at } 25°C$$

corresponding with a solubility product of $2 \times 10^{-12.07}$. This figure differs slightly from that given in the original paper because of a correction arising from the re-evaluation of pK_2 of oxalic acid. Further reference to this electrode is made in the last section of this chapter.

F. PICRATE

Brief mention will be made of a single ingenious application of this electrode. The possibilities of the cell,

$$\text{Pt, H}_2 \mid \text{picric acid (aq)} \mid \text{Hg}_2\text{Pi}_2 \mid \text{Hg}$$

(Pi = picrate), were first discussed by Brönsted (183), who nevertheless realized the incompatibility of the hydrogen electrode and picric acid solutions. The cell

$$\text{glass electrode} \left| \begin{array}{c} \text{picric acid (aq)} \\ \text{(saturated)} \end{array} \right| \text{Hg}_2\text{Pi}_2 \mid \text{Hg}$$

was, however, quite successfully used by Bell and Fendley (184) in a study of the free energy of formation of naphthalene picrate. They prepared pure mercurous picrate (as yellow needles) from aqueous mercurous nitrate and sodium picrate solutions, and added a layer of it to a mercury pool in contact with picric acid solution. The cell emf was reproducible to better than a millivolt, but no evaluation of $E^{\circ}_{Hg_2Pi_2}$ was attempted.

G. ELECTRODES OF THE THIRD KIND

In a single but extensive paper by Leblanc and Harnapp (185), the use of the mercurous oxalate, and also the mercurous tungstate electrode, in a special connection is described. If, for example, the mercurous oxalate electrode is used in a solution which is kept saturated with calcium oxalate, then its potential becomes dependent on the calcium ion activity. It may therefore be used to evaluate the concentration of calcium ions, or in a similar way, of any ionic species which forms an insoluble oxalate, provided that legitimate assumptions about activity coefficients can be made.

Both the mercurous oxalate and mercurous tungstate electrodes were prepared by adding an equilibrated paste of the mercurous salt mixed with the other insoluble salt to a mercury pool. They were then incorporated into cells of the type

$$\text{Hg} \mid \text{Hg}_2\text{Ox} \mid \text{CaOx} \mid \text{Ca(NO)}_3 \text{ (aq)} \; \vdots \; \frac{\text{KNO}_3}{\text{(saturated)}} \; \vdots \; \frac{N \text{ KCl}}{\text{calomel electrode}}$$

and

$$\text{Hg} \mid \text{Hg}_2\text{WO}_4 \mid \text{CaWO}_4 \mid \text{Ca(NO}_3)_2 \text{ (aq)} \; \vdots \; \frac{\text{KNO}_3}{\text{(saturated)}} \; \vdots \; \frac{N \text{ KCl}}{\text{calomel electrode}}$$

The emf's of these cells were reproducible to at least 1 mv and were used to evaluate the solubility products of calcium oxalate and calcium tungstate in various solutions. The use of silver, lead, cadmium, and zinc as the basis of electrodes of the third kind was also demonstrated and a further extension of this principle to the determination of ions other than calcium is clearly possible.

References

1. Ostwald, W., "Hand- und Hilfsbuch zur Ausfuhrung Physikochemische Messungen." Akademische Verlagsges., Leipzig, 1894.
2. Lewis, G. N., and Sargent, L. W., *J. Am. Chem. Soc.* **31**, 363 (1909).
3. Acree, S. F., Loomis, N. E., and Meyers, C. N., *Am. Chem. J.* **46**, 585 (1911); **50**, 396 (1913).
4. Ellis, J. H., *J. Am. Chem. Soc.* **38**, 737 (1916).
5. Chow, Ming, *J. Am. Chem. Soc.* **42**, 497 (1920).
6. Loomis, N. E., and Meacham, M. R., *J. Am. Chem. Soc.* **38**, 2310 (1916).
7. Loomis, N. E., Essex, J. E., and Meacham, M. R., *J. Am. Chem. Soc.* **39**, 1133 (1917).
8. Lewis, G. N., Brighton, T. B., and Sebastian, R. L., *J. Am. Chem. Soc.* **39**, 2243 (1917).
9. Linhart, G. A., *J. Am. Chem. Soc.* **41**, 1175 (1919).
10. MacInnes, D. A., and Parker, K., *J. Am. Chem. Soc.* **37**, 1445 (1915).
11. Harned, H. S., *J. Am. Chem. Soc.* **42**, 1808 (1920); **44**, 2729 (1922); **48**, 326 (1926).
12. Gerke, R. H., *J. Am. Chem. Soc.* **44**, 1686 (1922).
13. Mukherjee, J., and Kumar, K. K., *J. Am. Chem. Soc.* **52**, 2179 (1930).
14. Randall, M., and Beckenridge, G. F., *J. Am. Chem. Soc.* **49**, 1435 (1927).
15. Randall, M., and Young, L. E., *J. Am. Chem. Soc.* **50**, 989 (1928).
16. Scatchard, G., *J. Am. Chem. Soc.* **47**, 696 (1925).
17. Mueller, F., and Reuther, H., *Z. Elektrochem.* **48**, 220 (1942); **49**, 176 (1943).
18. Hills, G. J., and Ives, D. J. G., *Nature* **165**, 530 (1950).
19. Hills, G. J., and Ives, D. J. G., *J. Chem. Soc.* 311 (1951).
20. Fales, H. A., and Mudge, W. A., *J. Am. Chem. Soc.* **42**, 2435 (1920).

21. Johnson, R. J., and Ubbelohde, A. R., *Proc. Roy. Soc.* **A206**, 275 (1951).
22. Cueilleron, J., Meyer, P., Schneider, R., and Zieger, J. J., *Bull. Soc. Chim. France* **16**, 628 (1949).
23. Darbyshire, J. A., *Electronics Forum, No. 3*, 19 (1946).
24. Gordon, C. L., and Wichers, E., *Ann. N. Y. Acad. Sci.* **65**, 369 (1957).
25. Hulett, G. A., *Phys. Rev.* **32**, 257 (1911).
26. Hulett, G. A., and Lipscombe, G. F., *J. Am. Chem. Soc.* **38**, 20 (1916).
27. Pennycuick, S. W., and Best, R. J., *Australian J. Exptl. Biol. Med. Sci.* **3**, 173 (1926).
28. Hahn, F. L., *J. Am. Chem. Soc.* **57**, 2537 (1935).
29. Pinching, G. D., and Bates, R. G., *J. Research Natl. Bur. Standards* **37**, 311 (1946).
30. Midland Silicones, Ltd., Silicone Notes G1–5 (1956).
31. Finklestein, N. P., and Verdier, E. T., *Trans. Faraday Soc.* **53**, 1618 (1957).
32. Schwabe, K., and Ziegenbalg, S., *Z. Elektrochem.* **62**, 172 (1958).
33. Hills, G. J., and Ives, D. J. G., *J. Chem. Soc.* 319 (1951).
34. Guggenheim, E. A., and Prue, J. E., *Trans. Faraday Soc.* **50**, 231 (1954).
35. Hills, G. J., unpublished, 1957.
36. Grzybowski, A. K., *J. Phys. Chem.* **62**, 550 (1958).
37. Gupta, S. R., Ph.D. Thesis, London, 1957.
38. Gupta, S. R., Hills, G. J., and Ives, D. J. G., in preparation.
39. Pouradier, J., and Chateau, H., *Compt. rend. acad. sci.* **237**, 711 (1953).
40. Birge, R. T., *Revs. Mod. Phys.* **13**, 233 (1941).
41. Dumond, J. W. M., and Cohen, E. R., *Revs. Mod. Phys.* **25**, 691 (1953).
42. Harned, H. S., and Ehlers, R., *J. Am. Chem. Soc.* **55**, 2179 (1933).
43. Swinehart, D. F., *J. Am. Chem. Soc.* **74**, 1100 (1952).
44. Das, S. N., and Ives, D. J. G., in preparation.
45. Lietzke, M. H., and Vaughen, J. V., *J. Am. Chem. Soc.* **77**, 876 (1955).
46. Lapworth, A., and Partington, J. R., *J. Chem. Soc.* **99**, 1417 (1911).
47. Newbery, E., *J. Chem. Soc.* **105**, 2553 (1914); **107**, 1520 (1915).
48. Murata, F., *J. Chem. Soc. Japan* **56**, 588 (1935).
49. Schwabe, K., and Schwenk, W., *Z. Elektrochem.* **63**, 441 (1959).
50. Schwabe, K., and Hertzsch, R., *Z. Elektrochem.* **63**, 445 (1959).
51. Grzybowski, A. K., *J. Phys. Chem.* **62**, 555 (1958).
52. Haissinsky, M., and Cotten, M., *J. chim. phys.* (Paris) **46**, 476 (1949).
53. King, E. L., *J. Am. Chem. Soc.* **71**, 3553 (1949).
54. Seaborg, G. T., *Chem. Revs.* **27**, 199 (1940).
55. Wolfgang, R. L., and Dodson, R. W., *J. Phys. Chem.* **56**, 872 (1952).
56. Gerischer, H., and Staubach, K. E., *Z. physik. Chem. (Frankfurt)* **6**, 118 (1956).
57. Oldham, K. B., *Trans. Faraday Soc.* **53**, 80 (1957).
58. Reichardt, H., and Bonhoeffer, K. F., *Z. Physik* **67**, 780 (1930).
59. Stock, A., Cucuel, F., Gerstner, F., Köhle, H., and Lux, H., *Z. anorg. u. allgem. Chem.* **217**, 241 (1934).
60. Moser, H. C., and Voigt, A. F., *J. Am. Chem. Soc.* **79**, 1837 (1957); *J. Inorg. & Nucl. Chem.* **4**, 354 (1957).
61. Schwarzenbach, G., and Anderegg, G., *Helv. Chim. Acta* **37**, 1289 (1954).
62. Abel, E., *Z. anorg. Chem.* **26**, 376 (1901).
63. Forsling, W., Hietanen, S., and Sillén, L. G., *Acta Chem. Scand.* **6**, 901 (1952).
64. Infeldt, G., and Sillén, L. G., *Svensk Kem. Tidskr.* **58**, 104 (1946).
65. Sillén, L. G., *Svensk Kem. Tidskr.* **58**, 52 (1946).
66. Hietanen, S., and Sillén, L. G., *Arkiv Kemi* **10**, 103 (1956).

67. Hietanen, S., and Sillén, L. G., *Suomen Kemistilehti* **29B**, 31 (1956).

68. Linhart, G. A., *J. Am. Chem. Soc.* **38**, 2356 (1916).

69. Lewis, G. N., and Randall, M., "Thermodynamics," p. 419. McGraw-Hill, New York, 1923.

70. Bray, W. C., and Hershey, A. V., *J. Am. Chem. Soc.* **56**, 1892 (1934).

71. Bonner, O. D., and Unietis, F. A., *J. Am. Chem. Soc.* **75**, 5111 (1953).

72. El Wakkad, S. E. S., and Salem, T. M., *J. Phys. Chem.* **54**, 1371 (1950).

73. Carter, S. R., and Robinson, R. A., *J. Chem. Soc.* 267, 1912 (1927).

74. Popoff, S., Riddick, J. A., Wirth, V. I., and Ough, L. D., *J. Am. Chem. Soc.* **53**, 1195 (1931).

75. Popoff, S., Kunz, A. H., Riddick, J. A., and Becker, W. W., *Proc. Iowa Acad. Sci.* **36**, 263 (1929).

76. Kolthoff, I. M., and Barnum, C., *J. Am. Chem. Soc.* **62**, 3061 (1940).

77. Cartledge, G. H., *J. Am. Chem. Soc.* **63**, 906 (1941).

78. Higginson, W. C. E., *J. Chem. Soc.* 1438 (1951).

79. Adamson, A. W., *J. Phys. Chem.* **56**, 876 (1952).

80. Armstrong, A. M., Halpern, J., and Higginson, W. C. E., *J. Phys. Chem.* **60**, 1661 (1956).

81. Gurney, R. W., *J. Chem. Phys.* **6**, 499 (1938).

82. Richards, T., and Archibald, E. H., *Z. physik. Chem.* **40**, 385 (1902).

83. Sherill, M. S., *Z. physik. Chem.* **40**, 385 (1902); **47**, 103 (1904).

84. Dry, M. E., and Gledhill, J. A., *Trans. Faraday Soc.* **51**, 1119 (1955).

85. Sillén, L. G., *Acta Chem. Scand.* **3**, 539 (1949).

86. Hietanen, S., and Sillén, L. G., *Acta Chem. Scand.* **6**, 747 (1952).

87. Carrière, E., Guiter, H., and Lafitte, M., *Bull. soc. chim. France* **15**, 23 (1948).

88. Rummel, R. E., *Dissertation Abstr.* **12**, 816 (1952).

89. Thirsk, H. R., *Proc. Phys. Soc. (London)* **66B**, 129 (1953).

90. Havighurst, R. J., *Am. J. Sci.* **10**, 15 (1925).

91. Havighurst, R. J., *J. Am. Chem. Soc.* **48**, 2113 (1926).

92. Hylleraas, E., *Z. Physik* **36**, 862 (1926).

93. Dana, E. S., "System of Mineralogy," 7th ed., Vol. II, p. 25. Wiley, New York, 1951.

94. Cousens, R. H., Ives, D. J. G., and Pittman, R. W., *J. Chem. Soc.* 3973 (1953).

95. Dibbs, H. P., Ives, D. J. G., and Pittman, R. W., *J. Chem. Soc.* 3370 (1957).

96. Cornish, D. C., Ph.D. Thesis, London, 1960.

97. Clark, W. M., "The Determination of Hydrogen Ions," 3rd ed., Chapter 15. Williams & Wilkins, Baltimore, 1928.

98. Zobell, C. E., and Rittenberg, S. C., *Science* **86**, 502 (1937).

99. Salminen, A., *Suomen Kemistilehti* **11A**, 9 (1938).

100. Carpeni, G., *Bull. soc. chim. France* **7**, 776 (1940).

101. Banus, G., *Science* **93**, 601 (1941).

102. Levin, L. E., *Zavodskaya Lab.* **10**, 328 (1941).

103. Shaw, E. H., *J. Chem. Educ.* **18**, 330 (1941).

104. Gaddis, S., *Chemist Analyst* **32**, 9 (1943).

105. Hahn, F. L., *Science* **98**, 140 (1943).

106. Land, J. E., *Chemist Analyst* **32**, 87 (1943).

107. Coates, G. E., *J. Chem. Soc.* 489 (1945).

108. Scott, B. A., *Analyst* **70**, 476 (1945).

109. Van der Burg, B., *Chem. Weekblad* **44**, 417 (1948).

110. Smith, G. S., *Trans. Faraday Soc.* **45**, 752 (1949).

111. Bruniholz, G., *Anal. Chim. Acta* **10**, 470 (1954).

112. Lewin, S., *J. Sci. Instr.* **31**, 302 (1954).

113. Landry, A. S., *Chemist Analyst* **47**, 72 (1958).

114. Ingruber, O. V., *Ind. Chemist* **32**, 573 (1956).

115. Lauchlan, A. D. E., and Page, J. E., *Nature* **151**, 84 (1943).

116. Strafelda, F., and Polej, B., *Chem. listy* **50**, 185 (1956).

117. Strafelda, F., and Polej, B., *Collection Czechoslov. Chem. Communs.* **21**, 1397 (1956).

118. Strafelda, F., and Polej, B., *Chem. Premyzl* **7**, 240 (1957).

119. Harned, H. S., *J. Am. Chem. Soc.* **38**, 1986 (1916).

120. Ewing, W. W., *J. Am. Chem. Soc.* **47**, 301 (1925).

121. Spencer, H. M., *J. Am. Chem. Soc.* **54**, 3647 (1932).

122. Guggenheim, E. A., and Schindler, T. D., *J. Phys. Chem.* **30**, 533 (1934).

123. Hamer, W. J., *Trans. Electrochem. Soc.* **72**, 45 (1937).

124. Hitchcock, D. I., and Taylor, A. C., *J. Am. Chem. Soc.* **59**, 1812 (1937).

125. Hitchcock, D. I., and Taylor, A. C., *J. Am. Chem. Soc.* **60**, 2710 (1938).

126. Britton, H. T. S., and Welford, G., *J. Chem. Soc.* 1846 (1937).

127. Glasstone, S., "Electrochemistry of Solutions," 2nd. ed. Methuen, London, 1937.

128. MacInnes, D. A., Belcher, D., and Shedlovsky, T., *J. Am. Chem. Soc.* **60**, 1094 (1938).

129. Dole, M., "The Glass Electrode." Wiley, New York, 1941.

130. Manov, G. G., De Lollis, N. J., and Acree, S. F., *J. Research Natl. Bur. Standards* **34**, 115 (1945).

131. Bates, R. G., "Electrometric pH Determinations." Wiley, New York, 1954.

132. Findlay, A., *in* "Practical Physical Chemistry" (J. A. Kitchener, ed .) p. 252. Longmans, Green, New York, 1954.

133. Chateau, H., *J. Chem. Phys.* **51**, 590 (1954).

134. Britton, H. T. S., "Hydrogen Ions," 2nd ed. Chapman and Hall, London, 1955.

135. Potter, E. C., "Electrochemistry." Cleaver-Hulme, London, 1956.

136. Wingfield, B., and Acree, S. F., *J. Research Natl. Bur. Standards* **19**, 163 (1937).

137. Nomura, K., *J. Biochem. (Tokyo)* **18**, 301 (1933).

138. Leonard, J. E., *Symposium on pH Measurements, A.S.T.M., Spec. Tech. Publ.* **190**, 16 (1956).

139. Hawksworth, W. A., and Raw, C. J. G., *J. Chem. Phys.* **31**, 1421 (1959).

140. Agar, J. N., "The Structure of Electrolytic Solutions" (W. J. Hamer, ed.) Chapter 13. Wiley, New York, 1959.

141. Ebert, F., and Woitinek, H., *Z. anorg. Chem.* **210**, 269 (1933).

142. Wyckoff, R. W. G., "Crystal Structures." Interscience, New York, 1949.

143. Sidgwick, N. V., "The Chemical Elements and their Compounds," p. 293. Oxford Univ. Press, London and New York, 1950.

144. Koerber, G. G., and De Vries, T., *J. Am. Chem. Soc.* **74**, 5008 (1952).

145. Bjerrum, J., Schwarzenbach, G., and Sillén, L. G., "Stability Constants." Vol. II, Chemical Society, London, 1958.

146. Marcus, Y., *Acta Chem. Scand.* **11**, 599 (1957).

147. Scaife, D. B., and Tyrrell, H. J. V., *J. Chem. Soc.* 386 (1956).

148. Bethge, P. O., Jonevall-Westöö, I., and Sillén, L. G., *Acta Chem. Scand.* **2**, 829 (1948).

149. Goodwin, H. M., *Z. physik. Chem.* **13**, 577 (1894).

150. Bugarsky, S., *Z. anorg. Chem.* **14**, 145 (1897).

151. Gerke, R. H., and Geddes, J. R., *J. Phys. Chem.* **31**, 886 (1927).

152. Ishikawa, F., and Ueda, Y., *J. Chem. Soc. Japan* **51**, 59 (1930).

153. Ishikawa, F., and Ueda, Y., *Sci. Repts. Tôhoku Imp. Univ., First Ser.* **22**, 249 (1933).

154. Larson, W. D., *J. Am. Chem. Soc.* **62**, 764 (1940).

155. Dakin, T. W., and Ewing, D. T., *J. Am. Chem. Soc.* **62**, 2280 (1940).

156. Crowell, W. R., Mertes, R. W., and Burke, S. S., *J. Am. Chem. Soc.* **64**, 3021 (1942).

157. Harned, H. S., Keston, A. S., and Donelson, J. G., *J. Am. Chem. Soc.* **58**, 989 (1936).

158. Booth, H. S., "Inorganic Syntheses," Chapter 1, p. 115. McGraw-Hill, New York, 1939.

159. Oeholm, L. W., *Acta Soc. Sci. Fennicae* **41**, 1 (1913).

160. Cohen, E., and Bruins, H. R., *Z. physik. Chem.* **93**, 53 (1918).

161. Ishikawa, F., and Shibata, F. L. E., *Bull. Chem. Soc. Japan* **1**, 169 (1926).

162. Yoshida, T., *J. Chem. Soc. Japan* **3**, 64, 136 (1921).

163. Obata, J., *Proc. Phys.-Math. Soc., Japan* **1**, 169 (1919).

164. Vosburgh, W. C., *J. Am. Chem. Soc.* **49**, 2222 (1927).

165. Gerke, R. H., *Chem. Revs.* **1**, 385 (1925).

166. Vosburgh, W. C., *J. Am. Chem. Soc.* **50**, 2386 (1928).

167. Bates, R. G., and Vosburgh, W. C., *J. Am. Chem. Soc.* **59**, 1188, 1583 (1937).

168. Owen, B. B., *J. Am. Chem. Soc.* **57**, 1526 (1935).

169. Vosburgh, W. C., Derr, P. F., Cooper, G. R., and Bates, R. G., *J. Am. Chem. Soc.* **61**, 2592 (1939).

170. Bates, R. G., *J. Am. Chem. Soc.* **63**, 399 (1941).

171. De Vries, T., and Cohen, D., *J. Am. Chem. Soc.* **71**, 1114 (1949).

172. Larson, W. D., *J. Phys. Chem.* **54**, 310 (1950).

173. Mason, C. M., and Blum, W. M., *J. Am. Chem. Soc.* **69**, 1246 (1947).

174. Bates, R. G., *J. Research Natl. Bur. Standards* **47**, 127 (1951).

175. Elmore, K. L., Mason, C. M., and Christensen, J. H., *J. Am. Chem. Soc.* **68**, 2528 (1946).

176. Haring, M. M., and Zapponi, P. O., *Trans. Electrochem. Soc.* **80**, 203 (1941).

177. Haring, M. M., and Kraybill, H. F., *Trans. Electrochem. Soc.* **80**, 213 (1941).

178. Takaćs, I., *Magyar Chem. Folyoirat* **49**, 33, 100 (1943).

179. Larson, W. D., and MacDougall, F. H., *J. Phys. Chem.* **41**, 493 (1937).

180. Larson, W. D., and Tomsicek, W. J., *J. Am. Chem. Soc.* **61**, 65 (1939).

181. Larson, W. D., and Tomsicek, W. J., *J. Am. Chem. Soc.* **63**, 3329 (1941).

182. Harned, H. S., and Fallon, L. D., *J. Am. Chem. Soc.* **58**, 989 (1936).

182a. Pinching, G. D., and Bates, R. G., *J. Research Natl. Bur. Standards* **40**, 405 (1948).

183. Brönsted, J. N., *Z. physik. Chem.* **77**, 284 (1911).

184. Bell, R. P., and Fendley, J. A., *Trans. Faraday Soc.* **45**, 121 (1949).

185. Leblanc, M., and Harnapp, O., *Z. physik. Chem.* **A166**, 321 (1933).

Chapter Four

Silver–Silver Halide Electrodes

G. J. Janz

I. Introduction and Theory

A. Status of the Silver–Silver Halide Electrodes

As reference standards the silver–silver halide electrodes fall into the class of reversible electrodes of the *second kind*. In contrast to the electrodes of the *first kind*, which are reversible only with respect to the ions of the metal phase, electrodes of the second kind have a solid phase in the form of a sparingly soluble salt in equilibrium with a saturated solution of this salt participating in the electrode reaction.

The most important asset of silver–silver chloride electrodes is that they are small, compact, can be used in any orientation, and do not usually significantly contaminate any medium in which they are immersed. Further, since many equilibria are influenced by addition of neutral halide only insofar as the ionic strength may be modified (a matter easily dealt with either by Debye-Hückel calculations, or by extrapolation to zero ionic strength), these electrodes lend themselves to the setting up of thermodynamic cells without liquid junctions. This frequently brings in unambiguous information which is either unobtainable with liquid-junction cells, or which supplements the data available from them in important ways.

As a standard or reference electrode, the silver–silver halide electrode is ostensibly used to measure the activity of the halide ion[1] in the aqueous, or other, solution phase. This is clearly possibly only if the components in the other phases are in reproducible standard states. It is in attaining this condition that the primary difficulty lies with the silver–silver halide electrodes. Where solid phases are involved which may vary in thermodynamic properties because of mechanical strain, variation in crystal structure, impurity, nonstoichiometry, surface films, and the like, the basic problem is to obtain the electrode components in their most stable, or ground, states of minimum energy. For the silver–silver halide systems, efforts by various authorities to achieve stability, sensitivity, and reproducibility led to four main kinds of electrode construction: (i) electrolytic, the electrolytic deposition of both silver and silver halide; (ii) thermal, the decomposition in a furnace of a paste of silver oxide, silver halate (chlorate, bromate, iodate), and water to form the silver–silver halide couple; (iii) thermal-electrolytic, the electrolytic formation of the silver halide on thermally reduced silver oxide paste; and (iv) miscellaneous, such as the use of precipitated silver halide on silver. That the four methods are still in use reflects the fact, in part, that these difficulties have not yet been completely resolved.

B. Thermodynamic Principles

The thermodynamic principles of this reference electrode system may be illustrated by the most familiar example, the silver–silver chloride electrode:

$$Ag \mid AgCl \mid Cl^-$$

which consists of solid silver chloride on silver and in contact with a solution of a soluble chloride. As the solution is saturated with AgCl, the activity of silver chloride in solution is constant. The silver–silver chloride electrode is thus essentially equivalent to the $Ag \mid Ag^+$ electrode at which the silver ion activity is controlled by the activity solubility product which is invariant at a given temperature:

---

[1] The indeterminacy of single ion activities, and of single electrode potentials, and the permissible use of these concepts, has been discussed in Chapter 1.

$$K_s = a_{Ag^+} \cdot a_{Cl^-} \tag{1}$$

Thus the potential of the silver–silver chloride electrode is given by the expression:

$$E = E^\circ_{Ag,Ag^+} + \frac{RT}{F} \ln a_{Ag^+} = E^\circ_{Ag,Ag^+} + \frac{RT}{F} \ln \frac{K_s}{a_{Cl^-}} \tag{2}$$

from which it readily follows that:

$$E^\circ_{Ag,AgCl} = E^\circ_{Ag,Ag^+} + \frac{RT}{F} \ln K_s \tag{3}$$

where the constant terms are now contained in the definition of $E^\circ_{Ag,AgCl}$, the standard potential of the silver–silver chloride electrode. The potential therefore depends on the activity of chloride ions, i.e., the electrode is reversible to chloride ions in the same way as the chlorine electrode would be. It must not be supposed that the thermodynamic framework within which the electrode operates necessarily conveys anything about its mechanism.

It follows from the preceding discussion that the solubility of silver chloride, s_0, may be accurately predicted from a knowledge of the standard potentials for the silver–silver chloride and silver electrodes. Thus for the cell

$$Ag \mid AgCl \mid Cl^- \parallel Ag^+ \mid Ag \tag{A}$$

the emf has been deduced by Guggenheim and Prue (1) as $E^\circ = 576.9 \pm 0.2$ mv in a reconsideration of the data for the standard potentials of these electrodes in light of the precise values for the mean activity coefficients for HCl reported by Hills and Ives (2), and the results for the cell

$$Ag \left| AgCl \left| \begin{array}{c} KCl\ (xm) \\ KNO_3\ (m - xm) \end{array} \right| KNO_3\ (m) \left| \begin{array}{c} AgNO_3\ (xm) \\ KNO_3\ (x - xm) \end{array} \right| Ag \right. \tag{B}$$

reported by Owen (3). The ideal solubility at zero ionic strength, thermodynamically related to E° by

$$\ln s_0 = \frac{F}{2RT} \{E^\circ_{Ag,AgCl} - E^\circ_{Ag,Ag^+}\} \tag{4}$$

is thus predicted to be $1.33_1 \times 10^{-5}$ mole kg^{-1} with an uncertainty of $\frac{1}{2}\%$. Gledhill and Malan (4) determined the solubility of silver chloride to be $1.334 \pm 0.005 \times 10^{-5}$ mole liter^{-1} at 25°C, by a conductometric method using water of exceptional purity and correcting for dissolution of glass during the experiment. Extrapolation to zero ionic strength, by the Debye–Hückel formula gives a value of $1.332 \pm 0.004 \times 10^{-5}$ moles liter^{-1} for s_0.

The value of s_0 estimated by Brown and MacInnes (5) is suggested (1) to be in error by 3% from such considerations, due to an unfortunate guess at the activity coefficient for silver chloride in the presence of potassium nitrate in the solution.

Precise values for the standard potentials as a function of temperature for the silver–silver chloride, bromide, and iodide electrodes are known from 0° to 95°, 50° and 40°C, respectively (cf. Tables I and II, below). A knowledge of the standard potentials for the silver electrode as a function of temperature would make possible accurate predictions for s_0, the ideal solubility of the silver halides at zero ionic strength by the same calculations. Experimental values for the solubilities of AgCl and AgBr from 5° to 55°C are available from the very careful investigations of Gledhill and Malan (6, 7).[2]

C. Silver–Silver Halide–Electrolyte Interfaces

Some knowledge of the conditions existing in a silver–silver halide electrode, at the silver–silver halide interface and also at the silver halide–electrolyte interface is desirable to gain a more fundamental understanding of these electrode systems. The contact between a solid and a liquid electrolyte, using the silver–silver bromide system for specific attention, has been examined theoretically by Grimley and Mott (8, 9). A summary of the results and general principles relating to this problem follows.

The condition for equilibrium between a binary salt and an electrolyte is that the free energy change accompanying the transfer of an ion from the interior of the crystal to its hydrated state in the solution is zero. In an arbitrary electrolyte this condition can be satisfied only if the two phases are charged. The charge in an electrolyte occurs, at least in part, as a space charge of the hydrated ions, the space charge being highest near the interface and falling exponentially to zero in the bulk of the electrolyte. This charged layer is assumed to be balanced by an opposite charge carried by the crystal in the form of ions absorbed on the surface (thus usually known as the double layer, see Chapter 1). An essential point of the treatment by Grimley and Mott is that the balancing charge actually resides inside the crystal in the form of a space charge of lattice defects.

The nature of the silver–silver bromide solid interface predicted by this

---

[2] A study of the solubility of AgCl in HCl solutions from 25° to 300°C has been completed recently (see R. J. Raridon, Ph.D. Thesis, p. 93. Vanderbilt University, Nashville, Tennessee, 1958). Greely, Smith, Lietzke, and Stoughton, elsewhere (158), have reported the parameters for a solubility equation

$$\log s = a + b \log m_{HCl} + c(\log m_{HCl})^2$$

fitted at each temperature by least squares.

treatment is illustrated schematically in Fig. 1. The concentrations of the interstitial silver ions, $n_i(x)$, and vacant lattice points, $n_h(x)$, are shown as a function of the distance d from the interface. The charge density is highest near to the interface and falls exponentially to zero inside the crystal. It is apparent that in a layer of the crystal about 10^{-6} cm thick near the interface, the concentration of the vacant lattice points exceeds by several

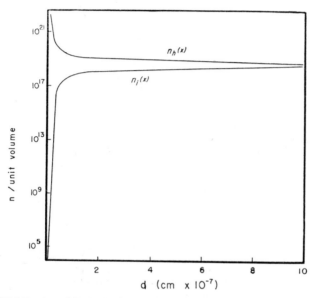

Fig. 1. Distribution of interstitial silver ions and vacant lattice points near a silver–silver halide interface. The curves n_h and n_i show the variation in concentrations of the interstitial silver ions and vacant lattice points, respectively, as a function of the distance, d, from the Ag,AgBr interface (8).

powers of 10 the concentration in the bulk of the crystal. The conductivity of a surface layer of this thickness deposited on silver would be expected to be greatly enhanced. The possibility of a rapid change in potential, actually at the interface, due to a relative displacement of positive and negative ions was recognized (8) but could not be taken into account owing to the lack of knowledge of the nature of the short-range forces between the ions. Refinements of this theoretical treatment will bring some changes in these results accordingly, but the general conclusion, namely the enhanced conductivity of the thin layer of silver bromide on metallic silver, is expected to hold.

The results of similar theoretical calculations for the silver bromide–electrolyte interface show that the electrical potential difference between the crystal surface and the bulk of the electrolyte is strictly the true zeta-potential of silver bromide. As illustrated in Fig. 2, the calculations show that the zeta-potential of silver bromide should be negative over a wide range of silver ion concentrations for the electrolyte. For the case where the electrolyte contains only silver and bromide ions, the concentrations of the silver and bromide ions in the electrolyte and the concentrations of

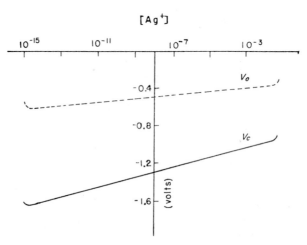

FIG. 2. Electrical potential difference between solid silver halide and the bulk of the electrolyte. The curves V_c and V_e show how the calculated electrical potential of the bulk of the crystal and the crystal surface for silver bromide, respectively, varies with silver ion concentration [Ag$^+$] (9). The potential in the bulk of the electrolyte is taken as zero.

the interstitial silver ions and vacant lattice points in the crystal both near the interface were calculated. Inside the silver bromide, in a layer 10^{-6} cm thick there is a distribution of interstitial ions and holes near the silver bromide–electrolyte interface of the same type illustrated in Fig. 1 for the silver–silver bromide interface.

In the electrolyte a diffuse double layer is predicted with the concentration of silver ions greatly enhanced in a layer approximately 10^{-6} cm thick near the crystal interface.

In this treatment it is assumed that the defects in the silver halides are the Schottky type (i.e., isolated positive or negative ion vacancies), and that the charge in the crystal arises through the presence of vacant cation and anion sites in unequal concentrations. An insight on the nature of these systems can be gained from experimental studies of self-diffusion and electrical conductivity of the solid silver halides. The technique of nuclear magnetic resonance also has been recently applied to the study of imperfect crystals. Thus conductivity measurements (10, 11) indicate that Br$^-$ ions remain relatively immobile in AgBr up to very high temperatures. Nuclear magnetic studies (12) give some evidence for association of defects at low temperatures. It appears that the onset of dissociation of the defects begins at about $-73°C$, and that the motion of the Ag vacancies leads to a characteristic minimum of the nuclear relaxation time at about $0°C$. Measurements of the electrical conductivity and self-diffusion coefficients recently completed over the range 350–450°C (13, 14a) show that the diffusion coefficient of the chloride ion is about 10^{-3} that of the silver ion. Conductivity and diffusion data with pure silver bromide crystals have likewise been reported (14b). These data and the conductances are in good agreement with the assumption that the transport of silver occurs by the vacancy mechanism in the silver halides.

D. Anodic Deposition of Halides

The porosity of anodically formed silver chloride layers has been investigated by Kurtz (15), and more recently by Lal, Thirsk, and Wynne-Jones, (16), Briggs and Thirsk (17), and Jaenicke, Tischer, and Gerischer (18). In the latter study the resistances of the halide layers were measured by a direct method, using a conductance cell, whereas in the former two investigations, it was obtained directly from a knowledge of the polarization overpotentials during the anodic processes.

The specific conductances of the solid silver halides at room temperature are in the range of $1–2 \times 10^{-7}$ ohm^{-1} cm^{-1}. The specific conductances of the anodically formed silver halide films were found in each investigation to be 10 to 100 times greater than that for the corresponding solid silver halides (recrystallized from melts). While Kurtz (15) interpreted this difference in terms of porosity, the results of the other investigations (16–18) have shown that the nature of the problem is undoubtedly more complex. At the moment it appears difficult to justify a quantitative approach to explain the lowered resistance of the anodic chloride layers on this concept alone.

At low current densities, less than 18 ma cm^{-2}, the anodic chloride layers were always a purplish-grey (16, 17) or red-brown (10) color, whether formed in the presence or absence of light. The silver bromide layers were yellow deposits, coherent and brittle; the silver iodide was also yellow, but of a powdery and fragile nature (16, 17).

Jaenicke Tischer, and Gerischer (18) used the criterion that if the resistance of the anodic halide layer showed a dependence on the concentration of the electrolyte in the conductance cell, this indicated a porous texture. Independence of the resistance from the electrolyte concentration was taken to show a dense coherent and pore-free layer. The specific resistance was measured for layers up to 30 μ thick, and formed with various current densities. The essential results are illustrated in Fig. 3 where a graph of the resistance as a function of the layer thickness under various anodic currents for growth is shown. It is apparent that the specific resistance becomes larger the more slowly the layer has been formed, and that for the pore-free silver halide layers, it is about one-tenth that of the single crystal, 5×10^{-6} ohm cm (19). It would appear that the layer growth proceeds along inner boundary interfaces.

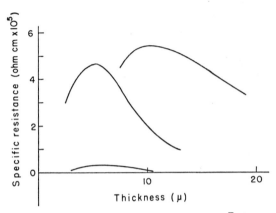

Fig. 3. Specific resistance of the covering halide layer in relation to thickness of layer. The anodic current densities were 30, 2.7 and 0.075 ma cm^{-2}, respectively, for the curves in increasing order of specific resistance (18).

Observations on the nature of the anodic silver chloride layers by microscopy have also been reported by Gerischer et al. (18). At current densities less than 3 ma cm^{-2} it was noted that the layer grew only at a few places on the silver metal surface, but with increasing polarization, the layer formation spread to the open areas until the various patches had grown together. In this layer the crystal surfaces were very varied, differing greatly in orientation. In the range 3 to 18 ma cm^{-2}, the polarization initially is already sufficiently great to promote the uniform growth of a dense coherent halide layer, red-brown in color.

The structure of anodically formed silver halide films has been investigated with an electron microscope by Huber (20). The specimens were prepared by anodizing highest purity silver sheets at current densities less than 10 ma cm^{-2} using 0.1 N halide solutions, followed by dissolution of the silver metal in nitric acid and mounting of the film in the conventional manner. The nature of the surface as seen under such high magnification is illustrated in Fig. 4a. It was noted that the structure is essentially nonporous, or more exactly that no pores penetrating entirely through the film to the metal surface were evident. From the nature of the cup-like depressions it is apparent that the film growth does not proceed uniformly with a planar front but penetrates into the metal by numerous independent depressions. A schematic representation of three possible types of silver–silver halide surfaces is shown in Fig. 4b. From the above it is apparent

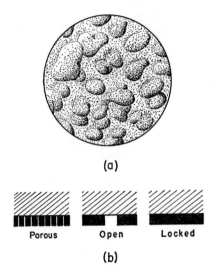

(a)

Porous   Open   Locked

(b)

Fig. 4. The structure of anodically formed silver halide films. (a) Silver–silver halide contact surface viewed under an electron microscope (20); (b) Schematic representation of three kinds of silver–silver halide surfaces (20).

that the anodically formed halide layers on silver may be classed as locked surfaces, in contrast to the porous and open surfaces. The latter are undoubtedly realized in the thermal silver–silver halide electrodes, prepared by the decomposition of a paste of silver oxide and silver halate or halide at moderately high temperatures.

At current densities somewhat greater than 18 ma cm^{-2}, quite a different growth mechanism apparently dominates. The silver surface was first seen to become dark, almost black, and then change through the various interference colors until finally a white covering halide layer was obtained, stable to careful washing but very readily rubbed off. The time to form the white layer seemed inversely proportional to the chloride ion concentration in the solution. It would appear that the process is one in which depletion of the chloride ions in the pores occurs with the formation of the initially observed black film. Hydrated silver ions then migrate through this layer to form silver chloride at the electrolyte diffusion interface, with the consequent formation of a soft, white halide layer of very low specific conductance.

Similar studies on the process of cathodic reduction of chloride layers on silver metal (18) showed that silver forms along the inner crystal grain boundaries. The resistance of the anodically formed halide layers thus vanishes rapidly in the process of cathodic reduction. At high reducing current densities, secondary rearrangements in the halide film were noted due to migration on the interface surfaces of the very finely divided electro-deposited silver particles. These however required times from several seconds to minutes.

II. Standard Electrode Potentials

A. Aqueous Media

In accordance with the Stockholm Convention (see Chapter 1, Section IV), the standard potential of the silver–silver chloride electrode is identified with the emf of the hypothetical cell

$$\text{H}_2 \text{ (ideal, 1 atm)} \mid \text{HCl (ideal, } m = 1) \mid \text{AgCl} \mid \text{Ag} \qquad \text{(C)}$$

in which all the reactants are in their standard states. This standard emf is determined from the measured emfs of the experimental cell by means of the thermodynamic relation

$$E = E° - \frac{2RT}{F} \ln (m_\pm \, \gamma_\pm)_{\text{HCl}} \qquad (5)$$

which may be rearranged to

$$E + \frac{2RT}{F} \ln m_\pm = E° - \frac{2RT}{F} \ln \gamma_\pm \qquad (6)$$

It can be seen that, provided the mean ion activity coefficient, $\gamma_\pm$, can be expressed as an acceptable function of $m_\pm$, this equation can be made the basis of an extrapolation to zero concentration, where $E°$ is obtained as an intercept. Methods of performing this extrapolation have been discussed elsewhere (Chapter I, Section V).

A variety of techniques, electrodes, and analytical methods have been used in the determination of the standard electrode potentials for the silver–silver halide electrodes. In Tables I and II some of these results are summarized, with the values retained to the number of significant figures reported by each investigator to reflect the precision of the experimental work.

The values of the standard potentials for the Ag,AgCl electrode from 0° to 95°C, found in Table I, are taken from two investigations (21, 22) of cells of type (C) and one (23) of type (D), i.e.,

$$\text{H}_2 \mid \text{HCl (0.01), MCl (} m) \mid \text{AgCl} \mid \text{Ag} \qquad \text{(D)}$$

TABLE I

THE STANDARD Emf OF THE CELL: $H_2 \mid HCl\ (m) \mid AgCl \mid Ag$
AS A FUNCTION OF TEMPERATURE

t (°C)	Values of $E°$ (abs volts)			
	Harned and Ehlers (21)	Bates and Bower (22)	Harned and Paxton (23)	Greely et al. (158)
0	0.23642	0.23655	0.23652	—
5	0.23400	0.23413	0.23405	—
10	0.23134	0.23142	0.23137	—
15	0.22854	0.22857	0.22849	—
20	0.22558	0.22557	0.22549	—
25	0.22246	0.22234	0.22239	—
30	0.21919	0.21904	0.21908	—
35	0.21570	0.21565	0.21570	—
40	0.21207	0.21208	0.21207	—
45	0.20828	0.20835	0.20833	—
50	0.20444	0.20449	0.20449	—
55	0.20042	0.20056	—	—
60	0.19627	0.19649	—	0.19676
70	—	0.18782	—	—
80	—	0.1787	—	—
90	—	0.1695	—	0.1696
95	—	0.1651	—	—

t (°C)	125	150	175	200	225	250	275
$E°$ (volts)[a]	0.1330	0.1032	0.0708	0.0348	−0.0051	−0.054	−0.090

[a] See reference 158.

in which strontium chloride and hydrochloric acid served as electrolyte. In the most recent work (22), all solutions were more dilute than 0.113 m, and some six hundred measurements with 81 different cells were made. The extended Debye-Hückel equation was used and the best value for the ion-size parameter a at each temperature was found by the method of least squares. The standard deviations of the individual $E°$ values ranged from 0.05 mv at 15°C to 0.28 mv at 95°C.

The equation given by Bates and Bower (22) for the temperature range 0°–95°C is:

$$E° = 0.23659 - 4.8564 \times 10^{-4}t - 3.4205 \times 10^{-6}t^2 + 5.869 \times 10^{-9}t^3 \quad (7)$$

In both the investigations of Harned and Ehlers (21) and Bates and Bower (22), thermal-electrolytic electrodes were used. The uncertainty in

TABLE II

A. The Standard Emf of the Cell: $H_2 \mid HCl \ (m) \mid AgBr \mid Ag$
as a Function of Temperature

t (°C)	$E°$ (abs volts) Harned and Donelson (25)	$E°$ (abs volts) Owen and Foering (26)	t (°C)	$E°$ (abs volts) Harned and Donelson (25)	$E°$ (abs volts) Owen and Foering (26)
0	0.08168	—	30	0.06874	0.06878
5	0.07994	0.07989	35	0.06604	0.06602
10	0.07804	0.07803	40	0.06302	0.06306
15	0.07596	0.07599	45	0.05997	—
20	0.07379	0.07376	50	0.05668	—
25	0.07129	0.07136	—	—	—

B. The Standard Emf of the Cell: $H_2 \mid HI \ (m) \mid AgI \mid Ag$
as a Function of Temperature (28)

t (°C)	$E°$ (abs volts)	t (°C)	$E°$ (abs volts)
5	−0.14717	25	−0.15230
10	−0.14810	30	−0.15401
15	−0.14925	35	−0.15591
20	−0.15067	40	−0.15792

the value of $E°$ at 25°C is likely to be due in part to the limited reproducibility of these electrodes, discussed later in this chapter. A practical standardization of the potential of this electrode based on recommended values for γ_{HCl} has been recently proposed (24) (see Chapter 1, Section V).

The values of the standard potentials of the Ag,AgCl electrode above 95°C in Table I are from the work of Greely, Smith, Lietzke, and Stoughton (158) for cells of type (C) in which the apparatus was modified for work at elevated temperatures. Thermal silver–silver chloride electrodes were used. At 25°C the measured $E°$ was 0.22233 volt (cf. 0.22234 volt, Bates and Bower (22)). The values fit the following equation:

$$E° = 0.23735 - 5.3783 \times 10^{-4}t - 2.3728 \times 10^{-6}t^2 \text{ volts} \qquad (7')$$

to within 0.19 mv to 200°C, and extrapolate to $E° = -0.138$ volt at 300°C.

The standard potential of the silver–silver bromide electrode has been established through measurements (25) on cells similar to the two types described for silver chloride, and a third type (26) in which the silver bromide electrode and silver chloride electrode are directly compared in borate buffer solutions containing the corresponding halides. The use of borate solutions under certain prescribed conditions has the advantage of eliminating the need for an extrapolation to infinite dilution (see Chapter 1, Section V). The agreement is within 0.05 mv over the range. These data differ from the earlier values reported by Harned and co-workers (27) for the cell containing the acid only by amounts varying from 0.1 to 0.3 mv.

The standard electrode potential of the silver–silver iodide electrode has been more difficult to establish by direct means [cells of types (C) and (D)], largely because of the experimental problems inherent in measurements with HI solutions (e.g., oxidation). Owen (28) has measured the standard potential of the silver–silver iodide electrode, using the thermal-electrolytic type of electrode and the borate-buffered cell technique.

B. Mixed Solvents

The standard emf values of the cell

$$H_2 \mid HCl\ (m) \text{ in solvent } (X), \text{ water } (100 - X) \mid AgCl \mid Ag \qquad (E)$$

where X is the weight per cent of an organic solvent in a partly aqueous medium, have been investigated. The difference between the standard emf's of cells (C) and (E) gives the free energy of transfer of the solute, HCl, from water to the mixed solvent in question, i.e.,

$$\underset{w \to s}{\Delta G} = nF(E_w^\circ - E_s^\circ) \qquad (8)$$

and, since from the definitions of E_w° and E_s°, ionic interactions are not concerned, this is the difference between the free energies of solvation of HCl in the two media. From measurements over a temperature range, differences in entropies and heats of solvation may be obtained by the usual thermodynamic methods.

The standard potentials for the silver–silver chloride electrode as a function of temperature in various aqueous organic solutions are summarized in Table III. Within experimental error, the results were found to fit the empirical quadratic equation:

$$E^\circ = E_{t_r}^\circ + b(t - t_r) + c(t - t_r)^2 \qquad (9)$$

where t_r is the reference temperature. More detailed tabulations and discussions may be found in the works of Harned and Owen (29) and Conway (30) and the original papers (5, 27, 32–39).

A feature common to all the mixtures, is that the values of the standard potential decrease with falling dielectric constant of the medium. The results at 25°C for various aqueous organic solutions, based on the recent

TABLE III

THE STANDARD Emf (MOLAL) OF THE CELL: $H_2 \mid HCl\ (m) \mid AgCl \mid Ag$
(MIXED SOLVENT) AS A FUNCTION OF TEMPERATURE
IN ORGANIC SOLVENT–WATER MIXTURES

Organic solvent (wt %)	$E_m{}^\circ = a + b(t - t_r) + c(t - t_r)^2$		
	a	$b \times 10^4$	$c \times 10^6$
Dioxane–water, $t_r = 25°C$ (0–50°C)			
20	0.20303	−7.605	−3.70
45	0.16352	−11.35	−3.70
70	0.06395	−17.67	−3.70
82 (32)	0.0611	−25.73	−9.65
Methanol–water, $t_r = 20°C$ (0–40°C)			
10	0.21818	−55.563	−4.128
20	0.21151	−52.910	−4.706
Methanol–water, $t_r = 25°C$ (5, 25)			
43.3	0.1941	−7.262	−6.594
64.0	0.1764	−9.512	−1.739
84.2	0.1319	−13.241	−4.303
94.2	0.0840	−14.064	−5.435
Ethanol–water, $t_r = 20°C$ (0–40°C)			
10	0.21900	−5.03	−3.82
20	0.21025	−4.19	−6.00
2-Propanol–water, $t_r = 20°C$ (0–40°C)			
5	0.22110	−5.7425	−3.8357
10	0.21666	−5.3324	−4.7405
20	0.20905	−4.9001	−6.8362
Glycerol–water, $t_r = 25°C$ (0–40°C)			
10	0.21650	−6.52	−3.3
30	0.20221	−6.68	−3.4
50[a]	0.18392	−7.45	−3.0

[a] Valid from 0° to 90°C, inclusive.

compilations (29, 40) and latest results (41–43) are summarized in Table IV. Values for $E_N{}^\circ$ and $E_c{}^\circ$, the mole fractions, and the densities of the solutions may also be found in the compilation by Feakins and French (40).

If it is assumed that the ions are spheres of radii r_+ and r_- in a uniform dielectric medium, the free energy of transfer for the solute species from water to the mixed solvent system should be given by the well-known Born expression (44).

TABLE IV

The Standard Potential (Molal) of the Silver–Silver Chloride Electrode
in Organic Solvent–Water Mixtures at 25°C (29, 40)

					Ethanol[a]				
	10	20	30	40	50	71.9	88.5	98	100
D	72.8	67.0	61.1	55.0	49.0	37.0	27.4	25.1	24.3
$E_m°$	0.2144	0.2073	0.2003	0.1945	0.1859	0.1554	0.1053	0.0215	−0.0813

					Methanol				
	10	20	40	60	80	90	94.2	100	
D	74.18	69.99	60.94	51.67	42.60	37.91	35.76	32.66	
$E_m°$	0.2155	0.2094	0.1968	0.1818	0.1492	0.1135	0.0841	−0.0099	

					Acetone			
	5	10	20	40	50	90	100	
D	75.9	73.0	67.0	54.6	48.2	24.0	19.1	
$E_m°$	0.2190	0.2156	0.2079	0.1859	0.158	−0.034	−0.53	

					Ethylene glycol			
	5	10	15	20	30	40	60	
D	76.9	75.6	74.2	72.8	69.8	66.6	59.4	
$E_m°$	0.2190	0.2161	0.2133	0.2101	0.2036	0.1972	0.1807	

	Dioxane					D-Glucose			
	20	45	70	82		5	10	20	30	50
D	60.8	38.5	17.7	9.5	D	77.3	76.1	73.4	70.5	—
$E_m°$	0.2031	0.1635	0.0639	−0.0614	$E_m°$	0.2186	0.2142	0.2045	0.1935	0.1634

	D-Fructose			Propanol-1			Propanol-2		
	5	10		10	20		5	10	20
D	77.3	76.1	D	71.8	64.9	D	74.9	71.4	64.1
$E_m°$	0.2190	0.2150	$E_m°$	0.2141	0.2066	$E_m°$	0.2180	0.2138	0.2063

		Glycerol				Methyl ethyl ketone		
	4.9	10	21.2	30	50		10	20
D	77.1	75.5	72.5	70.1	64.0	D	71.8	64.9
$E_m°$	0.2196	0.2165	0.2084	0.2022	0.1940	$E_m°$	0.2153	0.2078

	Propylene glycol			2,3-Butylene glycol	
	10	20		10	20
D	74.2	70.7	D	73.2	69.0
$E_m°$	0.2150	0.2077	$E_m°$	0.2144	0.2067

[a] All concentrations in wt %.

$$-\Delta G = F(E_w° - E_s°) = \frac{Ne^2}{2}\left(\frac{1}{D_s} - \frac{1}{D_w}\right)\left(\sum \frac{1}{r}\right) \qquad (10)$$

where D is the dielectric constant and the other symbols have the conventional significance. If one of the ions transferred is the "hydrogen ion," considered to be H_3O^+, the transfer will involve, effectively, desolvation in one medium and resolvation in the other. This is equivalent to the transfer of H_2O in the opposite direction, for which there will be a free energy change $\Delta G = -RT \ln a_w$, where a_w is the activity of water in the mixed solvent. These considerations suggest that $E°$ or $(E° - RT \ln a_w)$ should be a linear function of $1/D$, with a negative slope. Whilst in the first instance this approach based on the Born equation seems to be broadly successful (29), Feakins and French in a critical study of all the available data (40) noted that smooth curves rather than straight lines are generally obtained, the decrease in $E°$ being less than predicted by the Born relations for an increase in $1/D$, and that the $E°$ values in various mixtures of equal dielectric constants show an apparent dependence on the nature of the organic component in the mixture.

According to structural theories of ion solvation (Chapter 1, Section V), the formation of a primary solvation sheath of firmly held solvent molecules, in which dielectric saturation occurs, is responsible for the greater part of the free energy of solvation. Feakins and French made the exploratory assumption that when hydrogen chloride is transferred from water to a partly aqueous solvent, this primary ionic *hydration* remains unchanged. Then, by a similar argument to that used above, the free energy of transfer must involve a term

$$\Delta G = n(\mu_{H_2O}^w - \mu_{H_2O}^s) \tag{11}$$

where n is the number of water molecules involved in the primary hydration, and the μ terms are the chemical potentials of water in the two media. The further assumptions were made that this effect accounts for the *whole* of the free energy change, and that the water-organic solvent mixture can be considered ideal. Then,

$$\Delta G = -nRT \ln N_w \quad \text{and} \quad \Delta S = -nR \ln N_w \tag{12}$$

or

$$\Delta G = -nRT \ln \phi_w \quad \text{and} \quad \Delta S = -nR \ln \phi_w \tag{13}$$

according to whether mole fraction or volume fraction statistics are applicable. These relations imply that either $E°_{N,s}$ or $E°_{C,s}$ should be linear functions of $\log N_w$ or of $\log \phi_w$. The second of these alternatives was found to fit the data for all the available systems, the correlation being outstandingly better than anything based on the Born equation. The value of n determined from the slope of the plot was 2.2, which compares favorably with that deduced from diffusion measurements (45), i.e., $n = 2.1$, but is considerably less than values found by other methods. It was admitted that this treatment involved gross approximations; thus, entropy data, when available, often are very far removed from the requirements of Eq. 13. Nevertheless, the success of the method is striking, and results are awaited from studies of other systems (bromides, iodides, etc.).

For the calculation of the standard potential at 25°C in solvents moderately rich in the organic component (e.g., 70 wt % methanol), Oiwa (47) has proposed the equation:

$$E_N^{°*} = E_N° - \left[\frac{9.2}{P - 3.19} \right] RT \ln a_w \tag{14}$$

where P the polarization of a polar solvent is calculated by the Kirkwood (46) relation:

$$P = \frac{(D-1)(2D+1)}{9D} \qquad (15)$$

using the dielectric constant D of the pure solvent. The agreement between the calculated and observed values is within a few millivolts.

C. Nonaqueous Media

In discussing dilute aqueous solutions, difficulties associated with the use of alternative composition scales were not obtrusive. This is no longer the case when it becomes necessary to deal with nonaqueous, or partly aqueous solutions, and it is appropriate to consider these difficulties at the present stage.

The scales are those of mole fraction, N, molality, m, and molar concentration, C. For a given solution, these quantities are related[3] by the self-evident equations

$$N = \frac{m}{m + (1000/M_1)} = \frac{C}{C + [(1000d - CM_2)/M_1]} \qquad (16)$$

$$= \frac{mM_1}{mM_1 + 1000} = \frac{CM_1}{C(M_1 - M_2) + 1000d} \qquad (17)$$

where M_1 and M_2 are the molecular weights of solvent and solute, and d is the density of the solution in gm cm^{-3}.

For a given solution, the chemical potential of the solute is independent of any concentration scale or choice of standard state, so that,

$$\mu - \mu_N^\circ + RT \ln N\gamma_N = \mu_m^\circ + RT \ln m\gamma_m = \mu_C^\circ + RT \ln C\gamma_C \qquad (18)$$

notwithstanding that the standard states, the standard chemical potentials, and the activity coefficients appropriate to the three scales are all different. The task is, to find the relationships between these quantities.

This can be done by considering that in a solution of extreme dilution, all three activity coefficients tend to unity. For such a solution, Eq. (18) becomes

$$\mu_0 = \mu_N^\circ + RT \ln N_0 = \mu_m^\circ + RT \ln m_0 = \mu_C^\circ + RT \ln C_0 \qquad (19)$$

where the subscript zeros are used to denote extreme dilution. Comparing Eq. (18) and (19), it is seen that the quantity $\mu - \mu_0$, which is independent of concentration scales, is given by

$$\mu - \mu_0 = RT \ln \frac{N}{N_0}\gamma_N = RT \ln \frac{m}{m_0}\gamma_m = RT \ln \frac{C}{C_0}\gamma_C \qquad (20)$$

[3] The fact that 1 liter = 1000.027 cm^3 is ignored, but need not be.

so that

$$\frac{N}{N_0} \gamma_N = \frac{m}{m_0} \gamma_m = \frac{C}{C_0} \gamma_C \qquad (21)$$

For the extremely dilute solution, it is also clear that Eq. (17) becomes, in the limit,

$$N_0 = m_0 M_1/1000 = C_0 M_1/1000 d_0 \qquad (22)$$

where d_0 may be identified with the density of the pure solvent. Substitution from Eq. (17) and (22) into (20) leads to relations between mole fractional, molal and molar activity coefficients, which may be represented

$$\gamma_N = \gamma_m \ (1 + m M_1/1000) \qquad (23)$$

$$\gamma_N = \gamma_C \ [(d/d_0) + C(M_1 - M_2)/1000 d_0] \qquad (24)$$

$$\gamma_m = \gamma_C \ [(d/d_0) - CM_2/1000 d_0] \qquad (25)$$

For the standard emf of cell C, it is clear that

$$E_N{}^\circ - 2k \log N_0 = E_m{}^\circ - 2k \log m_0 = E_C{}^\circ - 2k \log C_0 \qquad (26)$$

where $k = (RT/F) \ln 10$. Use of Eq. (22) then leads to

$$E_C{}^\circ = E_m{}^\circ + 2k \log d_0 \qquad (27)$$

$$E_N{}^\circ = E_m{}^\circ + 2k \log (M_1/1000) \qquad (28)$$

For a mixed solvent, M_1 becomes an average molecular weight, thus if 100 grams of mixed solvent are made up of X grams of A and $(100 - X)$ grams of B, the average molecular weight is the total weight divided by the total number of moles, i.e.,

$$M_{AB} = 100 \left/ \left[\frac{X}{M_A} + \left(\frac{100 - X}{M_B} \right) \right] \right. \qquad (29)$$

For electrolytic solutes of various valency types, appropriate relationships may be derived in a similar manner, bearing in mind the general definition of mean ionic quantities typified by

$$m_\pm = (m_+{}^{\nu_+} m_-{}^{\nu_-})^{1/\nu} \qquad (30)$$

for an electrolyte which dissociates into ν_+ cations and ν_- anions per "molecule," and $\nu = \nu_+ + \nu_-$.

The use of the silver–silver chloride electrode as reference standard in pure methanol (D, 31.5) has been investigated by Nonhebel and Hartley (48), by Oiwa (49), and by Austin and co-workers (50, 50a); pure ethanol (D, 24.31) by Woolcock and Hartley (51), Harned and Fleysher (52), Mukherjee (53), and Taniguchi and Janz (42); pure acetone (D, 19.1) by Feakins and French (40); pure formamide (D, 109.5) by Mandel and Decroly (54); pure acetonitrile (D, 38.8) by Ulich and Spiegel (55); formic acid (D, 58.5) and acetic acid (D, 7.15) by Mukherjee (*56*). In the acetonitrile instability is observed, probably owing to the tendency to complex formation of silver chloride in this solvent. On this point it is of interest to note that Popov and Geske (*57*) have reported that if the acetonitrile solution is saturated with silver chloride and trimethylammonium chloride, the Ag,AgCl electrode is sufficiently reproducible and nonpolarizable for use in polarographic studies in this solvent. A summary of the results for absolute ethanol at 25°C is given in Table V. At 25°C, the most probable

TABLE V

THE STANDARD Emf OF THE CELL: H_2 | HCl (m) | AgCl | Ag
IN ETHANOL AT 25°C

Reference	$E_m°$ (abs volts)[a]
Harned and Fleysher (*52*)	−0.0552
Scatchard (*58*)	−0.0668
Woolcock and Hartley (*51*)	−0.0883
MacInnes (*59*)	−0.0740
Mukherjee (*53*)	−0.00977
Janz and Taniguchi (*42*)	−0.08131

[a] The wide variations from the most recent value (*42*) are most probably due to nonanhydrous alcohols.

values of $E_m°$ are: −0.0099, −0.0813, −0.53, 0.204, −0.1200, and −0.6180 volts, in methanol, ethanol, acetone, formamide, formic acid, and acetic acid, respectively.

According to the data of Austin and co-workers (*50*), the temperature dependence of this electrode potential in methanol is given by the equation:

$$E_t° = -0.0103 - 12.080 \times 10^{-4} (t - 25) - 4.00 \times 10^{-6} (t - 25)^2 \quad (31)$$

The standard potentials of the silver–silver bromide electrode in pure methanol and ethanol at 25°C have been measured by Kanning and Campbell (*60*), and Mukherjee (*61*) with thermal electrodes. The values for $E_m°$ are −0.1328 and −0.0815 volt, respectively. For the silver–silver iodide electrode in ethanol at 25°C, the standard potential $E_m°$ has been reported (*61*) at −0.2530 volt.

Traces of moisture in these solvents result in an increase of the electromotive force of the cell, e.g., 0.01% by weight of water added to a 0.1 m solution of hydrogen chloride in methanol and ethanol increased the emf by about 1 mv.

III. Preparation of Chemicals and Electrodes

A. CHEMICALS

A good grade of conductivity water should be used in all purifications or preparations. While water of specific conductance of 10^{-6} ohm^{-1} cm^{-1} and less may be readily achieved by ion exchange resins available commercially, this treatment does not ensure the removal of organic and related impurities (cf. Chapter 1, Section VII,D). The use of conductance water prepared by distillation methods is recommended to minimize this contamination hazard.

1. Potassium Silver Cyanide

The recommended concentration of silver-plating solution for the preparation of the electrolytic electrodes is approximately 10 gm $KAg(CN)_2$ per liter. The salt is most conveniently prepared by a double recrystallization of C.P. grade $KAg(CN)_2$ using the fourfold solubility change between 100° and 20°C. It can also be prepared by the addition of silver cyanide (41 gm) to an aqueous solution of potassium cyanide (20 gm) after the procedure of Bassett and Corbett (62). The recrystallized product may be oven-dried at 55°C, or over $CaCl_2$ in a desiccator, and stored in a glass stoppered bottle until required. The silver plating solution may be used about five times, but dilute $AgNO_3$ should be added dropwise to remove free cyanide by precipitation before plating, until a faint cloudiness is produced.

2. Silver Oxide

A paste of Ag_2O of high purity is required for the preparation of both the thermal-electrolytic and the thermal types of electrodes. The silver oxide is precipitated by adding a solution of NaOH to a vigorously stirred solution of $AgNO_3$ (one-half equivalent of C.P. $AgNO_3$ in 750 ml water). Vigorous stirring is continued until homogeneity and complete precipitation is ensured. An important precaution (63) in the purification of the silver oxide is the thorough washing of the resulting precipitate to ensure the removal of all water-soluble impurities. It was found that as an empirical criterion approximately 30 washings, each with shaking or stirring, proved sufficient for this step. For this step, alternatively, Soxhlet extraction with conductance water may be used with advantage. The specific conductance of the water from the final washings should not exceed 3×10^{-5} ohm^{-1} at room temperature (approximately 10^{-5} ohm^{-1} cm^{-1} are expected from the solubility of pure silver oxide). The Ag_2O is recovered in a sintered glass filter. The subsequent use of this material as an aqueous paste necessitates only a superficial drying by a short continuation of the suction.

3. Silver Chlorate

The preparation of $AgClO_3$ from $AgNO_3$ and $NaClO_3$ is recommended (64) as more dependable than the methods based on passing chlorine into an aqueous suspension of silver oxide or silver carbonate, or a solution of silver fluoride, or by the action of chloric acid on silver oxide, silver carbonate, or finely divided silver metal, to yield silver chlorate of 99.7% purity. Equal portions of concentrated sodium chlorate (10 N) and silver nitrate (10 N) solutions, preheated to 85°C, are mixed and slowly cooled to 0°C. The crystalline $AgClO_3$ is separated by decantation, washed, and recrystallized for further purification. The recrystallizations should suffice to yield $AgClO_3$ of 99.7% purity. It may be dried in an oven or in vacuum. $AgClO_3$ (m.p. 230°C) decomposes on heating above its melting point to $AgCl$. It should be stored in a dark bottle since it decomposes slowly, with darkening, when exposed to light.

4. Silver Bromate and Silver Iodate

These salts are most readily prepared in a pure state by recrystallization of C.P. purity grade chemicals. They may also be prepared (65) much after the manner of the chlorate, from $AgNO_3$, with $KBrO_3$ or $NaIO_3$, respectively. Both salts may be oven-dried at 100°C, and should be stored in dark bottles. When heated, these salts decompose to form the bromide and iodide, respectively.

5. Silver Perchlorate

Concentrated perchloric acid (70%) is diluted approximately twofold, and neutralized by the addition of highly purified Ag_2O. After a few minutes digestion near the boiling point, the solution is filtered through a sintered glass funnel to remove any excess Ag_2O. The filtrate is evaporated under reduced pressure, or on a steam bath. The drying is completed over P_2O_5 in a vacuum desiccator since silver perchlorate is very hygroscopic.

The final product corresponds to a monohydrate, $AgClO_4 \cdot H_2O$. The thermal decomposition of silver perchlorate has recently been investigated (65) with the aid of a thermobalance. The results show that the salt decomposes rapidly to form silver chloride at 460°C.

6. Hydrochloric Acid

The recommended concentrations of the anodizing solutions for the electrolytic electrodes and the thermal-electrolytic electrodes are 0.1 and 1 N respectively. These solutions are prepared from carefully distilled constant boiling hydrochloric acid. The azeotrope (b.p. 108.6°/760 mm) has a density of 1.0959/25°C, and contains 20.2 wt % HCl. For the distillation, hydrochloric acid (C.P.), diluted to a density of 1.10 gm/ml is recommended (*66*) as starting material. The azeotrope is twice redistilled in the conventional type of apparatus with quartz condenser and receiver, only the middle fraction being collected each time. The final distillate should be bromide-free (see Section III, A, 7) and is stored in a quartz flask until required for use.

When there is a need for pure *anhydrous* HCl, the addition of sulfuric acid to sodium chloride, with subsequent drying of the gas, is commonly used. An all-glass anhydrous hydrogen chloride generator of simple design (*67*) is illustrated in Fig. 5. The required amount of sodium chloride is

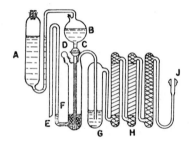

Fig. 5. Anhydrous hydrogen chloride generator. An all glass system for anhydrous HCl preparation showing the sulfuric acid (A, B) and sodium chloride (F) reservoirs, and drying trains (G, H) leading to the stock solution port (J) (*67*).

charged through side arm D to the reaction chamber, F. The glass beads in F are helpful in preventing caking of the chloride charge once the sulfuric acid is added. In practice, reservoir A is filled with more than sufficient concentrated sulfuric acid for the experiment. By gentle suction, an aliquot volume of sulfuric acid can be transferred to the dropping funnel, B, from the storage reservoir. Stopcock C controls the rate of sulfuric acid addition to the chloride in the reaction vessel. The rate of hydrogen chloride evolution is indicated by the bubbler, G, containing concentrated sulfuric acid. The latter thus serves for the preliminary drying of the hydrogen chloride. The three towers, H, are packed with calcium sulfate (Drierite) and glass wool. The stock solution receiving the anhydrous hydrogen chloride connects in at the exit of train J.

A novel feature is that the spent reaction mixture can be siphoned from chamber F through outlet E by applying gentle suction. Preparation for a new charge can thus be effected with very little labor and a minimum of hazard. In addition, by maintaining the bulk of the sulfuric acid in A, the danger of a serious acid spill through failure of stopcock C is effectively avoided. A safety tube, consisting of a mercury bubbler open to the atmosphere, is used in practice between F and G.

The generator operates equally well with concentrated hydrochloric acid as with a solid chloride for the reaction charge. From chamber F to exit J, escape of the hydrogen chloride to the atmosphere is impossible, for the apparatus is a continuous glass unit. Once the storage reservoir, A, has been charged, all transfers of the sulfuric acid, and of the spent reaction mixture can be effected by siphoning action.

7. Alkali Metal Chlorides

The need for careful purification of the chlorides was strikingly demonstrated by Pinching and Bates (68). Traces of bromide (0.01 mole per cent) were found to exert marked disturbing effects on the potential of the silver–silver chloride electrode.

The formation of red eosin (tetrabromofluorescein) by the action of bromine on fluorescein has been utilized for the detection of small amounts of bromide. Pinching and Bates replaced fluorescein with uranine, its sodium salt, to develop a rapid, sensitive, and reliable color test for bromide in the presence of chloride. The procedure is as follows: 0.2 ml of saturated chromic acid solution is added to an equal volume of a saturated solution of the alkali metal chloride in a test tube. A circular piece of filter paper is dipped into the uranine dye solution and placed over the test tube mouth. The tube is heated for 6 minutes in a boiling water bath. From an inspection of the color developed on the filter paper, and comparison with simultaneously run tests in solutions having known amounts of bromide, the amount of bromide present in the unknown can readily be determined. For very small amounts of bromide, comparison of the colors under ultraviolet light is recommended. The test is *sensitive* to about ±0.002 mole %, and can be used to detect the presence of one-thousandth mole % of bromide. The aqueous uranine dye solution, about 0.05 wt %, was found to have good stability and did not require a daily adjustment of test conditions such as necessary with fluorescein. If this test is to be tried on concentrated HCl, the acid must be neutralized with Br-free carbonate, otherwise chromyl chloride masks the test (69).

The following method has been found most effective for the purification of sodium and potassium chlorides. A filtered solution of reagent grade NaCl or KCl, saturated at room temperature, is treated with chlorine by bubbling for ten minutes, and then boiled for five minutes to remove free halogens. The alkali metal chloride is reprecipitated twice from such aqueous saturated solutions using gaseous HCl, collected on sintered glass filters, washed with small amounts of conductance water, and dried at 180°C. Pinching and Bates report a 60–85% yield of salt containing only 0.001 mole % bromide by this method.

Recent measurements have shown (70, 71) that with high vacuum pumping, both sodium and potassium chlorides can be readily obtained in a dry state at temperatures well below their respective melting points. Fusion is recommended however for the chloride purified by the preceding method since the recovered crystals may well contain occluded hydrochloric acid and water. Fusion of the salt in platinum under a dry nitrogen atmosphere is therefore recommended as a final step in the purification procedure. Since the chlorides in the molten state wet platinum, and on solidification adhere tightly to the walls of the fusion vessels, Pinching and Bates (68) followed the procedure of transferring the salt, while still molten, into a second platinum vessel at a lower temperature so that the salt did not stick so tightly. An arrangement for this is illustrated in Fig. 6.

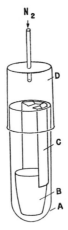

FIG. 6. Assembly for fusion of alkali metal halides under controlled atmospheres. The components are: A, quartz test tube; B, C, platinum crucible and trough respectively; D, loosely fitting Pyrex glass cover with entry tube for dry nitrogen gas (63, 68).

The platinum crucible, B, containing the salt (air-dried at 180°C), fits snugly into a clear quartz rimless test tube, A. The platinum trough, C, made from 0.005 inch thick foil shaped to form a dam at the upper end, and the Pyrex cover, D, are placed in position as shown. The cover is wired in position, and the assembly is placed in a crucible furnace in a vertical position for fusion. A slow stream of dry nitrogen is passed for 5 minutes to replace the moisture-laden air, and the fusion is effected at 1000°C over a period of 10–15 min. When all the salt has been melted, the tube is withdrawn from the hot zone, tilted to flow the molten salt into the cooler trough. It is thus placed on its side and allowed to cool with N_2 still flowing.

By this procedure, neutral NaCl and KCl can be fused without introducing by hydrolysis more than 0.001 mole % of free alkali. NaCl, predried at 180°C, can usually be fused in this apparatus without the use of dry nitrogen with satisfactory results. KCl, for which the tendency toward hydrolysis at elevated temperatures is less marked than NaCl, will usually contain up to 0.003 mole % of free alkali when it is fused in an open platinum crucible exposed to the atmosphere. With the apparatus and procedure above, the fused salts are nearly neutral (*63, 68*).

B. Electrodes

1. *Electrolytic*

Platinum metal is generally used as the electrode base, on which a layer of silver is electrodeposited and chloridized by anodizing in a dilute solution of HCl or a chloride salt. In its simplest form, the electrode base consists of a thin smooth platinum wire (approx. 26 B&S gauge) sealed in a soft

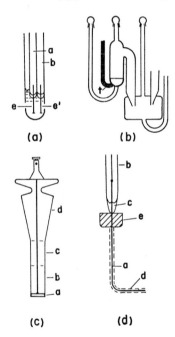

Fig. 7. Totally electrolytic silver–silver halide electrodes. (a) Brown wire electrodes; (b) Shedlovsky truncated cone electrode; (c) Gordon disc electrode; (d) Kennard wire electrode.

glass stem, leaving a 1 cm length of the wire exposed for use as the electrode. Four modifications of this design are illustrated in Fig. 7, namely, the Brown electrode (*a*) the Shedlovsky electrode (*b*) the Gordon electrode (*c*) and the Kennard electrode (*d*).

In the Brown electrode (5), two wire electrodes (e, e') are mounted in inner and outer tubes (a, b). An extension of the outer tube (b) protects the sensitive electrode surfaces from mechanical disturbance. Free access of solution to the electrodes is provided by holes in this outer hood. To overcome the need for the preparation of the electrodes outside the cell, the Shedlovsky electrode (72), shown in Fig. 7b, was designed. Two hollow truncated cones of platinum (t) serve as bases for an electrode pair. The outer surfaces are sealed to the glass cell wall, and the electrical contact is made through the mercury contact tubes. The Gordon electrode (73, 74) shown in Fig. 7c, consists of a platinum disk (a) sealed into a hollow cylinder of soft-glass (b) and used as the base. The soft-glass cylinder is sealed to a Pyrex standard-taper inner joint (d) through a graded seal (c). The danger of mechanical disturbance of the sensitive silver–silver chloride layer is minimized in this design by the rigid structure of the platinum base.

The preceding three forms have all been used with success in precise studies of the thermodynamic properties of alkali metal halides in the dilute solution region.

The Kennard electrode (75), Fig. 7d, was developed specifically for biological and physiological investigations. In the original system, a silver wire (a) was fixed into the glass tube (b) by a polythene seal (c) fused as shown. The electrode wire is threaded through a sleeve (d) of appropriate size made from ligature silk so that the latter projects beyond the end of the wire. The coated wire is bent to the desired shape and chloridized in the usual manner. It is small and readily made. The sleeving may be changed and rechloridizing performed with very little cost of time. The cotton wool (e) may be used to keep structures in contact with it moist. The projecting end of the sleeve can be used for contacting delicate surfaces, and it has been particularly useful for stimulating nerves and muscle in chambers, and *in vivo*, and in inaccessible places. The relatively large area of contact, by virtue of the wick, adds to stability in making the electrode system less polarizable. The emerging wick may be made rigid by employing a glass fiber covered with silk. Microelectrodes, and related techniques, are discussed in detail in Chapter 11 of this book.

The instructions for the preparation of the Gordon electrode, which embodies the features of rugged construction and is readily capable of preparation with intercomparison (bias) potentials in the range of 0.02 mv, and generally constant to ±0.005 mv are as follows. The details given are for the silver–silver chloride electrode, but the procedure would be the same for the silver–silver bromide and silver–silver iodide electrodes, except for the use of a bromide and iodide respectively for the anodic halide layer formation.

The platinum base in the Gordon electrode consists of a disc approximately 1 cm in diameter by 0.5–1 mm thick, sealed into a soft-glass standard-taper ground glass cone extension joint (Fig. 7c). Electrical contact with the external circuit is made from the brass terminal and copper wire which is silver-soldered to the short length of platinum wire welded to the back of the disc. Before the latter is sealed into the glass support, its surface must be given a high polish, using various grades of carborundum, and finally jewelers' rouge, or preferably γ-alumina. The discs are next boiled in concentrated nitric acid, washed, annealed, and finally sealed into the joint using a glass blowing lathe. The resulting electrode base presents a more rugged structure than the wire or gauze types also in use, minimizing the danger of disturbing the electrode surface by mechanical shock and offering a large working surface to the electrolyte. The platinum-to-glass seals may be tested for imperfections by allowing them to stand first in NaOH solution and then in phenolphthalein solution.

The electrodes should be cleaned by anodizing in concentrated nitric acid, e.g., 30 minutes, 1 ma, and well washed before being silver plated. For silver plating, a simple arrangement of two 250 ml beakers to serve as anode and cathode compartments, connected with an M type siphon as salt bridge, and with mechanical stirring in the cathode compartment, may be used. An apparatus of smaller volume has also been used, consisting of a U-tube divided into two compartments by a sintered glass diaphragm. In this case the whole cell may be mechanically rocked to stir the solution. A simple platinum (wire, gauze, or foil) electrode serves as the anode in the silver deposition circuit. Before use, the $KAg(CN)_2$ solution (10 gm per liter) should be freed from excess cyanide with dilute silver nitrate as recommended in an earlier paragraph. Two such cells are used in series for the preparation of the electrodes in sets of two. Silver deposition is continued for approximately six hours at 0.4 ma cm^{-2}. The silver plate obtained is snowy white and velvet-like in appearance, and should wet uniformly. Lack of uniform wetting has been observed to result in erratic electrodes after chloridizing. The nonwetting spots show up as darker silver chloride. When the plating is finished, the electrodes are soaked in concentrated NH$_4$OH from 1 to 6 hours and washed with water for 1 to 3 days. The electrodes are then chloridized in the same cell vessels by making them anodes in the circuit. The current density and period should be about 0.4 ma cm^{-2} and about 30 minutes, using 0.1 N HCl as the electrolyte. The electrodes should be washed with conductance water for 1 to 2 days before testing. The color of the fresh electrodes seems very variable. Sepia electrodes are obtained after chloridizing in the dark (*69*), whereas artificial lighting or diffuse daylight during chloridizing generally results in pale tan or brown electrodes (*69, 73, 76*). After the washing period, the color will have changed to a pink or plum shade (*73, 76*).

TABLE VI

PREPARATION OF THE ELECTROLYTIC SILVER–SILVER CHLORIDE ELECTRODE

Reference electrode base	(83, 84) Pt gauze	(85, 86) Pt gauze	(87) Pt wire	(5) Pt wire	(72) Pt cone	(73, 76) Pt disk
Silver Deposition:						
(i). Solution $KAg(CN)_2$	—	No excess cyanide	Excess cyanide	No excess cyanide	No excess cyanide	No excess cyanide
(ii). Time (hr)	24	8	120	2–6	2–6	5–6
(iii). Current density (ma cm^{-2})	6	2	0.9	8	0.6	0.4
Silver Washing:						
(i). NH_4OH	Not specified	Not specified	Not specified	Specified	Specified	Specified
(ii). Water	1 day	5 days	2 days	16 hr	16 hr	8 hr
Chloride Deposition:						
(i). Solution	Dilute halide	Dilute HCl	$0.75\,N$ HCl	$0.1\,N$ HCl	$0.1\,N$ HCl	$0.1\,N$ HCl
(ii). Time (hr)	0.33	1	120	0.5	0.5	0.5
(iii). Current density (ma cm^{-2})	5–7	1	0.2	10	1.0	0.4
Silver as AgCl:						
Per cent	1.5	5	0.5	25	25	8–10
Color[a]	Plum	White	—	Plum	Plum	Plum
Reproducibility (mv)	±0.02	±0.01	±0.1	±0.02	±0.02	±0.02
Light	No effect	Unstable	—	No effect	No effect	No effect

[a] Plum: this shade embraces colors from deep pink to purple-brown.

For testing, the same procedure as outlined in the next section for the thermal-electrolytic type electrodes is recommended. Fresh electrodes show the aging effect if tested immediately after preparation.

Normal electrodes have bias potentials rarely exceeding 0.1 mv, and generally constant to 0.005 mv. The useful life is somewhat uncertain. An electrode pair, in concentration cell measurements, may generally be used for five to fifteen experiments over a period of one to two months, and generally equilibrate with the cell solutions within an hour or so. Failure of an electrode pair is indicated by erratic values in the emf and longer equilibration periods in experiments even though the bias potentials may still appear normal. This method, until recent times, has been more widely used than any other for the preparation of the silver–silver chloride electrodes.

For the silver–silver bromide and silver–silver iodide electrodes, approx. 0.1 N KBr or KI solutions, sometimes made weakly acid with the appropriate acid, are used in the anodic halide deposition step. A somewhat lower current density, 0.25 ma cm^{-2}, and longer period of electrolysis, about 40 min, are found more suitable for these electrodes. The color of fresh electrodes varies from tan to yellow. The electrodes are generally more erratic than the corresponding chloride electrodes, but are capable of ±0.02 mv reproducibility (77–82).

The data in Table VI presents a summary of the procedures used over the period of the last fifty years for the preparation of the electrolytic silver–silver chloride electrodes. The current densities were estimated from the limited details available and must be considered as approximate values only. The work of MacInnes (83, 84) may be regarded as the first application of electrodes of this kind to measurements of high precision, although the relative amount of silver chloride is somewhat lower than desirable (see Section IV,B). It is of interest to note that the white electrodes of Carmody (85, 86) gave excellent results, but these have not been obtained in any of the subsequent studies. Afanasiev (87), from the results obtained through his procedure, was led to comment that "the reproducibility of the electrolytic electrodes depends on many factors, either accidental or imperceptible." This remark is readily appreciated by those who have had to recapture the "magic recipe" from the scanty and frequently contradictory information found in the original publications.

2. Thermal

The thermal electrodes are prepared by the decomposition of a proper mixture of silver oxide and silver chlorate, bromate, or iodate, applied as an aqueous paste to the platinum wire spiral serving as electrode base. The preparation of thermal electrodes suitable for measurements with bromides in dilute solution was first described by Keston (*88*). The apparent advantages of this electrode over the electrolytic electrode were the ease and speed of preparation, the absence of any possibility for the electrolyte to be occluded or adsorbed during its preparation, and a lower sensitivity to light.

The electrode base may be a spiral (1 mm diameter) of 2–3 turns of 24–26 gauge Pt wire. This is sealed into a 4–6 mm diameter glass tube as illustrated in Fig. 8a, or a ground glass extension joint, so as to leave the

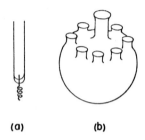

(a)   (b)

F<small>IG</small>. 8. Thermal and thermal-electrolytic silver–silver halide electrodes, and bias emf test vessel. The electrode base (a) consists of a 2–3 turn spiral, 1 mm dia, of Pt wire (24–26 gauge). The bias emf vessel (b) is a form readily made from a round bottom flask and convenient for comparison of a set of freshly prepared electrodes with aged reference standards.

end of the wire protruding inside the tube for a mercury contact. No observable differences in ultimate bias potentials has been found to be attributable to the glass used. If subjected to sudden thermal shock rather than the gradual increase recommended below, it is practically impossible to achieve platinum–glass seals that will withstand the heating-cooling cycle by the use of anything but soft glass. The seals do not necessarily break visibly, but a narrow channel develops, permitting the slow passage of mercury along the wire. Before applying the paste, the Pt spirals are cleaned by boiling briefly in concentrated HNO_3 followed by repeated rinsings with distilled water and boiling in conductance water.

The mixture of silver oxide and silver chlorate, bromate, or iodate, is made up by weight. The moist silver oxide (see above, chemicals) is dried in a tared weighing bottle, and the requisite amount of the other salt added to give the desired proportions. The most commonly used proportions have been approximately 90% silver oxide, 10% silver chlorate, bromate, or iodate (*28, 60, 88–90*). Conductance water is next added in slight excess, and mixed thoroughly to form a smooth paste. The latter is permitted to dry slightly to give a firmer consistency before use.

The platinum spiral is covered with this paste to form a ball of suitable dimensions (at least 4 or 5 mm diameter), and heated at first slowly to

100°C, and then finally to the decomposition temperature at which it is maintained for a period up to one hour. The electrodes are left in the furnace to cool slowly to room temperature. The temperatures and times for final decomposition to form the silver–silver halide deposit are: oxide–chlorate, and oxide–bromate, 650°C for 7 min (*88, 91*); oxide–iodate, 650°C for 7 min (*28*). A paste of silver oxide and silver iodide in the same proportions as the oxide–iodate mixture above, heated at 450°C for 10–15 min has been used successfully by Bates (*89*) for the preparation of the silver–silver iodide electrode. Loss of AgI, which may be appreciable in the oxide–iodate technique since the temperatures are above the decomposition temperature of silver iodide itself (550°C), is thus minimized.

The use of silver perchlorate rather than silver chloride in this method, with decomposition temperature and time of 520°C and 1 hr has been explored (*65, 92*). While within any one set of electrodes thus prepared the reproducibility and stability appeared satisfactory, it was noted that appreciably high bias potentials relative to an aged comparison electrode were frequently retained even weeks after the preparation (*92*).

While the equilibrium potential is independent of the type of electrode, the electrolytic and thermal-electrolytic types appear more reliable, possibly because the methods are better adapted to reproducibility of surface conditions.

The method of bias potentials, as outlined for the thermal-electrolytic-type electrodes, is used for testing these electrodes also.

3. Thermal-Electrolytic

With the exception of the electrolyte used for the deposition of the halide layer, the procedure for the preparation of thermal-electrolytic silver–silver chloride electrodes is generally applicable to the three different halide types. The electrode base most frequently used is identical in design to that described for the thermal electrodes (see Figure 8a).

The silver oxide when mixed with water, forms a paste such that it can be applied easily to the Pt spirals with a small spatula. With the inside of the spiral completely filled and the wire totally covered (except for a few mm between glass and spiral), a sphere of 3–4 mm diameter is obtained. Before applying the paste, the Pt spirals are cleaned as already described in the preceding section.

Electrodes for the thermal reduction are suspended in the central portion of the furnace well by means of a simple support fashioned from two parallel squares of heat-resistant asbestos board separated by 1½ inch spacers. A centrally located hole admits a thermocouple.

In order to preclude the possibility of sputtering by the rapid formation of steam, the electrodes should be maintained in the furnace at just below

100°C for $\frac{1}{2}-1$ hr to permit superficial drying. The temperature is then raised at a uniform rate to 450°C, at which it is held for $\frac{1}{2}$ hr. The electrodes are permitted to cool within the furnace to avoid thermal shock. In the application of a second coat, a paste of much thinner consistency is used, so that it almost yields to gravity when held on a spatula or when suspended from the sphere of silver. Reduction of the second coat of silver oxide proceeds in the same way. The electrodes are finally stored in a desiccator for protection until required for chloridizing.

The silver electrode is chloridized by making it the anode in a simple U-tube cell. The electrode chambers may be 8 cm long and 2 cm in diameter. The central portion is constricted to about 1 cm while fashioning the U-bend. Platinum spirals, similar to those used for the preparation of silver electrodes, serve as cathodes. A current of 10 ma is passed through an assembly consisting of 6–12 cells in series. Generally, about 10–20% of the Ag should be converted to AgCl, assuming 100% current efficiency.

Two solutions are commonly used for chloridizing, 0.05 N KCl and 1 N HCl, both electrolytes being readily obtained in a high degree of purity. The freshly prepared electrodes vary in color from almost white to dark brown. Bates has noted that after repeated use of the same HCl chloridizing solution, white or light gray electrodes are invariably obtained. These have high reproducibility and stability. Pre-electrolysis of the freshly prepared HCl solution may be desirable.

The cell used for intracomparison is illustrated in Fig. 8b. It may be a one liter flask modified to take the set of electrodes in a circle of short necks concentric to the main neck. A slow stream of oxygen-free nitrogen is introduced through the latter to agitate and deoxygenate the test solution. After chloridizing, the electrodes are removed from the U-tube cells, rinsed in conductance water, and transferred to the bias cell. All tests are carried out under a nitrogen atmosphere in oxygen-free solutions.

To observe the time required for the potential to attain its equilibrium value, i.e., aging of the set of electrodes, the following procedure is recommended. The new electrodes are measured relative to a set of two or more electrodes that have been aged for at least one week before use. Selection of the electrodes for the aged reference standards is arbitrary, guided only by the constancy (± 0.005 mv) of the bias potential which is taken as a criterion of the stability of the equilibrated state.

A semimicro form of this electrode for pH titrations was used by Bates and associates (93–94). The loops of platinum wire (16 mg), 6 mm in length, were covered with 0.16 gm of silver by thermal decomposition of silver oxide. The silver chloride was formed in 1 M hydrochloric acid for 15 min at 1 ma. The agreement of these electrodes with each other was within 0.04 mv.

Dilute KBr and KI solutions may be used for the anodic deposition of the halide layer for the silver bromide and silver iodide electrodes respectively as already described for the totally electrolytic electrodes.

4. Others

Gerke (*95*), Güntelberg (*96*), and Pearce and Fortsch (*97*) have described precipitated silver–silver halide electrodes. In this type of electrode the conventional silver–silver halide layer is replaced by a mass of finely divided silver in intimate contact with the silver halide. The silver is deposited electrochemically at a fine platinum wire from silver nitrate solution, using a high current density to give fine crystals. Silver halide, chemically precipitated, is washed and stored under water in darkness until needed. The electrode is simply prepared by first repeatedly washing the required amounts of the silver and silver halide with the solution to be investigated, and placing the silver halide on the silver in the bottom of the half-cell. No information is given in the literature as to the relative amounts of each present. The electrodes are slow to come to equilibrium; in some instances the period was as long as 30 days. The Güntelberg precipitated silver–silver chloride electrodes equilibrated with the solution in 1 to 2 days, and frequently were constant to ±0.02 mv for periods up to three weeks.

The design of the Güntelberg half-cell is illustrated in Fig. 9a. The

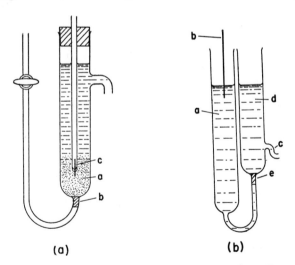

(a)   (b)

Fig. 9. Precipitated silver–silver halide electrode and molten silver chloride electrode. The Güntelberg electrode (a) is one in which the solution is introduced through a bed of crystalline silver mixed with precipitated silver halide (*93*, *96*). The silver–silver chloride half-cell (b) was used at 600–900°C by Senderoff and Brenner (*103*).

layer (a) of crystalline silver mixed with the silver halide rests on a cotton wool plug (b) in the bottom. The solution is introduced through a filling arm opening at the bottom of the half-cell so that on entering the compartment the solution washes through the silver–silver chloride electrode. Electrical contact (c) is made in the conventional manner. Güntelberg claimed that such half-cells could be used for extended periods without change if protected from light. The silver chloride was a crystalline form prepared from an ammoniacal solution by slow evaporation (over sulfuric acid). Randall and Young (98) specified silver chloride prepared metathetically by precipitation from silver chlorate solutions. It was heated for 24 hr at about 100°C with dilute hydrochloric acid before being washed and used. Electrodes prepared in this manner never varied by more than ±0.04 mv. This type of electrode was also used by Harned (99) in studying alkali halides.

From the data available it follows that three problems exist with the use of the precipitated electrode: (i) the length of time required for the electrode to come to concentration equilibrium with the solution; (ii) the preparation of finely crystalline silver in a strain-free reproducible form; and (iii) the apparent susceptibility of this type of electrode to oxidation by air dissolved in the solutions.

A "silver mirror electrode" has been described by Purlee and Grunwald (100, 101). It is reported to last indefinitely, to be entirely free from aging effects (reaching equilibrium in 10–15 min), to be reproducible to better than 0.05 mv, and to be especially suited for use in media of low dielectric constant. A description of its preparation is as follows. A platinum foil, 0.001 inch thick of total area 2 cm^2 is welded to a platinum wire and mounted in the contact tube in the usual manner. It is cleaned with conc. HNO_3, conc. NH_4OH, and finally washed well with doubly distilled water. Silver is deposited upon the foil by the Rochelle salt mirror process.[4] The silver layer is developed in three successive depositions, each requiring 1 hr. The silver coating (about 1.6 mg) is anodized in 0.05 N HCl for 2–3 min at 1.0 ma cm^{-2} (15–25% conversion of Ag to AgCl is recommended). The mirror electrode has been used by Grunwald and co-workers to excellent effect (102).

A form of the silver–silver chloride electrode suitable for emf measurements in molten salts as described by Senderoff and Brenner (103) is illus-

---

[4] Rochelle salt mirror process: A silver nitrate solution (1–2%) is diluted with NH_4OH until the precipitate is not quite entirely redissolved, and filtered. A second solution of silver nitrate (500 ml, 0.2% $AgNO_3$) is heated to boiling and about 0.8–0.9 gm Rochelle are added in a little water. Boiling is continued until a gray deposit forms, after which this solution is filtered and diluted to 500 ml. For plating, equal volumes of the cool solutions are simply mixed and the platinum foil is introduced.

trated in Fig. 9b. The reference half-cell was made of fused silica, and was designed for electrode polarization measurements in the temperature range of 600–900°C. For measurements of equilibrium potential the design of this reference half-cell can be simplified in that the Luggin capillary (c) on arm (d) would not be necessary. In practice molten silver chloride is poured into tube a and suction is applied to d until a tiny bead of silver chloride is drawn through the asbestos plug in constriction e. The silver reference electrode, b, is then inserted into a and the molten electrolyte from the other half-cell enters d through capillary c forming a liquid junction with the molten silver chloride at e. It should be noted that the high-temperature Ag,AgCl (liquid) half-cell is an electrode of the first kind; namely, a metal immersed in a liquid containing its own ions to which it is directly reversible.

IV. Properties

The literature reveals conflicting data and opinions on the various properties of the silver–silver chloride electrode and their bearing on the reproducibility and stability of its potential. Since many of the points are still open to question, a survey of the contributions seems appropriate.

The problem of the drift in potential of the silver–silver chloride electrode is generally resolved in experimental work by preparing a set of several electrodes at one time, and using from two to four electrodes in each compartment of the cell. The stability of the electrode potential may be readily observed by using a number of combinations of these in any measurements. In concentration cells, a check on the difference in the potentials of the electrodes may be obtained by making two measurements with the same solutions under investigation, but with a reversal of positions of the solutions within the cell for the second measurement. If the apparatus is designed symmetrically, the difference in emf should be twice the directly measured difference of potential of the electrodes. This has been found true within a few microvolts (72, 73).

A. AGING EFFECT

The aging effect, i.e., change in potential with age, of the silver halide electrodes was first noted by MacInnes and Parker (83). It was observed that older electrodes were slightly positive to new electrodes, and that the effect was always in the same direction and of the same order of magnitude, within 0.05 mv. It has been the subject of careful studies by Smith and Taylor (104) and more recently again by Taniguchi and Janz (105). A typical aging history for a set of thermal-electrolytic electrodes taken from the latter study is shown in Fig. 10.

It was demonstrated that the aging effect was practically the same for electrodes protected or exposed to diffuse daylight or artificial light in dilute sodium chloride as well as potassium chloride solutions, and in the presence or absence of dissolved oxygen. The possibility of bromide impurities contributing to this aging effect was eliminated by very careful purification of the potassium chloride. Only in dilute hydrochloric acid solutions was it confirmed that dissolved oxygen has a disturbing influence (106) on the silver chloride electrode. For both the thermal-electrolytic and the thermal electrodes similar aging effects were noted, the over-all change in potential, however, being less than for the electrolytic kind.

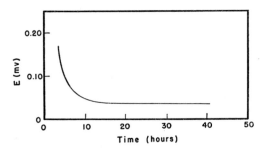

Fig. 10. Aging history for thermal-electrolytic silver–silver chloride electrode. Intercomparison emf (E) of a freshly prepared electrode relative to an aged silver–silver chloride electrode selected as standard (equilibrated) for aging tests (105).

Smith and Taylor (104) have suggested that the aging effect might be due to the occurrence of concentration polarization during the electrolytic chloridation. In the latter stages of this process, the electrode reaction may occur beneath a porous deposit of silver chloride of increasing thickness. Within the pores of this deposit, concentration polarization may cause the solution to become largely depleted of electrolyte, and this depletion may persist when the electrode is transferred to the solution in which its bias potential is to be measured. If the intercomparison cell is made up from a fresh and an aged electrode, it may then be regarded as a concentration cell

$$\text{Ag} \mid \text{AgCl} \mid \text{MCl }(C) \mid \text{MCl }(C - \delta) \mid \text{AgCl} \mid \text{Ag} \qquad \text{(F)}$$

in which δ is the defect of concentration of electrolyte within the pores of the freshly made electrode. The emf of this cell is:

$$E = \frac{2t_+ RT}{F} \ln \frac{C}{C - \delta} \qquad (32)$$

where t_+ is the transference number of the ion M^+ in the chloride solution concerned. It follows that a freshly prepared electrode should be positive relative to the aged reference standard since the solution in the pores of the new silver chloride electrode has become more dilute in the process of chloridizing electrolytically. The role of concentration-polarization was clearly shown by oppositely polarizing a set of two electrolytic electrodes that had been at equilibrium. It was found that the electrodes retained the polarity imposed on them during the electrolysis. The electrode which had been made the anode in passing the current was positive.

Similar effects were observed when polarization was caused by chemical rather than electrical means. Thus, in dilute HCl an oxidation occurs in the presence of dissolved air, which causes a slight decrease in the concentration of the acid within the interstices of the silver chloride layer so that the electrode is positive to an oxygen-free one. In a particular experiment, the change in potential was 0.21 mv, which corresponds with a change in effective concentration of the acid of about 0.5%.

Smith and Taylor (104) have pointed out that the aging period of freshly prepared electrodes may vary from a few minutes to 1–20 days. Hornibrook, Janz, and Gordon (73) had found no indication of aging after periods of 25–40 min., and questioned the credibility of concentration polarization being responsible for aging periods as long as 20 days. If the problem is considered in terms of linear diffusion, the concentration differences should decline at a rate proportional to exp. $(-\pi^2 Dt/x^2)$ where D is the diffusion coefficient, t is time, and x is the length of the path. For $x = 0.1$ cm in potassium chloride at 25°C, about 10 min would be required for the concentration difference to fall to 10^{-4} from 0.1 N. The question is resolved by recognizing the difference in electrode preparation used in these two investigations. The thickness of coating and current densities in chloridizing used by Smith and Taylor were 13.4 and 5.6 times as large as those used by Gordon and associates. Assuming a period of 10 min for the aging effect for the thinly coated electrodes, it follows that for a layer thirteen times this thickness about 28 hr would elapse before the effect was over. Thus for a small thickness of silver chloride deposited at a low current density, the aging effect would be over in a time so short as to be negligible.

It is clear that the porosity of an electrode is an important factor in determining its aging behavior. For purely electrolytic electrodes, it is only the silver chloride layer which is porous, but for the others, the silver substrate is porous as well. Using the surface area as an indication of the nature of the electrode surface, Taniguchi and Janz (105) have investigated this factor with reference to the aging period for the thermal-electrolytic electrodes. The results are summarized in Table VII. The surface areas were determined by N_2 adsorption using the conventional B.E.T. adsorption apparatus. The aging histories of the thermal-electrolytic electrodes prepared from these thermal silver deposits were carried out under nitrogen in oxygen-free solutions. The potentials of the new electrodes

TABLE VII

SURFACE AREA OF THERMAL SILVER (91)

Wt (gm) of Ag electrode			Surface area (m² gm⁻¹)	Equilibrium time (hr)
First coat	Second coat	Total	$(m^2\ gm^{-1})$	(hr)
0.0406	None	0.0406	3.4	15
0.0321	None	0.0321	39	150
0.1422[a]	None	0.1422	1.2	8
0.0441	0.0151	0.0592	0.3	6

[a] This sample was degassed at 400°C for 17 hr. All others were degassed at 120°C for periods up to 18 hr.

relative to the aged reference standards were in accord with the predictions of the concentration-polarization concepts. Results of these measurements leave little doubt that the application of a second coat of silver as recommended by Bates (63) insures a smooth, i.e., coherent, surface and leads to electrodes that rapidly age to steady bias potentials.

Minima and maxima have been observed in the aging history during the initial approach to equilibrium (e.g., see Fig. 11). Since all the electrodes are undergoing slow adjustment of the electrolyte concentration within their pores at widely different rates, fluctuations of this nature are to be expected.

The aging effect observed with the totally thermal type electrodes, which are prepared by a procedure that gives electrodes dry and completely free from electrolyte before immersion in the solution, has also been attributed to concentration polarization (104, 106), but the reasons for the effect are not so readily apparent. The relatively large surface areas attained by thermal decomposition may undoubtedly lead to concentration gradients by physical adsorption or related surface phenomena. The aging effect would thus again be the equilibration of the solution within the porous electrode with the main body of the test solution. The suggestion (73) that there is a change in the nature of the surface, such as the uncovering of "hot spots" in the silver chloride, is not ruled out.

A thermal treatment as part of the aging cycle has been used with success. Greely, Smith, Lietzke, and Stoughton (158), in using the totally thermal electrodes, found that practically all variation in potential of one electrode from another was removed by the following method. The set of freshly prepared electrodes were immersed in HCl solution of the same composition as to be used in the test, interconnected, and, in this solution, heated to 75°C. After cooling and standing approximately 12 hr the intercomparison emf values were, with few exceptions, ±0.05 mv for the six electrodes of the set.

The possibility of the occurrence of an aging effect may not have been recognized in some of the earlier work. This may have led some to discard the electrolytic type of electrodes in favor of the thermal-electrolytic (107), or to report the thermal-electrolytic type more positive to the thermal electrodes (91), and may in part account for differences reported for the standard electrode potential of the silver–silver electrode.

B. Silver–Silver Chloride Ratio

From an inspection of Table VI in which some of the previous and present practices have been summarized, it appears that for stable and reproducible electrodes, approximately 10–25% of the silver deposit should be changed to silver chloride, assuming 100% current efficiency in the electrolysis.

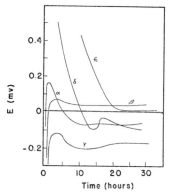

Fig. 11. Electrodes with increasing ratio of silver–silver chloride ratio. The intercomparison emf (E) of a set of five electrodes all relative to the same standard (equilibrated) silver–silver chloride electrode. The silver on the electrodes α, β, γ, δ, and ϵ had been electrolyzed to yield 16, 20, 30, 50, and 90% as AgCl respectively (105).

This factor has recently been investigated by Taniguchi and Janz (105) using the thermal-electrolytic type of electrode as the reference standard. Since a constant current was used, each electrode had to be chloridized for a different length of time. This was accomplished by placing all the electrodes as before in the U-cells, but leading the current initially only through the electrodes to be most highly chloridized. At proper time intervals, the current was led through additional electrodes until the desired extent of chloridation had been attained. In this manner, all the electrodes were in contact with the electrolyte for the same length of time and could be removed together so that the aging tests could be initiated on the set simultaneously. The results illustrated in Fig. 11 where electrodes α, β, γ, δ, and ϵ

have 16, 20, 30, 50 and 90% of the thermal silver electrolyzed to form silver chloride, respectively.

The results indicate that much above 20% leads to a thick coat of AgCl which added very little to the stability and tended to make the electrode more sluggish. In this series of measurements, the chloridizing solution (1 N HCl) was ten times more concentrated than the test solution. The electrodes with less than 30% AgCl were initially negative to the aged electrodes, and it would appear that the depletion of the electrolyte within the pores was not yet sufficient to attain a concentration less than that of the test solution.

The spread in potential, from +0.05 to −0.2 mv in this set, is somewhat larger than in a typical set of thermal-electrolytic electrodes prepared under identical conditions. It does serve to stress the need for evaluation of each set relative to an aged electrode as comparison electrode.

C. COLOR AND LIGHT

A point which has been, and still is, the subject of conflicting views concerns the sensitivity of the silver chloride electrodes to light. The electrodes have been used in darkness or subdued light by a large number of investigators (85–87, 96, 108) and the results of Carmody's studies on this point indicated that light did cause an appreciable change in potential of the electrolytic silver–silver chloride electrode. On the other hand, there have been a number of reports to the effect that these electrodes were not appreciably sensitive to light (68, 73, 104, 106). In the latter instances, the aged electrodes were a plum shade in color, and on direct exposure to light did not appreciably change in potential or color. The electrodes that were reported by Carmody to be sensitive to light were white. On exposure to light, these changed in potential and darkened to a brown color. The data of Harned (99), Brown (109), MacInnes and associates (5, 72), Gordon and associates (73, 74, 110), and Smith and Taylor (104) indicate that the shade of color of the silver chloride electrode had no effect upon its potential for all three types, electrolytic, thermal-electrolytic, and thermal. The colors of the above electrodes are in accord with the results observed for anodically formed chloride layers at current densities less than 18 ma cm^{-2}.

By contrast to the electrolytic type for which, with the one exception above, the color of the best electrodes has been noted to be pink or a plum shade, the best type of thermal-electrolytic electrodes have been reported to be light gray or white in color (63, 105). An empirical observation on the color of the electrodes and history of the chloridizing acid is of interest on this point. With a fresh chloridizing solution of HCl, highly colored (brown) electrodes were obtained which, while showing satisfactory intra-agreement, tended to equilibrate to rather high bias values (0.1–0.3 mv) relative to the aged reference standard. With repeated use of this chloridizing solution, the light gray and white thermal-electrolytic electrodes, which showed the satisfactory reproducibility and stability, were obtained.

It may well be that the white electrolytic electrodes can be obtained with a chloridizing solution that has been repeatedly used as in the case of the thermal-electrolytic electrodes. The color may not be due to adsorbed cyanide impurities in the electrolytic silver deposit as suggested by Carmody (*85, 86*) but rather due to some trace impurity in the hydrochloric acid which is depleted with continued use as chloridation electrolyte. Another possibility, since the solutions are quite strong, is that repeated use might lead to some $AgCl_2^-$ in the solution which in turn might critically affect the habit of the deposited AgCl.

Marked photovoltaic effects with the silver–silver halide electrodes may be observed if one electrode of the cell is kept in the dark while the other is exposed to light. In Fig. 12 the effect as observed (*111–113*) from

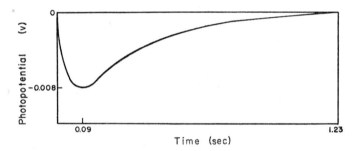

Fig. 12. Photovoltaic phenomenon with silver–silver halide electrodes. The variation in potential of an Ag,AgBr electrode, after exposure to Hg arc illumination, measured relative to an identical electrode maintained in the dark (*111–113*).

such a cell with silver–silver bromide electrodes is illustrated. Thus two main phases in the phenomenon are evident, an initial, inertia-less negative effect, attaining a maximum value in the period AB (about 0.1 sec), after which the potential difference becomes positive and finally levels off. In this instance the silver bromide was illuminated with a mercury arc at 150 volt placed about 21 cm before the electrode. The mechanism of the effect has been the subject of widespread investigations, especially in view of its bearing on photographic development (*111–118*). At metal-free AgBr the mechanism is most probably a photochemical decomposition with liberation of free bromine atoms and electrons. The free bromine can diffuse into the aqueous solution, hydrolyzing to form hypobromite and bromide ions, whereas the electrons may react to form silver atoms or simply diffuse into the lattice. For the silver–silver halide electrodes the photovoltaic effect mechanism is more complex. The photoconducting electrons in the initial (primary effect) tend to charge the metallic silver phase negatively; a secondary effect may be the chemical attack of the bromine on the silver phase which would result in a reverse (relative to the primary) movement of the electrons.

It appears that this factor of light is one of the least understood. Investigations on the light effect with silver–silver chloride electrodes are in progress (119). A good precaution would be to avoid daylight exposure or strong illumination of the electrodes during emf measurements until the "light effect" is better understood.

D. Oxygen

In addition to the controversial question of the effect of light, a drift in the potential of silver–silver chloride electrodes has been attributed to the effect of air dissolved in the solution (30, 98, 120, 121). The cause for this poor behavior in acid solutions was probably a slow oxidation reaction:

$$2Ag + 2HCl + \tfrac{1}{2}O_2 \rightarrow 2AgCl + H_2O$$

As mentioned in a preceding section, it was noted in a typical experiment that the change in effective concentration was about 0.5% corresponding to a 0.2 mv change in potential relative to an oxygen-free electrode. A similar effect was noted using silver–silver bromide electrodes.

The results of the measurements in nonacid media, i.e., aqueous potassium chloride, showed (104, 106) that the reproducibility among individual electrodes when silver–silver chloride electrodes were prepared at the same time was ±0.02 mv, irrespective of the electrode type and the presence, or absence, of air. For the silver–silver iodide electrodes, a marked oxygen effect was noted in both neutral and acid solutions. The "oxygen effect" is being reinvestigated with silver–silver chloride electrodes (119).

E. Electrolyte Impurities

Small concentrations of impurity, such as bromide, will give rise to relatively large bias potentials with silver–silver chloride electrodes. Some results taken from the careful work of Pinching and Bates (68) are summarized in Table VIII to illustrate the effects. Thermal-electrolytic electrodes were first equilibrated in a modified H-cell containing pure chloride solution. Each limb was then filled with carefully deaerated portions of the chloride solution, one portion containing a small added amount of the foreign salt. Hydrogen was used as the pressure gas in the filling process, each limb being flushed 2 or 3 times before the final filling. The potential difference ΔE, in general reached a constant value within an hour, but

TABLE VIII

EFFECT OF SMALL CONCENTRATIONS OF FOREIGN SALTS ON THE POTENTIAL OF
THE SILVER–SILVER CHLORIDE ELECTRODE IN HALIDE SOLUTIONS AT 25°C (68)

| Foreign salt | Molality | | Mole % of foreign salt | ΔE (mv) |
	Halide	Foreign salt $\times 10^5$		
	Sodium chloride solutions			
KBr	0.02	1.3	0.064	0.87–1.08
	0.05	25	0.5	1.90
KI	0.05	2.5	0.05	0.05
	0.05	25	0.5	0.17[a]
KCN	0.05	2.5	0.05	0.23
	Potassium chloride solutions			
KBr	0.05	2.5	0.05	0.50
	0.05	6	0.12	0.73–2.30
	Hydrochloric acid solutions			
KBr	0.05	2.5	0.05	0.46–3.64

[a] The electrode was yellow at the end of the experiment.

when the electrodes were immersed in solutions containing bromide as impurity, the emf rose slowly during 24–48 hr. The effects of salts, such as sodium sulfate, sodium oxalate, disodium hydrogen phosphate, and sodium sulfide were also checked in addition to the impurities listed in Table VIII. Of these the latter caused the largest change in potential (0.71 mv), and the electrodes were black at the end of the experiment.

With certain impurities, such as iodide and sulfide, the effect on the electrode potential may be explained through the formation of a salt of lower solubility than silver chloride on the surface of the electrode. An accurate computation of the molality of bromide or iodide ion necessary to form solid silver bromide or iodide on the surface of a silver–silver chloride electrode is possible with the aid of the standard electrode potentials: namely, 0.2224 (AgCl), 0.0713 (AgBr), and −0.1522 (AgI) in volts at 25°C. The relation between these and the standard potential of the silver electrode is given by:

$$E^\circ_{Ag,AgX} = E^\circ_{Ag} - \frac{RT}{F} \ln K_s \tag{33}$$

$$= E^\circ_{Ag} - 0.05912 \log (f_{Ag^+} f_{X^-})(m_{Ag^+} m_{X^-})$$

where K_s is the solubility product constant of the respective silver halide salt. Thus, for the silver electrode in equilibrium with a solution saturated with both silver chloride and silver bromide, this expression becomes

$$E^\circ_{AgBr} - E^\circ_{AgCl} = 0.05914 \log (m_{Cl^-}/m_{Br^-}) \qquad (34)$$

since f_{Cl^-} and f_{Br^-} are nearly equal. The value for m_{Br^-} in equilibrium with solid silver bromide is 0.00279 m_{Cl^-} or 0.28 mole %. Small traces of bromide (Table VIII) have an abnormally large effect on the potential of the silver–silver chloride electrode. The explanation of the abnormal bromide effect likely lies in the fact that silver bromide and silver chloride form solid solutions whereas silver iodide and silver chloride do not.

In view of the magnitude of the error due to the small amounts of bromide present frequently in commercial samples of potassium chloride, the removal of bromide is important in purification of the salt for precise electrochemical work. Pinching and Bates developed a sensitive colorimetric test to determine bromide in the presence of chloride, developed the various methods of purifying sodium chloride and potassium chloride relative to removal of bromide impurity, and constructed an apparatus of simple design for diminishing the hydrolysis of sodium and potassium chlorides during fusion to remove occluded acid. Treatment with chlorine, precipitation with hydrogen chloride and, after washing, fusion in a nitrogen atmosphere was found to give chlorides with less than 0.002% bromide, free of iodide and significant amounts of inert impurities. Instability, and large fluctuating bias potentials frequently observed with freshly prepared electrodes by anodic chloride deposition, may well be due in large part to the presence of bromides as impurities in trace amounts.

Neither traces of chloride nor traces of bromide affected the potential of the silver iodide electrode in potassium iodide. With the silver bromide electrode in sodium bromide solution, traces of chloride had no effect, but traces of iodide had a larger effect on the potential than predicted by calculation from the standard electrode potentials. Adsorption effects may be responsible for this abnormally large effect.

F. Reproducibility and Stability

The impression from all the published work is that with careful attention to details on purity and procedure, each of the three types of electrodes can be prepared to give reproducibly good reference electrodes having stable intercomparison potentials of ±0.02 mv or less. More frequently than not, in practice, it is found that intercomparison of electrodes from different sets of the same type, or intercomparison of electrodes of the three types shows an irreproducibility quite unpredicted and outside these limits. This is illustrated by the fact that Noyes and Ellis (*107*) rejected electrolytic electrodes, in spite of their previous successful use by MacInnes and Parker (*83*) and Jahn (*122*), in favor of the thermal-electrolytic, whereas Rule and LaMer (*91*) rejected all but the thermal type.

It is also significant to note that the careful determinations of the standard potential of the Ag,AgCl electrode by Harned and Ehlers (*21*) and by Bates and Bower (*22*) (Table I) differ by 0.18 mv at 25°C, i.e., by a value far outside the normally claimed limits of reproducibility (±0.02 mv) of these electrodes. Both groups of investigators used the thermal-electrolytic electrodes. That the reproducibility of the Ag,AgCl electrode can be far better than this is seen from a comparison of the values of Bates and Bower (*22*) with earlier ones. Comparison with Carmody's data (*85, 86*) at 25°C at seven molalities in the region from 0.001 to 0.1 shows the values differ on the average by only 0.01 mv, while Young's values at two comparable molalities differ by 0.07 and 0.04 mv. The average difference between Güntelberg's measurements (*96*) at 20°C and those of Bates and Bower at the same temperature is only 0.05 mv for four molalities. It would appear that experimental factors other than the reproducibility of the Ag,AgCl electrode such as differences in the structure of the solid phases must contribute in part at least to the large discrepancy above.

Later work (*105*) has shown that within a set of electrodes prepared simultaneously, the limits of ±0.02 mv in reproducibility are readily achieved. Indeed stable equilibrated electrodes with bias potentials as low as ±0.005 mv and constant over periods of a month can be expected. These observations are in accord with the earlier results. The limits of reproducibility, however, were found (*91*) to be ±0.1 mv when stable and equilibrated electrodes from different sets were compared. The selection of the aged reference standard is quite arbitrary and must be made by intercomparison of numerous aged equilibrated electrodes. From these, the electrode negative in potential to all the rest is to be selected as the comparison reference standard, being in a state of lowest free energy and, accordingly, a more stable state than the other electrodes. In testing new electrodes, the agreement of the electrodes with the aged reference standard selected as above to ±0.02 mv should be the criterion that the potentials have come to a true equilibrium value. Relative to removal of factors contributing to the variation in potential of one electrode from another, the added treatment of heating in solution to 75° while interconnected (see this chapter, p. 216) has been reported for the thermally prepared electrodes. The solubility of AgCl is higher at the higher temperature and any AgCl in a higher free energy state can more easily dissolve and reprecipitate in the lowest free energy state. Any electrolytic reaction between the interconnected electrodes having initially different potentials would occur more rapidly at the higher temperatures. However no results were given for the comparison of the electrodes in such a set with aged reference standards as described by Taniguchi and Janz (*105*).

The silver–silver bromide electrode has been investigated in anhydrous HCN by Coates and Davies (*123*) for reversibility and reproducibility. All tests were made in 0.02 M KBr in hydrogen cyanide. Electrodes of the thermal type showed some erratic fluctuations but were capable of agreement within 1 mv. An aging effect of about 1 mv was observed in 8–10 days. Electrodes of the thermal-electrolytic type agreed within themselves to 1–2 mv initially, and after 14 days, to 0.5 mv. In aqueous solution the electrodes returned to the original bias potential of 0.2 mv. A slight aging effect was noted. When this type was bromidized in a hydrogen cyanide solution of potassium bromide, the reproducibility was 0.5 mv. The electrolytic type was initially found to be 2 mv positive to the thermal-electrolytic type, but this difference decreased with long standing. The aging effect was short (less than 24 hr) for this type, and reproducibility was 1 mv within the set.

V. Applications

Perhaps the most important application of the silver–silver chloride electrode has been in the investigation of the thermodynamics of electrolytes in aqueous and partly aqueous (*29, 59, 74*) and nonaqueous solutions (*48, 51*) from the potentials of thermodynamic cells. The emf method has the advantages that it is applicable over a wide range of temperatures and does not deteriorate rapidly in precision with falling concentrations of solution. A very powerful method for measurement of the thermodynamic properties of dissolved electrolytes is the isopiestic method (*124–126*). The absolute standards of reference for this method were established by emf measurements in concentration cells, using silver chloride electrodes in sodium and potassium chloride solutions (*73, 74*). Theories of ionic interaction have been investigated in aqueous media in similar cells (*110, 127*).

In addition, these electrodes have seen widespread use, being employed in cells for measuring: (i) standard electrode potentials (*45, 128*); (ii) activity coefficients, by use of cells with and without liquid junctions, both directly and, as already indicated, indirectly by standardizing the isopiestic method (*124–126*); (iii) ionization constants of acids (*29, 129*), bases (*126*), and the overlapping constants of polybasic acids (*59, 130*); (iv) the ionic product of water (*131–133*); (v) standards for the pH scale (*63, 134–137*); (vi) solubility products of sparingly soluble salts (*59, 127, 138*); (vii) transference numbers (*59, 139*); (viii) conductances of halide solutions by high-precision dc methods (*140–141*); (ix) thermodynamic metal chelate stability constants (*142*); and many other quantities involved, for example, in studies of electrocapillarity (*143*), corrosion (*144, 145*), electroanalytical chemistry (*57, 138*), colloidal electrolytes (*145, 146*) and a host of biological problems (*75, 147–150*).

The silver–silver halide electrodes have seen application in very con-

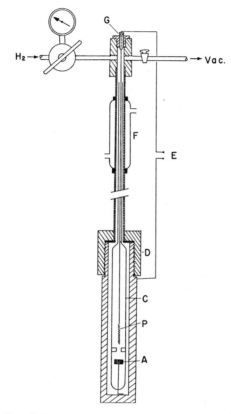

Fig. 13. Silver–silver halide electrode arrangement for superatmospheric pressures and elevated temperatures. The high pressure – high temperature assembly consisted of the hydrogen and Ag,AgCl electrodes (P, and A respectively) in a glass vessel (C) enclosed in a steel shell (D), fitted with a condenser (F), gas and vacuum inlets, and electrode contacts (G, E) (*156*).

centrated aqueous solutions of HCl (*151, 152*), and inorganic chlorides (*153*). Investigations on the solubility of AgCl in the presence of either common ion (*154, 155*) have served to emphasize the need for solubility data in media containing a common ion before making definitive interpretations concerning the thermodynamic data involving the Ag,AgCl electrode in such media.

The application of the silver–silver halide electrodes to measurements at elevated temperatures and superatmospheric pressures (*156–158*) is a development of current interest. An experimental arrangement, such as illustrated in Fig. 13, has been used successfully for rapid and continuous pH measurement from 1 to 40 atm pressures at temperatures up to 250°C. In a one compartment cell as illustrated, the hydrogen reaching the silver–silver chloride electrodes was found to have considerable effect on the potential of the latter. It was suggested that the diminution by hydrogen of the potential of the Ag,AgCl electrode toward that of a hydrogen electrode may be due to the coexistence of simultaneous hydrogen and AgCl electrodes at the hydrogenated AgCl electrode (*156*). Another possible explanation (*157*) is that reduction of part of the AgCl in the electrode has occurred with an accompanying increase of the acid concentration in the AgCl coating. A silica sheath to isolate the Ag,AgCl electrode, with electrolyte contact through a porous silica frit, was used in the Teflon-lined autoclave assembly (*158*) for determining activities of hydrochloric acid solutions and the standard potentials of the silver–silver chloride electrode at elevated temperatures.

REFERENCES

1. Guggenheim, E. A., and Prue, J. E., *Trans. Faraday Soc.* **50**, 231 (1954).

2. Hills, G. J., and Ives, D. J. G., *J. Chem. Soc.* 305 (1951).

3. Owen, B. B., *J. Am. Chem. Soc.* **60**, 2229 (1938).

4. Gledhill, J. A., and Malan, G. McP., *Trans. Faraday Soc.* **48**, 258 (1952).

5. Brown, A. S., and MacInnes, D. A., *J. Am. Chem. Soc.* **57**, 1356 (1935).

6. Gledhill, J. A., and Malan, G. McP., *Trans. Faraday Soc.* **49**, 166 (1953).

7. Gledhill, J. A., and Malan, G. McP., *Trans. Faraday Soc.* **50**, 126 (1954).

8. Grimley, T. B., and Mott, N. F., *Discussions Faraday Soc.* **1**, 3 (1947).

9. Grimley, T. B., *Proc. Roy. Soc.* **A201**, 40 (1950).

10. Kurnick, S. W., *J. Chem. Phys.* **20**, 218 (1952).

11. Teltow, J., *Ann. Physik.* **5**, 63 (1950).

12. Rief, F., *Phys. Rev.* **100**, 1597 (1955).

13. Compton, W. D., *Phys. Rev.* **101**, 1209 (1956).

14a. Compton, W. D., and Maurer, R. J., *J. Phys. Chem. Solids* **1**, 191 (1956).

14b. Miller, A. S., and Maurer, R. J., *J. Phys. Chem. Solids* **4**, 196 (1958).

15. Kurtz, L. J., *Compt. rend. acad. sci. U.R.S.S.* **2**, 305 (1935).

16. Lal, H., Thirsk, H. R., and Wynne-Jones, W. K. F., *Trans. Faraday Soc.* **47**, 70, 999 (1951).

17. Briggs, G. W. D., and Thirsk, H. R., *Trans. Faraday Soc.* **48**, 1171 (1952).

18. Jaenicke, W., Tischer, R. P., and Gerischer, H., *Z. Elektrochem.* **59**, 448 (1955).

19. Lehfeldt, W., *Z. Physik.* **85**, 717 (1933).

20. Huber, K., *Z. Elektrochem.* **59**, 693 (1955).

21. Harned, H. S., and Ehlers, R. W., *J. Am. Chem. Soc.* **55**, 2179 (1933).

22. Bates, R. G., and Bower, V. E., *J. Research Natl. Bur. Standards*, **53**, 282 (1954).

23. Harned, H. S., and Paxton, T. R., *J. Phys. Chem.* **57**, 531–5 (1953).

24. Bates, R. G., Guggenheim, E. A., Harned, H. S., Ives, D. J. G., Janz, G. J., Monk, C. B., Prue, J. E., Robinson, R. A., Stokes, R. H., and Wynne–Jones, W. F. K., *J. Chem. Phys.* **25**, 361 (1956); **26**, 222 (1957).

25. Harned, H. S., and Donelson, J. G., *J. Am. Chem. Soc.* **59**, 1280 (1937).

26. Owen, B. B., and Foering, L., *J. Am. Chem. Soc.* **58**, 1575 (1936).

27. Harned, H. S., Keston, A. S., and Donelson, J. G., *J. Am. Chem. Soc.* **58**, 989 (1936).

28. Owen, B. B., *J. Am. Chem. Soc.* **57**, 1926 (1935).

29. Harned, H. S., and Owen, B. B., "Physical Chemistry of Electrolytic Solutions," 3rd ed. Reinhold, New York, 1958.

30. Conway, B. E., "Electrochemical Data," Elsevier, Houston, Texas, 1952.

31. Akerlöf, G., *J. Am. Chem. Soc.* **54**, 4125 (1932).

32. Crockford, H. D., Knight, S. B., and Staton, H. A., *J. Am. Chem. Soc.* **72**, 2164 (1950).

33. Harned, H. S., and Donelson, J. G., *J. Am. Chem. Soc.* **60**, 339, 2128 (1938).

34. Harned, H. S., and Morrison, J. O., *J. Am. Chem. Soc.* **58**, 1908 (1936).

35. Harned, H. S., and Nestler, F. H. M., *J. Am. Chem. Soc.* **68**, 665 (1946).

36. Knight, S. B., Crockford, H. D., and James, F. W., *J. Phys. Chem.* **57**, 463 (1953).

37. Knight, S. B., Masi, J. F., and Roesel, D., *J. Am. Chem. Soc.* **68**, 661 (1946).

38. Lucasse, W. W., *J. Am. Chem. Soc.* **48**, 627 (1926).

39. Patterson, A., and Felsing, W. A., *J. Am. Chem. Soc.* **64**, 1478 (1942).

40. Feakins, D., and French, C. M., *J. Chem. Soc.* p. 3168 (1956); pp. 2284, 2581 (1957).

41. Everdell, M. H., *J. Chem. Soc.* p. 2289 (1949).

42. Taniguchi, H., and Janz, G. J., *J. Phys. Chem.* **61**, 688 (1957).

43. Danyluk, S. S., Taniguchi, H., and Janz, G. J., *J. Phys. Chem.* **61**, 1679 (1954).

44. Born, M., *Z. Physik* **1**, 45 (1920).

45. Robinson, R. A., and Stokes, R. H., *Trans. Faraday Soc.* **36**, 740 (1940).

46. Kirkwood, J. G., *J. Chem. Phys.* **7**, 911 (1939).

47. Oiwa, I. T., *J. Phys. Chem.* **61**, 1587 (1957).

48. Nonhebel, G., and Hartley, G. S., *Phil. Mag.* [6] **50**, 729 (1925).

49. Oiwa, I. T., *J. Phys. Chem.* **60**, 754 (1956).

50. Austin, J. M., Hunt, A. H., Johnson, F. A., and Parton, H. N., unpublished, see reference 50a.

50a. Robinson, R. A., and Stokes, R. H., "Electrolyte Solutions," 3rd ed. Academic Press, New York, 1959.

51. Woolcock, J. W., and Hartley, H., *Phil. Mag.* [7] **5**, 1133 (1928).

52. Harned, H. S., and Fleysher, M. H., *J. Am. Chem. Soc.* **47**, 87 (1925).

53. Mukherjee, L. M., *J. Phys. Chem.* **58**, 1042 (1954).

54. Mandel, M., and Decroly, P., *Nature* **182**, 794 (1958).

55. Ulich, H., and Spiegel, G., *Z. physik. Chem.* **A177**, 103, 187 (1936).

56. Mukherjee, L. M., *J. Am. Chem. Soc.* **79**, 4040 (1957).

57. Popov, A. I., and Geske, D. H., *J. Am. Chem. Soc.* **79**, 2067 (1957).

58. Scatchard, G., *J. Am. Chem. Soc.* **48**, 2026 (1926).

59. MacInnes, D. A., "The Principles of Electrochemistry." Reinhold, New York, 1939.

60. Kanning, E. W., and Campbell, A. W., *J. Am. Chem. Soc.* **64**, 517 (1942).

61. Mukherjee, L. M., *J. Phys. Chem.* **60**, 974 (1956).

62. Bassett, H., and Corbett, A. S., *J. Chem. Soc.* p. 1672 (1924).

63. Bates, R. G., "Electrometric pH Determinations," p. 206. Wiley, New York, 1954.

64. Fernelius, W. C., Inorganic Syntheses, Vol. 2, p. 4. McGraw-Hill, New York, 1946.

65. Ishikawa, F., and Matsuo, S., *Sci. Rpts. Tôhoku Univ., First Ser.* **33,** 228 (1949).
66. Foulk, C. W., and Hollingsworth, M., *J. Am. Chem. Soc.* **45,** 1220 (1923).
67. Taniguchi, H., and Janz, G. J., *Anal. Chem.* **28,** 287 (1956).
68. Pinching, G. D., and Bates, R. G., *J. Research Natl. Bur. Standards* **37,** 311 (1946).
69. Pittman, R. W., and Godly, T., Birkbeck College, London, private communication, 1959.
70. Gardner, H. J., Brown, C. T., and Janz, G. J., *J. Phys. Chem.* **60,** 1458 (1956).
71. Laitinen, H. A., Ferguson, W. S., and Osteryoung, R. A., *J. Electrochem. Soc.* **104,** 516 (1957).
72. Shedlovsky, T., and MacInnes, D. A., *J. Am. Chem. Soc.* **58,** 1970 (1936).
73. Hornibrook, W. J., Janz, G. J., and Gordon, A. R., *J. Am. Chem. Soc.* **64,** 513 (1942).
74. Janz, G. J., and Gordon, A. R., *J. Am. Chem. Soc.* **65,** 218 (1943).
75. Kennard, D. W., *Proc. Physiol. Soc.* **39 P,** 20–21 (1953).
76. Thompson, P. T., Ph.D. Thesis, Pittsburgh, Pennsylvania, 1956.
77. MacWilliam, E. A., and Gordon, A. R., *J. Am. Chem. Soc.* **65,** 984 (1943).
78. Halla, F., *Z. Elektrochem.* **17,** 179 (1911).
79. Jones, G., and Hartmann, M., *J. Am. Chem. Soc.* **37,** 752 (1915).
80. Taylor, H. S., *J. Am. Chem. Soc.* **38,** 2300 (1916).
81. Gelbach, R. W., *J. Am. Chem. Soc.* **55,** 4857 (1935).
82. Harned, H. S., and Douglas, S. M., *J. Am. Chem. Soc.* **48,** 3095 (1926).
83. MacInnes, D. A., and Parker, K., *J. Am. Chem. Soc.* **37,** 1445 (1915).
84. MacInnes, D. A., and Beattie, J. A., *J. Am. Chem. Soc.* **42,** 1117 (1920).
85. Carmody, W. R., *J. Am. Chem. Soc.* **51,** 2901 (1929).
86. Carmody, W. R., *J. Am. Chem. Soc.* **54,** 3647 (1932).
87. Afanasiev, A. L., *J. Am. Chem. Soc.* **52,** 3477 (1930).
88. Keston, A. S., *J. Am. Chem. Soc.* **57,** 1671 (1935).
89. Bates, R. G., *J. Am. Chem. Soc.* **60,** 2983 (1938).
90. Stokes, R. H., and Stokes, J. M., *Trans. Faraday Soc.* **41,** 2 (1945).
91. Rule, C. K., and LaMer, V. K., *J. Am. Chem. Soc.* **58,** 2339 (1926).
92. Janz, G. J., and Taniguchi, H., unpublished work, 1957.
93. Bates, R. G., Siegel, G. L., and Acree, S. F., *J. Research Natl. Bur. Standards* **30,** 347 (1943).
94. Bates, R. G., and Pinching, G. D., *J. Research Natl. Bur. Standards* **43,** 519 (1949).
95. Gerke, R. H., *J. Am. Chem. Soc.* **44,** 1684 (1922).
96. Güntelberg, E., *Z. physik. Chem.* **123,** 199 (1926).
97. Pearce, J. N., and Fortsch, A. R., *J. Am. Chem. Soc.* **45,** 2852 (1923).
98. Randall, M., and Young, L. E., *J. Am. Chem. Soc.* **50,** 989 (1928).
99. Harned, H. S., *J. Am. Chem. Soc.* **51,** 416 (1929).
100. Purlee, E. L., and Grunwald, E., *J. Phys. Chem.* **59,** 1112 (1955).
101. Purlee, E. L., and Grunwald, E., *J. Chem. Phys.* **27,** 990 (1957).
102. Grunwald, E., *J. Am. Chem. Soc.* **76,** 3855 (1954); **79,** 1366, 1372 (1957); **80,** 3840, 3844 (1958); *J. Org. Chem.* **20,** 747 (1955).
103. Senderoff, S., and Brenner, A., *Trans. Electrochem. Soc.* **101,** 31 (1954).
104. Smith, E. R., and Taylor, J. K., *J. Research Natl. Bur. Standards* **20,** 837 (1938).
105. Taniguchi, H., and Janz, G. J., *J. Electrochem. Soc.* **104,** 123 (1957).
106. Taylor, J. K., and Smith, E. R., *J. Research Natl. Bur. Standards* **22,** 307 (1939).
107. Noyes, A. A., and Ellis, J. H., *J. Am. Chem. Soc.* **39,** 2532 (1917).
108. Owen, B. B., *J. Am. Chem. Soc.* **60,** 2229 (1938).
109. Brown, A. S., *J. Am. Chem. Soc.* **56,** 646 (1934).

110. Butler, J. P., and Gordon, A. R., *J. Am. Chem. Soc.* **70**, 2276 (1948).
111. Sheppard, S. E., Vanselow, W., and Hall, V. C., *J. Phys. Chem.* **33**, 1403 (1929).
112. Vanselow, W., and Sheppard, S. E., *J. Phys. Chem.* **33**, 331 (1929).
113. Sheppard, S. E., Vanselow, W., and Happ, G. P., *J. Phys. Chem.* **44**, 411 (1940).
114. Sanders, H. L., and Kolthoff, I. M., *J. Phys. Chem.* **44**, 936 (1940).
115. Anthanasiu, G., *Ann. phys.* **4**, 377 (1935).
116. Brown, F. C., *J. Phys. and Chem. Solids* **4**, 206 (1958).
117. Ansler, H., *Z. Elektrochem.* **57**, 801 (1953).
118. Matjic, R., *Z. Elektrochem.* **62**, 1100 (1958).
119. Pittman, R. W., and Godly, T., Birkbeck College, London, private communication, 1959.
120. Macfarlane, A., *J. Chem. Soc.* 3212 (1931).
121. Macfarlane, A., and Hartley, H., *Phil. Mag.* [7] **13**, 425 (1932).
122. Jahn, H., *Z. physik. Chem.* **33**, 545 (1900).
123. Coates, G. E., and Davies, R. H., private communication, 1953.
124. Gordon, A. R., *J. Am. Chem. Soc.* **65**, 221 (1943).
125. Robinson, R. A., and Sinclair, D. A., *J. Am. Chem. Soc.* **56**, 1830 (1934).
126. Scatchard, G., Hamer, W. J., and Wood, S. E., *J. Am. Chem. Soc.* **60**, 3061 (1938).
127. Buckley, P. S., and Hartley, H. H., *Phil. Mag.* [7] **8**, 320 (1929).
128. Bates, R. G., *J. Am. Chem. Soc.* **61**, 308 (1939).
129. Harned, H. S., and Robinson, R. A., *J. Am. Chem. Soc.* **50**, 3157 (1928).
130. Bates, R. G., *J. Am. Chem. Soc.* **70**, 1579 (1948).
131. Harned, H. S., *J. Am. Chem. Soc.* **47**, 930 (1925).
132. Harned, H. S., and Copson, H. R., *J. Am. Chem. Soc.* **55**, 220 (1933).
133. Harned, H. S., and Hamer, W. J., *J. Am. Chem. Soc.* **55**, 4496 (1933).
134. Bates, R. G., *J. Am. Chem. Soc.* **73**, 2259 (1951).
135. Bates, R. G., *Analyst* **77**, 653 (1952).
136. Bates, R. G., and Smith, E. R., *Compt. rend. conf. union intern. chim. pure et appl.* **17**, 72 (1951).
137. Smith, E. R., and Bates, R. G., *Comp. rend. conf. union intern. chim. pure et appl.* **15**, 119 (1949).
138. Lingane, J. J., "Electroanalytical Chemistry." Interscience, New York, 1953.
139. Allgood, R. W., LeRoy, J. D., and Gordon, A. R., *J. Chem. Phys.* **8**, 418 (1940).
140. Benson, G. C., and Gordon, A. R., *J. Chem. Phys.* **13**, 473 (1954).
141. Gunning, H. E., and Gordon, A. R., *J. Chem. Phys.* **10**, 126 (1942).
142. Hughes, U. L., and Martell, A. E., *J. Am. Chem. Soc.* **78**, 1319 (1956).
143. Grahame, D. C., *Chem. Revs.* **41**, 441 (1947).
144. Gilbert, P. T., *J. Sci. Instr.* **22**, 235 (1945).
145. Gilbert, P. T., *Discussions Faraday Soc.* **1**, 320 (1947).
146. *Discussions Faraday Soc.* (Colloidal Electrolytes) January, 1935.
147. Hitchcock, D. I., *J. Gen. Physiol.* **5**, 383 (1923).
148. Hitchcock, D. I., *J. Gen. Physiol.* **16**, 357 (1932).
149. Shedlovsky, T., ed., "Electrochemistry in Biology and Medicine." Wiley, New York, 1958.
150. *Discussions Faraday Soc.* **No. 13** (1953).
151. Akerlöf, G., and Teare, J. W., *J. Am. Chem. Soc.* **59**, 1855 (1935).
152. Jacques, H., *Helv. Chim. Acta* **29**, 1041 (1949).
153. Harned, H. S., and Gary, R., *J. Am. Chem. Soc.* **76**, 5924 (1954); **77**, 1994 (1955).
154. Pinkus, A., and Hangen, M., *Bull. soc. chim. Belges* **45**, 693 (1936).
155. Leitzke, M. H., and Stoughton R W., *J. Am. Chem. Soc.* **79**, 2067 (1957).

156. Roychoudhury, R. N., and Bonilla, C. F., *J. Electrochem. Soc.* **103**, 241 (1956).

157. Lietzke, M. H., and Vaughen, J. V., *J. Am. Chem. Soc.* **77**, 876 (1955).

158. Greeley, R. S., Smith, W. T., Lietzke, M. H., and Stoughton, R. W., *J. Phys. Chem.* **64**, 652, 1445 (1960). See also, Greeley, R. S., Ph.D. thesis, University of Tennessee, Knoxville, Tennessee, 1959.

Chapter Five

The Glass Electrode

R. G. Bates

I. Introduction

As an indicator electrode responding quantitatively to hydrogen ions over wide ranges of concentration, the glass electrode displays an amazing versatility. It is not influenced by oxidizing and reducing agents; it is not "poisoned" by heavy metals; it is not limited in its applications to aqueous solutions, but functions well in several nonaqueous or partly aqueous media.

The glass electrode, therefore, has many of the characteristics of an ideal indicator electrode for practical pH measurements, and for this purpose it is unique.

The development of the glass electrode can be credited, more than any other single factor, with the widespread use of pH measurement and control in the industry, commerce, and research of the present day. The glass electrode therefore occupies a place of outstanding importance among "standard reference electrodes" in the sense in which these have been defined in this work, i.e., those electrodes for which the parameters and use have become standardized in many fields of electrochemical inquiry (Chapter 1, Section I).

A. Hydrogen Ion Function of Glass Membranes

William Thomson, Lord Kelvin, appears to have been one of the first to study the electrolytic behavior of glass membranes (1), reporting in 1875 that two metallic electrodes separated by a glass plate formed a cell of approximately the same emf as that formed by dipping the same two metals in a liquid electrolyte. According to Kratz (2), the observations of Giese, a laboratory assistant of von Helmholtz, on potentials in Daniell cells in which glass replaced the usual diaphragm, and in Leyden jars, led to a confirmation of the electrolytic conductance of glass itself (3).

Nevertheless, it was Cremer (4) who discovered in 1906 that the potentials of glass electrodes blown in bulb form are remarkably sensitive to changes in the acidity of the medium in which the bulbs are immersed. The studies of Cremer also focused attention upon the phase-boundary potentials developed at surfaces of materials other than glass and laid the foundation for later important discoveries in physiology. The precise conditions under which glass electrodes would respond to hydrogen ions and the quantitative aspects of the hydrogen ion function were discovered three years later by Haber and Klemensiewicz (5). The surface potential was found by these authors and also by Borelius in 1914 (6) to change with hydrogen ion concentration in the same manner as the potential of the hydrogen electrode over a wide pH range.

B. Development of the Glass Electrode

Hughes (7) showed that the composition of the glass has an important bearing on the behavior of the glass electrode. He compared glass electrodes directly with hydrogen electrodes, and his elucidation of the great versatility of the electrode is largely responsible for transforming a laboratory curiosity into the major tool of chemical process control it is today.

Further impetus was given to the practical use of glass electrodes through the detailed studies of MacInnes and Dole (8) of the relation between pH response and the composition of soda lime glasses. The composition they selected as most suitable was 72.2 mole % SiO_2, 6.4 mole % CaO, and 21.4 mole % Na_2O. This glass, known commercially as Corning 015 in America and as Jena Schott 4073[III] in Germany, has a relatively low melting point, a comparatively low resistance, and is rather hygroscopic. For many years it was the most satisfactory glass for pH measurements. In recent years, however, other glasses with reduced errors in alkaline solutions have become available (9–11). The alkaline sodium errors of most of these glasses have been greatly reduced by the substitution of lithium for the sodium constituent.

Apart from the imperfect hydrogen ion response at the ends of the pH scale, about which more will be said in a later section, the most serious disadvantages of the glass electrode are its high electrical resistance and its relatively low durability, particularly in hot alkaline solutions. The electrical resistivity of glass may increase by a factor of 3,000 when the temperature is lowered from 100° to 0°C. The most durable electrodes have, in general, the lowest hygroscopicity and the highest resistance. Even though modern electronic electrometers permit accurate measurements of the potential of the glass membrane to be made in systems of very high resistance, it has proved difficult to fabricate electrodes of high durability at elevated temperatures without at the same time raising the low-temperature electrical resistance of the membrane to unsuitable levels. This dilemma has not been entirely resolved.

The most important developments in glass electrode design and construction from inception to the end of the year 1948 have been summarized in the books of Dole (12) and Kratz (2).

II. Theory of the Glass Electrode

The utility of the glass electrode rests on the fact that the magnitude of the phase-boundary potential between the surface of the glass membrane and the electrolytic solution in which the electrode is immersed is usually determined almost exclusively by the hydrogen ion concentration (or activity) in the solution. Glass is by no means the only material to give rise to phase-boundary potentials of possible usefulness. The phenomenon is, indeed, quite general in nature and is displayed by a large number of natural and artificial materials. Some of these are ion-exchange resins, clay and paraffin membranes, quartz and other minerals, and even systems of immiscible liquids. The study of phase-boundary potentials is of considerable importance to an understanding of the physiological phenomena that occur at cell walls.

Glass membranes are relatively easy to prepare, however, and their chemical compositions can be varied to produce an electrode with the most favorable combination of desirable properties. A satisfactory hydrogen ion response is not characteristic of all glass compositions, nor does it extend over the entire useful range of the pH scale.

The precise mechanism by which the electric potential at the surface of the glass membrane is altered as the pH of the solution changes has not been uniquely explained. Several views have been advanced but no unified, uncontested theory has evolved. Kratz (2) has classified these proposals as (a) adsorption theories, (b) distribution theories, and (c) statistical-mechanical theories.

These theories have certain common features, in that they attribute the potential difference to the change of free energy on the transfer of hydrogen ions across the phase boundary. In the pH region 1 to 9, where the 015 glass electrode displays practically the theoretical response, these different formulations yield the same result, reducing to a simple Nernst equation. The differences among them consist primarily in the different manner of treating the departures of the electrode from the theoretical emf/pH slope below pH 1 and above pH 9.

A. ADSORPTION POTENTIALS

Glass surfaces may acquire charges by adsorption of ions from the solutions with which they are brought into contact, in the same manner as graphite electrodes are known to do (13). Lengyel and Matrai (14, 15) showed that quartz surfaces will adsorb hydrogen, lithium, sodium, potassium, calcium, strontium, barium, and aluminum ions from aqueous solutions and function thereafter as adsorption electrodes, the potentials of which respond to changes in the concentration of the "indicator" ion in the solution phase. As is the case with the glass electrode (16), anions are without effect. Near pH 7, the response to hydrogen ions is about 45 mv per pH unit instead of the theoretical 59 mv per pH unit at 25°C.

It appears that the true adsorption electrode is formed only on the surface of an insulator of very high specific resistivity such as quartz. The adsorption model therefore probably represents a limiting case. As the conductivity of a glass membrane decreases, the equilibrium distribution of ions between the solution and the glass phase is established with increasing difficulty. At the same time adsorption phenomena become more pronounced, until with a perfect dielectric all thermodynamic response is lost and the electrode process is exclusively one of adsorption.

B. ION DISTRIBUTION

The X-ray study of glass reveals a three-dimensional network of oxygen and silicon atoms in which there is a residual negative charge (see below). The charge of this macro-anion is balanced by cations which occupy holes in the network and are held in many different levels of energy by the electrostatic forces which are centered on the neighboring oxygens (*17*).

It is well known that glass undergoes certain dimensional changes when it is brought into equilibrium with aqueous solutions. In solutions of pH between 1 and 9, where the 015 glass electrode is substantially error-free, the glass exhibits a noticeable swelling. Furthermore, the voltage departures which are manifest above pH 9 are accompanied by a definite attack of the silicon-oxygen lattice at the glass surface (*18*). On the other hand, the voltage departures that sometimes appear in very acidic media and in nonaqueous solutions seem to be associated with some dehydration of the swollen surface layer.

The earliest form of the distribution theory (*5*) pictured the swollen layer at the surface of a conditioned glass electrode as a solid aqueous phase of fixed hydrogen ion concentration functioning as a hydrogen electrode. This approach did not explain the observed errors of the glass electrode in a satisfactory way, even though variable transference numbers were postulated. The refinements introduced by Gross and Halpern (*19*) and by Ray *et al.* (*20*), wherein the aqueous phase was considered to be saturated with the constituents of the glass while the glass surface was saturated with water, likewise did not provide the explanation.

Nevertheless, the concept of a glass phase of constant hydrogen ion concentration seemed quite plausible, inasmuch as this swollen glass layer could be regarded as a buffer system consisting of solid silicic acid, sodium silicate, and calcium silicate. This view led Hughes (*21*) to observe that the hydrogen ion concentration of a buffer phase of this sort would not be expected to remain constant above pH 9. This limit is, of course, imposed by the dissociation constants of silicic acid, which are approximately $pK_1 = 9$ and $pK_2 = 13$. Above pH 9, where departures do in fact first become noticeable, Hughes (*21*) and Britton (*22*) have linked the failure of the electrode to progressive ionization of the solid acid and concomitant uptake of alkali ions.

Ion exchange theories of the electrode function appear to have sprung from the work of Horovitz (*23*, *24*), who regarded the glass as a solid electrolyte. The potential difference between glass and solution phases depends, according to Horovitz, on the concentrations of ions in both of these phases. The electrode function is therefore limited to those ions which can migrate into the glass surface, and these are exclusively cations (*25*), with hydrogen ion by far the most labile. These ideas, which lead to the concept of a mixed electrode capable of an emf response to more than one species of ion, are supported by the studies of Izmailov and Vasil'ev (*26*), who used radioactive tracers to reveal the penetration of ions into the membrane surface.

It seems well established that the freshly blown glass membrane behaves as a cation exchanger when the surface is conditioned by soaking in aqueous solutions. The careful experiments of Haugaard (27) with soda-lime glasses showed that a quantitative exchange of hydrogen ion from the solution with sodium from the glass membrane takes place. The earlier studies of MacInnes and Dole (8) are consistent with Haugaard's findings. A reservoir of hydrogen ions in the glass surface is presumably established in this fashion. The conditioned (swollen) surface contains stable sites for the accommodation of hydrogen ions, which appear to be able to penetrate the glass surface more easily than can other ionic species (28). Nicolsky (29) has accounted for the electrode function in alkaline solutions with the aid of an equilibrium constant for the exchange of sodium ions and hydrogen ions between the glass and solution phases.

There have also been attempts to utilize the concepts of the semipermeable membrane (Gibbs–Donnan equilibrium) and of the liquid–liquid junction in explaining the electrode behavior of the glass–solution interface. The membrane formulation leads to a reasonably satisfactory expression for the surface potential, provided the mobilities of anions in the glass phase are considered to be vanishingly small. Nevertheless, there is ample evidence that the behavior is not in actuality that of a permselective membrane. Likewise, Dole's representation of the phase boundary as an electrical double layer similar to a diffusion junction explained the alkaline errors of the glass electrode rather successfully (30). This equation was simplified somewhat by Gross and Halpern (31).

Schwabe and Glöckner (49) have observed the increase of the acid error with time and have been led to the belief that progressive absorption of acid by the outer gel layer causes the voltage departure. Similarly, the time dependence of the alkaline error can be attributed to a loss of hydrogen ions from the gel layer when the electrode is immersed in a highly alkaline solution. These authors visualize, therefore, a gel layer of constant hydrogen ion concentration in the pH region (2 to 9) where the electrode is substantially error-free.

C. Quantum-Mechanical Theory

Dole's satisfactory description of the glass electrode response and the voltage departures in alkaline solutions by a liquid-junction treatment appeared to require that the mobility of hydrogen ions in the glass phase be enormously greater than the mobility of sodium ions. Furthermore, the usefulness of the equation based upon this treatment is limited in practice by a lack of the needed mobilities and adequate information on their changes with concentration and pH. Hence, Dole (32) set out to examine further the basis for the earlier theory and to derive a new and more useful expression from the point of view of quantum statistics. For this purpose he utilized Gurney's statistical approach (*33*) to the electrochemical behavior of alloys. The glass surface was regarded as a solid lattice into which cations could migrate from the solution. Cations within the glass could occupy sites characterized by many different levels of energy. The transfer of cations between the solution phase and these sites within the glass phase depends upon the height of the energy barrier that must be traversed and is governed by the Boltzmann distribution law.

The equation derived by Dole is discussed in detail in his monograph (*12*) and is compared with the expression derived by Nicolsky (*29*) wholly from thermodynamic considerations. The expression for the alkaline error in volts (ΔE) is

$$\Delta E = 2.3026 \frac{RT}{F} \log \left(\frac{c_{Na^+} \exp[(Q_{Na} - Q_H)/RT] + c_{H^+}}{c_{H^+}} \right) \tag{1}$$

where c is molar concentration and R, T, and F are the gas constant per mole, the temperature in degrees Kelvin, and the faraday, respectively.

The key to Dole's equation is the quantity ($Q_{Na} - Q_H$), where Q represents the difference between the energies of the ion in the solution and in the lowest quantum level in the glass phase. Dole and Wiener (*34*) evaluated ($Q_{Na} - Q_H$) from observed voltage departures in solutions containing sodium ions. This quantity varied but little with temperature, even though the alkaline errors themselves are widely different. This finding is strong confirmation of the validity of the statistical equation and of the ion transfer model on which it is based. The Q quantity made unnecessary the assumptions regarding ionic mobilities that were a part of the earlier treatment.

III. pH Concept

A. THE HYDROGEN ELECTRODE

The quality of the "hydrogen ion function" or "pH response" of a glass electrode is assessed by comparing the change of the surface potential of the electrode with that of a hydrogen electrode as the acidity of the solution in which both electrodes are immersed is altered. The electrode process occurring at the platinum surface of the hydrogen electrode is

$$2H^+ + 2e^- = H_2 \text{ (g)}$$

For the sake of simplicity, we shall assume that the partial pressure of the gas is 1 atm, the customary standard state for a gaseous component. If this is not actually the case, the measured potential can easily be corrected to obtain the potential corresponding to this reference state.

Inasmuch as the standard potential for the hydrogen electrode reaction is zero at all temperatures by convention, the Nernst equation yields the following relationship between the electrode potential (E_e) and the activity of hydrogen ions, a_H:

$$E_e = \frac{2.3026RT}{F} \log a_H \qquad (2)$$

When the concentration and activity of hydrogen ions are less than unity, as they are in most dilute solutions, $\log a_H$ and E_e are negative. It is convenient, then, to define pH *formally* as follows:

$$\text{pH} = -\log a_H \qquad (3)$$

The potential of the hydrogen electrode is the fundamental basis for the establishment of all values for pH.

B. Modern Definition of pH

Unfortunately, it is not possible to determine the potential of a single electrode exactly, and for this reason Eqs. (2) and (3) cannot serve as a precise definition of a single practical pH scale of general utility. All emf measurements yield *potential differences* between two electrodes, which, by the Nernst equation, are translated into combinations of the activities of two or more ions, the activity of a single ionic species being as elusive as the potential of a single electrode (cf. Chapter 1, Section II).

The general adoption of the standard hydrogen electrode as the arbitrary zero of potential at all temperatures permits the *standard potentials* of other electrodes to be established. Unfortunately, it does not offer a means of evaluating the potentials of electrodes in other than their standard states. If a direct comparison of a given electrode with this primary standard is attempted, the measured difference of potential includes an indeterminate liquid-junction potential at the boundary of contact between the two different half-cell solutions. Secondary "reference electrodes" of fixed potential (e.g. saturated calomel) offer greater convenience, but their application to the measurement of the potential of a single electrode involves inescapably: (i) the evaluation of the activity of a single ion; or (ii) the evaluation of a liquid-junction potential; or (iii) the assumption that the liquid-junction potential remains unchanged when the same reference electrode is immersed in two different solutions.

Since 1909 when Sørensen first proposed the pH unit (35), pH numbers for "unknown" solutions (X) have been obtained from the emf of a cell of the type

$$\text{H}_2 \text{ (g, Pt)} \mid \text{Solution X} \vdots \text{KCl (bridge)} \vdots \text{Reference electrode} \qquad (4)$$

where the vertical dotted lines mark the sites of liquid junctions. The bridge solution, usually a saturated or 3.5 M solution of potassium chloride, is believed to lower the liquid-junction potential to small, relatively constant, values when the pH of solution X lies between 2 and 12. The reference electrode is usually a calomel electrode. The hydrogen electrode may be replaced by an electrode of glass, antimony, or quinhydrone for the sake of enhanced versatility and convenience.

Unfortunately, this well-established experimental method does not furnish values of "the acidity" or pH that have a simple fundamental meaning in terms of hydrogen ion concentration or activity. This experimental defect can be blamed largely on the indeterminate nature of the liquid-junction potential. Application of the Nernst equation to cell (4) suggests, however, that if the liquid-junction potential does not change when solution X_1 is replaced by solution X_2

$$\Delta E = \frac{2.3026RT}{F} \Delta(-\log a_{\mathrm{H}}) \tag{5}$$

where ΔE is the observed change in the emf of the cell and $\Delta(-\log a_{\mathrm{H}})$ is the corresponding change in the pH defined by Eq. (3). These considerations form the basis for the modern operational definition of pH, namely

$$\mathrm{pH} = \mathrm{pH(S)} + \frac{E - E_{\mathrm{s}}}{2.3026RT/F} \tag{6}$$

In Eq. (6), pH(S) is the assigned pH value of a standard reference solution and E_{s} is the emf measured when this reference solution replaces solution X in cell (4).

When the two solutions (reference and "unknown") are matched closely with respect to composition and concentration and when the pH of neither one is less than 2 nor greater than 12, the two liquid-junction potentials are thought to be nearly the same. Under these restricted conditions, it is possible to ascribe, if with some reserve, fundamental meaning to the measured pH. If the values of pH(S) represent the activity of hydrogen ions (pa_{H}) in the standard reference solution, by necessity conventionally defined, the pH measured in the range 2 to 12 will have approximately the significance prescribed by Eq. (3). The pa_{H} values established by the National Bureau of Standards for six reference solutions are given in Table I (36). The nature of the conventional activity scale is set forth in detail elsewhere (37).

IV. Limitations of the Glass Electrode

The mechanism through which the glass membrane alters its potential with a change of pH is not an electron-transfer process; hence, the glass

TABLE I

pH(S) OR pa_H OF SIX REFERENCE SOLUTIONS FROM 0° TO 95°C

t (°C)	0.05 M K tetroxalate	KH tartrate (saturated at 25°C)	0.05 M KH phthalate	0.025 M KH$_2$PO$_4$, 0.025 M Na$_2$HPO$_4$	0.01 M Borax	Ca(OH)$_2$, (saturated at 25°C)
0	1.67	—	4.01	6.98	9.46	13.43
5	1.67	—	4.01	6.95	9.39	13.21
10	1.67	—	4.00	6.92	9.33	13.00
15	1.67	—	4.00	6.90	9.27	12.81
20	1.68	—	4.00	6.88	9.22	12.63
25	1.68	3.56	4.01	6.86	9.18	12.45
30	1.69	3.55	4.01	6.85	9.14	12.30
35	1.69	3.55	4.02	6.84	9.10	12.14
40	1.70	3.54	4.03	6.84	9.07	11.99
45	1.70	3.55	4.04	6.83	9.04	11.84
50	1.71	3.55	4.06	6.83	9.01	11.70
55	1.72	3.56	4.07	6.84	8.99	11.58
60	1.72	3.56	4.09	6.84	8.96	11.45
70	1.74	3.58	4.12	6.85	8.93	—
80	1.77	3.61	4.16	6.86	8.89	—
90	1.80	3.65	4.20	6.88	8.85	—
95	1.81	3.68	4.23	6.89	8.83	—

electrode is completely unaffected by oxidizing and reducing agents. Dissolved gases do not disturb the surface potential, nor do such common electrode poisons as arsenic compounds, cyanides, sulfides, chloroform, phenols, alkaloids, and salts of the noble metals.

On the other hand, certain proteins cause erroneous results to be obtained, possibly through coagulation on the membrane surface. Nevertheless, no great difficulty is experienced in measuring the pH of whole blood, if contact with the electrode is not prolonged unduly (*38–41*). The adsorption of surface-active materials may cause trouble in some applications.

The best pH-responsive glasses are relatively soluble, and a perceptible alteration of the pH may result from their immersion in poorly buffered media. Solutions of hydrofluoric acid and other substances corrosive to glass provoke large errors, and dehydrating media can be used only with caution.

A. pH RESPONSE

Hughes (*7*) emphasized that suitable glass electrodes should have low electrical resistance, stable potentials, and low "electrode errors". In later sections we shall consider the electrical resistance of glass electrodes and the susceptibility of the glass membrane to chemical attack. The first of these factors decreases the ease and to some extent the accuracy with which the emf of glass electrode cells can be determined, and the second limits the useful life of the electrodes. The most serious limitation of the glass electrode is, however, its imperfect hydrogen ion response, that is, the failure of the membrane potential to parallel that of the hydrogen electrode over the entire pH range.

From Eqs. (2) and (3) it may be seen that the rate of change of the hydrogen electrode potential with pH is given by

$$dE_e/d\text{pH} = -2.3026RT/F \tag{7}$$

Thus, E_e is a linear function of pH at any given temperature. The "pH response" of a glass electrode is given by

$$\text{Response} = \frac{E_2 - E_1}{\text{pH}_2 - \text{pH}_1} \tag{8}$$

where E_1 and E_2 are values of the emf of the cell:

glass electrode | solution of defined pH || reference electrode

when the two electrodes are immersed in solutions of pH equal to pH_1 and pH_2, respectively. The double line indicates elimination or matching of the liquid-junction potential. It should be noted that the emf becomes more *positive* as the pH increases, for the electrode potential, E_e, of the glass electrode becomes more negative and that of the reference electrode remains constant. Evidently the ideal glass electrode would display a response of $2.3026RT/F$ volt per pH unit (0.0592 volt per pH unit at 25°C) over all intervals of pH.

In general, very thin membranes display the most nearly ideal pH response. The response falls progressively below the theoretical 2.3026 RT/F volt per pH unit as the strength of the membrane is increased. For many years a wall thickness of about 0.1 mm was preferred by the manufacturers of commercial electrodes. These electrodes possessed adequate durability and yet gave about 96 to 98% of the theoretical pH response (2). Newer glass formulations, however, permit very thick membranes of considerable mechanical strength to be used, presumably at no great sacrifice of response. It is believed that there is a critical thickness for each glass composition, above which voltage departures occur. This threshold thickness for electrodes of Corning 015 glass has been placed at 54 to 130 microns (42).

The most extensive studies of the pH response of glass electrodes relate to electrodes of Corning 015 glass. Between pH 1 and pH 9 at room temperature, the surface potential of moderately thin membranes formed of this glass changes by practically the same amount as does the hydrogen electrode potential, for a given change of pH. In other words, plots of E_{Gl} and E_{H_2} as a function of pH are straight lines of equal slope, maintaining a constant separation in the intermediate range of pH. Evidently the separation of the curves measures the standard electrode potential, E_{Gl}°, of the particular glass electrode. From Eqs. (2) and (3),

$$E_{Gl} = E_{Gl}^\circ - \frac{2.3026RT}{F} \, \text{pH} \tag{9}$$

B. Alkaline Errors

In most highly alkaline solutions, particularly those containing sodium ion, the Corning 015 electrode is somewhat more *positive* (or less negative) than the potential that would be expected from the linear emf/pH plot established at pH values between 1 and 9. As Eq. (9) shows, a departure in this direction yields a pH value that is too low. The corrections that must be applied to the "observed" pH numbers are therefore positive.

These so-called "voltage departures" are surprisingly reproducible. For this reason, it is often possible to utilize the 015 glass electrode for measurements up to pH 12, provided that the sodium ion concentration does not exceed 0.1 M, that the temperature is not greater than 35°C, and that the compositions and corresponding corrections are known and applied. In alkaline solutions, cations are the offenders; anions have been found not to disturb the surface potential (16).

In general, the alkaline errors caused by cations not present in the glass decrease with increasing ionic radius, presumably because the larger ions experience difficulty in penetrating the silicon-oxygen lattice. Indeed, the smaller the cations in the glass and the larger the cations in the solution the smaller are the voltage departures observed (9). A useful, though only approximate, rule for 015 glass electrodes is that the lithium ion error is one-half as large as the sodium ion error and the error caused by potassium ions is one-fifth as large as the sodium error. Magnesium is without effect (43), while barium and ammonium ions are nearly so (18, 44).

The alkaline errors of the Corning 015 glass electrode are about the same at 10°C as at 25°C. The pH range over which the "ideal" pH response is maintained becomes progressively narrowed as the temperature is elevated and the ionic strength of the solution is increased. According to Humphreys (45), the theoretical response is limited to the range pH 6.0 to 7.4 at 100°C. A part of the loss of response can doubtless be attributed to the increased thickness of the glass membrane needed to withstand the corrosive action of aqueous solutions at this temperature.

Ssokolof and Passynsky (9) discovered that the alkaline error of glass electrodes in most common test solutions can be substantially eliminated up to pH 13 by replacing the sodium constituent of the glass with lithium. This work led to the development of other formulas for improved lithium glasses suitable for the fabrication of electrodes with very low alkaline errors. Fortunately, these glasses do not have the excessively high electrical resistance that characterized the original formulation.

TABLE II

SODIUM ION ERRORS OF GLASS ELECTRODES[a]
(AT 25°C, IN MILLIVOLTS)

True pH	Corning 015 Schott 4073[III]	Beckman general purpose	Beckman type E	Cambridge Alki	Leeds and Northrup black dot
Na$^+$ (0.1 M)					
9.5	1.8	—	—	—	—
10.0	3.3	0.6	—	—	—
10.5	6.0	1.8	—	—	—
11.0	10.4	2.8	—	—	—
11.5	16	4.4	—	—	—
12.0	24	7.6	—	—	—
12.5	—	12	0.6	—	—
13.0	—	19	1.7	—	1.0
13.5	—	—	4.3	—	5.5
Na$^+$ (1 M)					
9.0	3.0	0.6	—	—	—
9.5	5.0	1.5	—	—	—
10.0	9.5	2.8	—	—	—
10.5	16	4.8	—	—	—
11.0	24	7.7	—	—	—
11.5	—	12	0.6	—	—
12.0	—	19	1.2	0	—
12.5	—	—	3.2	1.2	1.1
13.0	—	—	5.0	3.6	6.4
13.5	—	—	8.5	7.8	13

[a] Sodium ions make the potential of the glass electrode too positive; hence, these voltage departures are to be subtracted from the apparent electrode potential.

The Electronic Instruments GHS electrode displays an error of about 1.2 mv in a 0.1 M solution of sodium hydroxide at 25°C and about 9 mv in 1.0 M sodium hydroxide (78). The errors of the Doran Alkacid electrode in 0.1 M and 1.0 M solutions of sodium hydroxide are about 1.2 mv and 6 mv, respectively. The Electronic Instruments Code BH15 glass (intended for use above 50°C) is said to have a negligible error in 1.0 M sodium hydroxide at 25°C (private communication from Dr. G. Mattock).

The sodium ion errors (voltage departures) of four commercial glass electrodes at 25°C are compared with those of the 015 glass electrode in Table II. The Leeds and Northrup black dot electrodes are known to contain lithium as a constituent, and the Cambridge Alki and the Beckman type E electrode are presumed also to contain this element. The lithium errors of these electrodes are therefore expected to be two to three times as large as the sodium errors. An appreciable lithium error is, however, much less serious in practice than an error caused by sodium ions, which are present in a large fraction of test solutions.

Glasses with a large alkali metal error and relative insensitivity to hydrogen ion have practical applications in the potentiometric determination of sodium and potassium (54). In general, the response to alkali metal cations is enhanced by the substitution of alumina or boric oxide for a part of the silica of the glass. The interference by 1 M potassium chloride in the determination of sodium ion concentrations by sodium aluminosilicate electrodes is not serious if the concentration of sodium (present as the chloride) exceeds 0.001 M (54a). The introduction of boric oxide into the glass, however, results in a deterioration of the specificity. Sodium ion electrodes are available commercially. Their pH response is not entirely nullified; hence, sodium ion determinations are usually made on solutions buffered in the pH range 8 to 10.

C. Acid Errors

In highly acidic solutions and in certain nonaqueous media, the Corning 015 glass electrode is somewhat more *negative* (or less positive) than the potential that would be expected from the linear emf/pH plot established at pH values between 1 and 9. The value of the pH found from Eq. (9) will therefore be too high. A negative correction must be applied to the "observed" pH numbers.

This "acid error" or "negative error" does not appear to be a specific disturbance due to certain types of ions as is the case with the alkaline error. Neither cations nor anions appear to effect the acid error in any specific way, although there is recurrent evidence (26) that anion adsorption may sometimes play a part. The acid error is, furthermore, not as reproducible as the alkaline error, nor is it particularly sensitive to temperature. It is claimed that some glass electrodes display little or no acid error.

The magnitude of the error is not fixed by the pH of the solution exclusively. From studies of the behavior of 015 electrodes in solutions of hydrochloric acid and sulfuric acid, Dole (46) found that the acid error became apparent at much higher pH values when alcohol was present in the solution than in its absence. In solutions of hydrochloric acid and sulfuric acid of pH -1, the glass electrode reading is too high by 0.30 and 0.13 pH unit, respectively. In 95 vol % ethanol the measured value is too high by 0.71 pH unit (42 mv). The voltage departures in strong solutions of acids found by Goldman and Hubbard (47) are given in Table III.

TABLE III

VOLTAGE DEPARTURES IN CONCENTRATED SOLUTIONS OF ACIDS

Solution	Voltage departure (mv)
25% H_2SO_4	10
75%	100
96%	525
75% H_3PO_4	10
85%	20
75% HCOOH	10
90%	32
75% CH_3COOH	12
99%	220

An examination of the glass surface shows that the onset of the acid error is accompanied by a reduction in the thickness of the swollen surface layer of the glass (18). Dole (46) attributed the error in strongly acidic, highly concentrated, or nonaqueous solutions to the difference in water activity on the two sides of the glass membrane. The equations he developed by treating the membrane as a reversible "water transfer" electrode account very successfully for the acid error and lend support to the belief that each of the hydrogen ions entering the glass surface carries one molecule of water with it.

It is well known that little or no impairment of the glass electrode function results when the contact with the reference side of the membrane is made through a metal coating or pool of mercury rather than through an aqueous solution. Dole's theory can apply as well to the transfer of water across the phase boundary as to that across the entire membrane. The interesting observation (48) that Jena borosilicate thermometer glass containing sodium and aluminum is practically devoid of an acid error at pH values as low as -1.4 has led to the suggestion (2) that unhydrated protons may participate in the voltage response of durable glasses of low hygroscopicity. The ions that migrate into the glass network in establishing the electrode function can presumably be no larger than the holes left there by the leaching out of cations during the conditioning process. It is therefore possible that the relatively large hydronium ions do not find an abundance of suitable sites for easy penetration of the surface, although protons are still able to do so.

Schwabe and Glöckner (*49*) attribute the negative error to an excessive gain of protons through acid sorption by the gel layer. It has also been suggested (*50*), that some of the many protons available in solutions of low pH seek out acceptors of lower energy in the gel structure, in addition to the customary exchange sites (whatever those may be). The result is a modification of the quantitative response of the surface potential to changes in pH. Explanations of electrode errors are, however, largely speculative. There is as yet no general agreement as to the exact cause of the voltage departures in strongly acidic solutions.

V. Composition of Electrode Glasses

The most comprehensive investigations of the relation between the behavior of glass electrodes and the composition of the glass membrane are those of Hughes (*21, 51*), MacInnes and Dole (*8*), Ssokolof and Passynski (*9*), Lengyel and Blum (*52*), and Perley (*10, 53*). These studies (with the exception of Perley's) have been discussed most thoroughly and capably by Dole (*12*) and Kratz (*2*).

It is perhaps helpful to recall at this point that the pH-responsive glass will have three and possibly four distinguishable structural units. The primary network is formed from silicon atoms, covalently bound to four tetrahedrally disposed oxygen atoms. Each oxygen atom is, in turn, usually shared by two silicons. If all the valencies are satisfied, the limiting composition is that of pure silica, SiO_2. Chains and networks are formed, randomly disposed in the vitreous state.

When not all the oxygens are shared by two silicons, the network acquires a negative charge which may be balanced by cations situated within the holes or interstices in the network. These cations are held by electrostatic forces but can move, no doubt by activated jumps, from one site to another, giving rise to a finite electrical conductance which increases rapidly with rising temperature. The charge-balancing cations are normally singly or doubly charged. They find their most stable sites when their co-ordination by surrounding oxygen atoms is greatest.

In addition, tervalent elements may actually replace silicon in the covalent network. These substitutions give the network an extra negative charge which must be balanced by a corresponding extra interstitial cation. Glasses can in this way be tailored to some degree to produce a desired combination of favorable characteristics. They can indeed be designed to yield a useful sodium ion response if desired (*14, 54*).

The first essential property of a suitable glass is that it be workable and stable. Glasses which have high softening points or which devitrify easily are unsatisfactory, as are those which are too soluble for extended use in aqueous solutions. The criteria by which the most suitable compositions are chosen include electrical resistance of the membrane, magnitude and stability of the "asymmetry potential" (the difference of potential displayed by the two membrane surfaces in contact with identical solutions), the pH response, and the magnitude of the electrode errors.

Perley studied the properties and stabilities of electrodes made from over 500 pH-responsive glasses. His conclusions regarding the specific effects of the various constituents of the glass on the characteristics of the electrode are of considerable importance and are summarized in the following paragraphs.

Electrode glasses have at least three constituents. These are SiO_2, R_2O, and MO or M_2O_3, where R is an alkali metal and M is a bivalent or trivalent metal. The R_2O constituent may be a mixture of two alkali metal oxides; MO is often CaO, BaO, or SrO; and Perley regards lanthanum oxide as the most successful of the M_2O_3 constituents. The usual limits of composition are as follows: SiO_2, 60 to 75 mole %; R_2O, 17 to 32 mole %; and MO or M_2O_3, 3 to 16 mole %.

It is not surprising that the function of these various constituents cannot be indicated exactly. Perley's studies, however, confirm the suggestion made by Ssokolof and Passynsky (9) that ionic radii are of primary importance. In addition, Perley focuses attention on the co-ordination number (the number of oxygen atoms of the silicon-oxygen network which are nearest neighbors of an interstitial cation) and on the degree of stability it imparts to the labile ionic constituents of the glass. It is, of course, this lability that gives rise to the conductivity and to the concept of glass as a "solid electrolyte."

Perley's data illustrate most strikingly the great superiority of lithium oxide glasses over their sodium oxide counterparts with respect to the alkaline error. They also demonstrate a close tie between the alkaline sodium error and the sodium content of the glass. In fact, the replacement of 1 mole % lithium oxide in a glass of the following composition: 25 mole % Li_2O, 1 mole % Na_2O, 7 mole % BaO, 2 mole % La_2O_3, 65 mole % SiO_2; by the corresponding quantity of sodium oxide raises the alkaline error observed in 2 N sodium solution, pH 12.8, from 0.40, to 0.60 at 25°C.

Lithia glasses, however, have higher resistances than soda glasses of similar composition, a fact that seems surprising in view of the smaller size of lithium and consequent greater ease of migration through the interstices of the lattice. A high degree of hydration of lithium might explain this anomaly were there not evidence that lithia glasses absorb much less water than soda or potash glasses (55).

The relatively high resistance of many lithia glasses does not constitute a serious problem, for the resistance decreases as the lithium content is increased and drops to suitable levels before the glass becomes so soluble as to be unsatisfactory for the fabrication of electrodes. Glasses high in lithium oxide, however, often show a relatively large increase of resistance with time of use. Robust glasses of low resistance are rather hard to achieve.

The resistance of glasses containing both lithium and sodium oxides in constant total amount of 26 mole % passes through a maximum at a composition near that where both oxides are present in equal molal amounts. When the amount of either oxide is greater than 4 mole % and less than 22 mole per cent in these glasses, the electrical resistance is too high to permit pH measurements at 25°C to be made.

Studies of glasses with different MO or M_2O_3 constituents show that the larger cations (barium and strontium) are more effective than the smaller ones (calcium, magnesium, beryllium) in extending the ideal pH response to highly alkaline solutions and in imparting stability to the response at high pH over long time periods. Nevertheless, the replacement of calcium by barium or strontium in the formulation of the glass raises the electrical resistance considerably. An M_2O_3 oxide can replace all or a part of the alkaline earth constituent with favorable effects on the stability without undue increase of the resistance.

Some interesting effects are produced by the addition of uranium dioxide (UO_2), titanium dioxide (TiO_2), or germanium dioxide (GeO_2) to pH glasses. Schwabe (56) has found that the replacement of 5 to 6% of the SiO_2 in Corning 015 glass by UO_2 gives a glass with 10 times the electrical conductivity of the 015 glass, whereas the pH response is not appreciably altered. Some titania glasses appear to be useful for pH measurements at high temperatures. Simon and Wegmann (57) have shown that the replacement of 1 to 4 mole % of silicon dioxide by germanium dioxide improves the workability of some electrode glasses, although the alkali error may be slightly increased.

Lengyel and his associates have examined the relationship between electrical resistance and compositions of the glass (58) and, pursuing the studies of Schwabe, have selected a glass of the composition: Li_2O, 30%; BaO, 5%; UO_2, 2%; and SiO_2, 63% on the basis of its low resistance, good pH response, and satisfactory workability (59). Bulbs of this glass 10 mm in diameter with a membrane thickness of 0.1 to 0.2 mm are said to have resistances of 0.1 to 0.5 megohm at room temperature.

Perley concludes that the alkali metal oxide is the constituent essential for the pH response. Its role in the electrode function undoubtedly depends to a degree on the hydration of the alkali metal ions in the glass surface. Glasses containing as much as 28 mole % lithium oxide together with a little rubidium oxide or cesium oxide have very low alkaline sodium errors and low resistances. Furthermore, small amounts of lanthanum oxide are effective in eliminating the instability of resistance and response at high pH that would severely limit the useful life of electrodes fabricated from this glass.

A suitable composition is 65 mole % SiO_2, 28 mole % Li_2O, 3 mole % Cs_2O, and 4 mole % La_2O_3 (10). For the construction of electrodes with low sodium errors, Cary and Baxter (11) recommend a glass of the composition: 68 mole % SiO_2, 25 mole % Li_2O, and 7 mole % CaO. It must be remembered that an increase in temperature increases greatly the attack of a thin glass membrane by an aqueous solution and that a decrease of temperature brings about an enormous increase in electrical resistance. For these reasons, a single glass composition may be unable to span satisfactorily the 0° to 100°C range over which glass electrodes are commonly used. This problem has been solved by the fabrication of electrodes for use within certain specified ranges of temperature.

VI. Chemical Properties of Glass Electrodes

A. Hygroscopicity

The importance of water in the development of the pH response of a glass membrane is well recognized. The exact role of water is still in doubt, just as the exact role of ionic constituents in the electrochemical behavior of glass surfaces is not yet clearly understood.

The experiments of Haugaard (27) and others (8, 23) demonstrate with remarkable clarity that the conditioning of a freshly blown 015 glass membrane in an aqueous solution is accompanied by a type of ion exchange in which sodium ions are removed from the glass surface and replaced by an equal number of hydrogen ions from the solution. It is probable that each of these hydrogen ions consists of at least one molecule of water in combination with a proton. There exists on the conditioned surface of the glass a swollen layer of hydrous silica which appears to be necessary for the proper pH function. Dimensional changes of the glass surface can be measured with an interferometer, and it is found that decreases in the normal thickness of the swollen layer are usually accompanied, in acidic as well as in alkaline solutions, by departures from the linear pH/emf relationship. In strongly acidic and nonaqueous solutions, the dimensional changes are presumably associated with dehydration of the swollen layer; in alkaline solutions they appear to be caused by attack of the silicon-oxygen network, about which we shall have more to say in the next section.

When glass electrodes are allowed to become dry, the electrical resistacne increases enormously (28) and the pH response falls below the theoretical value. Drying ordinarily does no harm to the electrode, but the conditioning process must, of course, be repeated before the electrode is capable of yielding stable potentials once more. After the electrode has once been put in service, the ion exchange process which characterized the initial conditioning presumably does not occur again. Conditioning of the dry membrane probably consists thereafter in a simple hydration of the silicon-oxygen skeleton left by the extraction of sodium, lithium, calcium and other ionic constituents from the glass surface when it was first immersed in water. Although a conditioning period of 2 to 12 hours is usually recommended, Perley (53) obtained constant potentials from lithia-silica glass electrodes 20 minutes after they were immersed in a pH 6.86 phosphate buffer.

Experience shows that the hydration-dehydration of the lattice is usually reversible; exhaustive drying may, however, result in a shrinking of the surface layer and irreparable damage to the electrode. Annealing of unleached electrodes has no marked effect on their behavior after conditioning. Annealing of leached electrodes, however, results in large permanent voltage departures (60). When the "dead" skeleton of silica is removed by dipping the electrode in a dilute solution of hydrofluoric acid, however, the normal pH function is promptly restored.

It has also been observed that glasses whose pH response is imperfect sometimes show an improvement in response after treatment with superheated water under pressure. The studies of Hubbard (61) have demonstrated that the hygroscopicity of the powdered glass shows a very direct correlation with the pH response of electrodes fabricated from the glass. This close relationship is evident in Table IV. These data suggest that

TABLE IV

HYGROSCOPICITY AND pH RESPONSE OF 10 TYPES OF GLASS

Glass	Water sorbed (mg cm^{-3})	pH response (mv/pH unit)
Corning 015	358	59
Dish	88	58
American Ceramic Society No. 1	40	57
Window	39	56
Electric hygrometer	39	56
Blue bottle	30	54
BSC 517	5.5	43
F 620	4.8	39
Ba C 572	2.2	33
Pyrex	1.8	18

glasses far less hygroscopic than Corning 015 glass display very nearly the theoretical response (59 mv per pH unit at 25°C). Lithium pH glasses were unfortunately not included in the study.

B. DURABILITY

The life of a glass electrode is determined not only by the composition and thickness of the pH-sensitive membrane but also by the compositions and temperatures of the solutions in which the electrode is immersed. In the normal case, the processes of corrosion and leaching bring its period of service to an end after 9 months to 2 years.

The mechanism by which glass is attacked in aqueous solutions involves sorption of water and the penetration of the water ever more deeply into the layers of glass. The corrosive action of the lye formed by extraction of the alkaline constituents from the body of the glass promotes the destruction of the silicon-oxygen network in the surface. The decomposition proceeds inward from both surfaces of the membrane until cracks eventually develop. The end is usually heralded by a drop in the pH response and by an instability of the measured emf.

Attack of the glass by water and dilute acids proceeds somewhat differently from that produced by alkalies. Water and acids release the ionically bound basic constituents, replacing them with hydrogen ions. The water-soluble reaction product is extracted, leaving in the surface an amorphous swollen layer of hydrous silica which resists further attack by water or dilute acid. If the glass electrode is kept immersed in water, its useful life may be appreciably extended (*62*). Alkalies, however, react with the silicic acid skeleton, exposing the deeper layers of the glass to attack; no protective layer can be built up.

The chemical stability of the glass surface is of great importance in the measurement of the pH of water and poorly buffered solutions. Consequently many investigators have attempted to study the rate of release of alkali by titration or by the observation of pH changes. There are two other ways in which the durability of the glass has been measured, namely by the conductance method and by the interferometric method. The first of these has been described in detail by Kratz (*62*). It is particularly well suited to studying the durability of the large bulb-type electrodes of diameter about 3 cm. The electrode is immersed in a sample of conductance water contained in a rotating conductance cell of resistant glass which is in turn mounted in a constant-temperature bath. The relation between conductance and concentration is established by standardization of the apparatus with dilute solutions of potassium chloride or sodium hydroxide.

When a freshly blown glass bulb is first dipped into the water, the conductivity increases rapidly. After 30 minutes, however, the release of soluble glass constituents becomes approximately a linear function of the time of immersion.

The interferometric method (*18, 63*) cannot be applied directly to electrodes. The durability of rectangular specimens of many electrode glasses has, however, been measured successfully in this way. Much of this work has been done by Hubbard and his associates. Citations will be found in one of their later papers (*64*). The surfaces were sufficiently flat to show interference bands when the specimens were placed under optical flats of fused quartz, and the displacement of the bands could be observed after each piece had been immersed to part of its length in various solutions for 6 hours at 80°C. The results revealed the normal swelling due to hydration of the surface layer. In addition, attack was unmistakably evident above pH 9.0, beginning at about the pH where the onset of the alkaline error is observed. It is noteworthy that the neutralization of hydrous silica (silicic acid) should commence at about this same pH.

A uniform durability over a wide pH range appears to be characteristic of the best pH-responsive glasses. Accelerated attack is nearly always associated with pronounced voltage departures. This fact is illustrated by the conspicuous errors displayed by the 015 electrode in alkaline solutions and hydrofluoric acid solutions which attack the glass surface. Furthermore, the durability of 015 glass in a concentrated ammonia solution of pH 13.3 is greater than in a more dilute ammonia solution of pH 12.5 (*18*). This change of durability with concentration is of opposite sign to that found with strong alkalies, and the corresponding voltage departures have been found to be of opposite sign also.

The chemical durability of electrode glasses decreases sharply with elevation of the temperature, following closely the exponential type of curve which characterizes the change of electrical resistance of the glass with change of temperature (*65*). The increase in attack rate has been estimated to be twofold for an increase of 10°C and tenfold for an increase of 25°C. Ingruber (*66*) has found that electrodes designed for use up to 130°C have a very short life at temperatures of 180° to 200°C.

VII. Physical Properties of Glass Electrodes

A. Electrical Resistance

The electrical resistance of a glass electrode is not a function of the pH of the solutions in contact with the two membrane surfaces. Furthermore, it has no direct bearing on the pH response of the electrode, although both properties are dependent on the composition of the glass and to some extent on its thickness. The very high resistance of glass membranes is, however, the source of a large part of the difficulties associated with the measurement of the emf of glass electrode cells. In addition, the large change of resistance with temperature restricts the useful temperature range of electrodes of a given composition to rather narrow limits. The direct-current resistances of commercial glass electrodes are usually from 5 to 500 megohms at the temperatures of intended use. Attempts to reduce the resistance below 1 megohm either by changes in the composition of the glass or by reducing the thickness of the membrane are impractical because of the attendant decreases in durability. Increasing the area of an electrode is likewise not usually a practical means of effecting an appreciable reduction of the electrical resistance.

The ac resistance of glass membranes is a function of frequency, as the measurements of MacInnes and Belcher (67) have clearly demonstrated. A typical Corning 015 glass electrode with dc resistance of 81 megohms had an ac resistance of only 2.55 megohms at a frequency of 1020 cps and 1.27 megohms at 3380 cps. Glass is primarily a dielectric with only slight electrical conductivity. The high resistance to the flow of direct currents has only a small ohmic component, which is thought to be of the order of magnitude of the ac resistance. The larger resistive component is attributable to the considerable polarization capacity of the glass, i.e., to the establishment of a back emf.

As electrical analogues, a series connection of a capacitance and an ohmic resistance, with or without a second parallel capacitance, have been suggested. The series capacitance arises from chemical polarization, and the parallel capacitance is electrostatic in origin. If the resistance of the electrode is too high, there is an objectionable lag in the response attributable to the so-called RC (resistance times capacitance) time constant of the measuring circuit.

The flow of current through the glass as the dc voltage is varied nonetheless indicates that Ohm's law is obeyed and that the dc resistance remains constant. It appears therefore that the glass electrode displays a polarization proportional to the imposed difference of potential and independent of the direction and duration of current flow. This polarization is reflected in an elevation of the dc resistance above that found by ac measurements.

There is general agreement that the current is carried through the glass membrane almost entirely by the ions of the alkali metals. Even after conditioning of the glass surface, a process accompanied by exchange of alkali ions for hydrogen ions, the passage of current is apparently still associated with the migration of alkali ions exclusively (8, 27).

We have already offered a picture of the three-dimensional structure of glass as an irregular spatial network in which each silicon atom is linked to four oxygens in a tetrahedral arrangement and each oxygen is bonded to two silicon atoms. The alkali ions occupy the spaces between these tetrahedra and are held loosely by electrovalence forces made available through incomplete or ruptured oxygen bridges. These cations can move, albeit with difficulty, from one site to another through the glass under the influence of an electric field. Both surfaces of the conditioned membrane consist of a thin swollen layer of hydrous silica enclosing a relatively thick center layer of unaltered alkali silicate. With the passage of small currents, the middle layer shifts in one direction or the other, depending on the direction of the current. Haugaard (27) has calculated that a shift of about 10^{-11} cm takes place when a current of 0.01 μa is passed for 1 sec. With the measuring apparatus of the present day, the current passed through the electrode during a measurement may be only 10^{-6} μa, or even less. Electrolytic destruction of the glass membrane is therefore of little practical concern.

The percentage change of the electrical resistance of glass for a change of 1°C in the temperature is 9 to 10%, as compared with 1 to 2% for electrolytes and a few tenths of a per cent (in the opposite direction) for metals. The Rasch and Hinrichsen formula (65), which can be written in the form

$$\frac{d \log R_{Gl}}{dT} = \frac{-Q}{2.3026 \, RT^2} \tag{10}$$

suggests that the logarithm of the resistance ($\log R_{Gl}$) is a linear function of the reciprocal of the absolute temperature, and this prediction has been

TABLE V

TEMPERATURE RANGES AND RESISTANCE OF SOME COMMERCIAL GLASS ELECTRODES

Electrode	Temperature range (°C)	Approximate dc resistance (megohms at 25°C)
Beckman General Purpose (clear glass)	−5 to 50	50 to 200
Beckman Type E (blue glass)	5 to 40	—
Beckman Amber (amber glass)	20 to 130	1000
Cambridge Alki	10 to 50	400
Doran M4996	<60	150
Doran Alkacid M4999	<60	300
Electronic Instruments GG	8 to 60	—
Electronic Instruments GHS	15 to 110	200
Leeds and Northrup–Blue Dot	0 to 20	18 to 30
Leeds and Northrup–Black Dot	10 to 60	40 to 100
Leeds and Northrup–Two White Dots	50 to 90	250 to 1500
W. G. Pye 11126 (lithium glass)	0 to 100	100 to 500
W. G. Pye 11128 (sodium glass)	0 to 65	100 to 500

confirmed (68). The quantity Q may be regarded as an activation energy, the average magnitude of the energy barrier that the mobile ion must surmount in order to migrate to the next stable site in the glass network.

Glasses whose durability and resistance make them suitable for use at high temperatures may have excessive resistances at lower temperatures. For this reason, different glass compositions are usually chosen for different temperature ranges. The approximate resistances of some commercial glass electrodes at 25°C and the temperature ranges for which these electrodes were designed are shown in Table V.

Inasmuch as the *change* of the surface potential is the quantity of interest in most applications of the glass electrode, the large change of resistance with temperature, if unrecognized, may be the source of occasional difficulties. This will be the case only when measurements are made at different temperatures and when the currents drawn are sufficiently large to yield an appreciable "IR drop." Under these relatively rare conditions, correct results will be obtained only by correcting for the alteration in the IR drop between successive measurements or between the standardization and subsequent use of the glass electrode cell.

B. ASYMMETRY POTENTIAL

The asymmetry potential, as its name implies, is the difference between the potentials generated at the two surfaces of the glass membrane under identical conditions. For its measurement, two identical reference electrodes are immersed in two portions of the same solution (of good buffer capacity), and the solutions are brought into contact with opposite sides of the glass membrane. Silver–silver chloride electrodes immersed in 0.1 M solutions of hydrochloric acid are suitable for this purpose. The cell formed is represented as follows:

$$\text{Ag} \mid \text{AgCl} \mid 0.1\ M\ \text{HCl} \mid \text{Glass} \mid 0.1\ M\ \text{HCl} \mid \text{AgCl} \mid \text{Ag}$$

If the silver–silver chloride electrodes have been shown to be identical by a prior comparison in the same solution of hydrochloric acid, the measured emf of this cell is the asymmetry potential of the glass membrane. The asymmetry potential of sealed commercial glass electrodes cannot readily be measured in this fashion. Its day-to-day fluctuations, however, can be observed by repeated measurements of the emf of the cell

$$\text{glass electrode} \mid 0.1\ M\ \text{HCl} \mid \text{AgCl} \mid \text{Ag}$$

provided that the potential of the inner reference half-cell remains constant. Asymmetry potentials commonly fall in the range 0 to ± 10 mv.

The fact that the electrochemical behavior of the two surfaces of a glass membrane is not the same was first recognized by Cremer (4), and this phenomenon was termed the "asymmetry potential" by Hughes (21). The studies of Laug (69), Yoshimura (70), and Bräuer (71) clarified the role of membrane thickness, water content, and mechanical and chemical attack of the glass [see also Beck and Wynne-Jones (72)]. Hamilton and Hubbard (73) showed that differences in the capacities of the two surfaces to adsorb ions may have a bearing on the magnitude of the asymmetry potential. Kratz has discussed these investigations thoroughly in his monograph (2).

The chief cause of asymmetry appears to lie in differences of composition of the outer and inner surface layers, specifically to differences in alkali metal content resulting from unequal leaching of the surfaces. There is a consequent difference in water sorption and an inequality in the thickness of the swollen layer. Any influence capable of altering the alkali content, water content, or ion-exchange capacity of one membrane surface preferentially is therefore capable of elevating the asymmetry potential. Some of these may be summarized as follows:

1. Alteration of water-sorptive capacity. Loss of alkali in the flame while the glass bulb is being fabricated.
2. Dehydration of the swollen surface layer. Drying, or immersion in dehydrating solutions.
3. Destruction of the swollen layer. Mechanical damage (grinding or polishing); chemical attack (etching by alkalies or hydrofluoric acid).
4. Disturbance of the exchange capacity for hydrogen ions (adsorption of foreign ions; grease films, proteins and surface-active agents).

In most applications of the glass electrode, only *changes* of the asymmetry potential are of concern. The asymmetry potential normally drifts slowly from day to day. Large and sudden fluctuations are to be expected only when the electrode is subjected to severe dehydration or damage of the sort indicated above. For a short series of measurements, therefore, the asymmetry potential can be considered to be constant and can be "balanced out" in the standardization of the electrode.

For work of the highest accuracy, the change with time can be determined and a correction applied in the ingenious and effective manner described by Covington and Prue (74). These investigations used the large glass electrodes manufactured by Jenaer Glaswerk Schott und Gen., combined with a silver–silver chloride electrode in a cell without liquid junction. The pH-sensitive bulb of these glass electrodes is about 30 mm in diameter, and the electrical resistance is about 0.5 megohm.

The emf data sought by Covington and Prue were obtained by subtraction of the emf values of two cells at the moment when the asymmetry potential of the same glass electrode was identical in the two solutions. The authors were able to measure the emf with an accuracy of 0.01 mv and to observe readily the change of asymmetry potential with time, first in one cell and then in the other. By a time-extrapolation procedure, the emf of the two cells at the moment of transfer of the glass electrode was obtained. It appears that the hydrogen ion function of the glass electrode was established nearly instantaneously. A second study of cells with transference containing two glass electrodes yielded highly precise data for the activity coefficient of hydrochloric acid. When rigorous precautions in regard to insulation and screening were taken, Covington was able to use the Jena electrode satisfactorily at 0°C (74a).

VIII. Glass Electrode Half-Cells

To complete the electrical circuit for the measurement of the surface potential of a glass electrode it is customary to place a solution of good buffer capacity and a reference electrode of constant potential on the "reference side" of the membrane, which usually means within the glass bulb. Nevertheless, metal-filled electrodes in which the circuit is completed through a metal film (e.g. silver) deposited directly on the glass surface or by a filling of mercury give satisfactory results (27, 75).

A. INNER REFERENCE CELLS

It is convenient to regard the glass electrode with the solution in which it is immersed as a half-cell reversible to hydrogen ions. The inner assembly of the glass electrode is, however, a complete galvanic cell in itself. It may be represented as follows:

Reference electrode, X, H$^+$ | Glass

where X represents the ion to which the reference electrode is reversible. The emf of this inner cell is part of the measured potential difference between the outer glass surface (indicating surface) and the solution in all attempts to determine the potential of the outer surface. Inasmuch as the useful information to be acquired from glass electrodes comes from the *differences* or alterations in the surface potential, constancy of the emf of this inner assembly is necessary and sufficient for nearly all purposes.

To achieve the desired constancy of potential, the solution must be stable and must not attack the glass. Since alkali will unavoidably be leached from the inner surface of the membrane, the buffer capacity must be high. This buffer capacity β is defined as $db/d\mathrm{pH}$, where b is an increment of strong base, in gm equiv liter^{-1}. A value of at least 0.05 for β is recommended. It is achieved in a solution of hydrochloric acid of molar concentration 0.025 or greater and in a buffer solution containing a weak acid and its salt, both at a concentration of 0.05. Similarly, the solution should not be too dilute with respect to the ion X, and the reference electrode should be of high stability. Calomel and silver–silver chloride electrodes in solutions of hydrochloric acid or buffered chloride solutions meet these requirements satisfactorily.

The magnitude of the emf developed by the inner cell is of concern only in the design of the measuring instrument. Electrodes for use with direct-reading meters of the deflection type are often designed in such a way that the emf of the pH cell (consisting of the glass electrode and external reference electrode) will have an emf of zero when the electrodes are immersed in a solution of pH 7. This adjustment can be accomplished by a suitable choice of the pH and of the concentration of ions X in the inner solution. Some slow change of the emf of the inner cell is, of course, inevitable. A provision is made in the pH meter for compensating these variations, along with the asymmetry potential, whenever the instrument is standardized. If the inner electrode and solution are of inadequate stability, the drift may exceed the correcting range of the instrument.

Calomel and silver–silver chloride elements are the most common inner reference electrodes. At temperatures above 80°C, however, the calomel electrode becomes unstable. The Jenaer Glaswerk has developed a "Thalamid" reference electrode that is said to be stable at temperatures up to 135°C. The electrode consists of a 40% thallium amalgam in contact with solid thallous chloride and a solution saturated with potassium chloride.

One of the most important considerations in the selection of inner electrode and solution is the minimizing of the errors due to temperature fluctuations. The inner reference electrode should be located within the pH-sensitive bulb, and this bulb should always be completely immersed in the solution. Inasmuch as the temperature coefficient of the emf of the total cell depends, *inter alia*, on the pH and composition of the unknown solution, it is manifestly impossible to design a cell system that will be uniformly insensitive to temperature changes. Nevertheless, the temperature effect can be compensated fairly completely under certain "average" conditions, for example at pH 7 (*37*).

Fricke (*76*) has found that the pH of a buffer solution composed of acetic acid (1 N) and sodium acetate (1 N) and saturated with potassium chloride is almost unaffected by changes of temperature in the range 20° to 100°C. It is possible, therefore, to design a symmetrical pH cell the standard potential of which is substantially constant (except for changes in the asymmetry potential and differences in the Nernst slope) over this considerable range of temperatures. Figure 1 is a plot of the change of emf with pH for a cell consisting of inner and external Thalamid electrodes and an inner acetate buffer solution saturated with potassium chloride. The lines have the theoretical Nernst slope at 20°, 60°, and 100°C and intersect

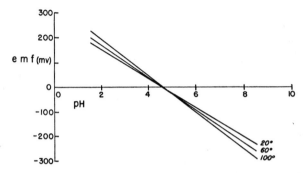

Fig. 1. Isotherms of a symmetrical pH cell [after Fricke (76)].

the line of zero emf at a common point ("Isothermenschnittpunkt"). The automatic instrumental compensation of changes in the standard potential of the glass electrode has been described by Electronic Instruments Ltd. (77).

B. Commercial Glass Electrodes

The properties of glass membranes discussed in the foregoing sections determine the design, selection, and use of commercial electrodes. The primary obstacle has always been that electrodes with suitable electrical resistances at low temperatures are susceptible to rapid chemical attack when immersed in aqueous solutions at high temperatures. Conversely, electrodes of compositions that yield adequate durability at high temperatures have such high electrical resistances at low temperatures that they are incapable of yielding accurate results rapidly. The most satisfactory solution of this difficulty has been to design electrodes specifically for certain ranges of temperature. The temperature ranges for which six commercial electrodes were designed are indicated in Table V.

The large alkaline errors that rendered the 015 glass electrode useless in solutions containing sodium ions at high pH are of far less concern since the general introduction of the lithia glasses. Errors in the pH response, though not eliminated, are relatively small and reproducible, and correction tables and charts are usually provided by the manufacturer. Some of these corrections are given in Table II. Simon and Wegmann (78) have compared the pH response, asymmetry potentials, and electrode errors of thirteen commercial glass electrodes.

In the early stages in the development of the glass electrode considerable effort was directed toward the design and fabrication of electrodes of very low resistance. These attempts were largely abandoned when excellent electronic amplifiers capable of measuring emf accurately in circuits with resistances of 1,000 megohms or greater were developed. Bulb-type electrodes with a diameter of 3.0 cm and a resistance of about 0.4 megohm can still be obtained from the Jenaer Glaswerk Schott und Gen., Mainz, Germany, under the designation "Niederohmige Glaselektroden Nr. 9000." These low-resistance electrodes are well suited to accurate investigations of the sort conducted by Covington and Prue (74, 74a).

Some pH electrodes are fabricated from glass of such low resistance that a thick multilayered membrane can be used. The durability of this glass is understandably not high, but as corrosion proceeds the leached silicon-oxygen skeleton is said to fall away, exposing a fresh pH-responsive surface. A layered glass consisting of a very conducting membrane within

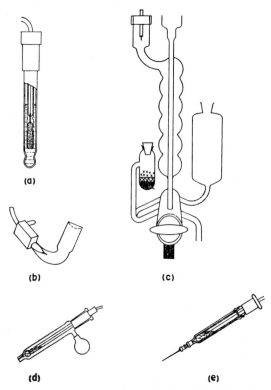

(a)

(b)   (c)

(d)   (e)

Fig. 2. Some types of glass electrodes. (a) Leeds and Northrup immersion electrode; (b) Beckman one-drop assembly; (c) MacInnes-Belcher condenser-type electrode; (d) Doran hanging-drop electrode; (e) Electronic Instruments hypodermic electrode.

a layer of more durable glass has also been fabricated. Unfortunately, no detailed information on the performance of these newer types of glass electrodes is available.

Most commercial glass electrodes are sealed for protection from evaporation and contamination. If intended for use outside a shielded electrode compartment, they are also provided with a shielded stem and a shielded lead which should be grounded to the case or electrostatic shield of the measuring instrument. The stem should be of high-resistance glass.

As a glance at the manufacturers' literature will indicate, glass electrodes are made in a wide variety of sizes and shapes and for many special applications. A few of these are shown in Fig. 2. Many are intended for immersion in the test solution, but syringe electrodes and capillary electrodes are becoming increasingly popular for blood pH and micro measurements. Some of these are water-jacketed for temperature control. The construction of a micro glass electrode of the capillary type has been described by Hartree (79). Although the so-called micro electrodes require only 0.05 to 0.3 ml of solution, it must be realized that errors in the measurement due to solubility of the pH-sensitive glass membrane are enhanced by the use of such small samples. The MacInnes-Belcher condenser-type electrode (67) shown in Fig. 2 has been widely favored, particularly in biochemical studies.

Inner reference cells usually consist of a calomel or silver–silver chloride electrode immersed in a solution of hydrochloric acid or in a chloride solution buffered with acetate, citrate, or other suitable buffer system. The Thalamid electrode is employed in some of the glass electrodes manufactured by Jenaer Glaswerk Schott und Gen. Quinhydrone electrodes, formerly widely used within the glass bulb, have been found to be insufficiently stable and have been abandoned.

C. Reference Glass Electrodes

The glass electrode is rarely (if ever) used in a reference half-cell of fixed potential for the measurement of the potentials of other electrodes, as is, for example, the calomel electrode. The reasons are readily apparent. The glass electrode, unless metal-filled, requires an inner reference electrode of its own, and the interposition of the glass membrane between this electrode and the solution in the half-cell is unnecessary. Furthermore, because of its changing asymmetry potential, the glass electrode cannot be depended upon to maintain a constant potential from day to day and must be standardized frequently against another more reliable reference.

This standardization is accomplished, for example, by joining the glass electrode half-cell (electrode plus its buffer solution) to a saturated calomel electrode through a saturated solution of potassium chloride, measuring the emf of the cell so composed, and subtracting this emf from the known potential of the calomel electrode. According to the Stockholm convention for electrode potentials set forth in Chapter 1, the emf (E) of the cell

$$\text{Glass electrode} \mid \text{buffer soln.} \vdots \text{KCl (satd)} \mid \text{Hg}_2\text{Cl}_2 \mid \text{Hg}$$

is given by $E_r - E_l$, where E_r and E_l are the electrode potentials of the right and left electrodes, respectively. Consequently, the potential of the glass electrode half-cell is given by $E_l = E_r - E$, provided that proper regard is taken for the sign of E, namely that E has a positive sign if the calomel and glass electrodes form the positive and negative poles, respectively, of the cell. The potential of the saturated calomel electrode (E_r) may be taken as 0.2508 volt at 15°C, 0.2444 volt at 25°C, and 0.2391 volt at 35°C (*37*).

This procedure for the standardization of a glass reference electrode is most satisfactory when the half-cell solution that makes contact with the saturated solution of potassium chloride has a pH between 2 and 9.5. In this region of pH, the saturated solution of potassium chloride reduces the liquid-junction potential to a small value that is little affected by variations in pH. When the solution in the half-cell has a pH less than 2, an abnormal liquid-junction potential dependent on the pH and composition of the solution is usually developed at the boundary between the two liquid phases.

The glass electrode reference half-cell finds its real advantage in experimental situations where, through its use, the liquid-junction potential can be minimized or eliminated. When the test solutions, for example, have pH values between 0 and 2, a reference half-cell of corresponding pH can be assembled. The residual liquid-junction potential will normally be rather small, especially if a saturated solution of potassium chloride is interposed between the test and reference solutions.

Reference half-cells of pH less than 2 should be standardized against the hydrogen electrode in a cell without liquid junction. The solution in contact with both the hydrogen electrode and the outer surface of the glass membrane should be one of known pH(S), that is, pa_H. The cell is formulated

$$\text{Glass reference electrode} \mid \text{Solution} \mid \text{Pt, H}_2$$

and the reference electrode potential (E_l) is given once again by $E_r - E$, where the sign of the emf (E) is determined in accordance with the Stockholm convention. The value of E should, of course, be corrected in the usual way to correspond to a partial pressure of 1 atm of dry hydrogen. The potential of the hydrogen electrode (E_r) is computed from the pa_H by

Eq. (2). The values for two useful half-cell solutions of pH less than 2 are given in Table VI.

TABLE VI

POTENTIAL OF THE ELECTRODE: SOLUTION | Pt, H_2 (GAS, 1 ATM) IN STRONGLY ACIDIC SOLUTIONS

Solution	Potential (volts)		
	15°C	25°C	35°C
0.1 M hydrochloric acid	−0.0629	−0.0651	−0.0673
0.05 M potassium tetroxalate	−0.0955	−0.0994	−0.1033

The most common reference application of the glass electrode is in the measurement of *changes* in the potential of a second electrode in a medium of fixed, and usually rather high, hydrogen ion concentration. The liquid junction can be avoided in this way. As an example, the titration of silver ion in a solution of sulfuric acid with a silver indicator electrode may be mentioned. The glass electrode also has important uses as a reference in the measurement of oxidation-reduction potentials, especially in redox titrations. For these applications, a standardization of the reference electrode is often not required.

IX. Glass Electrode Techniques

The use of the glass electrode as an indicator electrode in pH determinations and the means for measuring glass-electrode potentials have been discussed in considerable detail in other books (*2, 12, 37*). Instrumentation has also been the subject of an excellent review article (*80*). In the remaining sections of this chapter the techniques of particular importance in the reference applications of the glass electrode will be summarized.

A. MEASUREMENT OF GLASS ELECTRODE POTENTIALS

The surface potentials of the large bulb-type electrodes of resistance 0.3 to 0.5 megohms can be measured quite satisfactorily with a precision low-resistance potentiometer and a galvanometer of high sensitivity. Galvanometers with current sensitivities as high as 5×10^{-10} amp per mm are available commercially. These instruments should provide a voltage sensitivity of about 0.3 mv per mm when used to measure the surface potentials of these low-resistance forms of glass electrode.

The common commercial forms of glass electrode usually have resistances in excess of 10 megohms (see Table V). Their potentials can be measured with an accuracy of 1 to 2 mv by the many commercial designs of electronic voltmeters or pH meters available. The majority of these utilize a dc amplifier either in a direct-reading circuit with a deflection meter of large scale or to amplify the null current from a compensation (potentiometer) circuit. Negative feedback is often used with advantage to ensure linearity of the meter reading with respect to the input voltage and to remove the restrictions imposed by nonlinear vacuum tube characteristics (*80, 81*).

In recent years new circuitry has provided enormous increases in the stability of these measuring devices. This is accomplished through the use of dynamic condensers or choppers with subsequent amplification of the ac signal. The vibrating-reed electrometer has extended considerably the sensitivity of emf measurements through very high resistances. With the newer instruments it is possible to achieve an accuracy of 0.1 mv or better in measuring the potentials of commercial glass electrodes with resistances in the 10 to 500 megohm range.

Attempts to measure the emf of glass electrode cells have been plagued from the earliest days by the grid-current error. The electronic instruments utilized for the measurements drew a small current from the cell, even at balance. Although this current rarely exceeded 10^{-11} amp, it was sufficient to cause an appreciable IR drop, and hence an error in the measured emf, when the cell had a resistance greater than 100 megohms. In pH measurements, the IR drop will "cancel out" to a large extent if the temperatures of standard and "unknown" solutions (and hence the resistances in the two measurements) are the same (*37*). It is likewise of no concern when the glass electrode is being used to observe *changes* of potential of an indicator electrode, if the temperature remains constant. The grid currents drawn by the vibrating-reed electrometer and some of the other newer measuring instruments are negligible.

The measurement of IR drop can be utilized to determine the resistance of glass electrodes. In the method of Eckfeldt and Perley (*68*), an electrometer of high input impedance is used. The open-circuit emf (E_G) of a cell with glass and calomel electrodes is measured. The cell is then connected in series with a known voltage (V) from a precision potentiometer of low resistance and shunted with a known high resistance (R_c), after which a new value of the emf (E_R) is determined. The resistance of the glass electrode cell (R_G) is then calculated by the equation

$$R_G = R_c \left(\frac{V + E_G - E_R}{E_R} \right) \tag{11}$$

Electrodes for general purpose use will normally have resistances less than 200 megohms at 25°C, whereas high-alkalinity electrodes and microelectrodes may have resistances as high as 500 megohms. The resistances of electrodes intended for use at high temperatures may, of course, be considerably in excess of 500 megohms at 25°C, as may be seen in Table V.

B. Nonaqueous Solutions

The importance of water to the development of the hydrogen ion response of the glass electrode has already been emphasized, and in Section IV,C we have seen that the response departs progressively from the line of theoretical slope as the activity of water in the solution is lowered. Nevertheless, the glass electrode is capable of yielding useful results in partially aqueous and nonaqueous solutions if properly utilized and if the limitations of the data are clearly recognized.

First of all, excessive dehydration of the glass membrane must be carefully avoided. Satisfactory results cannot be obtained in strongly dehydrating media, and even in partially aqueous solutions the electrode must usually be reconditioned in water frequently to restore its pH response. Application of a correction, determined by an occasional comparison with the hydrogen electrode in the same solvent mixtures often enhances the value of the data obtained in water-deficient media.

Nevertheless, Bacarella, Grunwald, Marshall, and Purlee have used the glass electrode successfully to determine dissociation constants for several carboxylic acids and aniline derivatives in methanol-water mixtures containing as much as 95 vol % methanol (82). It appears that a given set of electrodes was used only in solvents of a particular composition; furthermore, these electrodes were kept in this solvent rather than being returned to water frequently for reconditioning. A suitable standardization was made in each solvent mixture by measurement of a solution of hydrochloric acid. The results for the dissociation constant of formic acid in methanol-water mixtures agree well with those obtained by Shedlovsky and Kay (83) by a conductance method.

The primary effect on the response of the glass electrode of adding alcohol or acetone to the water solvent has been described as a contraction of the linear portion of the emf/pH curve (84, 85). In 40% ethanol, the theoretical slope is said to be maintained from pH 3 to pH 9.5, but in 70% ethanol departures appear at pH 7. The interpretation of these findings is obviously dependent on what is meant by pH in these partially aqueous media. When proper care is taken to keep the pH-sensitive membrane of the glass electrode saturated with water, useful data can be obtained in mixtures of benzene and isopropyl alcohol. The electrode has been used in glacial acetic acid, and, very likely, is capable of yielding data of some utility in many other media of very diverse nature, as the studies of Schwabe indicate (56). The glass electrode behaves well in hydrogen peroxide (86, 87). In order to use the glass electrode successfully as a proton electrode in this solvent, however, Mitchell and Wynne-Jones found it necessary to make corrections for dehydration and for the changing asymmetry potential.

The glass electrode has been conspicuously successful in indicating the end-points of acid-base titrations in many different solvent systems and undoubtedly serves as a satisfactory reference for the observation of the changes in potential of other indicator electrodes in these media. It must be emphasized, however, that the validity of the measured potentials themselves is never subject to test, in the absence of a direct comparison with the hydrogen electrode.

C. Care of Glass Electrodes

The rationale of the maintenance of the glass electrode in a manner consistent with a long life and satisfactory performance is contained in the discussions of the properties of the electrode in the foregoing sections. The pH-sensitive membrane is essentially a fragile silicon-oxygen lattice swollen by sorption of water and rendered pH-responsive through the exchange of its alkali metal ions for some of the hydrogen ions present in the aqueous solution in which it was initially conditioned. When the membrane is kept immersed in water, the leaching of alkali metal ions and the deterioration of the inner layers of glass by deeper penetration of water is arrested and the life of the electrode is prolonged. The membrane is, however, a labile structure readily susceptible to chemical attack. Its ion-exchange properties are impaired by dehydration, and the silicon-oxygen bonds that give it form and substance are destroyed by alkalies, particularly at high temperatures. For these reasons, the life of glass electrodes can be prolonged by keeping the surface wet with water and by limiting its exposure to dehydrating and corrosive solutions to relatively brief periods.

Mechanical damage of the membrane may result from contact with solution cups, scratching by abrasive solids, or from the etching effect of corrosive solutions. Mechanical stresses, resulting from chemical attack followed by drying, may produce minute cracks in the glass membrane. Cracks may likewise appear after many months of use, simply as the result of normal thinning and deterioration of the membrane. Whatever the cause, mechanical failure is often undetected for a time, and the user may be unaware that erroneous results are being obtained. To guard against this unfortunate occurrence, the pH response of glass electrodes should be checked frequently by measurement of the emf of a glass–calomel cell with two buffer solutions that differ in pH by several units. For this purpose, the phthalate and borax solutions are satisfactory. The pH values of these solutions are given in Table I.

The pH response is also impaired by surface deposits which interfere with rapid establishment of equilibrium between the solution phase and the glass phase. Films of metallic silver, petrolatum, or silicone grease only 30 Å in thickness have been found to lower the pH response of the glass electrode from 59 to 52 mv per pH unit (88). Some colloidal materials adhere tenaciously to the glass surface. Needless to say, the electrode should be kept free of all such deposits. Washing with water and gentle rubbing with soft tissue is the preferred method of removing them. Cleaning in a 6 M solution of hydrochloric acid followed by thorough rinsing with water is the next expedient. Organic material not removed by this treatment is sometimes readily dissolved by a 70% ethanol solution. Glass electrodes often become sluggish in their response after prolonged or severe attack, but attempts at rejuvenation by immersing them in fluoride solutions cannot be recommended.

Water-repellent silicone coatings to retard fouling of the electrode are available commercially. It is likely that a repellent coating of this sort may have substantial advantages in many applications of the glass electrode, for example in retarding the clotting of blood at the glass surface, which is a source of considerable difficulty in many physiological studies. Unfortunately, it appears that the coating is destroyed by contact with solutions of high pH, so that it is probably incapable of offering prolonged protection of the membrane from attack by alkaline solutions.

The effect of hydrophobic coatings on the water content of the swollen layer and on the asymmetry potential of the glass electrode is an intriguing subject which has not, to the author's knowledge, been adequately examined.

REFERENCES

1. Thomson, W., *Proc. Roy. Soc.* **A23**, 463 (1875).
2. Kratz, L., "Die Glaselektrode und Ihre Anwendungen." Steinkopff, Frankfurt am Main, Germany, 1950.
3. von Helmholtz, H., *J. Chem. Soc.* **39**, 277 (1881).
4. Cremer, M., *Z. Biol.* **29**, 562 (1906).
5. Haber, F., and Klemensiewicz, Z., *Z. physik. Chem.* **67**, 385 (1909).
6. Borelius, G., *Ann. Physik.* **45**, 929 (1914); **50**, 447 (1916).
7. Hughes, W. S., *J. Am. Chem. Soc.* **44**, 2860 (1922).
8. MacInnes, D. A., and Dole, M., *J. Am. Chem. Soc.* **52**, 29 (1930).
9. Ssokolof, S. I., and Passynsky, A. H., *Z. physik. Chem.* **A160**, 366 (1932).
10. Perley, G. A., *Anal. Chem.* **21**, 394 (1949).
11. Cary, H. H., and Baxter, W. P., *U. S. Patent* 2,462,843 (1949).
12. Dole, M., "The Glass Electrode." Wiley, New York, 1941.
13. Lengyel, B., *Z. physik. Chem.* **153**, 425 (1931); **154**, 371 (1931).

14. Lengyel, B., *Z. physik. Chem.* **159**, 145 (1932).

15. Lengyel, B., and Matrai, T., *Z. physik. Chem.* **159**, 393 (1932).

16. Dole, M., Roberts, R. M., and Holley, C. E., *J. Am. Chem. Soc.* **63**, 725 (1941).

17. Warren, B. F., *Chem. Revs.* **26**, 237 (1940).

18. Hubbard, D., Hamilton, E. H., and Finn, A. N., *J. Research Natl. Bur. Standards* **46**, 168 (1951).

19. Gross, P., and Halpern, O., *Z. physik. Chem.* **115**, 54 (1925); **118**, 255 (1925).

20. Ray, R. C., Ganguly, P. B., and Sarkar, B. P., *J. Indian Chem. Soc.* **19**, 61 (1942).

21. Hughes, W. S., *J. Chem. Soc.* p. 491 (1928).

22. Britton, H. T. S., "Hydrogen Ions," 4th ed., Vol. I. Van Nostrand, Princeton, 1956.

23. Horovitz, K., *Z. Physik.* **15**, 369 (1923).

24. Horovitz, K., *Z. physik. Chem.* **115**, 424 (1925); Horovitz, K., and Zimmerman, J., *Sitzber. Akad. Wiss. Wien Abt. IIa* **134**, 355 (1925).

25. Lark-Horovitz, K., *Naturwissenschaften* **19**, 397 (1931); *Nature* **127**, 440 (1931).

26. Izmailov, N. A., and Vasil'ev, A. G., *Zhur. Fiz. Khim.* **29**, 1866, 2145 (1955); **30**, 1500 (1956).

27. Haugaard, G., *Nature* **120**, 66 (1937); *Compt. rend. trav. lab. Carlsberg* **22**, 199 (1938); *Glastech. Ber.* **17**, 104 (1939).

28. MacInnes, D. A., and Belcher, D., *J. Am. Chem. Soc.* **53**, 3315 (1931).

29. Nicolsky, B. P., *Acta Physicochim. U.R.S.S.* **7**, 597 (1937).

30. Dole, M., *J. Am. Chem. Soc.* **53**, 4260 (1931).

31. Gross, P., and Halpern, O., *J. Chem. Phys.* **2**, 136 (1934).

32. Dole, M., *J. Chem. Phys.* **2**, 862 (1934).

33. Gurney, R. W., *Proc. Roy. Soc.* **A134**, 137 (1931); **A136**, 378 (1932).

34. Dole, M., and Wiener, B. Z., *Trans. Electrochem. Soc.* **72**, 107 (1937).

35. Sørensen, S. P. L., *Biochem. Z.* **21**, 131, 201 (1909); *Compt. rend. trav. lab. Carlsberg* **8**, 1 (1909).

36. Bower, V. E., and Bates, R. G., *J. Research Natl. Bur. Standards* **59**, 261 (1957).

37. Bates, R. G., "Electrometric pH Determinations," Chap. 2, 4, 7, 8, and 9. Wiley, New York, 1954.

38. Sendroy, J., Jr., "Symposium on pH Measurement," p. 55. ASTM Tech. Publ. No. 190, Philadelphia, 1957.

39. Sendroy, J., Jr., Shedlovsky, T., and Belcher, D., *J. Biol. Chem.* **115**, 529 (1936).

40. Yoshimura, H., *J. Biochem. (Japan)* **23**, 335 (1936).

41. Yoshimura, H., and Fujimoto, T., *J. Biochem. (Japan)* **25**, 493 (1937).

42. Diamond, J. J., and Hubbard, D., *J. Research Natl. Bur. Standards* **47**, 443 (1951).

43. Amis, E. S., and Gabbard, J. L., *J. Am. Chem. Soc.* **59**, 557 (1937).

44. Dole, M., *J. Phys. Chem.* **36**, 1570 (1932).

45. Humphreys, R. G., *Glastech. Ber.* **17**, 277 (1939).

46. Dole, M., *J. Am. Chem. Soc.* **54**, 2120, 3095 (1932).

47. Goldman, R. G., and Hubbard, D., *J. Research Natl. Bur. Standards* **48**, 370 (1952).

48. Lengyel, B., and Vincze, J., *Glastech. Ber.* **19**, 359 (1941).

49. Schwabe, K., and Glöckner, G., *Z. Elektrochem.* **59**, 504 (1955).

50. Boksay, Z., Csákvári, B., and Lengyel, B., *Z. physik. Chem. (Leipzig)* **207**, 223 (1957).

51. Hughes, W. S., *Chem. Eng. Mining Rev.* **20**, 105 (1927).

52. Lengyel, B., and Blum, E., *Trans. Faraday Soc.* **30**, 461 (1934).

53. Perley, G. A., *Anal. Chem.* **21**, 391, 559 (1949).

54. Eisenman, G., Rudin, D. O., and Casby, J. U., *Science*, **126**, 831 (1957).

54a. Isard, J. O., *Nature* **184**, 1616 (1959).

55. Hubbard, D., *J. Research Natl. Bur. Standards* **36**, 365 (1946).

56. Schwabe, K., "Fortschritte der pH-Messtechnik." Verlag Technik, Berlin, 1953; *Chem. Tech. (Berlin)* **6**, 301 (1954).

57. Simon, W., and Wegmann, D., *Helv. Chim. Acta* **41**, 2099 (1958).

58. Lengyel, B., Somogi, M., and Boksay, Z., *Z. physik. Chem. (Leipzig)* **209**, 15 (1958).

59. Lengyel, B., and Till, F., *Egypt. J. Chem.* **1**, No. 1, 99 (1958).

60. Hubbard, D., and Rynders, G. F., *J. Research Natl. Bur. Standards* **40**, 105 (1948).

61. Hubbard, D., *J. Research Natl. Bur. Standards* **36**, 511 (1946).

62. Kratz, L., *Glastech. Ber.* **20**, 305 (1942).

63. Berger, E., *Glastech. Ber.* **14**, 351 (1936).

64. Hubbard, D., Black, M. H., Holley, S. F., and Rynders, G. F., *J. Research Natl. Bur. Standards* **46**, 168 (1951).

65. Rasch, E., and Hinrichsen, F. W., *Z. Elektrochem.* **14**, 41 (1908).

66. Ingruber, O. V., *Ind. Chemist*, December (1956).

67. MacInnes, D. A., and Belcher, D., *Ind. Eng. Chem., Anal. Ed.* **5**, 199 (1931).

68. Eckfeldt, E. L., and Perley, G. A., *J. Electrochem. Soc.* **98**, 37 (1951).

69. Laug, E. P., *J. Am. Chem. Soc.* **56**, 1034 (1934).

70. Yoshimura, H., *Bull. Chem. Soc. Japan* **12**, 359, 443 (1937).

71. Bräuer, W., *Glastech. Ber.* **19**, 268 (1941), *Z. Elektrochem.* **47**, 638 (1941).

72. Beck, W. H., and Wynne-Jones, W. F. K., *J. chim. phys.* **49**, C97 (1952).

73. Hamilton, E. H., and Hubbard, D., *J. Research Natl. Bur. Standards* **27**, 27 (1941).

74. Covington, A. K., and Prue, J. E., *J. Chem. Soc.* 3696, 3701 (1955); 1567 (1957).

74a. Covington, A. K., *J. Chem. Soc.*, 4441 (1960).

75. Thompson, M. R., *J. Research Natl. Bur. Standards* **9**, 833 (1932).

76. Fricke, H. K., "Beiträge zur Angewandten Glasforschung" (E. Schott, ed.), p. 175. Wissenschaftliche Verlagsges., Stuttgart, 1959.

77. Electronic Instruments Ltd., "Temperature Effects in pH Measurements and the Use of the Isopotential pH." TDS-pH-2, April 29, 1959.

78. Simon, W., and Wegmann, D., *Helv. Chim. Acta* **41**, 2309 (1958).

79. Hartree, E. F., *Biochem. J.* **52**, 619 (1952).

80. Clark, W. R., and Perley, G. A., "Symposium on pH Measurement," p. 34. ASTM Tech. Publ. No. 190, Philadelphia, 1957.

81. Beckman, A. O., "The Development of pH Instrumentation." Reprint No. R-36, National Technical Laboratories, South Pasadena, California, 1950.

82. Bacarella, A. L., Grunwald, E., Marshall, H. P., and Purlee, E. L., *J. Org. Chem.* **20**, 747 (1955); *J. Phys. Chem.* **62**, 856 (1958).

83. Shedlovsky, T., and Kay, R. L., *J. Phys. Chem.* **60**, 151 (1956).

84. Izmailov, N. A., and Bel'gova, M. A., *Zhur. Obschei Khim.* **8**, 1873 (1938).

85. Izmailov, N. A., and Frantsevich-Zabludovskaya, T. F., *Zhur. Obschei Khim.* **15**, 283 (1945).

86. Mitchell, A. G., and Wynne-Jones, W. F. K., *Trans. Faraday Soc.* **51**, 1690 (1955).

87. Kolczynski, J. R., Roth, E. M., and Shanley, E. S., *J. Am. Chem. Soc.* **79**, 531 (1957).

88. Hubbard, D., and Rynders, G. F., *J. Research Natl. Bur. Standards* **41**, 163 (1948).

Chapter Six

The Quinhydrone Electrode

G. J. Janz and D. J. G. Ives

I. Introduction

A. STATUS OF THE QUINHYDRONE ELECTRODE

In 1904, Haber and Russ (*1*) established the fact that *p*-benzoquinone (quinone) and its hydroquinone (quinol) form an electrochemically reversible oxidation-reduction system in which hydrogen ions participate. It may be represented

$$C_6H_4O_2 + 2H^+ + 2e^- \rightleftharpoons C_6H_4(OH)_2$$

It was not until 1921 that Biilmann (*2*) and, independently, Granger and Nelson (*3*) realized the potentialities of this discovery. Rapid exploitation followed, no doubt stimulated by concurrent growth of interest in organic oxidation-reduction systems, associated particularly with the names of Conant, Fieser, and Michaelis. A new alternative to the hydrogen electrode had appeared, simple and convenient, capable of high precision, and suitable for application in biological, medical, agricultural, and industrial fields. Interest in the new electrode reached a maximum between 1924 and 1928, and then quite rapidly declined. This was undoubtedly due to the rise of the glass electrode, which has supplanted all others as the most versatile and convenient, even if not the most accurate, instrument for pH determination. At present the quinhydrone electrode appears to be so infrequently used as to be obsolescent, but an objective reappraisal suggests that it is more out of favor than its limitations warrant. Its more desirable properties may be summarized as follows.

Under restricted but well-defined conditions, the quinhydrone electrode potential responds theoretically to pH and is reproducible to a few microvolts (4, 5). Equilibrium is attained rapidly ["almost instantaneously" to "in a few minutes" (5–7)]. Unlike the glass electrode, the quinhydrone electrode is of low impedance and, under normal conditions, has a reasonably high exchange current (8); this allows it to be applied in simple titration techniques which require no potentiometric equipment except a galvanometer (9–11), and in differential potentiometric titrations of excessively dilute solutions, e.g., 0.0004 N acetic acid (12). The quinhydrone electrode is open to the objection that its use requires the addition of a foreign substance to the solution under investigation, but, in the "unsaturated electrode," the minimum addition required is extremely small; 0.00016 M quinhydrone is capable of sustaining electrode potentials definable to 0.1 mv (6) and 0.00033 M is adequate for pH determination to ±0.05 pH unit (13).

Unlike the hydrogen electrode, the quinhydrone electrode is insensitive to barometric pressure and normally exerts no reducing action on any component in solution. It can be used in the presence of nitric acid (2) at concentrations as high as 1 M (14), or in the presence of ethylenic, acetylenic and halogen-substituted acids (2, 15) and of many metallic salts, e.g., Zn, Cd, Hg (5), Ni, Co, Fe, and even Cu (16). The quinhydrone electrode can therefore be used in cells without liquid junction under circumstances which would preclude use of the hydrogen electrode, and can thus provide thermodynamic results of a precision hard to obtain otherwise. It can also be used for accurate measurements in solutions which must be maintained in equilibrium with carbon dioxide (17), a matter which is important in the study of biological fluids (18). It is applicable in many partly aqueous and many nonaqueous media, including methanol (19), ethanol (20), n-butanol (21), acetone (22–24), and formic acid (25). It can be used in the presence of phenols and cresols (26). One of its congeners, the chloranil electrode, has been outstandingly successful in studies of anhydrous, "superacid" systems (27).

The quinhydrone electrode is simple in construction and is suitable for expeditiously preparing reference half-cells of fixed potential (28–31) which are highly reproducible and respond more rapidly than calomel half-cells to changes in temperature (29); they are, however, less permanent (32) and are no longer used in the construction of glass electrodes (33). The electrode is easily adapted to the micro-scale for dealing with a few drops of solution (2), and many convenient micro–half-cells have been described (18, 34–36). It is also suitable for assessing the pH of very viscous or semi-solid materials (37) and has, in its day, been applied to almost every conceivable kind of system from nickel-plating baths (38) to cheese (39). Bibliographies dealing with these applications have appeared (4, 18) covering the peak period of publication up to 1930.

The quinhydrone electrode has been used in fundamental studies requiring considerable accuracy of measurement. Apart from the early work of Schreiner (40) and of Larsson (41), outstanding examples are found in the classical studies of Auerbach and Smolczyk (42) on the pH titration curves of dibasic acids, in the measurements by Güntelberg and Schiødt (17) of the mean ion activity coefficients of hydrogen and bicarbonate ions in strong electrolyte solutions, and, more recently, in the extensive work of the Sillén school (43) on the hydrolysis of metal ions. It is fair to note, however, that some of the latter work has had to be repeated with use of a glass electrode (44) because of a previously unsuspected and uncommon error due to the basic properties of quinone.

B. Basic Theory

The essential theory of the quinhydrone electrode was understood by its discoverers (1–3). It has been frequently expounded in reviews (15, 45) and elaborated (46–48) and is given in standard texts (18, 33, 49–51). Only a brief outline is therefore required in the present section.

In the cell

$$\text{H}_2, P = 1 \text{ atm}, \text{Pt} \mid \text{HCl}, m \mathrel{\vdots} \text{HCl}, m, \text{Q}, \text{QH}_2 \mid \text{Pt or Au}$$

where Q and QH_2 represent small concentrations of quinone and hydroquinone in solution, there is no appreciable liquid-junction potential, and the cell reaction is the reduction of quinone to hydroquinone,

$$\text{Q} + \text{H}_2 = \text{QH}_2$$

The emf of the cell is

$$E = E° + \frac{RT}{2F} \ln \frac{a_Q}{a_{QH_2}} = E° + \frac{RT}{2F} \ln \frac{C_Q}{C_{QH_2}} + \frac{RT}{2F} \ln \frac{f_Q}{f_{QH_2}} \quad (1)$$

in which the terms representing activities, concentrations and activity coefficients are self-evident. If the ratio of the concentrations of quinone and of hydroquinone is kept constant, and if the ratio of their activity coefficients remains equal to unity (for nonelectrolytic solutes in dilute solution this condition is likely to be satisfied), it is clear that the emf of the cell will be independent of the concentration of the electrolyte, hydrochloric acid, and of the concentrations (in fixed ratio) of quinone and hydroquinone. For the p-benzoquinone system it is a very convenient circumstance that the quinone and its hydroquinone form a stable, sparingly soluble 1:1 molecular compound, called quinhydrone, $Q \cdot QH_2$. Use of this compound, which is extensively dissociated in aqueous solution (52), automatically fixes the concentration ratio of its components at unity. For cells made up with the use of quinhydrone, Biilmann (2) showed the emf to be independent of quinhydrone concentration from 0.005 M to saturation (0.018 M at 25°C) and of hydrochloric acid concentration (with reservations to be discussed in due course). It follows that the potential of the quinhydrone electrode must vary as a function of hydrogen ion activity in the same way as the potential of the hydrogen electrode. Biilmann took the view that, indeed, the electrode may be regarded as a hydrogen electrode kept in equilibrium with an extremely low partial pressure of hydrogen provided by the quinone–hydroquinone system. Whilst it may be legitimate to say that there is a definite, if very low, chemical potential of hydrogen associated with this system at each temperature, the pressure of hydrogen corresponding with the cell emf at 25°C, 0.6990 int volt, is $10^{-23.64}$ atm. As pointed out by La Mer and Parsons (53), this pressure (which would be provided by 1.4 molecules in 22.4 liters) is far too small to be anything but a thermodynamic fiction, and its derivation can carry no implication that the mechanism of the quinhydrone electrode reaction is anything like that of the hydrogen electrode reaction. That it is not is strongly suggested by the fact that the former will occur freely at a metal substrate which cannot catalyze the latter. The matter is settled by the observation (54) that quinone, deliberately presented with hydrogen atoms, prefers to undergo reduction (in aqueous solution) by successive electron and proton additions.

The electrode reaction is best discussed in terms of the equilibrium

$$Q + 2H^+ + 2e^- \rightleftharpoons QH_2$$

and the corresponding expressions for the electrode potential,

$$E = E^\circ + \frac{RT}{2F} \ln \frac{a_Q \cdot (a_{H^+})^2}{a_{QH_2}} \tag{2}$$

$$= E^\circ + \frac{RT}{2F} \ln \frac{a_Q}{a_{QH_2}} + \frac{RT}{F} \ln a_{H^+} \tag{3}$$

Equation (3) shows that, provided the second term on the right-hand side can be kept constant (ideally, at zero), the electrode will show a "proper hydrogen electrode function." It is in meeting this requirement precisely that difficulties arise.

C. Sources of Departure from Ideal Behavior

These may be summarized, as a preliminary to detailed treatment in Section III, as follows.

(i) As with all reference electrodes, inadequate exchange currents will lead to difficulties associated with ready polarization, or with displacements of potential caused by mixed control, arising from the entry of undesired electrode processes.

(ii) Hydroquinone is a dibasic acid. Although the first dissociation constant is small, and the second still smaller, this property must become of increasing significance with rising pH, and limits the pH range over which the quinhydrone electrode is useful. According to circumstances, the errors become appreciable at pH values in excess of 6 to 9. Two effects enter; one is the partial transfer of potential control to an alternative process, such as

$$Q + 2e^- + H^+ \rightleftharpoons QH^-$$

or

$$Q + 2e^- \rightleftharpoons Q^{2-}$$

which give a different, or no dependence of potential on pH. The other effect is alteration of the pH of the solution under investigation because the electrode sets up its own, competing buffer system. If the original solution is poorly buffered, it may suffer considerable change in pH.

(iii) Hydroquinone is a reducing agent and undergoes aerial oxidation at a rate which increases quite abruptly with rising pH at around pH 8, because it is the ions of hydroquinone which are principally concerned. The oxidation is irreversible, leading to the formation of colored products of high molecular weight, and possibly to hydrogen peroxide. Although this action may be obviated by use of nitrogen-swept solutions, it places a restriction on the pH range in which the electrode can be freely used.

(iv) Quinone is a base, and is capable of accepting a proton to form an ion QH^+. Errors due to this are not obtrusive, but may enter significantly in strongly acid solutions; they have been mentioned in relation to Sillén's work (43).

(v) Quinone is an oxidizing agent. Although this does not usually cause trouble (hydrogen, of course, must be excluded from a quinhydrone electrode based on platinum), there is the general point that the oxidation-reduction system proper to the electrode is formally capable of interacting with another oxidation-reduction system that may be present in the solution. The fact that often it does not do so seems usually to be a happy accident of reaction kinetics, the undesired reaction being so much slower than the electrode response.

(vi) Quinone is chemically reactive in other ways. It is chlorinated with remarkable ease, even by aqueous hydrochloric acid. There is some doubt as to how significant this reaction may be under normal circumstances, but "creeping potentials" have been assigned to it. Quinone also reacts with amino compounds, and is even not entirely indifferent to ammonium ions, let alone free ammonia. This was the source of "protein errors" which proved to be a grave nuisance in biochemical studies. In the presence of nitric acid and oxygen, quinone is oxidized to black, polymeric products. Probably the impermanence of quinhydrone electrodes is to be principally ascribed to quinone, for it is said to undergo photochemical decomposition in aqueous solutions. Quinone is also volatile, and this introduces some difficulty in ensuring that quinhydrone (especially in relation to the surface layers of the crystals) is, and remains, strictly stoichiometric.

(vii) Both quinone and hydroquinone show departures from ideal behavior (i.e., deviations from Henry's law) when the solution phase contains electrolytes, and these are best considered first in terms of a single, non-electrolytic solute. At a given temperature, the activity of such a solute in its saturated solution is fixed by equilibrium with the solid phase, and this remains true even when the solubility is reduced by the salting-out effect of an added electrolyte. Thus, $a = Cf$ remains constant because when the activity coefficient, f, is increased from its ideal value of unity, the concentration, C, diminishes to the extent required to maintain equilibrium.

Conditions are somewhat different in a saturated solution of quinhydrone because it is *unsaturated* with respect to each of the dissociation products, quinone and hydroquinone. The activities of these substances in solution are therefore not *separately* fixed. While their concentrations are necessarily always equal, mass action law requires the *product* of their activities to remain constant, i.e., in any saturated solution of quinhydrone at a given temperature, the following conditions must always be satisfied:

$$\frac{C_Q}{C_{QH_2}} = 1$$

$$C_Q f_Q \cdot C_{QH_2} f_{QH_2} = \text{constant}$$

(4)

If, now, the activity coefficients f_Q and f_{QH_2} are increased by salting-out, the concentrations C_Q and C_{QH_2} will be diminished, but they must be *equally* diminished. Thus, unless the activity coefficients also remain equal to each other, the ratio of the activities of the components cannot remain equal to unity. This means that the second term on the right-hand side of Eq. (3) cannot remain equal to zero. Since salting-out effects upon quinone and hydroquinone are unequal, the activity coefficients, when not equal to unity, are different. This gives rise to "salt errors," which are present at all finite concentrations of electrolyte in solution. In practice, however, these errors are often less than errors from experimental sources, or, if this is not the case, they can frequently be treated by fairly satisfactory quantitative methods.

(viii) There must also be an effect upon ionic activities exerted by quinone and hydroquinone, but this is less clear-cut and normally far less significant. It cannot be denied, however, that the presence of these molecular solutes may alter the properties of the solvent, which can no longer be considered strictly as pure water.

(ix) Finally, in the presence of solutes of high molecular weight, or of colloids or precipitates, preferential adsorption effects may cause difficulties.

II. Theory of the Quinhydrone Electrode

A. Oxidation-Reduction Systems

1. General Considerations

Ideally, the inert metal electrode in a homogeneous oxidation-reduction system serves only to acquire the electrochemical potential of electrons (cf. Chapter 1, Section II) determined by the prevailing redox equilibrium in solution. The metal participates in the specific charge transfer which is going on throughout the solution phase, and is called upon only to act as a donor and acceptor of electrons. It is immaterial what metal is used (provided it is sufficiently noble), and this has been experimentally confirmed in a number of cases (*55*). Then, since no solid phases are involved as reactants or products in the electrode reaction, no difficulties in bringing solid substances into reproducible states can enter, and such electrodes should be well-behaved above all others.

Some of the expectations based upon such an oversimplified picture of how these electrodes work are illusory. Electron-transfer processes in solution are anything but simple and require an activation energy (*56*), so that the electrode may well be required to act catalytically. In any case, the rate of transfer of electrons across the surface of a metal is critically dependent upon the state of the surface, particularly in relation to the presence of films of oxide or impurity. Poisoning can reduce the exchange current of an electrode of this kind to 1% of its maximal value (*57*). On balance, however, it is a fact that these oxidation-reduction electrodes are well-behaved, rapidly attaining reproducible equilibrium potentials. But they have no general application for reference purposes (and are therefore not discussed, as such, in this book), unless the oxidation-reduction reaction involves hydrogen ions, when electrode potential becomes dependent on pH. For practical purposes, exploitation of this fact is limited to the quinone–hydroquinone systems with which this chapter deals.

2. Organic Oxidation-Reduction Systems

Most organic reductions involve hydrogen ions, but are irreversible because they produce electron-pair covalent bonds which do not ionize sufficiently to sustain a reverse reaction. Thus, for the complete reaction

$$R + 2e^- \rightarrow R^{2-}$$

$$R^{2-} + 2H^+ \rightarrow R \begin{array}{c} H \\ \diagup \\ \diagdown \\ H \end{array}$$

to be effectively reversible, both R–H bonds must have appreciable acidic dissociation. If, for example, R is an aldehyde and RH_2 is a primary alcohol, one of these bonds is C–H; although this does not necessarily preclude ionization, it usually does inhibit any significant back reaction. For effective reversibility, both of the bonds must normally be formed between hydrogen and an atom of adequate electronegativity, such as oxygen or nitrogen.

It is necessary to distinguish between *reductions* in which electrons and protons are successively taken up, as in the above scheme of reaction, and *hydrogenations*, which proceed by addition of hydrogen atoms. This distinction was made by Conant and Cutter (*58*) and is clearly seen in the marked differences (e.g., in the effects of poisons) between cathodic reductions and catalytic hydrogenations (*59*). For the reverse processes, the distinction is the same as that between heterolytic and homolytic reactions (*60*). Only reversible reductions involving electron transfer are of direct electrochemical interest.

Conditions favoring the easy occurrence of such reactions are summarized in the Shaffer-Michaelis theory of 1-electron transfer steps. Shaffer (*61*) proposed a "principle of equi-valence change," according to which transfer can occur as a result of bimolecular collision only if the valency changes of the reducing and oxidizing entities are numerically the same. Otherwise, transfers with no electrons "left over" could occur only in relatively improbable multiple encounters. In such a case, the barrier to reaction arising from inequality of the numbers of electrons offered and required (e.g., Tl^+ and Ce^{4+}) is annulled by addition of a mediator (e.g., Mn^{2+}) capable of stepwise valency variation, and thus able to bridge the gap by passing electrons one or two at a time. There are, however, alternative explanations for the slowness of certain oxidations (62), upon which this theory was based.

The Michaelis principle (63, 64) is that "whenever a bivalent oxidation can be brought about by two successive univalent oxidations, then the kinetics of such a reaction will be greatly enhanced." The view has recently been expressed (65) that it cannot be generally valid. The situation is that later work with new techniques has shown the problems of charge transfer to be more complex than was formerly supposed. But if some of the earlier conclusions cannot be supported in detail, the combined statement of these two principles in the simplest form — that reaction is all the easier when the valency changes of the two reactants are equally matched, particularly when both are unit changes — remains rooted in common sense and certainly provides useful general guidance. This is specially true of organic reactions.

If a reduction reaction produces one stable organic compound from another, it must involve the transfer of at least two electrons in order to form one electron-pair bond. If, by the Michaelis principle, this must proceed by two successive 1-electron steps, there must be an intermediate radical which contains an odd number of electrons. Since such radicals are normally very unstable, this necessity would correspond with the existence of a high potential barrier to the reaction. But in certain systems there are structural features which confer a degree of stability upon the radicals, and it is strong support for the Michaelis theory that such systems provide most, if not all, of the organic charge transfer reactions which can be used to establish reversible electrodes. Most of the substances concerned have "double-ended" molecules with, in the oxidized form, terminal oxygen or nitrogen atoms which are linked with each other by a conjugated system of double and single bonds. Such are quinones (hydroquinones), quinone imines (aminophenols), quinone diimines (phenylenediamines), diphenoquinone (pp'-dihydroxydiphenyl) and many quinonoid dyes (corresponding leuco-compounds); extensive lists have been tabulated (66). The radical QH, or its ion, Q^-, derived from a quinone ("holoquinone"), Q, is called a semiquinone and is stabilized by resonance; alternatively, the odd electron is accommodated in a nonlocalized molecular orbital. Direct evidence has been obtained for the existence of semiquinone species in solution by magnetic and spectroscopic methods (66). Their behavior in solution must be considered in terms of three reactions (67); dismutation into fully oxidized and fully reduced products, dimerization to form a meriquinone (e.g., quinhydrone) and, because of their reactivity, their removal by any irreversible reaction, perhaps condensation with some other constituent, or oxidation to polymeric products. The equilibrium constant for semiquinone formation (or the dismutation constant) varies with pH (68). If the semiquinone is anionic in nature (quinones), its formation is favored by rising pH. If, on the other hand, it is cationic (p-phenylenediamine), the reverse is the case. There is a clear relation with the well-known tendencies of these systems to undergo oxidative "decomposition" in alkaline and acid media, respectively.

The behavior of such oxidation-reduction systems has been extensively studied by a potentiometric titration method pioneered by Clark (69) in which, for example, the potential of a platinum or gold electrode in a solution of a quinone is followed, at constant pH, throughout the course of a titration with titanous chloride solution. Alternatively, a hydroquinone may be titrated in a similar way with an oxidizing agent, such as potassium ferricyanide, dichromate, or some other quinone. The theory of these titrations has been reviewed by Michaelis and Schubert (70) and is outlined in standard texts (66, 71). It therefore need not be discussed, except to say that the shape of the titration curves varies in a calculable way according to whether the value of the semiquinone formation constant is large or small. In the former case, the curve has two well-marked inflections corresponding with two distinct 1-electron transfer steps; in the latter, it has but one inflection and has a shape indistinguishable from that expected for a single-step, 2-electron transfer (for an illustration, see reference 49, p. 298).

From such titrations, "formal" oxidation-reduction potentials [defined by equality of concentrations of oxidized and reduced forms (72)] at each fixed pH may be easily derived. The values so obtained agree, as would be expected, with those derived from normally established cells, or by polarographic methods (73). If such data, determined over a pH range, are plotted as a function of pH, curves are obtained which clearly indicate the state of ionization of the entities participating in the redox reaction. Thus, if a 2-electron reduction is accompanied by the addition of two hydrogen ions to form an undissociated hydroquinone, a linear plot of slope 0.059 volt at 25°C is obtained, in accordance with the appropriate Nernst equation. If, however, the singly-charged hydroquinone ion is formed, the line will have half this slope, and if the doubly-charged ion, zero slope. In general, the plot will show linear segments over the pH ranges within which these alternatives predominantly occur, and their points of intersection may be used to read off the pK values for the first and second dissociations of the hydroquinone. Such a plot was obtained from the study of anthraquinone β-sulfonate in one of the earlier papers of Conant and Fieser and their co-workers (71, 74). In some cases the acidic dissociations of oxidized, semi-quinone and reduced forms may all be significant in distinguishable pH ranges; this was so in the interesting case of pyocyanine (66, 68), for which the ranges for two-step reduction (pH < 6) and one-step reduction (pH 6–10) were also clearly marked by characteristic color changes.

The titration method was applied by Conant and Fieser (75) to measurements over a range of temperatures, in order to determine free and total energies of reduction of quinones. The effect of variation of solvent on these quantities has been studied (76) and a range of benzo-, naphtho-, and anthraquinones has been surveyed (77). Many systems, including hydroxy-quinones, phenanthrenequinones, aminonaphthoquinones and naphtho-quinones have been studied in this way by Fieser (78, 79). The method has been developed and extended by Geake (80). The results of such studies are of predominant interest in theoretical organic chemistry and have been extensively discussed in this connection by Branch and Calvin (81), and such discussions continue (82–84). It appears that there is a need for more accurate thermochemical data on quinone–hydroquinone systems for purposes of advancing theoretical interpretations of free energies of reduction (85) in terms of the difference in resonance energy between benzenoid and quinonoid structures, or otherwise. Strictly, data appertaining to the gaseous state should be used for such a purpose (86).

Compounds in this group provide most of the important redox indicators, and several semiquinonoid systems act as potential mediators by which oxidations or reductions, otherwise extremely slow, can be accomplished. In either case, the desired function depends upon the reversibility of successive 1-electron transfer steps (87).

Quinones are also important agents in organic "hydrogen transfer reactions" (88), performing dehydrogenations. These reactions occur best in polar solvents by a heterolytic fission mechanism, in which a hydrogen atom, with its pair of bonding electrons, is taken by the quinone, Q, from the hydro-aromatic donor to form the hydroquinone anion, QH^-. This rate-limiting step is followed by rapid proton transfer to form the molecule, QH_2. The reaction is catalyzed by proton donors which form the *cation* QH^+, which has an even greater affinity than the quinone for "anionoid hydrogen." It is interesting that the free energies of activation of these reactions are related linearly to the standard redox potentials of the quinone–hydroquinone systems concerned.

3. Electrochemical Applications of Quinone–Hydroquinone Systems

From the brief survey of organic oxidation-reduction systems given in the preceding section, it might be thought that there is a wide choice for setting up reference electrodes for pH measurement. The earlier studies of quinone systems by the titration method suggested that this might well be so. This applies particularly to the careful survey made by La Mer and Baker in 1922 (89); the $E°$ values (pH = 0) at 25°C for eight quinones in aqueous solution covered a potentially useful range, were easily determinable with 0.1 mv accuracy or better and, where valid checks could be made (quinone and toluquinone), agreed precisely with the results of Biilmann (2) from normally established cells. La Mer and Baker's data are shown in Table I.

TABLE I

$E°$ Values (pH = 0) for Quinone-Hydroquinone Systems[a,b]

Bromoquinone	0.7151	p-Xyloquinone	0.5900
Chloroquinone	0.7125	p-Thymoquinone	0.5875
Quinone	0.6990	Dimethoxyquinone	0.5139
Toluquinone	0.6454	1,4-Naphthoquinone	0.4698

[a] Int volts at 25°C.   [b] La Mer and Baker (89).

In contrast with this expectation, only the unsubstituted benzoquinone system has been extensively applied to pH determination, in the quinhydrone electrode. A few other systems have been explored, but have not been generally adopted; only the fully chlorinated derivative has been used to a considerable extent for a specialized purpose. It is possible that some of these electrode systems are worthy of further exploitation, but there are good reasons for the existing situation, and it may be useful to examine them.

There are a number of ways in which pH-responsive quinone–hydroquinone electrodes could be set up. The two components could be added to the solution so that precisely equal concentrations were attained; only the ratio of the two concentrations would need critical adjustment. This procedure is not used, although, apart from the slight extra trouble and possibility of experimental error involved, there seems no reason why it should not be. A carefully made up stock solution containing both components could be dispensed dropwise into the experimental solution (cf. ref. 13). If the two components form a stable quinhydrone, trouble is saved, for a means is apparently provided of ensuring exact equivalence of concentrations. If, in addition, the quinhydrone is a sparingly soluble solid, still more trouble is saved and conditions are more closely standardized by using it in saturated solution. It must, however, be of low enough solubility (but not too low for effective potential control) to avoid undue contamination, or change, of the solution under test. If, on the other hand, no quinhydrone is formed, the same trouble-saving effect could be attained by saturating the solution with both components. This has some advantages, but *both* must have solubilities not too high and not too low, and it is asking rather a lot to expect many systems to meet this double requirement.

Clearly, the most desirable systems are those which *either* form a well-defined, stable quinhydrone, *or* which do not form one at all, and at the same time meet rather stringent requirements in solubilities, as well as stability. It is in this way that the restrictions arise. Benzoquinone, toluquinone, thymoquinone, and 1,4-naphthoquinone form reasonably stable quinhydrones and all of them have been used, or advocated for use, for pH-indicating electrodes. Monochloroquinone does form a quinhydrone, but the hydroquinone itself is soluble in little more than its own weight of water. The three dichloroquinones and trichloroquinone form ill-defined quinhydrones, difficult to isolate. Tetrachloroquinone (chloranil), tetramethylquinone (duroquinone), and *p*-xyloquinone do not form quinhydrones, but their solubilities are too low for serviceable use in aqueous solutions. Thus, the simplest of the available systems is probably the best for general use. In other words, little is to be gained by using substituted quinone systems, for substitution seems invariably to decrease the tendency to form a stable quinhydrone of low solubility (*76*). It remains possible, however, that there may be useful exceptions to this generalization.

B. STRUCTURAL AND MECHANISTIC ASPECTS

1. The Structure of Quinhydrone

The first X-ray examination of quinhydrone was made by Foz and Palacios (*90, 91*), who, after correcting certain erroneous preliminary conclusions, established that the structure contained chains of alternating quinonoid and benzenoid units. This result was confirmed both by Anderson's X-ray measurements (*92*), which also revealed plane-to-plane stacking of the two kinds of aromatic ring, and by magnetic anisotropy measurements (*93*). The structural problem, however, called for explanations for the high density of quinhydrone (s.g. at 20°C = 1.401, as compared with 1.318 for quinone and 1.358 for hydroquinone), its deep color (which is confined to the solid state), and an identification of the forces responsible for the considerable stability, and low solubility of the crystals. Closely related problems awaited solution in relation to the formation, stability, and color of a very large class of molecular compounds, of which quinhydrone is often considered to be typical.

The first complete structure analysis of a molecular compound was made in 1943 by Powell, Huse, and Cooke (*94*), who examined the dark red product of interaction of *p*-iodoaniline with *s*-trinitrobenzene and found that the intermolecular distances between the components in the crystal were far too great for any normal kind of valency bond to exist. There was one weak hydrogen bond (length, 3.1 A) which was clearly of no great significance; certainly hydrogen bonding could not be generally invoked to explain the existence of molecular compounds, which are formed under circumstances where hydrogen bonding is inconceivable. This is the case for the purple compound between chloranil and hexamethylbenzene, later examined by Harding and Wallwork (95), and for many others. In both of these cases a structural feature appeared which recalls Anderson's findings (92), and which now seems to be common to the molecular compounds formed between aromatic components. It is the alternating, plane-to-plane stacking of the two kinds of aromatic ring, at distances from each other which are usually not less than the distances of normal van der Waals approach, and it appears that some special force of interaction is to be associated with this arrangement. If this is so, the forces concerned must be of quite long range, and various suggestions have been made about them. An early suggestion, due to Weiss (96), was that electrostatic attractions are set up as a result of 1-electron transfers from one component to the other, but this has been criticized (97, 101) on the grounds that the heats of formation are too small, and that the products are neither salt-like nor paramagnetic. Another suggestion is that the forces are due to co-operative attractions between alternating polarizing and polarizable molecules; the name "polarization bond" has been introduced in this connection (98). Deferring further consideration of their nature, it appears that some rather specialized "molecular compound forces" contribute to the stability of quinhydrone, and to these must be added the dispersion forces which normally hold the components of organic crystals together and, in all probability, rather strong hydrogen bonding as well. The problem then arises as to which of these may be predominant in controlling structure and properties in the solid state.

A partial answer was provided by Wallwork and Harding (99, 100) in their determination of the structure of phenoquinone, which is closely similar to quinhydrone. This compound is formed from two molecules of phenol and one of quinone, and was again found to contain the characteristic columnar stacking of aromatic rings with, in this case, a quinone sandwiched between two phenols as the repeating unit. The phenol–quinone interplanar distance, 3.33 Å, was again not shorter than those of normal intermolecular contacts, but each phenolic hydroxyl group was found to form a strong hydrogen bond (length, 2.64 Å) with the oxygen of a quinone molecule in an adjacent column. The important point is that the requirements of maximal hydrogen bonding were decisive in determining the 2:1 stoichiometry of the compound, as opposed to the requirements of maximal "molecular compound bonding," which would presumably be attained in a 1:1 compound. It may be noted that, in quinhydrone, both requirements are fully satisfied by 1:1 combination.

This qualitative conclusion to the effect that hydrogen bonding is an important factor was put into perspective by the semiquantitative thermodynamic studies of Suzuki and Seki (101). From heats of solution of quinhydrone and its components in acetone, and from entropies derived from data assembled by Schreiner (102), they found for the reaction

$$Q \text{ (solid)} + QH_2 \text{ (solid)} = Q \cdot QH_2 \text{ (solid)}$$

$\Delta H = -5.41$ kcal, $\Delta G = -3.54$ kcal and $\Delta S = -6.28$ cal deg^{-1} at 24°C. The rather high entropy loss on forming solid quinhydrone from its crystalline components is noteworthy, indicating a marked increase in efficiency of packing, or in strength of binding, or both. But the more important result was obtained by using heats of sublimation to calculate for the hypothetical reaction

$$Q \text{ (gas)} + QH_2 \text{ (gas)} = Q \cdot QH_2 \text{ (solid)}$$

a value of $\Delta H \sim -43$ kcal. To this quantity, hydrogen bonding could contribute no more than -10 to -12 kcal, whilst dispersion forces must account for about -27 kcal, leaving only -4 to -6 kcal to be accounted for in terms of other more specialized forces. Thus, although hydrogen bonding does, apparently, make a substantial contribution to the stability of solid quinhydrone, it seems to be less significant than other factors associated with crystal packing, upon which both dispersion and other specialized forces are critically dependent.

The matter was settled by the complete structural analysis of quinhydrone carried out by Matsuda and co-workers in 1958 (103), the essential features of which may be outlined, with the aid of the diagrams in Fig. 1.

Quinone and hydroquinone molecules are linked alternately by hydrogen bonds of length 2.71 Å, forming zig-zag chains which extend throughout the crystal. These chains are arranged side-by-side so that, running across them in the same plane, the now familiar columnar stacks of alternating quinone and hydroquinone molecules, face-to-face, are generated. The sheets thus formed are built up into a layer structure, but the aromatic rings in one sheet do not lie in planes parallel with those in the next, and the distances between the sheets is such that no nonbonded atoms approach closer than 3.31 Å. Within the columns, the perpendicular distance between the averaged molecular planes is 3.16 Å, which is significantly shorter than the normal van der Waals distance between aromatic molecules, which usually exceeds 3.4 Å. This means that there must be a force of attraction between neighboring rings strong enough to nullify the repulsion that would normally exist at so short a distance of separation; a similar inference could be drawn from certain distortions of the rings. The evidence for a special kind of bonding is therefore strong. The authors refer to an observation by Nakamoto (104), arising from a study of the di-

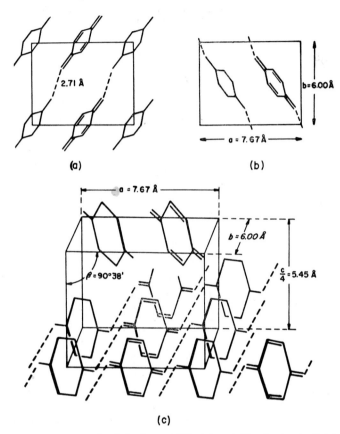

FIG. 1. The structure of quinhydrone (103). (a) and (b), sheets parallel to (001) at $z = 0$ and $z = \frac{1}{4}$, respectively; (c), perspective view.

chroism of quinhydrone, that there is an unusual electron mobility in a direction perpendicular to the plane of the aromatic rings, and they favor an explanation in terms of the charge-transfer mechanism proposed by Mulliken (105).

Mulliken regarded the ground state, N, of a molecular compound, AB, formed between an acceptor molecule A and a donor B, to be represented by a wave function

$$\psi_N = a\psi_0 + b\psi_1 + \text{minor terms} \tag{5}$$

where ψ_0 is a "no-bond" wave function and ψ_1 is a "dative" wave function, corresponding with the transfer of an electron from B to A, accompanied by the establishment of a covalent bond between the odd electrons in A^- and B^+, usually a weak one because of the large distance between A and B. This recalls the electron-transfer theory of Weiss (96), but the essential difference is that the attraction which is established is primarily due to exchange forces and is therefore much more dependent upon the factors of distance and symmetry than would be the case for electrostatic forces alone. The covalent bond need not be formed between specific atoms, but is rather intermolecular; thus when B is an aromatic molecule, the odd electron in B^+ occupies one of the delocalized π molecular orbitals. This is consistent with the ideas previously advanced by Dewar (106). Mulliken (105) asserts that these charge-transfer forces are alone capable of explaining the existence of complexes like molecular compounds, and it is an essential part of his theory that these complexes should show characteristic light absorption. Thus, if Eq. (5) represents the ground state electronic wave function, it necessarily follows that there is an excited state function

$$\psi_E = a^*\psi_1 - b^*\psi_0 + \ldots \tag{6}$$

with $a^* \sim a$ and $b^* \sim b$, and the existence, and intensity, of an absorption spectrum corresponding with the transition $\psi_N \rightarrow \psi_E$ can be predicted. If $a^2 \gg b^2$, ψ_N has nearly pure no-bond character and ψ_E nearly pure ionic character; the spectrum can then be called an intermolecular charge-transfer spectrum, light absorption causing an electron to jump from B to A.

Such charge-transfer forces may often co-operate with dispersion forces in making up the total of van der Waals attractions, particularly in systems containing more than one component. They also have, like dispersion forces, the property of approximate additivity, so that the fact that one molecule is bound to another does not, in itself, prevent a third from being attracted. This is particularly significant in the formation of solid state complexes like quinhydrone, which may be almost completely dissociated in solution.

It is an important aspect of this theory that the donor molecule B can be regarded as a Lewis base, and the acceptor A as a Lewis acid. Mulliken refers to "π bases" and "π acids" in connection with the aromatic systems which form molecular compounds of the kind in question; maximum interaction between the two arises when the molecular planes are parallel and close. The effect of this is apparent in the solid structure feature of columnar packing. It is interesting to note that these properties for quinone and hydroquinone can be inferred from their behavior in solution (this chapter, Section I,C).

An interesting example of an intramolecular acid-base function of this kind has recently been reported (107).

Apart from satisfying at last the curiosity of electrochemists about the structure of quinhydrone, it is probable that the main outcome of the structural studies is as follows. The geometrical requirements for simultaneously satisfying the forces of hydrogen bonding and charge-transfer bonding are somewhat complicated, and it is evident that substitution in the quinonoid or benzenoid rings is likely to cause steric obstruction and oppose the attainment of the uniquely favorable structure. This is no doubt why progressive substitution tends to decrease the stability of the quinhydrone and eventually prevents its formation. It is also clear that little is likely to be gained by exploring alternatives to quinhydrone to find an improvement for electrochemical use.

2. Quinhydrone in Aqueous Solution

Quinhydrone is extensively dissociated into its components in solution. The dissociation equilibrium has been studied by means of solubility determinations in the absence and in the presence of excess of either quinone or hydroquinone by Luther and Leubner (108), Biilmann (2), Granger and Nelson (3) and Sørensen and his co-workers (109), with results in substantial concordance. Such measurements were extended to cover a temperature range by Berthoud and Kunz (110) and their results are shown in Table II.

TABLE II

Solubility and Dissociation of Quinhydrone in Aqueous Solution (110)

Temp (°C)	Solubility		K (mole liter^{-1})	% dissociated
	(mole liter^{-1} × 10^3)	(gm(100 cm^3)$^{-1}$)		
5	5.13[a]	0.111[a]	—	—
15	12.24	0.267	0.223	95.1
25	18.70	0.408	0.259	93.7
35	27.88	0.608	0.291	91.8
45	34.0[a]	0.742[a]	—	—

[a] Interpolated from Coons (13).

A somewhat lower value than that shown in the table for the dissociation constant at 25°C, 0.225 mole liter^{-1}, was obtained by Wagner and Grünewald (52), who also presented evidence, based on light absorption, that the undissociated quinhydrone in solution is meriquinonoid. There seems to be no apparent explanation for the unfortunate disagreement about the value for the dissociation constant at 25°C.

3. The Mechanism of the Quinhydrone Electrode Process

The first study of the kinetics of the quinhydrone electrode reaction was made by Rosenthal, Lorch, and Hammett (111). Using highly purified materials, in rigorously deoxygenated solutions under conditions which precluded concentration polarization, they studied the dependence of cathodic and anodic currents upon electrode potential and, in turn, how the resulting polarization curves varied with the nature of the metal phase and the concentrations of quinone, hydroquinone, and hydrogen ions.

It was found that platinum electrodes were always unsteady in behavior in solutions which contained dissolved oxygen. Apart from this, it was found that the exchange current (as a function of the slope of the polarization curve as it passed through the rest potential) depended strongly on the nature and state of the metal phase. Approximate relative catalytic activities for various electrodes determined in this way are shown in Table III, which might well serve as a guide for the best procedure in setting up electrodes for reference purposes.

TABLE III

RELATIVE CATALYTIC ACTIVITIES OF ELECTRODES FOR THE QUINHDYRONE ELECTRODE REACTION[a,b]

Electrode	Relative catalytic activity	Electrode	Relative catalytic activity
Blank platinum	1	Blank gold	0.5
Grey platinum on gold	10	Bright palladium on gold	1
Bright platinum on gold	80	Mercury	0.3
Bright gold on platinum	3		

[a] Rosenthal, Lorch, and Hammett (111).
[b] Subject to wide variation with aging and composition of electrolyte; 0.1 N H_2SO_4 solution, saturated with quinhydrone.

In all cases the activity of an electrode declined with use, and was not restored by normal cleaning processes. Heating for an hour at 400°C in air, nitrogen or hydrogen was the only method found for substantially increasing activity, but the enhancement (sometimes multiplying the exchange current by 10 or 20) fell away very rapidly, the activity reaching a steady value, considerably higher than before, after one or two days. Exposure to moist air, or strong cathodic polarization, had slight activating effects, but anodization did not, in strong contrast to electrodes used for the hydrogen electrode reaction.

Under these circumstances, it was difficult to obtain results sufficiently reproducible for kinetic analysis, but although rectilinear Tafel lines could not be obtained, the authors established the following facts. The cathodic reduction of quinone was first order with respect to quinone and also with respect to hydrogen ions. The anodic oxidation of hydroquinone was first order with respect to hydroquinone, but was retarded by hydrogen ions. Apart from the exclusion of reactions involving hydrogen atoms or molecular quinhydrone, no definite conclusions could be reached about mechanism, except that no one reaction path was adequate to cover the whole range of working conditions.

This study was taken up again by Vetter (8) in 1952, using a refined technique, and with the advantage of developments in knowledge of electrode kinetics that had taken place in the interim. He was able to obtain linear Tafel plots for both cathodic and anodic processes, limited at one end by the incidence of back reaction, and at the other by diffusional rate control. This enabled him to apply established tests for the occurrence of a two-step electrode process (112), by which he showed that the reaction does involve consecutive 1-electron transfers. A more detailed analysis of the reaction orders was possible, but cannot now be discussed in detail. It led to the conclusion that the reaction path varies over the pH range in the following way:

Lower pH values	Higher pH values
$H^+ + Q \rightleftharpoons QH^+$	$Q + e^- \rightleftharpoons Q^-$
$QH^+ + e^- \rightleftharpoons QH$	$H^+ + Q^- \rightleftharpoons QH$
$H^+ + QH \rightleftharpoons QH_2^+$	$QH + e^- \rightleftharpoons QH^-$
$QH_2^+ + e^- \rightleftharpoons QH_2$	$H^+ + QH^- \rightleftharpoons QH_2$

The transition from one mechanism to the other is continuous. In both cases electron and proton transfers alternate, and in both a semiquinone molecule or ion is an essential intermediate, in spite of the fact that the concentrations of these entities are, in this case, undetectably low in aqueous solution. This mechanism provides strong support for the Michaelis theory (67). It is also noteworthy that the basic properties of quinone (and of the semiquinone) are in evidence in the more strongly acid solutions.

III. The Nonideality of the Quinhydrone Electrode

A. Acid-Base Functions of Hydroquinone and Quinone

Biilmann (2) attributed the failure of the quinhydrone electrode in alkaline solution to the ionization of hydroquinone as a weak dibasic acid.

The pH of about 8 at which deviations began was consistent with the value of the first dissociation constant, $K_1 = 1.1 \times 10^{-10}$ at 18°C, determined conductometrically by Euler and Bolin (113). The constants for 25°C now generally accepted were determined potentiometrically by Sheppard (114), who obtained $K_1 = 1.75 \times 10^{-10}$ and $K_3 = 4 \times 10^{-12}$, the latter being "to some extent hypothetical." Values of 1.22×10^{-10} and 9.2×10^{-13} for these constants at 30°C have been reported (115).

The increasing effect of these dissociations with rising pH may be formally considered in terms of a progressive change in the electrode process from

$$Q + 2H^+ + 2e^- \rightleftharpoons QH_2$$

through

$$Q + H^+ + 2e^- \rightleftharpoons QH^-$$

to

$$Q + 2e^- \rightleftharpoons Q^{2-}$$

The corresponding expressions for electrode potential are

$$E = E° + \frac{RT}{2F} \ln \frac{Q(H^+)^2}{QH_2} \tag{7}$$

$$E = E°' + \frac{RT}{2F} \ln \frac{Q \cdot H^+}{QH^-} \tag{8}$$

$$E = E°'' + \frac{RT}{2F} \ln \frac{Q}{Q^{2-}} \tag{9}$$

where the symbols Q, QH_2, QH^-, Q^{2-}, and H^+ signify concentrations of the entities concerned. In the present argument, the distinction between activity and concentration is to be ignored for the sake of simplicity; this need not be done, but there is no point in using precise formulations to consider problems associated with errors and corrections. From these equations, the change in pH response is obvious, and can be considered in relation to the previous discussion of redox titrations (this chapter, Section II,A,2). Since

$$K_1 = \frac{QH^- \cdot H^+}{QH_2} \quad \text{and} \quad K_2 = \frac{Q^{2-} \cdot H^+}{QH^-} \tag{10}$$

it can easily be shown that

$$E°' = E° + \frac{RT}{2F} \ln K_1$$

and

$$E°'' = E° + \frac{RT}{2F} \ln K_1 K_2 \tag{11}$$

Since, in a given solution, all these entities remain in equilibrium with each other, the single-valued potential of an electrode in the solution could equally well be calculated by any of the Eq. (7) to (9), together with Eq. (11). It is convenient to use Eq. (7) in order to find the extent to which these dissociations may cause deviations from normal behavior in the not too high pH range.

Let the total concentration of hydroquinone in whatever form in the solution be represented by M; then

$$M = QH_2 + QH^- + Q^{2-} \tag{12}$$

and, substituting from (10),

$$M = QH_2 \left\{ 1 + \frac{K_1}{H^+} + \frac{K_1 K_2}{(H^+)^2} \right\} \tag{13}$$

If there were *no* dissociation, Eq. (7) would read

$$E = E^\circ + \frac{RT}{2F} \ln \frac{Q(H^+)^2}{M}$$

but if dissociation occurs, it must be modified to

$$E = E^\circ + \frac{RT}{2F} \ln \frac{Q(H^+)^2}{M} \left\{ 1 + \frac{K_1}{H^+} + \frac{K_1 K_2}{(H^+)^2} \right\}$$

For the saturated quinhydrone electrode, $Q = M$ under all conditions, so that

$$E = E^\circ + \frac{RT}{2F} \ln \{ (H^+)^2 + K_1 \cdot H^+ + K_1 K_2 \} \tag{14}$$

appears to be the general equation for the potential of this electrode, subject to the approximation that activities and concentrations have been identified with each other. When $(H^+)^2$ is the predominant term within the bracket on the right-hand side, Eq. (14) approximates to Eq. (7), but as H^+ is decreased, the second and third terms predominate in turn. Using the constants determined by Sheppard, $(H^+)^2$ is 100 times $K_1 \cdot H^+$ at pH = 7.8, and is equal to it at pH = 9.8. Between pH 9.8 and 11.4, $K_1 \cdot H^+$ is the largest term; above 11.4, $K_1 K_2$ exceeds the others. Although these calculations clearly set an upper limit to the pH range in which accurate use of the quinhydrone electrode is possible, they are otherwise not of practical interest because further disturbing factors intervene. This is not so for all systems, and Eq. (14) has been experimentally confirmed in other cases; a very clear account of this is given by MacInnes (*116*). La Mer and Parsons (*53*) have tabulated pH corrections to be used for the quinhydrone electrode, based upon Eq. (14); these are shown in Table IV.

The more serious effect of the acidic ionization of hydroquinone arises from the disturbance of the pH of the solution under test. It is readily calculated from Sheppard's data that a saturated solution of quinhydrone in water at 25°C has a pH of 5.75, in reasonable agreement with the value.

TABLE IV

pH CORRECTIONS FOR THE DISSOCIATION OF HYDROQUINONE[a,b]

pH	$0.0295 \log \left\{ 1 + \dfrac{K_1}{H^+} + \dfrac{K_1 K_2}{(H^+)^2} \right\}$	pH correction
	(volts)	
7.60	0.0001	+0.002
8.00	0.0002	+0.003
8.50	0.0007	+0.01
8.80	0.0012	+0.02
9.00	0.0023	+0.04
9.30	0.0038	+0.07
9.50	0.0056	+0.10

[a] LaMer and Parsons (53).   [b] At 25°C.

5.85, determined by Kolthoff and Bosch (117). Hence, at pH values higher than this, the electrode itself must have a buffering action, the effect of which will depend on the other constituents of the solution. If the solution is very dilute and is not itself buffered, then, according to Best (118), any initial pH greater than 5 is disturbed. On the other hand, if the solution is well buffered, then, according to Kolthoff (119), the electrode may be used up to pH 9.2 at 18°C with an error not exceeding 0.04 pH unit. Both of these limits are rather more extreme than general experience suggests, and it seems safe to say that caution is necessary within the range pH 6 to 8, and extreme caution at pH > 8. The effect may be considered quantitatively in the following way.

If a given solution contains a total concentration, x, of an acid of dissociation constant K_a, partially neutralized by addition of y gm equiv of a strong base such as sodium hydroxide, and if it also contains a concentration M of quinhydrone, the resultant pH can be calculated by standard methods based on Eq. (12) and on the electroneutrality equation

$$H^+ = A^- + QH^- + 2Q^{2-} + OH^- - Na^+ \tag{15}$$

This leads to

$$H^+ = \frac{K_a x}{(K_a + H^+)} + \frac{M(K_1 H^+ + 2K_1 K_2)}{\{(H^+)^2 + K_1 H^+ + K_1 K_2\}} + \frac{K_w}{H^+} - y \tag{16}$$

in absence of activity coefficient terms. It is not usually practicable, and certainly not convenient, to use such expressions to calculate correction terms for observed pH values.

The basic properties of quinone have already been mentioned as a source of error in measurements with the quinhydrone electrode, and a particular case has been discussed by Granér, Olin, and Sillén (*120*). These properties, not hitherto mentioned in texts dealing with the quinhydrone electrode, have been brought to attention in relation to salt effects, dehydrogenation reactions, the structure of quinhydrone, and the mechanism of the quinhydrone electrode. They are to be expected to come into evidence in strongly acid media (*121*), but will not otherwise be very significant. This is shown in the study carried out by Biedermann (*122*), who found that in aqueous solutions maintained at an ionic strength of 3 M with sodium perchlorate, the ratio Q/QH_2 did not remain constant as Na^+ was replaced by H^+ up to 0.6 M. On the basis that this effect was due to the equilibrium

$$Q + H^+ \rightleftharpoons QH^+$$

he obtained a value for $K = QH^+/Q \cdot H^+ = 0.1 \pm 0.05$. The equation analogous to Eq. (14) to allow for this equilibrium is

$$E = E^\circ + \frac{RT}{2F} \ln \frac{(H^+)^2}{(1 + H^+K)} \qquad (17)$$

and the errors in electrode potential caused by neglect of the effect can be calculated as -1.2 mv at pH $= 0$, and -0.1 mv at pH $= 1$. It is, however, uncertain how such data, relating to a medium of very high ionic strength, could be applied under more normal conditions, when it is likely that this source of deviation would be less significant. It could, however, disturb measurements of high precision at very low pH values.

B. Salt Errors

Biilmann (*2*) was aware that the quinhydrone electrode is sensitive to the presence of salts in solution, but left detailed investigation of this to Sørensen and co-workers (*109*), who carried out much pioneer work in the early 1920's in co-operation with him. These authors made measurements of the emf, given by Eq. (1), of the hydrogen–quinhydrone cell, and realized that its variation with salt concentration must, in all probability, be due to changes in the ratio of the activity coefficients, f_Q/f_{QH_2}. They confirmed this by measuring the solubilities of quinone and of hydroquinone in salt solutions. Thus, in any saturated solution of quinone, $a_Q = C_Q f_Q$ is fixed, so that $f_Q = a_Q/C_Q$. If a_Q is identified with the solubility of quinone at zero concentration of electrolytic solute, S_0, then $f_Q = S_0/S$, where f_Q is the activity coefficient of quinone in a medium in which its solubility is S. This involves the assumption that the nonideality of the quinone in solution is entirely due to its interactions with ions. A similar argument was applied in the case of hydroquinone. The results are shown in Table V.

Substituted in Eq. (1), the activity coefficients led to calculated emf values for the hydrogen–quinhydrone cell which agreed quite well with

TABLE V

SOLUBILITIES AND ACTIVITY COEFFICIENTS OF QUINONE AND OF HYDROQUINONE
IN 0.01 N HCl + ADDED NaCl[a,b]

HCl + NaCl (mole liter^{-1})	S_Q (mole liter^{-1})	f_Q	S_{QH_2} (mole liter^{-1})	f_{QH_2}	$\dfrac{f_Q}{f_{QH_2}}$
0	0.10390 = S_0 (extrap)	—	0.51200 = S_0 (extrap)	—	—
0.01	0.10368	1.0021	0.51030	1.0033	0.9988
0.1	0.10094	1.0293	0.49762	1.0289	1.0004
0.5	0.09608	1.0814	0.42704	1.1990	0.9019
1.0	0.09049	1.1482	0.35794	1.4304	0.8027
2.0	0.08036	1.2929	0.24956	2.0516	0.6302
3.0	0.07262	1.4307	0.17523	2.9219	0.4896
4.0	0.06614	1.5709	0.11994	4.2688	0.3680

[a] Sørensen, Sørensen, and Linderstrøm-Lang (109).
[b] At 18°C.

experiment. This comparison is best made by use of the later and more
accurate measurements of Linderstrøm-Lang (123), and is illustrated in
Table VI.

TABLE VI

CORRELATION OF ACTIVITY COEFFICIENT AND emf DATA
FOR 0.01 N HCl + ADDED NaCl[a,b]

HCl + NaCl (mole liter^{-1})	0.028884 × $\log \dfrac{f_Q}{f_{QH_2}}$ (volts)	emf calcd. (volts)	emf obs. (volts)	Δ (volts)
0	—	0.70475 = 0.70475		—
0.01	−0.00002	0.70473	0.70471	−0.00003
0.1	0.00000	0.70475	0.70428	−0.00047
0.5	−0.00130	0.70345	0.70351	+0.00006
1.0	−0.00276	0.70199	0.70214	+0.00015
2.0	−0.00579	0.69896	0.69934	+0.00038
3.0	−0.00898	0.69577	0.69636	+0.00059
4.0	−0.01254	0.69221	0.69320	+0.00099

[a] Linderstrøm-Lang (123).   [b] At 18°C.

Apart from an unexplained eccentricity in the case of the 0.1 N hydrochloric acid solution, the differences between observed and calculated emf
values are not large and, plotted against concentration, lie close enough to

a smooth curve to indicate that the accuracy of measurement was high (better than ±0.05 mv). These differences are probably physically significant and may well arise from the fact that the concentrations of the saturated solutions of quinone and of hydroquinone involved in the solubility measurements were much higher than those in the cell solutions, which were in equilibrium with solid quinhydrone. There can be no doubt, however, that this work identified the source of the salt errors.

In extended studies with various electrolytes, Linderstrøm-Lang (124) found that the simple relations

$$\log f_Q = k_Q C \quad \text{and} \quad \log f_{QH_2} = k_{QH_2} C \quad (18)$$

where C is concentration of electrolyte in gm equiv liter^{-1}, usually applied, in general agreement with experience of salting-out effects (e.g., 125, 126). Values of the salting-out coefficients, k_Q and k_{QH_2}, for aqueous solutions at 18°C were tabulated, and some of them are shown in Table VII. They can be used to correct "apparent pH values" for salt errors by means of the relation

$$pH_{true} = pH_{app} + \frac{1}{2}(k_Q - k_{QH_2})C \quad (19)$$

TABLE VII

SALTING-OUT COEFFICIENTS FOR QUINONE AND HYDROQUINONE IN AQUEOUS SALT SOLUTIONS[a,b]

Salt	k_{QH_2}	k_Q
$\frac{1}{2}CaCl_2$	0.148	ca. 0.060
HCl	0.108	−0.027
LiCl	0.160	0.066
NaCl	0.157	0.056
KCl	0.113	0.023
RbCl	0.078	0.019
CsCl	0.014	0.010
KCl	0.113	0.023
KBr	0.107	−0.040
KI	0.095	−0.128

[a] Linderstrøm-Lang (124).
[b] At 18°C.

Table VII shows that hydroquinone is usually salted out more than quinone. Regularities are seen in salting-out coefficients for series of salts with a common ion (potassium halides; alkali metal chlorides), and sometimes molecule–ion attractions lead to salting-in. The attraction between quinone and hydrogen ion is apparent, but the effects are too complex in origin for generalizations to be made. A possible exception is that ionic polarizability may be a significant factor, since the difference between the anion and cation refractivities is, for a series of alkali halides, smoothly related to $(k_{QH_2} - k_Q)$ (127).

This method of correcting salt errors has not found general favor. Strictly applied, it would need two solubility determinations for each emf measurement, which is hardly practicable as a general procedure. It is also open to objection because of the wide difference in conditions between the two types of experiment, and because, in solutions which contain quite high concentrations of both nonelectrolyte and electrolyte, more than one kind of interaction must be taken into account. There is evidence (128) that hydroquinone in saturated solution has appreciable effects on ionic activities, and it is unrealistic to assume that, in such solutions, activity coefficients are independent of *intermolecular* actions.

Acceptable salt error data have therefore mainly been determined by direct comparisons between quinhydrone and hydrogen electrodes. The work of Urmánczy (129, 130) led to the suggestion that the activity coefficients should be derived from equations of the form

$$\log f = a\mu + b \tag{20}$$

where μ is ionic strength and a and b are constants specific to each electrolyte, but this has not been substantiated, and some of these authors' results seem to be vulnerable to criticism (131).

The accurate measurements of the emf values of the cell

$$\text{H}_2, 1 \text{ atm, Pt} \mid \text{HCl } (N) \vdots \text{HCl } (N), \text{Q} \cdot \text{QH}_2 \mid \text{Au}$$

carried out by Hovorka and Dearing (132) had a reproducibility better than ± 0.03 mv, and provided the salt error data which are now generally accepted. Their measurements for hydrochloric acid solutions at 25°C are shown in Table VIII.

TABLE VIII

HOVORKA AND DEARING'S (132) emf VALUES, FOR THE CELL

$$\text{H}_2, 1 \text{ atm, Pt} \mid \text{HCl } (N) \vdots \text{HCl } (N), \text{Q} \cdot \text{QH}_2 \mid \text{Au}$$

N	E (int volts at 25°C)	pH error	f_Q/f_{QH_2}
0	0.69938 (extrap)	—	—
0.01	0.69935	−0.0005	0.998
0.04	0.69926	−0.0020	0.991
0.1	0.69906	−0.0054	0.976
0.5	0.69766	−0.0291	0.875
1.0	0.69583	−0.0601	0.758
2.0	0.69200	−0.1250	0.563

The salt errors, in terms of emf or pH deviations plotted against concentration, lie very close to a straight line passing through the origin. Similar results were obtained with cells containing 0.01 N hydrochloric acid and varying concentrations of salts, and were expressed by

$$\Delta pH = \frac{\Delta E}{0.05912} = \frac{AC}{0.05912} = BC \qquad (21)$$

where ΔpH and ΔE represent salt errors in terms of pH and electrode potential, A and B are coefficients characteristic of the added salt and C is the concentration of added salt in gm equiv liter^{-1}. Values of A and B for various electrolytes, and one nonelectrolyte, are assembled in Table IX; the figures for potassium nitrate and nitric acid are due to Stonehill (131).

TABLE IX

Salt Errors of the Quinhydrone Electrode [a, b]

$$\Delta pH = \frac{\Delta E}{0.05912} = \frac{AC}{0.05912} = BC$$

Salt	A [int volt (gm equiv liter)$^{-1}$]	B [pH unit (gm equiv liter)$^{-1}$]
HCl	−0.00364	−0.0616
LiCl	−0.00209	−0.0353
NaCl	−0.00244	−0.0413
KCl	−0.00220	−0.0372
MgCl$_2$	−0.00205	−0.0346
CaCl$_2$	−0.00217	−0.0367
SrCl$_2$	−0.00224	−0.0379
BaCl$_2$	−0.00259	−0.0438
H$_2$SO$_4$	−0.00186	−0.0314
Li$_2$SO$_4$	+0.00159	+0.0269
Na$_2$SO$_4$	+0.00134	+0.0227
K$_2$SO$_4$	+0.00141	+0.0238
MgSO$_4$	+0.00122	+0.0206
HNO$_3$	−0.00529	−0.0895
KNO$_3$	−0.00380	−0.0643
Mannitol	+0.00140	+0.0237

[a] Hovorka and Dearing (132).   [b] At 25° C.

The salt effects are found to be additive to quite a close approximation, except in cases where incomplete dissociation of the hydrogen sulfate ion, HSO$_4^-$, is concerned; thus, the addition 2NaCl + H$_2$SO$_4$ gives an acceptable result, but 2HCl + Na$_2$SO$_4$ does not. This is the basis for a very valuable facility for systematic correction for salt errors.

Where comparison can be made, there is quite good correlation between the two methods of determining salt error corrections. Thus the B factors calculated from Linderstrøm-Lang's solubilities at 18°C are, for eight electrolytes, 0.007 ± 0.002 unit more negative than Hovorka and Dearing's values for 25°C, but this does not always hold. There is no detailed information about the dependence of salt errors on temperature.

Variation of salt errors with pH has not been extensively investigated, but Gabbard (*133*) has presented evidence that it is insignificant up to a pH value of about 6. But above this, particularly in weakly buffered solutions, they increase very rapidly indeed, and any attempt to allow for them quantitatively becomes futile. This is no doubt because the ionization equilibrium of hydroquinone is affected. This is yet another factor which limits the working pH range of the quinhydrone electrode. To offset this, it should be mentioned that salt errors are minimized by use of cells in which the errors are largely cancelled by symmetry, or in which the errors must remain a constant factor which has no influence on the comparison of two emf values. Devices of this kind have been used by Kirschman and co-workers (*134*) and by Kilpatrick and Chase (*135*).

C. Quino- and Hydro-Quinhydrone Electrodes

The reaction of the hydrogen–quinhydrone cell is

$$\text{Q (dissolved)} + \text{H}_2 \text{ (1 atm)} = \text{QH}_2 \text{ (dissolved)} \tag{A}$$

whether the cell solution is saturated with quinhydrone or not. This is because the individual activities of quinone or of hydroquinone are not fixed, and it is in this way that salt errors arise. If a cell can be devised in which the essential reaction involves solid phases alone, the free energy change of the reaction, and the cell emf, become independent of variations in activity of substances in solution and salt errors must vanish. There are three possible ways of attaining this objective for cells based on quinone–hydroquinone redox systems.

If the system is one which forms no quinhydrone, the half-cell solution must be kept saturated with both the quinone and the hydroquinone. When the other half-cell is a hydrogen electrode, the reaction is

$$\text{Q (solid)} + \text{H}_2 \text{ (1 atm)} = \text{QH}_2 \text{ (solid)} \tag{B}$$

and the emf is not only free from salt errors, but is also independent of what solvent is used to make up the electrolyte. This is the basis of the chloranil electrode.

If the system is one which forms a solid quinhydrone, the half-cell solution must be kept saturated both with the quinhydrone and *one* of its components; either the quinone, or the hydroquinone. Then, for cells completed with the hydrogen electrode, the reactions are either

$$2Q \text{ (solid)} + H_2 \text{ (1 atm)} = Q \cdot QH_2 \text{ (solid)} \tag{C}$$

or

$$Q \cdot QH_2 \text{ (solid)} + H_2 \text{ (1 atm)} = 2QH_2 \text{ (solid)} \tag{D}$$

These are cells based on the "quino-quinhydrone" and "hydro-quinhydrone" electrodes, respectively, and both are free from salt errors.

The cell reactions (B), (C), and (D) are obviously interrelated; thus (C) + (D) = 2(B), and similar relations apply to the free energy changes and the emf values. It can also be seen that $\frac{1}{2}[(C) - (D)]$ is the reaction

$$Q \text{ (solid)} + QH_2 \text{ (solid)} = Q \cdot QH_2 \text{ (solid)}$$

It was on this basis that Conant and Fieser (76) were able to determine free energies for solid phase reductions of quinones to hydroquinones, and free energies of formation of solid quinhydrones from their solid components for a whole range of systems.

The quino- and hydro-quinhydrone electrodes are as old as the quinhydrone electrode itself. They were investigated by Granger and Nelson (3), by Sørensen, Sørensen, and Linderstrøm-Lang (109), and by Biilmann and Lund (34); the pioneer papers appeared in 1921. They are indeed free from salt errors, but have so many other disadvantages that they are quite unsuitable for general use as reference electrodes. This can be seen by inspection of procedures which have been used. Biilmann and Lund (34) used about 0.1 gm of quinhydrone, mixed with 0.4 to 0.5 gm of quinone, or 1.0 gm of hydroquinone, all finely powdered, to equilibrate with 15 ml of half-cell solution; an ignited platinum spiral was immersed in the mush. Schreiner (102) used even larger quantities, and noted that equilibration must be carried out in the electrode vessel itself in the absence of air, otherwise the systems darkened, particularly those containing excess quinone; it was also necessary to make measurements quickly. It is quite obvious that where one or other of two quite highly reactive substances have to be used in excessive concentrations, the chances of obtaining stable electrodes which do not alter the solutions in which they are placed (in pH or otherwise) are remote. This is reflected in the rather poor agreement between determined standard potentials, which are collected in Table X. The figures attributed to Schreiner are interpolated from measurements at other temperatures, Clark's are critically assessed and not original, and Stonehill's result for the quino-quinhydrone electrode is admittedly open to doubt. Although these electrodes are obviously limited in application, Stonehill's assessment of the salt errors due to nitric acid and potassium nitrate provide one example of their use.

TABLE X

STANDARD POTENTIALS OF QUINO- AND HYDRO-QUINHYDRONE ELECTRODES[a]

Authors	Reference	Quino-quinhydrone			Hydro-quinhydrone		
		0°	18°	25°	0°	18°	25°
Biilmann and Lund	*34*	—	0.7562	—	—	0.6179	—
Sørensen *et al.*	*109*	—	0.7548	—	—	0.6191	—
Schreiner	*102*	0.7706	0.7555	0.7495	0.6293	0.6176	0.6130
Conant and Fieser	*76*	0.7699	—	0.7488	0.6272	—	0.6126
Stonehill	*131*	—	—	0.7459	—	—	0.6141
Clark	*18*	0.7716	0.7564	0.7505	0.6294	0.6177	0.6132

[a] Potentials in int volts.

D. OXIDATION REACTIONS

One advantage of the quinhydrone electrode is that it can be used for rapid pH determination in solutions containing dissolved air. Oxygen exerts no oxidizing action on hydroquinone in acid solution, although milder reagents, such as ferric ions, do so. It follows that hydroquinone is not thermodynamically invulnerable to oxidation in aerated solutions, and it is fortunate that the reaction is normally too slow to be significant. This might not be so in the presence of a suitable catalytic agent. With rising pH, the resistance of hydroquinone to oxidation must deteriorate, perhaps rather rapidly because of the formation of reactive semiquinone radicals; ultimately, in strongly alkaline solutions, it is well known to absorb oxygen avidly.

La Mer and Rideal (*136*) studied the rate at which hydroquinone in solution absorbs oxygen from the gas phase as a function of pH; typical results are shown in Table XI.

TABLE XI

RATE OF OXYGEN ABSORPTION BY 0.001 MOLE HYDROQUINONE
IN BORATE BUFFER SOLUTIONS[a,b]

pH	7.32	7.56	7.74	8.04	8.24	8.32	8.40	8.56
O_2 absorption, cm^3 min^{-1}	0.04	0.19	0.34	1.00	2.00	2.95	3.90	6.00

[a] La Mer and Rideal (*136*).   [b] At 25°C.

The rates of absorption from air were naturally less than those from pure oxygen; in effect, the rate–pH curve was shifted 0.5 unit along the pH scale, i.e., the rate with air at pH 7.8 was the same as that with oxygen at pH 7.3. In these experiments, steps were taken to ensure that oxygen supply was not a rate-limiting factor, solution and gas being enclosed in a vessel mounted in a shaker. This is not the procedure used in electrochemical measurements, so that Table XI may present an over-gloomy view of the disturbing effects of this reaction. Thus, in still solution initially saturated with air, the reaction might well become insignificant when the 0.0003 mole liter^{-1} of dissolved oxygen originally present had been taken up. It is, however, quite clear that the exclusion of oxygen is highly desirable when precise measurements with the quinhydrone electrode are to be made.

The oxidation reaction has further implications. La Mer and Rideal (*136*) found that it proceeded beyond the 1:1 ratio of hydroquinone to oxygen, and that its velocity was proportional, in dilute solution, to $[H^+]^{-3/2}$ and to $[QH_2]$ where the terms in brackets represent concentrations. Taking into account the known acidic dissociation constants of hydroquinone (*114*), they showed that the concentrations of QH^- and Q^{2-} ions could be of kinetic significance, and proposed a reaction mechanism which fitted the rate–concentration relationships they had observed. This mechanism involved the formation of a hydrogen-bonded complex ion, which underwent "autoxidation," with formation of hydrogen peroxide. It can be represented

$$2QH_2 \rightarrow 3H^+ + QH^- + Q^{2-} \rightarrow 3H^+[QHQ]^{3-}$$

$$3H^+[QHQ]^{3-} + 2O_2 \rightarrow 2Q + 2H_2O_2$$

and perhaps the reddish colors which develop when alkali is added to hydroquinone, which cannot be due to semiquinone alone (*68*), are due to such complexes. There can be no doubt that, as pH is increased, there is an increasing tendency for anionic semiquinone radicals to be formed, and as soon as this happens, it is very likely to initiate the complex oxygen-peroxide equilibria which are discussed elsewhere (Chapter 7, Section III). Indeed, La Mer and Rideal drew attention to the analogy with the autoxidation of metals.

Further work on the kinetics of reaction of hydroquinone with oxygen, by Euler and Brunius (*47*) and by Reinders and Dingemans (*137*), led to different results. In both cases proportionality of rate to hydroquinone concentration was found, and inverse proportionality to the square of the hydrogen ion concentration, suggesting that the doubly-charged anion, Q^{2-}, is the only entity effectively concerned in reacting with oxygen. Above pH 7, however, the products are polymeric "humic acids" (*137*), indicating a reaction of some complexity. Apart from an observation that the oxidation depends strongly on the buffer system used (*138*), as well as on the pH range (*137*), this discrepancy has not been resolved. But the formation of

peroxide in such "autoxidations" has been known for a very long time
(*139*), and is now exploited for the large-scale production of hydrogen
peroxide (*140*), so that it cannot be disputed that La Mer and Rideal's
views are strongly supported. It therefore becomes obvious that the action
of dissolved oxygen on the quinhydrone electrode may, at pH values exceeding 7, be very deleterious in a complicated way. Apart from the disturbance of the quinone/hydroquinone ratio in solution, strongly acidic,
polymeric oxidation products may be formed, *and* hydrogen peroxide. This,
according to what metal is used for the electrode, may set up an "oxygen
electrode reaction," leading to mixed potential control.

E. Chemical Reactivity

Two other specific failings of the quinhydrone electrode due to unwanted chemical reactivity have already been briefly mentioned. The first
is the chlorination of quinone by aqueous hydrochloric acid, and is somewhat difficult to assess. Concentrated hydrochloric acid has long been
known to bring about this reaction (*141*), and it is important to know how
significant it may be in the much less reactive media in which the quinhydrone electrode is normally used. Conant and Fieser (*76*) referred to a
statement of Granger (*142*) that even 0.1 N hydrochloric acid adds to
quinone slowly, and La Mer and Baker (*89*) said that chlorination by
hydrochloric acid often occurred as a side reaction in their titrimetric reductions of quinones. Harned and Wright (*143*) ascribed a slow, positive
creep of their quinhydrone electrode potentials, even for very low concentrations of hydrochloric acid, to this reaction. This tendency was observed
to increase with rising temperature, and was said to be discernible in
Biilmann's original data (*2*).

One of the most remarkable things about this effect is the number of
occasions on which it has *not* been mentioned. Thus, Biilmann and Jensen
(*6*), Linderstrøm-Lang (*123*), Hovorka and Dearing (*132*), and others
recorded measurements to five significant figures of the emf values of cells
containing hydrochloric acid of normality 0.1 or more. Biilmann and
Krarup (*144*) used the quinhydrone electrode in 0.1 N hydrochloric acid
at 37°C without noting a difficulty. Semipermanent standard electrodes
containing hydrochloric acid have been frequently proposed. It is difficult
to avoid thinking that, where this trouble has been found, it may have been
an artifact arising in some other way. Perhaps in nonaqueous media the
chlorination reaction may be more prominent; this conclusion was reached
by Ebert (*19*) for the case of methanolic solutions, and he found it necessary
to extrapolate his readings to "zero time." It is clearly unsafe to make any
general statement on this supposed reactivity of quinone, except that it is

a possible, but unestablished, source of error to which due attention should be paid.

The second way in which the reactivity of quinone leads to difficulty relates to ammonium salts and amino compounds. Linderstrøm-Lang (123) studied "the ammonium sulfate error" and said that the slight trace of ammonia always present will react with quinone; red and blue colors are produced and the reaction increases with rising pH. Although electrode potentials were uncertain to about 0.3 to 0.4 mv at pH 4–5, he obtained a fairly good linear plot of potential against ammonium sulfate normality up to about 5 N, which agreed quite well with the activity coefficient corrections derived from solubility measurements. The salt error due to ammonium sulfate, evaluated in this way, was about equal in magnitude, but opposite in sign, to that due to sodium chloride. Shikata and Tachi (145) confirmed that the quinhydrone electrode is not satisfactory in operation in the presence of ammonium salts; interaction with quinone has an acidifying action which can sometimes be tolerated when readings are taken without delay for well-buffered systems.

Similarly, quinone reacts to a greater or less degree with amino compounds, giving colored products. Britton (146) lists triethanolamine, hydroxylamine, hexamine, p-toluidine, naphthylamine and casein as examples. Pring (22) reported that reaction varied greatly in rate from case to case; it was slow with tertiary bases, faster with secondary amines, and very rapid with primary amines. It may be noted, however, that Pring was able, using unsaturated as well as saturated quinhydrone electrodes, to study quite a wide range of amino compounds by extrapolating his emf readings, when necessary, to zero time. This device has been used by other workers (19, 147) under similar circumstances and it depends for its success on the rapidity with which the electrode equilibrium proper is attained.

Although Biilmann (2) successfully used the quinhydrone electrode in the presence of glycine, quinone does, in general, react with amino acids at measurable rates (148) and the early view expressed by Linderstrøm-Lang and Kodama (149) that the electrode is not susceptible to protein errors was soon found to be premature. At pH values around 6, red-brown colors are formed, accompanied by drifts of potential, which do not depend upon what metal (platinum or gold) is used for the electrode (119). Very large errors in pH determinations for biological fluids may occur (>1 pH unit for blood serum) because of reaction with proteins, or interaction with competing redox systems, as with whole blood (150). Nevertheless, the quinhydrone electrode, before the glass electrode era, was widely used with some success in protein-containing solutions of biological origin (45), and it appears that some proteins (acid casein, egg albumin) are relatively innocuous. Linderstrøm-Lang (123), although admitting that protein effects are highly specific, was able to set up an empirical scale of protein errors; although they varied as a function of pH, approximate additivity (with salt errors) was observed. His estimates of the corrections appropriate to milk and blood serum did not agree very well with others (*119, 151, 152*), but his data were "more carefully rationalized" (*18*). There is no longer very much point in detailed discussion of this topic.

IV. Experimental Procedures

A. MATERIALS

Biilmann's quinhydrone (*2*) was prepared by Valeur's method (*153*); 20 gm of hydroquinone in 40 ml of 95% ethanol were added to 10 gm of quinone in 300 ml of the same solvent and set aside for 24 hr. Filtration at the pump, drying first between filter papers, and then over concentrated sulfuric acid, afforded 17.5 gm of product, mp 172°C (rapid heating). Biilmann and Lund (*34*) prepared quinhydrone by oxidation of hydroquinone in aqueous solution with iron alum, and the method became widely used. The iron always present as an impurity was said to have no ill effect, and Biilmann and Jensen (*6*) claimed a reproducibility of 0.04 mv for electrodes using it. Britton (*146*), however, condemns the method, and it is not now used, since purer material is readily available commercially. For a substance required in such small amounts at a time, almost any reasonably pure stock is adequate for a set of *comparative* measurements, and much work has been carried out on this basis; it adds to the difficulty of comparing the results of different workers on an absolute scale. That variation in purity, and possibly state, of quinhydrone has an appreciable effect was shown by Clayton and Vosburgh (*5*), who observed bias potentials up to 0.2 mv between electrodes made up with various samples, including some prepared by "iron oxidation." But most of them were reduced to about 0.005 mv by the simple device of repeatedly washing the samples of quinhydrone with the cell solution before finally setting up the cell for measurements. It thus became clear that most of the variations were due to surface layers of the crystals of quinhydrone, which can lose quinone by reason of its exceptional volatility, even at room temperature. This effect has been demonstrated by setting up unsaturated electrodes prepared from successive extracts of quinhydrone that had been stored (*6*). Quinhydrone must never be dried by heating, and should be stored in a desiccator containing a little quinone (*101*).

Most workers aiming at measurements of high accuracy have preferred to purify their own materials, since washing the quinhydrone with cell solution is not always practicable (*143*). Recrystallization from acetic acid solution gives a product of admirable appearance, but it is under the suspicion of containing adsorbed acid. Any crystallization in the presence of air may lead to impurities produced by autoxidation. Both of these points have been taken into account in work which merits the closest attention. Hovorka and Dearing (132) prepared their quinhydrone by mixing equimolar quantities of the components, dissolved in minimal amounts of boiled-out distilled water, at a temperature of 60°C. The mixture was cooled in ice, filtered, the product washed with water and dried between filter papers at room temperature. Harned and Wright (143) recrystallized Eastman quinhydrone from boiled-out water at 70°C under a nitrogen atmosphere, and obtained a product melting sharply at 170°C. Rosenthal, Lorch, and Hammett (111) purified quinone by sublimation at atmospheric pressure, hydroquinone by thrice repeated vacuum sublimation, and recrystallized the quinhydrone prepared from these materials from 10^{-5} N hydrochloric acid at 70°C, under nitrogen. They strongly emphasized the importance of excluding oxygen at all stages. The sensitivity of quinhydrone to light is generally recognized, so that it should be stored in a dark container.

The device of checking the "standard state" of quinhydrone by means of an agreed standard cell in which a satisfactory sample should establish a known emf has been suggested (130, 131). Thus, Stonehill (131), for the hydrogen–quinhydrone cell containing 0.1 N hydrochloric acid at 25°C obtained an emf of 0.69904 int volt, in excellent agreement with Hovorka and Dearing's value (132) of 0.69906 int volt.

B. Metal Phase

Recommendations in the earlier literature as to the best metal to use as the basis for the quinhydrone electrode are conflicting. The main debate was concerned with platinum or gold as alternatives, and there was a fairly even balance between opposed conclusions. It would be pointless to survey all the *ad hoc* findings, since it is now possible to understand the main factors concerned in the light of quite a few systematic investigations, and of knowledge gained in other fields.

Electron transfer across a metal surface is sensitive to impurity or oxide films, so that extreme cleanliness is necessary, and noble metals alone can withstand the procedures normally available without extensive attack or oxidation. Metals which carry an oxide film are useless; they tend to set up metal–metal oxide couples which compete for potential control. This is the case for tungsten, which cannot be used with quinhydrone (154). The importance of the nature and state of the metal phase is enhanced by its catalytic action on the electrode process, clearly demonstrated in the very careful work of Hammett and associates (111). Their observation

(Table III) that bright platinum-plated gold is 80 times as active as massive platinum does not seem to have been exploited. Their findings that gold-plated platinum is 3 times as active as bright platinum agrees with Cullen and Biilmann's recommendation (35) that it is suitable for microelectrodes. That "blank platinum" is twice as active as "blank gold," indicated by their results, is supported by various references in the literature. But, apart from micro-applications, such differences are unimportant because in either case, if the area of the electrode is made large enough, an adequate exchange current can be attained. But it is very important that danger of mixed potential control should be eliminated as far as possible. It is of general significance that catalytic activity was found to be extremely variable, depending on the age of the electrode and the composition of the electrolyte; this may account for many of the discrepancies on record. It also agrees with reports that electrodes are susceptible to poisoning (23, 155) and suggests that the most active electrode, if fast in decay, may not be the most suitable for prolonged use. Gold has been found to be more sensitive to poisoning than platinum, especially when used for pH recording in flowing systems (13).

It is certain that the potential set up at an electrode by the uniquely defined redox equilibrium should be quite independent of what metal is used, and identical potentials for gold, platinum, or plated electrodes in equilibrium with the same solution have frequently been observed (e.g., 2, 76, 156). If this is found not to be the case (157) it is an infallible sign that something is wrong: either polarization or mixed potential control. Since the metal substrate is catalytic, its activity must be strictly confined to the desired process, otherwise difficulties will arise. From this point of view, platinum requires more careful scrutiny than gold. In some cases the difficulties are too obtrusive to be overlooked; thus platinum cannot be used in pH determinations of blood because it is an oxidative catalyst (10), and it cannot be used in formic acid solutions because it catalytically decomposes the solvent (25). But it has not been generally realized that platinum, however inefficiently, can catalyze the oxygen electrode reaction, and may lead to trouble on this account when used in solutions containing dissolved oxygen. The evidence for this, accumulated from scattered observations in the literature, is quite substantial.

Rosenthal, Lorch, and Hammett (111) noted in their kinetic studies that platinum electrodes were always erratic in oxygen-containing solutions. Lammert, Morgan, and Campbell (158) found that quinhydrone electrodes prepared in nitrogen were far more reproducible than those prepared in air. With use of nitrogen, 85% of the bias potentials, even for small platinum wire electrodes, were less than 5 μv, and equilibrium potentials were attained much more rapidly—"almost immediately." This agrees precisely with Clayton and Vosburgh's observation (5) that platinum–quinhydrone electrodes in nitrogen-swept solutions show bias potentials less than 5 μv within one minute. There can be no doubt that when platinum is used, electrode behavior is improved by exclusion of air from the electrode system, and this precaution is probably vital in work with excessively dilute solutions (12). On the other hand, replacement of air by nitrogen has no effect on gold electrodes, even in sensitive, unbuffered systems (133), and gold was preferred to platinum by Hovorka and Dearing (132) and by La Mer and Baker (89) because of its regularity of behavior and speed of attaining equilibrium.

It is possible that plated, or alloy, electrodes should be examined closely for greater catalytic activity than pure metal electrodes towards undesired reactions. This is often found when different metals in contact are exposed to the same solution — local action is fostered. Gold-plated platinum was found to be inferior for the quinhydrone electrode by Morgan and Lammert (159), and the effect of scratching the surface was disastrous. The large gold-plated electrodes of Larsson and Adell (160) needed 35 to 40 minutes to reach potentials recorded with only 0.2 mv accuracy. Since so many workers have found that the proper quinhydrone electrode equilibrium is established rapidly [oscillographic recording indicates that less than two seconds is required (7)], any slowly attained potentials must be regarded as dubious. Very likely, as in other cases, "potential creeps" are a function of undesired side-reactions.

Commercial platinum is normally hardened by alloying with other platinum metals and, in some connections, its catalytic activity is thereby increased. This is perhaps why Cullen (36) found that very pure platinum was "as good as gold" for quinhydrone electrodes. Morgan and Lammert (159) found that platinum alloys containing 10% of iridium or rhodium were always positive to normal platinum when used for quinhydrone electrodes in aerated solutions, but not in nitrogen-swept solutions. It can hardly be unrelated that iridium and rhodium are the two metals which have been used to establish a workable "air electrode" (161).

On balance, it seems very likely that Corran and Lewis (162) were justified in preferring gold to platinum on the grounds that the latter is likely to catalyze the oxidation of hydroquinone. Reference to Section III,D of this chapter suggests that such oxidation might be irreversible. If it should involve the formation of a trace of hydrogen peroxide, then the oxidation is likely to become autocatalytic, with very rapid deterioration. It is clear that these troubles can be avoided by excluding air, or, if this is inconvenient, by using gold electrodes.

Morgan, Lammert, and Campbell (4,158,159,163,164), without attempting to make measurements of absolute accuracy, set out to attain the

highest degree of reproducibility in quinhydrone electrodes. Using Eastman Kodak quinhydrone (mp 169–170°C) and 0.1 N hydrochloric acid or
(0.01 N HCl + 0.09 N KCl) as electrolyte, these dedicated workers made
22,000 measurements on 7500 cells; their findings, some of which have been
mentioned, merit attention. They recommended, with Biilmann, that electrodes should be large, since with decreasing size, trouble is encountered,
sooner with gold than with platinum, because of increasing polarizability.
Gold electrodes were found to have a smaller current-passing capacity than
platinum, but were less affected by air, and some of the best results were
obtained with large gold electrodes. Platinum improved with use, and old
and battered electrodes were as good as new. This was contrary to Biilmann
(6), who advised against the use of dulled platinum, and it is opposed by
Britton (51), who says that the platinum should be highly polished. Somewhat surprisingly, they recommended pencil leads (Venus 4B), sealed into
glass contact tubes with picein, as an alternative to noble metals; cheap,
a little slower to reach equilibrium and more difficult to clean, they showed
no sensitivity to air. More recently, boron carbide has been advocated as
an alternative to noble metals for unattackable electrodes (165).

Methods of preparing electrodes for use have been the subject of disagreement. Biilmann washed his platinum electrodes in water and heated
them to redness "sur un bec Bunsen à vapeur d'alcool" (2). This has been
usually translated as a direction to heat in an alcohol flame, and has been
followed by many, including Britton (51). Cullen (36) advises a hydrogen
flame; certainly a coal gas flame of any kind should not be used. Cray and
Westrip (23) say that heating is undesirable, leads to slow equilibration,
and is unnecessary, except for an electrode that has become poisoned.
Morgan, Lammert, and Campbell (163) found that heating had no beneficial effect and was disastrous if it led (as frequently) to the cracking of
platinum-through-glass seals. They recommended the following procedure
as the best of many which they explored.

The electrodes are placed in cold chromic-sulfuric acid cleaning mixture,
which is heated to 125°C and allowed to cool overnight. On removal, the
electrodes are rinsed in running tap water, soaked in distilled water for 5 to
10 minutes, washed in conductance water, and rinsed with absolute ethanol.
They are then dried in a current of scrubbed, dry air for 20 minutes. Rinsing
with cell solution before use had no advantage, and was even slightly
deleterious to platinum electrodes. This method has been widely used, but
Clayton and Vosburgh (5) found that drying in vacuum, followed by ad-
mission of nitrogen, was preferable to air-drying; equilibrium potentials
were attained, in out-gassed solutions, very much faster (to within 5 μv
in 1 minute, instead of 10 μv in 1 hour). This was not the experience of
Morgan, Lammert, and Campbell, but it does support the idea that oxygen

at any stage is undesirable in its effects on platinum electrodes. It is therefore worth noting that Coons (*13*) recommended a nonoxidizing cleaning method for platinum, finding that it led to a more rapid attainment of equilibrium. It consisted of treating the electrode in boiling 5–10% sodium bisulfite solution for not less than three minutes, followed by washing in water.

Inconsistent recommendations make the choice of cleaning method difficult. It must be made according to the intended use of the electrode, and other factors, such as convenience and time. Since many accurate measurements have been made with electrodes subjected to heating, there can be no harm in it for routine use when high accuracy is not desired; it is effective for reactivating poisoned electrodes. On the other hand, if it is intended to exploit the reproducibility of the quinhydrone electrode to the fullest extent, the preceding summary indicates what should be done.

C. Experimental Conditions and Techniques

Few additional general comments are needed since, apart from special applications, the quinhydrone electrode has the advantage of needing no characteristic half-cell design. It is also adaptable; Newbery's metallized glass electrodes [platinum or gold (*156*)] can be used with advantage with quinhydrone, and it allows full scope for ingenuity in the design of microelectrodes, some of which are illustrated in Fig. 2. If such electrodes are constructed with very small wires, the exchange current is likely to be small, and an electronic voltmeter may be needed to avoid serious polarization. Designs involving metal films on glass (*18*, *166*), or drops of liquid in contact with platinum foil (*167*), are therefore to be preferred.

Various criteria for satisfactory operation of quinhydrone electrodes have been proposed, some of which are common to other electrodes, such as indifference to stirring of the solution. Biilmann recommended that at least two electrodes should always be used in the same solution, so that interagreement can be checked; their potentials should also be independent of quinhydrone concentration (i.e., saturated and unsaturated electrodes should give identical results). Hall and Conant (*27*) proposed as criteria rapid attainment of final equilibrium, rapid recovery after polarization, and registration of the correct electrode potential in a standard buffer solution.

The quinhydrone electrode is well suited, and has been widely used, for potentiometric titrations (*168*). The accuracy of end-point determinations, as affected by "alkaline errors" has been studied by Rabinowitsch and Kargin (*169*). Similar studies were made by Klit (*170*), who found that 0.1% accuracy was attainable in titrating an acid with a dissociation constant exceeding 10^{-7} in 0.1 N solution, or exceeding 10^{-6} in 0.005 N solution, provided carbon dioxide was excluded. Ingenious differential titration methods have been devised (171), and methods by which known and unknown solutions are brought to equality of pH, so that accuracy is improved by partial cancellation of errors (10).

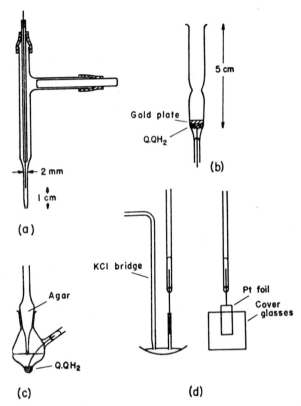

Fig. 2. Some microelectrodes. (a), Cullen (36); (b), Mozolowski and Parnas (166); (c), Ettisch (see reference 18); (d), Boëz (167).

Probably no other electrode could have been used for recording fast pH changes, such as those involved in the system,

$$H_2CO_3 \rightleftharpoons CO_2 + H_2O$$

studied by Buytendijk and Brinkman (7). They used a cell designed by Mislowitzer (172), consisting of concentric cylindrical vessels; the outer part contained a standard buffer, and the inner part the solution under investigation, both being saturated with quinhydrone. Connection between the two was made via a ground surface wetted with saturated potassium chloride solution. The electrode in the inner vessel served as a stirrer. It consisted of a platinum disk of diameter five-sixths that of the vessel, and was made to sweep out the whole solution volume by a vertical periodic motion of 10 c/s. Its potential responded to changes in the solution brought about by microtitration at a rate limited solely by the rate of mixing.

V. Numerical Data and Applications

A. REFERENCE ELECTRODES OF FIXED POTENTIAL

It has already been mentioned that the quinhydrone electrode is unsuitable for setting up permanent reference half-cells of fixed potential, and its use in this way was opposed by Sørensen and his co-workers (*32*). Yet it has advantages over the calomel electrode; it can be set up more quickly, is more reproducible, and responds faster to changes of temperature without hysteresis effects. Veibel (*28*) and Hovorka and Dearing (*29*) recommended the use of the quinhydrone electrode in equilibrium with "Veibel's solution," i.e., (0.01 N HCl + 0.09 N KCl) as an advantageous half-cell. The fixed potentials to be assigned to this, and to two analogous electrodes, have been recalculated and are shown in Table XII.

TABLE XII

POTENTIALS OF STANDARD QUINHYDRONE ELECTRODES

Temp (°C)	(0.01 N HCl + 0.09 N KCl) (abs volts)	0.1 N HCl (abs volts)	0.01 N HCl (abs volts)
18°	0.5750	0.6345	0.5787
25°	0.5831	0.6414	0.5868

The basis of the calculations was primarily Hovorka and Dearing's measurements (*132*) of the emf of hydrogen–quinhydrone cells at 25°C, corrected for salt errors where necessary. Values for 18°C were derived from these using Harned and Wright's temperature coefficient (*143*). In either case, earlier data in the literature (*6, 28, 123, 144*) were examined, and mean values adopted. The potentials of the nonstandard hydrogen electrodes used in these cells was assessed either by use of pH(S) values (cf. Chap. 5, Section III,B) assembled by Bates, Pinching, and Smith (*173*), or by identifying a_{H^+} with $C_{H^+}f_{\pm}$, the activity coefficients being taken from Harned and Owen (*174*) or elsewhere (*175*). Subtraction from the cell emf values gave the desired quinhydrone electrode potentials. Maximum divergences between values from different sources, or from different calculational routes, were slightly greater than 0.4 mv. The uncertainty in the adopted values is assessed at ±0.2 mv. Such electrodes could be used with a salt bridge and, for measurements with acid solutions, errors due to liquid junction potentials would be minimized by cancellation. More reliable data of this kind could be obtained by direct measurement, and this might well be a desirable project.

Cooper and Hand (*30*) have recommended 0.05 M potassium hydrogen phthalate solution as a basis for a standard quinhydrone half-cell, whilst Schomaker and Brown (*31*) used a solution of potassium tetroxalate prepared by saturation at 0°C. In the latter case, the following emf values were recorded for the cell completed with a saturated calomel electrode:

0°C, 0.36566 volt $\pm$ 0.07 mv

25°C, 0.35236 volt $\pm$ 0.04 mv

35°C, 0.34743 volt $\pm$ 0.06 mv

Ives and Swaroopa (*176*) used saturated potassium hydrogen phthalate electrodes in connection with dc conductance measurements.

B. STANDARD POTENTIAL

In order to obtain the best representative data, chief reliance must be placed upon the determinations of Harned and Wright (*143*) and of Hovorka and Dearing (*132*). Harned wished to use the quinhydrone electrode in cells without liquid junction in order to determine the dissociation constants of certain acids vulnerable to reduction by the hydrogen electrode. The necessary preliminary work was to determine the standard emf of the silver chloride–quinhydrone cell over a range of temperatures. This was done by means of an elegant technique, involving vacuum filling of the cells, similar to that adopted in many researches by the Harned school. They found that complete segregation of the quinhydrone and silver chloride half-cells was necessary. Large platinum foil electrodes were used, and all the precautions previously discussed in this chapter were adopted. Results of five figure significance were obtained for cells containing 0.01 N hydrochloric acid. Existing data for the silver–silver chloride electrode were then used to derive the $E°$ values required for the quinhydrone electrode.

The result at 25°C, 0.69969 int volt, did not agree with the carefully and directly determined value, 0.69935 int volt, of Hovorka and Dearing (*132*). On the other hand, the value at 18°C, 0.70482 int volt, agreed quite well with that of Biilmann and Jensen (*6*), 0.70479 int volt. The discrepancy at 25°C has not been adequately explained, although a private communication from Wright is cited by Hovorka and Dearing to the effect that his 25° electrode potential is 0.18 mv high. Until an experimental decision is made, it is best to follow Bates (*177*) in averaging the two 25° figures, and using the result, 0.69976 abs volt, to derive data at other temperatures by means of Harned and Wright's temperature coefficient,

which is close to that found by Biilmann and Krarup (*144*). This gives rise
to the figures in Table XIII, which are consistent with solutions of the
equation

$$E° = 0.69976 - 0.73606 \times 10^{-3}(t - 25) - 0.292 \times 10^{-6}(t - 25)^2 \text{ abs volt}$$

where t is temperature in °C.[1]

TABLE XIII

$E°$ Values of the Quinhydrone Electrode (*177*)

Temp (°C)	$E°$ (abs volt)	Temp (°C)	$E°$ (abs volt)
0	0.71798	25	0.69976
5	0.71437	30	0.69607
10	0.71073	35	0.69237
15	0.70709	40	0.68865
20	0.70343	—	—

C. Applications

Comprehensive bibliographies covering the years up to 1930 have been
given by Clark (*18*) and by Morgan and co-workers (*4*), and many references will be found in Britton's text (*51*). All that need be done is to record
some of the applications noted for the period 1930 to 1956.

The quinhydrone electrode has found its widest application in determinations of the pH of soils (*178–195*); errors in these determinations have
been considered by Crowther (*181*), and Hubbard (*184*) has compared
hydrogen, quinhydrone and antimony electrodes for use with alkaline soils.
In biological fields, the quinhydrone electrode has been used to study body
fluids (*196*), serum and plasma (*197, 198*), solid culture media (*199*), aqueous humor of rats (*200*), tissues (*201*) and the inhibition of bacterial
growth (*202*). The electrode has been applied in cereal chemistry (*203*);
it has been used in solutions containing tannin (*204, 205*, but cf. *206*) and
for the study of fruit juices (*207*) and the inversion of sucrose (*208, 209*).
Application to the measurement of the pH of semiplastic solids (*37*) and
gelatin gels (*210*) has been reported. In such cases, the electrode wire is
either dipped into powdered quinhydrone after being moistened with the
semiplastic or viscous liquid, or it is first treated with an acetone solution
of quinhydrone, which is allowed to dry off before the electrode is used.

---

[1] Redeterminations of emf's of the quinhydrous–silver chloride cell from 25° to 55°C
have recently been made by Hayes, J. C., and Lietzke, M. H., *J. Phys. Chem.* **64,** 374
(1960), and extrapolated to determine $E°$ values. This work does not resolve the above
discrepancy.

The quinhydrone electrode has been widely used in potentiometric titrations, and some examples have already been cited. Other publications worthy of attention deal with acid-base titrations (*211*), titrations of unsaturated acids (*212*), titrations in nonaqueous solvents (*213*), in mixed solvents (*214*) and in heavy water (*215*). It was first applied to the study of salt hydrolysis by Cupr (*216*).

VI. Alternative Systems

A. The Chloranil Electrode

Conant and Fieser (*76*) measured the emf of the hydrogen–chloranil cell, obtaining values of 0.664 volt at 25°C and 0.683 volt at 0°C. Using aqueous 0.1 N hydrochloric acid as electrolyte, they experienced some difficulty because of the low solubilities of tetrachloroquinone and its hydroquinone, but measurements with 50% ethanolic 0.1 N hydrochloric acid were easier and led to identical results. The cell reaction involves solid phases alone. No quinhydrone is formed, there are no salt errors and the emf of the cell is independent of the solvent, provided that the solid phases are invariant. The standard potentials of the chloranil electrode determined in this way are different from the $E°$ values of the redox couple in solution determined, for example, by the titration method. In the former case, the ratio of the activities of the oxidized and reduced members of the couple is determined by their relative solubilities; in the latter it is, by convention, unity. Thus, Conant and Fieser (*76*) found $E°$ for the homogeneous tetrachloroquinone–tetrachlorohydroquinone couple to be 0.695 volt for 0.5 N HCl and 0.703 volt for 1.0 N HCl at 25°C, both in 95% ethanol as solvent. These are no longer thermodynamically fixed constants. Applications of this electrode are discussed in Chapter 10.

B. Other Electrodes

1. Toluquinhydrone

This electrode was studied in Biilmann's original work (*2*), in the unsaturated form. At 18°C, 0.005 mole liter^{-1} of toluquinhydrone in solution, either in 0.1 N or 0.02 N sulfuric acid, established a potential against a hydrogen electrode in the same solution of 0.6506 volt; at 25°C, there was a slight discrepancy, 0.6458 volt and 0.6453 volt were obtained with these two solutions. Against the quinhydrone electrode, values of 0.6508 volt and 0.6452 volt at 18° and 25°C were found. The mean values adopted were 0.6507 and 0.6454 int volt. The second of these coincides with the value found by La Mer and Baker (*89*) by the titration method. The agreement between duplicate electrodes (platinum) in the same solution was as good as 0.03 mv, but this electrode has not been exploited. The free energy of formation of toluquinhydrone is substantially less than that of benzoquinhydrone (*76*), and it is more vulnerable to photochemical decomposition (*148*); it therefore cannot be seen to offer any advantages.

2. Thymoquinhydrone

The thymoquinone–thymohydroquinone system was investigated by La Mer and Baker (*89*), and a standard potential of 0.5875 volt at 25°C was determined by the titration method. The quinhydrone has a low free energy of formation from its components (*76*), is vulnerable to decomposition in sunlight (*148*) and it is much less soluble than benzoquinhydrone. Biilmann (*217*), although reporting emf's of the hydrogen–thymoquinhydrone cell (0.5927 volt at 18°C; 0.5866 volt at 25°C, both ±0.5 mv), said that they were not very constant, tending to increase with time. This difficulty was attributed by Tendeloo and his co-workers (*218*) to the fact that the quinhydrone is not only very sparingly soluble, but is also very slow in dissolving, so that Biilmann's electrodes did not in fact reach equilibrium. This is supported by comparing their standard potentials with La Mer and Baker's. The trouble is avoided by adding the thymoquinhydrone in the form of a solution in dioxane, and the electrode thus prepared was found to have admirable properties. Its temperature coefficient was said to be negligible, and it responded theoretically to pH over a range extending up to pH 10.5. Measurements of the emf of the saturated calomel–thymoquinhydrone cell containing ammonia–ammonium chloride buffer solutions gave rise, by application of the method of least squares, to the relation

$$\text{pH} = \frac{0.359 - E}{0.0577}$$

where E is the emf of the cell. The pH values derived from experimental emf's using this equation showed a mean deviation of ±0.02 pH unit from those determined by means of the hydrogen electrode.

On this evidence, the thymoquinhydrone electrode appears to have substantial advantages, for it operates well in alkaline solutions containing ammonia, without exclusion of air. It does not, in spite of this, seem to have attracted attention. Since the original paper is not very accessible, it is justifiable to provide some essential details of the work.

Thymoquinone can be obtained by oxidizing thymol by the method of Kremers, Wakeman, and Hixon (*219*); mp 47°–48°C. The thymohydroquinone is made by reduction of the quinone with aqueous sulfur dioxide at room temperature, the completion of the reaction being marked by the loss of the black color initially produced. The product is crystallized from ethanol and melts at 140°C. The quinhydrone is formed by mixing equimolar quantities of the components in alcoholic solution and allowing to crystallize; this can be facilitated by dilution with water. It is described variously as dark violet needles, or dark green crystals (mp 78°C, with decomp, 76°). The quinhydrone (1 gm) is dissolved in dioxane (15 ml) and is dispensed from a dropping bottle. It is possible that this electrode merits further study.

3. 1,4-Naphthoquinhydrone

Kläning (*220*) has studied this electrode, and the associated quino- and hydro-quinhydrone electrodes, obtaining values for the standard potentials at 20°C of 0.4817, 0.2092 and 0.2735 volt, respectively. The solubility of the naphthoquinhydrone was found to be 2.72×10^{-4} mole liter^{-1} at 20°C. Care was taken to exclude oxygen from the cells. No very definite assessment can be made of the merits of this electrode system.

To conclude, it may be remarked that the list of possible electrode systems has not been exhausted, but attention has been confined to those which might conceivably have some general application; thus it is doubtful if the alloxanthine and tetramethylalloxanthine electrodes described by Biilmann and Lund (*221*) meet this description.

REFERENCES

1. Haber, F., and Russ, R., *Z. physik. Chem.* **47**, 257 (1904).
2. Biilmann, E., *Ann. chim.* **15**, 109 (1921).
3. Granger, F. S., and Nelson, J. M., *J. Am. Chem. Soc.* **43**, 1401 (1921).
4. Morgan, J. L. R., Lammert, O. M., and Campbell, M. A., *Trans. Electrochem. Soc.* **61**, 405 (1932).
5. Clayton, W. J., and Vosburgh, W. C., *J. Am. Chem. Soc.* **59**, 2414 (1937).
6. Biilmann, E., and Jensen, E. L., *Bull. soc. chim. France* **41**, 151 (1927).
7. Buytendijk, F. J. J., and Brinkman, R., *Koninkl. Akad. Wetenschap. Amsterdam* **29**, 816 (1926).
8. Vetter, K. J., *Z. Elektrochem.* **56**, 797 (1952).
9. Cavanagh, B., *J. Chem. Soc.* **130**, 2207 (1927).
10. Meeker, G. H., and Oser, B. L., *J. Biol. Chem.* **67**, 307 (1926).
11. Martin, A. E., *J. Soc. Chem. Ind.* **56**, 179T (1937).
12. Clarke, B. L., and Wooten, L. A., *J. Phys. Chem.* **33**, 1468 (1929).
13. Coons, C. C., *Ind. Eng. Chem. Anal. Ed.* **3**, 402 (1931).
14. Stonehill, H. I., *Trans. Faraday Soc.* **39**, 72 (1943).
15. Biilmann, E., *Trans. Faraday Soc.* **19**, 677 (1923).
16. O'Sullivan, J. B., *Trans. Faraday Soc.* **21**, 319 (1925–6).
17. Güntelburg, E., and Schiødt, E., *Z. physik. Chem.* **A135**, 393 (1928).
18. Clark, W. M., "The Determination of Hydrogen Ions," Chap. 19. Williams & Wilkins, Baltimore, Maryland, 1928.
19. Ebert, L., *Ber. deut. chem. Ges.* **58**, 175 (1925).
20. Larsson, E., Dissertation, Lund, 1924.

21. Seltz, H., and Silverman, L., *Ind. Eng. Chem. Anal. Ed.* **2**, 1 (1930).
22. Pring, J. N., *Trans. Faraday Soc.* **19**, 705 (1923–4).
23. Cray, F. M., and Westrip, G. M., *Trans. Faraday Soc.* **21**, 326 (1925–6).
24. Izmaïlov, N. A., and Zabara, I. F., *Zhur. Fiz. Khim.* **20**, 165 (1946).
25. Pinfold, T. A., and Sebba, F., *J. Am. Chem. Soc.* **78**, 2095 (1956).
26. Roller, P. E., *J. Phys. Chem.* **34**, 367 (1930).
27. Hall, N. F., and Conant, J. B., *J. Am. Chem. Soc.* **49**, 3047 (1927).
28. Veibel, S., *J. Chem. Soc.* **123**, 2203 (1923).
29. Hovorka, F., and Dearing, W. C., *J. Am. Chem. Soc.* **56**, 243 (1934).
30. Cooper, C. A., and Hand, P. G. T., *J. Soc. Chem. Ind.* **55**, 341T (1936).
31. Schomaker, V., and Brown, D. J., *Ind. Eng. Chem. Anal. Ed.* **9**, 34 (1937).
32. Sørensen, S. P. L., Sørensen, M., and Linderstrøm-Lang, K., *Compt. rend. trav. lab. Carlsberg* **14**, No. 1 (1923).
33. Bates, R. G., "Electrometric pH Determinations," p. 180. Wiley, New York, 1954.
34. Biilmann, E., and Lund, H., *Ann. chim.* **16**, 321 (1921).
35. Cullen, G. E., and Biilmann, E., *J. Biol. Chem.* **64**, 727 (1925).
36. Cullen, G. E., *J. Biol. Chem.* **83**, 535 (1929).
37. Sanders, G. P., *Ind. Eng. Chem. Anal. Ed.* **10**, 274 (1938).
38. Seltz, H., and McKinney, D. S., *Ind. Eng. Chem.* **20**, 542 (1928).
39. Watson, P. D., *Ind. Eng. Chem.* **19**, 1272 (1927).
40. Schreiner, E., *Z. anorg. Chem.* **121**, 321; **122**, 201 (1922); **135**, 333 (1924).
41. Larsson, E., *Z. anorg. Chem.* **125**, 281 (1922).
42. Auerbach, Fr., and Smolczyk, E., *Z. physik. Chem.* **A110**, 65 (1924).
43. Sillén, L. G., *Quart. Revs. (London)* **13**, 146 (1959).
44. Olin, A., *Acta Chem. Scand.* **11**, 1445 (1957).
45. Biilmann, E., *Bull. Soc. Chim. France* **41**, 213 (1927).
46. Sørensen, S. P. L., Sørensen, M., and Linderstrøm-Lang, K., *Compt. rend. trav. lab. Carlsberg* **14**, No. 14 (1923).
47. Euler, H., and Brunius, E., *Z. physik. Chem.* **A139**, 615 (1928).
48. Brodsky, A. E., and Trachtenberg, F. I., *Z. physik. Chem.* **A143**, 287 (1929).
49. MacInnes, D. A., "The Principles of Electrochemistry." Reinhold, New York, 1939.
50. Glasstone, S., "An Introduction to Electrochemistry." Van Nostrand, New York, 1942.
51. Britton, H. T. S., "Hydrogen Ions," 4th ed. Chapman and Hall, London, 1955.
52. Wagner, C., and Grünewald, K., *Z. Elektrochem.* **46**, 265 (1940).
53. La Mer, V. K., and Parsons, T. R., *J. Biol. Chem.* **57**, 613 (1923).
54. Stackelberg, M., and Weber, P., *Z. Elektrochem.* **56**, 806 (1952).
55. Butler, J. A. V., Hugh, W. E., and Hey, D. H., *Trans. Faraday Soc.* **22**, 24 (1926).
56. Symposium on charge-transfer processes, Toronto, 1958. *Can. J. Chem.* **37**, 120 (1959).
57. Gerischer, H., *Z. Elektrochem.* **54**, 366 (1950).
58. Conant, J. B., and Cutter, H. B., *J. Am. Chem. Soc.* **44**, 2651 (1922).
59. Kobosew, N. I., *Zhur. Fiz. Khim.* **26**, 112 (1952).
60. Hey, D. H., *Ann. Repts. on Progr. Chem. (London)* **41**, 181 (1944); **45**, 139 (1948).
61. Shaffer, P. A., *J. Am. Chem. Soc.* **55**, 2169 (1933).
62. Weiss, J., *J. Chem. Soc.* 309 (1944).
63. Michaelis, L., *Trans. Electrochem. Soc.* **71**, 107 (1937).
64. Michaelis, L., and Smythe, C. V., *Ann. Rev. Biochem.* **7**, 1 (1938).

65. Halpern, J., *Can. J. Chem.* **37**, 148 (1959).

66. Remick, A. E., "Electronic Interpretations of Organic Chemistry," 2nd ed., Chapter 12. Wiley, New York, 1949.

67. Michaelis, L., Schubert, M. P., and Granick, S., *J. Am. Chem. Soc.* **61**, 1981 (1939).

68. Michaelis, L., *Chem. Revs.* **16**, 243 (1935).

69. Clark, W. M., *J. Washington Acad. Sci.* **10**, 255 (1920); *Chem. Revs.* **2**, 127 (1926).

70. Michaelis, L., and Schubert, M. P., *Chem. Revs.* **22**, 437 (1938).

71. MacInnes, D. A., "The Principles of Electrochemistry," p. 297. Reinhold, New York, 1939.

72. Charlot, G., Bézier, D., and Courtot, J., "Constantes sélectionnées, potentiels d'oxydo-réduction." Pergamon, New York, 1958.

73. Müller, O. H., and Baumberger, J. P., *Trans. Electrochem. Soc.* **71**, 181 (1937).

74. Conant, J. B., Kahn, H. M., Fieser, L. F., and Kurtz, S. S., *J. Am. Chem. Soc.* **44**, 1382 (1922).

75. Conant, J. B., and Fieser, L. F., *J. Am. Chem. Soc.* **44**, 2480 (1922).

76. Conant, J. B., and Fieser, L. F., *J. Am. Chem. Soc.* **45**, 2194 (1923).

77. Conant, J. B., and Fieser, L. F., *J. Am. Chem. Soc.* **46**, 1858 (1924).

78. Fieser, L. F., *J. Am. Chem. Soc.* **50**, 439 (1928); **51**, 3101 (1929); **52**, 4915 (1930).

79. Fieser, L. F., and Fieser, M., *J. Am. Chem. Soc.* **56**, 1565 (1934); **57**, 491 (1935).

80. Geake, A., *Trans. Faraday Soc.* **34**, 1395 (1938); Geake, A., and Lemon, J. T., *Trans. Faraday Soc.* **34**, 1409 (1938).

81. Branch, G. E. K., and Calvin, M., "The Theory of Organic Chemistry," Chapter VII. Prentice-Hall, New York, 1941.

82. Evans, M. G., and De Heer, J., *Quart. Revs. (London)* **4**, 94 (1950).

83. Fritz, G., and Hartmann, H., *Z. Elektrochem.* **55**, 184 (1951).

84. Basu, S., *Trans. Faraday Soc.* **52**, 6 (1956).

85. Pilcher, G., and Sutton, L. E., *J. Chem. Soc.* 2695 (1956).

86. Conant, J. B., *J. Am. Chem. Soc.* **49**, 293 (1927).

87. Waters, W. A., *Ann. Repts. on Progr. Chem. (London)* **42**, 1946 (1945).

88. Braude, E. A., Jackman, L. M., and Linstead, R. P., *J. Chem. Soc.* 3548 (1954).

89. La Mer, V. K., and Baker, L. E., *J. Am. Chem. Soc.* **44**, 1954 (1922).

90. Foz, O. R., and Palacios, J., *Anales fis. quím. (Madrid)* **30**, 421 (1932).

91. Palacios, J., and Foz, O. R., *Anales fis. quím. (Madrid)* **33**, 627; **34**, 779 (1935).

92. Anderson, J. S., *Nature* **140**, 583 (1937).

93. Banerjee, S., *Z. Krist.* **100**, 316 (1939).

94. Powell, H. M., Huse, G., and Cooke, P. W., *J. Chem. Soc.* 153 (1943).

95. Harding, T. T., and Wallwork, S. C., *Acta Cryst.* **8**, 787 (1955).

96. Weiss, J., *J. Chem. Soc.* p. 245 (1942).

97. Dewar, M. J. S., "The Electronic Theory of Organic Chemistry," p. 185. Oxford Univ. Press, London and New York, 1949.

98. McKeown, P. J. A., Ubbelohde, A. R., and Woodward, I., *Acta Cryst.* **4**, 391 (1951).

99. Wallwork, S. C., and Harding, T. T., *Nature* **171**, 40 (1953).

100. Harding, T. T., and Wallwork, S. C., *Acta Cryst.* **6**, 791 (1953).

101. Suzuki, K., and Seki, S., *Bull. Chem. Soc. Japan* **26**, 372 (1953).

102. Schreiner, E., *Z. physik. Chem.* **117**, 57 (1925).

103. Matsuda, H., Osaki, K., and Nitta, I., *Bull. Chem. Soc. Japan* **31**, 611 (1958).

104. Nakamoto, K., *J. Am. Chem. Soc.* **74**, 1739 (1952).

105. Mulliken, R. S., *J. Am. Chem. Soc.* **74**, 811 (1952).

106. Dewar, M. J. S., *J. Chem. Soc.* 406, 777 (1946).

107. Elvidge, J. A., and Lever, A. B. P., *Proc. Chem. Soc.* p. 123 (1959).

108. Luther, R., and Leubner, A., *J. prakt. Chem.* **85**, 314 (1912).
109. Sørensen, S. P. L., Sørensen, M., and Linderstrøm-Lang, K., *Ann. chim.* **16**, 283 (1921); *Compt. rend. trav. lab. Carlsberg* **14**, No. 14 (1923).
110. Berthoud, A., and Kunz, S., *Helv. Chim. Acta* **21**, 17 (1938).
111. Rosenthal, R., Lorch, A. E., and Hammett, L. P., *J. Am. Chem. Soc.* **59**, 1795 (1937).
112. Vetter, K. J., *Z. Naturforsch.* **7a**, 328 (1952).
113. Euler, H., and Bolin, I., *Z. physik. Chem.* **66**, 71 (1909).
114. Sheppard, S. E., *Trans. Electrochem. Soc.* **39**, 429 (1921).
115. Abichandani, C. T., and Jatkar, S. K. K., *J. Indian Inst. Sci.* **A21**, 417 (1938).
116. MacInnes, D. A., "The Principles of Electrochemistry," pp. 289–296. Reinhold, New York, 1939.
117. Kolthoff, I. M., and Bosch, W., *Biochem. Z.* **183**, 435 (1927).
118. Best, R. J., *J. Phys. Chem.* **34**, 1815 (1930).
119. Kolthoff, I. M., *Z. physiol. Chem.* **144**, 259 (1925).
120. Granér, F., Olin, A., and Sillén, L. G., *Acta Chem. Scand.* **10**, 476 (1956).
121. Hammett, L. P., "Physical Organic Chemistry," p. 48. McGraw-Hill, New York, 1940.
122. Biedermann, G., *Acta Chem. Scand.* **10**, 1340 (1956).
123. Linderstrøm-Lang, K., *Compt. rend. trav. lab. Carlsberg* **16**, No. 3 (1927).
124. Linderstrøm-Lang, K., *Compt. rend. trav. lab. Carlsberg* **15**, No. 4 (1923–1925).
125. Randall, M., and Failey, C. F., *Chem. Revs.* **4**, 285 (1927).
126. Harned, H. S., and Owen, B. B., "The Physical Chemistry of Electrolytic Solutions," 2nd ed. Reinhold, New York, 1958.
127. Linderstrøm-Lang, K., *Compt. rend. trav. lab. Carlsberg* **17**, No. 3 (1927–1929).
128. Biilmann, E., Klit, A., and Swaetichin, T., *Biochem. J.* **22**, 845 (1928).
129. Urmánczy, A., *Magyar Chem. Folyóirat* **39**, 125 (1933).
130. Kiss, A., and Urmánczy, A., *Z. physik. Chem.* **A169**, 31 (1934).
131. Stonehill, H. I., *Trans. Faraday Soc.* **39**, 67 (1943).
132. Hovorka, F., and Dearing, W. C., *J. Am. Chem. Soc.* **57**, 446 (1935).
133. Gabbard, J. L., *J. Am. Chem. Soc.* **69**, 533 (1947).
134. Kirschman, H. D., Wingfield, B., and Lucas, H. J., *J. Am. Chem. Soc.* **52**, 23 (1930).
135. Kilpatrick, M., and Chase, E. F., *J. Am. Chem. Soc.* **53**, 1732 (1931).
136. La Mer, V. K., and Rideal, E. K., *J. Am. Chem. Soc.* **46**, 223 (1924).
137. Reinders, W., and Dingemans, P., *Rec. trav. chim.* **53**, 209 (1934).
138. Saint-Maxen, A., *J. Chim. Phys.* **32**, 410 (1935).
139. Manchot, W., *Ann.* **314**, 177 (1901).
140. Wood, W. S., "Hydrogen Peroxide." *Roy. Inst. Chem. Monographs* **2** (1954).
141. Wöhler, F., *Ann.* **51**, 155 (1844).
142. Granger, F. S., Dissertation, Columbia Univ., March, 1920.
143. Harned, H. S., and Wright, D. D., *J. Am. Chem. Soc.* **55**, 4849 (1933).
144. Biilmann, E., and Krarup I., *J. Chem. Soc.* **125**, 1954 (1924).
145. Shikata, M., and Tachi, I., *J. Biochem. (Tokyo)* **10**, 115 (1928).
146. Britton, H. T. S., "Hydrogen Ions," 4th ed., Vol. I, Chapter 4. Chapman and Hall, London, 1955.
147. Cullen, G. E., and Earle, I. P., *J. Biol. Chem.* **76**, 565, 583 (1928).
148. Cooper, E. A., and Nicholas, S. D., *J. Soc. Chem. Ind. (London)* **46**, 59T (1927).
149. Linderstrøm-Lang, K., and Kodama, S., *Compt. rend. trav. lab. Carlsberg* **16**, No. 1 (1925–1927).
150. Meeker, G. H., and Reinhold, J. G., *J. Biol. Chem.* **77**, 505 (1928).

151. Kolthoff, I. M., *Rec. trav. chim.* **44**, 275 (1925).

152. Lester, V., *J. Agr. Sci.* **14**, 634 (1924).

153. Valeur, A. M., *Ann. Chim. Phys.* **21**, 546 (1900).

154. Flexner, L. B., and Barron, E. S. G., *J. Am. Chem. Soc.* **52**, 2773 (1930).

155. Biilmann, E., *Trans. Faraday Soc.* **19**, 819 (1923).

156. Newbery, E., *Trans. Electrochem. Soc.* **65**, 227 (1934).

157. Bhattacharya, A. K., and Jha, J. B., *Z. physik. Chem.* (*Leipzig*) **205**, 113 (1956).

158. Lammert, O. M., Morgan, J. L. R., and Campbell, M. A., *J. Am. Chem. Soc.* **53**, 597 (1931).

159. Morgan, J. L. R., and Lammert, O. M., *J. Am. Chem. Soc.* **53**, 2154 (1931).

160. Larsson, E., and Adell, B., *Z. physik. Chem.* **A156**, 352 (1931).

161. Perley, G. A., and Godshalk, J. B., U. S. Patent No. 2,416,949; British Patent No. 567,722 (June 10, 1942).

162. Corran, J. W., and Lewis, W. C. McC., *Biochem. J.* **18**, 1358 (1924).

163. Morgan, J. L. R., Lammert, O. M., and Campbell, M. A., *J. Am. Chem. Soc.* **53**, 454 (1931).

164. Lammert, O. M., and Morgan, J. L. R., *J. Am. Chem. Soc.* **54**, 910 (1932).

165. Mueller, T. R., Olsen, C. L., and Adams, R. N., *Proc. 2nd Intern. Congr. Polarography, Cambridge, 1959* (Pergamon, New York, 1960).

166. Mozolowski, W., and Parnas, J. K., *Biochem. Z.* **169**, 352 (1926).

167. Boëz, L., *Compt. rend. soc. biol.* **101**, 524 (1929).

168. Kolthoff, I. M., *Rec. trav. chim.* **42**, 186 (1923).

169. Rabinowitsch, A., and Kargin, V. A., *Z. Elektrochem.* **33**, 11 (1927).

170. Klit, A., *Z. physik. Chem.* **A131**, 61 (1928).

171. MacInnes, D. A., and Jones, P. T., *J. Am. Chem. Soc.* **48**, 2831 (1926).

172. Mislowitzer, E., *Biochem. Z.* **159**, 72 (1925).

173. Bates, R. G., Pinching, G. D., and Smith, E. R., *J. Research Natl. Bur. Standards* **45**, 418 (1950).

174. Harned, H. S., and Owen, B. B., "The Physical Chemistry of Electrolytic Solutions," 2nd ed., p. 547. Reinhold, New York, 1958.

175. Bates, R. G., Guggenheim, E. A., *et al.*, *J. Chem. Phys.* **25**, 361 (1956).

176. Ives, D. J. G., and Swaroopa, S., *Trans. Faraday Soc.* **49**, 788 (1953).

177. Bates, R. G., "Electrometric pH Determinations," p. 175. Wiley, New York, 1954.

178. Karraker, P. E., *J. Am. Soc. Agron.* **22**, 171 (1930).

179. Kuhn, I., *Z. Pflanzenernähr Düng.* **15A**, 13 (1929).

180. De Coninck, P., *Ann. soc. sci. Bruxelles* **B50**, 6 (1930).

181. Heintze, S. G., and Crowther, E. M., *Trans. 2nd Comm. Intern. Soc. Soil Sci.* **1929A**, 102.

182. Frognier, R., *Ann. soc. sci. Bruxelles* **B50**, 135 (1930).

183. Collins, E. R., *Iowa State Coll. J. Sci.* **5**, 321, 323 (1931).

184. Hubbard, P. L., *J. Assoc. Offic. Agr. Chemists* **16**, 193 (1933).

185. Naftel, J. A., Schollenberger, C. J., and Bradfield, R., *Soil Research* **3**, 222 (1933).

186. Naftel, J. A., *Alabama Polytech. Inst. Agr. Expt. Sta. 44th. Ann. Rept.* 17 (1933).

187. Dean, H. L., and Walker, R. H., *J. Am. Soc. Agron.* **27**, 429 (1935).

188. Hissink, D. J., Crowther, E. M., and Heintze, S. G., *Trans. 3rd. Intern. Congr. Soil Sci., Oxford* **1**, 127 (1935).

189. Dean, H. L., and Walker, R. H., *J. Am. Soc. Agron.* **27**, 519 (1935).

190. Gisiger, L., *Landwirtsch. Jahrb. Schweiz* **49**, 735 (1935).

191. Van der Spek, J., *Verslag. Landbouwk. Onderzoek.* **No. 41B**, 575 (1935).

192. Dean, H. L., and Walker, R. H., *Proc. Iowa Acad. Sci.* **42**, 105 (1935).

193. Klychnikov, V. M., *Vsesoyuz. Akad. Sel'skokhoz. Nauk im. V. I. Lenina, Nauch. Issledovatel. Inst. Udobrenii, Agrotekh i Agropochvovedniya im. K. K. Gedroitsa, Trudy Leningrad. Odtel* **2**, 3 (1938); *Chem. Zentr.* **II**, 2806 (1940).

194. Tovborg-Jensen, S., *Ingeniren* **52**, No. 31, 38 (1943).

195. Janekovic, G., *Zemljiste i biljka* **1**, 313 (1952).

196. Reimers, K., *Z. Ges. exptl. Med.* **67**, 327 (1929).

197. Laug, E. P., *J. Biol. Chem.* **88**, 551 (1930).

198. Hanke, M. E., *Proc. Soc. Exptl. Biol. Med.* **27**, 972 (1930).

199. Tilford, P. E., *Phytopathology* **25**, 362 (1935).

200. Pierce, J. A., *J. Biol. Chem.* **111**, 501 (1935).

201. Krantz, J. C., Carr, C. J., and Musser, R., *Science*, **85**, 127 (1937).

202. Glick, D. P., and Gee, L. L., *J. Bacteriol.* **33**, 34 (1937).

203. Sorg, L. V., *Cereal Chem.* **7**, 143 (1930).

204. Wallace, E. L., and Beck, J., *J. Research Natl. Bur. Standards* **4**, 737 (1930).

205. Gerngross, O., and Herfeld, H., *Collegium* 947 (1932).

206. Fornachon, J. C. M., *Ind. Eng. Chem. Anal. Ed.* **18**, 790 (1946).

207. Kauko, Y., and Knappsberg, L., *Angew. Chem.* **53**, 187 (1940).

208. Floyd, W. W., *Trans. Kansas Acad. Sci.* **36**, 118 (1933).

209. Cady, H. P., and Ingle, J. D., *J. Phys. Chem.* **40**, 837 (1936).

210. Swyngedauw, J., *Compt. rend. soc. biol.* **126**, 42 (1937).

211. Hahn, F. L., *Z. angew. Chem.* **43**, 712 (1930).

212. Hatcher, W. H., and Sturrock, M. G., *J. Am. Chem. Soc.* **52**, 3233 (1930).

213. Bereau, F. Y., and Tous, J. G., *Anales fis. quim. (Madrid)* **39**, 710 (1943).

214. Zhukov, I. I., and Vorokhobin, I. G., *J. Gen. Chem., U.S.S.R.* **2**, 399 (1932).

215. La Mer, V. K., and Korman, S., *J. Am. Chem. Soc.* **57**, 1511 (1935); *Science* **83**, 624 (1936).

216. Cupr, V., *Publ. fac. sci. Univ. Masaryk* **133**, 1 (1931).

217. Biilmann, E., and Muis, J., *Ber. deut. chem. Ges.* **64B**, 310 (1931).

218. Tendeloo, H. J. C., Buy, J. S., and Huyskes, J. A., *Landbouwk. Tijdschr.* **50**, 742 (1938).

219. Kremers, E., Wakeman, N., and Hixon, R. M., "Organic Syntheses," Collected Vol. I, 2nd ed., p. 511. Wiley, New York, 1941.

220. Kläning, U., *Acta Chem. Scand.* **9**, 1396 (1955).

221. Biilmann, E., and Lund, H., *Ann. Chim.* **19**, 137 (1923).

Chapter Seven

Oxide, Oxygen, and Sulfide Electrodes

D. J. G. Ives

I. Introduction

Metal–metal oxide electrodes find use in systems where, by reason of high alkalinity or elevated temperature, glass and quinhydrone electrodes fail. They can also be used when the hydrogen electrode would be poisoned, or when the passage of hydrogen might sweep away wanted volatile constituents. They are favored when a robust electrode is needed for control or routine estimation of pH. A few of them are capable of measurements of quite high accuracy; more are satisfactory for measuring pH within a useful tolerance and still more provide adequate end-point indicators in electrometric acid-base titrations. As a class, they present features of considerable general interest. The oxygen electrode, in a highly reversible form, is of comparatively recent inception; it has potentialities in various connections and very wide theoretical implications. It may be regarded as a relative of metal–metal oxide electrodes.

Sulfide-reversible electrodes are included in this chapter because of their obvious affiliations.

A. GENERAL PRINCIPLES OF METAL–METAL OXIDE ELECTRODES

Ideally, metal–metal oxide electrodes respond to pH in the same way as the hydrogen electrode, changing in potential by $RT/F \ln 10$ volt (i.e., $2.3026 RT/F$ volt) for each unit of pH change in the solution with which they are in contact. Their operation may be viewed in two thermodynamic ways.

They may first be regarded as a special sort of electrode of the second kind; special because the anionic part of the sparingly soluble metal "salt" participates in the self-ionization equilibrium of the solvent, namely, water. Thus, a reversible electrode represented by

$$M \mid MO \mid H^+ (aq)$$

must conform with the thermodynamic equilibria

$$M^{2+} + 2e^- \rightleftharpoons M$$

$$MO \text{ (solid)} \rightleftharpoons M^{2+} + O^{2-}$$

$$O^{2-} + H_2O \rightleftharpoons 2OH^-$$

$$2OH^- + 2H^+ \rightleftharpoons 2H_2O$$

Accordingly, the potential of such an electrode may be formulated

$$E = E^{\circ}_{M,M^{2+}} + \frac{RT}{2F} \ln a_{M^{2+}} \tag{1}$$

If, by analogy with other electrodes of the second kind, the solubility product of the oxide is defined by

$$K_s = a_{M^{2+}} \cdot a_{O^{2-}} \tag{2}$$

the situation is now different because oxide ions are in equilibrium with hydroxyl ions, so that

$$K_s' = a_{M^{2+}}(a_{OH^-})^2 \tag{3}$$

where K_s' is the solubility product of the hydroxide; indeed the sparingly soluble phase may be a hydroxide or an oxy-hydroxide — provided only that it is a well-defined invariant phase; that is all that matters. Hence,

$$E = E^{\circ}_{M,M^{2+}} + \frac{RT}{2F} \ln K_s' - \frac{RT}{F} \ln a_{OH^-} \tag{4}$$

and, so long as the ionic product of water,

$$K_w = a_{H^+} \cdot a_{OH^-} \tag{5}$$

can be regarded as constant,

$$E = E^\circ_{M,M^{2+}} + \frac{RT}{2F} \ln K_s' - \frac{RT}{F} \ln K_w + \frac{RT}{F} \ln a_{H^+} \tag{6}$$

$$E = E^\circ_{M,MO,H^+} + \frac{RT}{F} \ln a_{H^+}$$
$$\tag{7}$$
or $$\quad E = E^\circ_{M,MO,H^+} - \frac{RT}{F} \ln 10 \text{ pH}$$

which is of identical form with the Nernst equation for the potential of the hydrogen electrode. Strictly, this equation is valid only as long as zero concentration conditions prevail, because K_w is not a thermodynamic equilibrium constant. Clearly, the self-ionization of water is controlled in part by the activity of water and it can easily be seen that Eq. (7) should contain another term:

$$E = E^{\circ\prime}_{M,MO,H^+} + \frac{RT}{F} \ln a_{H^+} - \frac{RT}{F} \ln a_{H_2O} \tag{8}$$

Although, within limits of quite high accuracy, this extra term may be ignored for dilute aqueous systems, this will not be permissible when measurements are to be extended to concentrated solutions or to partly aqueous solvent systems. Cells of this kind have been used to measure activity coefficients of water in methanol-water mixtures (1).

The second view that may be taken is that these electrodes are equivalent to oxygen electrodes at which the partial pressure of oxygen controlling the electrode potential, in conjunction with the pH of the solution, is identified with the dissociation pressure of the metal–metal oxide system. The phase rule indicates that, at constant temperature, this is invariant. It is doubtful whether it is profitable to think in these terms, for the pressures involved (e.g., 10^{-53} atm for Ni, NiO at 25°C) can have no mechanistic significance. It is, however, more satisfying to consider that each metal–metal oxide system has, at each temperature, its own specific oxygen potential. This may be related to the chemical potential of oxygen gas in its standard state by

$$\mu = \mu^\circ + RT \ln \frac{P}{P^\circ} \tag{9}$$

where P is the dissociation pressure and P° is the standard pressure of gaseous oxygen.

In any event, instead of considering single electrode potentials (cf.

Chap. 1, Section II), it is better to base an unambiguous argument on the complete, thermodynamic cell

$$H_2, 1 \text{ atm, Pt} \mid \text{aqueous solution} \mid MO \mid M$$

in which the reaction will be

$$H_2 + MO = M + H_2O$$

The standard free energies of formation of the solid oxide and of liquid water obtained from authoritative sources (2, 3) will give $\Delta G°$ for the cell reaction and hence the standard emf of the cell, $E°$, which is to be identified with the standard potential of the metal–metal oxide electrode, $E°_{M,MO,H^+}$. It is to be noticed that, in this cell, both electrodes respond to pH in an identical way, so that the emf is independent of the pH of the cell solution.

If desired, the cell reaction can be considered in terms of

$$H_2 + \tfrac{1}{2}O_2 = H_2O$$

where the oxygen has the chemical potential characteristic of the metal–metal oxide couple concerned; for that matter, it can also be considered in terms of pressures, but it may be felt that this tends to place the imprint of fictitiousness on very real quantities by measuring them on an unsuitable scale.

Any satisfactory metal–metal oxide reference electrode must fit into this thermodynamic framework. But thermodynamics gives no clue to the mechanism by which the electrode process may proceed, nor any idea of the difficulties which may be encountered in getting the electrode to behave in the desired way.

B. Essential Properties of Solid Phases

If the electrode is to operate satisfactorily, the metal and its oxide must have the following properties.

The metal must be sufficiently noble to resist direct attack by all the solutions in which the electrode is to be used. Its standard electrode potential should be positive (Stockholm convention), so that the reaction

$$M + 2H^+ = M^{2+} + H_2$$

has no tendency to occur, even when any activation energy barrier to hydrogen ion discharge is lowered by the presence of dissolved oxygen, i.e., when the hydrogen evolution reaction is depolarized. This condition must be satisfied over a usefully wide pH range, otherwise the metal–metal oxide electrode will not be stable; it will seriously contaminate the solution in which it is placed and will not respond correctly to pH except in the higher ranges.

The metal must also have the properties which are desirable in the establishment of a reproducible electrode system of the first kind, i.e., a metal–metal ion electrode. It must be obtainable in a reproducible state of minimum free energy, and this means that it should not occur in different polymorphic forms, and should not be hard enough to sustain any strain or tempering effects determined by its previous mechanical or thermal treatments.

The oxide must be stable. It is important to notice that this requirement is somewhat opposed to the first, for the more noble the metal, the less stable the oxide.

The oxide phase must also be obtainable in a reproducible standard state. The first difficulty arises if the metal has more than one valency state, for the oxide commonly formed may then be a mixture of lower and higher oxides, or a mixed oxide. It is true that only the lowest oxide can exist at equilibrium in contact with the metal, but in solid–solid systems the rate of attainment of equilibrium is often exceedingly slow. There is a danger, in such a case, that more than one oxide phase may be present and the electrode potential is unlikely to be controlled by the single, clear-cut reaction desired. Apart from this, many oxides exist in alternative crystalline forms which differ in free energy except at a transition point. At ordinary temperatures, the rate at which the stable form is spontaneously produced from the others may be effectively zero. Unfortunately, metastable modifications of compounds are commonly produced in chemical reactions, and unless particular care is taken, it is clear that polymorphism may cause great difficulty in attaining a standard state for the oxide.

It is obviously desirable that the oxide should be very sparingly soluble, otherwise it will lead to contamination and alteration of pH in the solution in which it is placed (4). At the same time, it must be able to participate without undue hindrance in the equilibria which control electrode potential, and these equilibria must be mobile enough to endow the electrode with an adequate exchange current (cf. Chapter 1, Section III). If this is to be the case over a wide pH range, the oxide should be amphoteric. In terms of the formal system so far used as an example, this might be represented:

$$MO + H_2O$$

$$M^{2+} + 2OH^- \rightleftharpoons M(OH)_2 \rightleftharpoons MO_2^{2-} + 2H^+$$

$$\text{low pH media} \qquad\qquad\qquad \text{high pH media}$$

It is easily seen that if each balanced reaction is in equilibrium, the whole system is in equilibrium and Eq. (8) remains applicable. All that is necessary is that, at the pH extremes, $a_{M^{2+}}$ or $a_{MO_2^{2-}}$ should not attain unsuitably high values in the solution phase. The impression is to be gained from certain published papers that a change in the potential–pH relation is to be expected for such electrodes as the "isoelectric point" is crossed. That this is not so can be seen by considering the over-all reaction in the complete "hydrogen–metal oxide" cell. If such a change does occur, it means that there has been a change in the identity of the solid nonmetallic phase, or that potential control has been taken over by some other process unconnected with the proper metal oxide–aqueous solution equilibrium.

Difficulties may arise from the presence in solution of anions which form complexes with the metal cations. Although the linking of another equilibrium with those set out above should not, thermodynamically, cause any disturbance, in practice there will be an undesirable enhancement of total "solubility" and promotion of conditions under which true equilibrium is not attained. Complex formation is usually found to be fatal to the proper functioning of metal–metal oxide electrodes.

C. Methods of Forming Metal–Metal Oxide Couples

The metal and metal oxide phases may be prepared and brought together in various ways. The metal may be massive, in the form of a wire, a foil, or a cast stick; it may be electrolytically deposited upon a noble metal substrate, or it may be prepared in the form of a crystalline deposit or powder. The oxide may be prepared separately in crystalline form to be mixed with the metal powder, to be brought into contact with the massive metal phase, or to be added to the solution phase. It may be formed as an adherent layer on the metal by anodic oxidation, or by spontaneous oxidation in air (perhaps at an elevated temperature) or in a solution containing dissolved oxygen. In practice, and for the purposes of discussion, the various combinations are restricted to three.

1. Powdered Metal-Powdered Oxide in Admixture

This has the advantage that each phase can be given separate, careful treatment to bring it into the most stable and reproducible state. It involves the use of a half-cell of a kind developed by Brönsted (5) in which solution is caused to flow through a bed of metal and oxide. Such a cell was used by Güntelberg (6) for the silver–silver chloride electrode. Although inconvenient for general use and usually very slow to reach equilibrium, it appears that half-cells constructed in this way are suited to provide reproducible, thermodynamic results.

2. Aerial Oxidation

This is obviously extremely convenient, but the oxide is normally produced in vestigial amounts and an electrode formed with such small traces of one essential potential-determining phase will have a very small "electrochemical capacity." The problem also likely to arise is whether the properties of a limiting oxide film are very directly related to those of the pure bulk oxide which has been thermodynamically characterized. On the other hand, if a thick film is spontaneously formed, this usually amounts to runaway oxidation and the metal concerned will be far from satisfying the requirements of a reasonable degree of nobility.

3. Anodic Oxidation

Although in principle, this method is desirable because of the possibility of regulating the conditions of growth and thickness of the oxide film, it is little used for producing reversible metal–metal oxide couples because of difficulties which are discussed in the following section.

D. The Formation of Oxide Films

This subject has been extensively discussed in connection with corrosion (7) and the theory of oxidation of metals (8). A valuable article, with special reference to anodically formed films has recently appeared (9). All metals interact with gaseous oxygen to an extent which varies from the formation of a chemisorbed monolayer (in perhaps less than 10^{-2} sec) to the development of a well-defined oxide film. In many cases initial action is very rapid, but shows down rather abruptly when a limiting film, perhaps 20–100 Å thick, has been established (10). In the early stages, the oxide film tends to ape the structure of the metal substrate, and this it can do, provided that the degree of lattice misfit does not exceed about 15%, depending on the elastic constants of the oxide. Since conversion of metal to oxide involves expansion, such a film is highly compressed and is not in thermodynamic equilibrium. In some cases these extremely thin films may be very strong, both coherent and adherent, and self-repairing after damage. They are then often highly protective, forming "barrier layers." They will conduct electricity only under high potential gradients, by a process of activated jumps; they also show rectifying action. The metal is then passivated, and the exchange currents for any electrochemical process have fallen effectively to zero. In such cases (Al, Zr, Ta, etc.), there is little or no possibility of forming reversible metal–metal oxide electrodes.

In other cases, oxidation may proceed beyond this limiting stage, and will be accompanied by a recrystallization or fracturing process necessary to relieve the strain in the thickening film. The mechanism of further film growth depends on the facility with which charged particles can permeate the film, and may be illustrated by the case of copper, which has been extensively investigated by Garner and his co-workers (11). A detailed discussion of the mechanism of the oxidation of copper by gaseous oxygen is available (*12*). At the outer surface of the film, oxygen is dissociatively adsorbed to form a layer of ions, the charge being provided by electrons from the metal, passing outwards through the film. The layer of charge so established sets up a very high potential gradient in the film and, under its influence, cuprous ions migrate outwards. When they reach the outside, combination with oxide ions occurs to form a new layer of cuprous oxide. For an oxide film to provide such a means for extended film growth, it must possess semiconducting properties, and this is usually associated with a degree of nonstoichiometry; thus, cuprous oxide is an oxygen-excess (or metal-deficit) semiconductor. This, together with the decrepitation of the thickening film already mentioned, is not a circumstance favorable to the production of a "standard state oxide."

Oxidation in an aqueous medium containing dissolved oxygen may proceed by a similar mechanism supplemented, or perhaps replaced, by local cell action. If the existing air-formed film is nonuniform or pitted, the thicker sections are likely to be the sites of cathodic action, at which oxygen is consumed with production of (*inter alia*) hydroxyl ions. At the thinner sections, or in pits, anodic action can now send metal ions directly into solution. In the solution phase, some of these ions may combine with hydroxyl ions from nearby cathodic areas to produce precipitates which are not closely attached to the metal and are quite unlike the original oxide film. Such corrosion processes may be regarded as due to the operation of an "oxygen concentration cell" and have recently been reviewed (*13*). They may have the effect that an initially good electrode may deteriorate with use.

Attention may now be turned to the anodic oxidation of metals. Here the permeation of a limiting film by ions may be greatly assisted by the imposed field. The anodization of aluminum is familiar, and so is its result. It is obviously unlikely that any such forced process will produce anything but a highly passivating film. In all the other cases, in which film conduction is more facile, the metals concerned are of variable valency. Since the rapidly thickened film is bound to be fissured and porous, it turns out that even automatic potential control may be ineffective in preventing the attainment of a higher valency state than that desired, because of the conditions of concentration polarization prevailing in the depths of the pores. Then the oxide layer as a whole will be a mixture of lower- and higher-valent oxides, quite unsuitable for reproducible open-circuit behavior, even if a process of "self-discharge" tends to reduce the higher oxide.

It is clear that there are difficulties in securing homogeneous, stable oxide films on metals likely to be useful for reversible electrodes, and the reasons may be briefly summarized.

If the metal–metal oxide system is to be stable, the whole of the oxide film must consist of the lower-valent oxide. In oxygenated systems, there may be a tendency for the outer parts of the film to change into higher-valent oxide. If this is to be prevented, the lower oxide must be well enough conducting for the metal substrate to exert control over the whole film; this can only be the case if the oxide is a good semiconductor and the chances then are that it will not be stoichiometric. It will also be necessary for the metal to send ions through the film with some ease, and this will probably mean that it will not in any case be noble enough for the desired purpose.

If on the other hand, the lower oxide is not a good conductor, the outer regions of the oxide film may become completely oxidized to a higher-valent state. The possibility then occurs that the open circuit, potential-controlling redox system may not be metal–lower oxide couple, but lower oxide–higher oxide couple, and there is a bare chance that this might be serviceable. But since the metal is necessarily a reducing agent for its higher oxide, such a system cannot be in equilibrium, and can only persist if the lower oxide is a very poor conductor and offers a high barrier to the transfer of metal ions across it. Such an electrode is unlikely to be satisfactorily reversible, and probably will not pass the smallest current without significant polarization. The metal phase, in such a case, would better consist of a foreign, unattackable metal, and a "lower–higher oxide couple" had better be set up in some other way.

In anodically produced films, the oxidation gradient may be in the reverse direction, and this would seem to promise effective reduction of all the higher oxide by the metal. But the general situation seems to be that stoichiometric lower oxides are nonconductors. Increasing oxidation, within limits, fosters conducting power. Then there is an automatic regulation which prevents the oxide film from attaining either one definite, stoichiometric state or the other. Thus, if the conductance of the film tends to rise with oxidation, the metal substrate is able to exert its reducing power to an increasing extent. On the other hand, as the conductance of the film decreases with progressive reduction, the metal declines in its effective reducing power. The result is neither one thing nor the other, and the "resting potential" of the electrode will be anything but a thermodynamic fixture. This is why, even if an oxide is effectively used as a depolarizer in primary or secondary batteries, this does *not* imply that it will necessarily be suitable as a basis for a reference electrode of reproducible potential. Some examples may be quoted of how some apparently hopeful systems fail for this and other reasons.

E. Examples of mainly Unsatisfactory Systems

Manganese dioxide is used on the largest scale as a depolarizer. It exists in four modifications (14), of which only the β-form, pyrolusite, is suitable for thermodynamic use, since it has the lowest free energy. This is not the form, however, produced in anodic oxidation. The β-oxide can be used to set up an electrode

$$\text{Pt} \mid \beta\text{-MnO}_2 \mid \text{Mn}^{2+}, \text{H}^+$$

for which a reproducibility of ± 1 mv has been claimed ($E^\circ = 1.236 \pm 0.001$ volt at 25°C) (15), although later work has not confirmed this (16), the potentials varying quite widely from one sample of the β-oxide to another. In any case, such an electrode, requiring manganous ions in solution, would not be useful; there is the possibility of an electrode, however, in which two valency states are represented by sparingly soluble compounds, such as

$$\text{Pt} \mid \beta\text{-MnO}_2 \mid \text{MnOOH} \mid \text{H}^+$$

or

$$\text{Pt} \mid \beta\text{-MnO}_2 \mid \text{Mn}_2\text{O}_3 \mid \text{H}^+$$

Such electrodes have been extensively studied by Vosburgh and his co-workers in connection with the "self-discharge of the manganese dioxide electrode" (17) and have recently been briefly reviewed (18). It seems that the electrode potential can vary widely, but is determined mainly by the surface composition of the deposit. The potentials change gradually over prolonged periods, and this is attributable (19) to a slow migration of the lower surface oxide inwards. It is very interesting to note that if the lower-valent compound is the oxy-hydroxide, this can effectively take place by the movement of protons and electrons alone. Quite apart from "leaking" manganous ions into solution, it is obvious that any such electrode will be quite useless for reference purposes. It does, however, typify some of the difficulties to be expected of "oxide electrodes" in the broadest sense.

Nickel oxide electrodes are used in the Edison accumulator, and have recently been studied by Wynne-Jones and his collaborators (20–22) with results of a similar kind. The anodic generation of oxide films is opposed by passivation. Anodic and cathodic charging curves showed ill-defined arrests, not corresponding with stoichiometric oxidation states, and subject to a very marked hysteresis effect. No stable equilibrium potential could be recorded. No other phases than Ni(OH)_2 and NiOOH could be identified by X-rays; the oxide NiO_2 has never been isolated and, if it exists, is apparently "amorphous to X-rays." Nevertheless, nickel is present in three oxidation states, so that films with the same total oxygen content can differ radically in detailed specification. In the lowest valency state, Ni(OH)_2 is the stable phase, but it is a nonconductor. Oxidation probably proceeds by a proton transfer mechanism,

$$\text{Ni(OH)}_2 + \text{OH}^- = \text{NiO} \cdot \text{OH} + \text{H}_2\text{O} + \text{e}^-$$

and is accompanied by a rapid increase in conductance; the oxy-hydroxide tends to contain excess of oxygen and is a good conductor. Conway (23) has recently made a detailed study of the mechanism of self-discharge of the nickel oxide electrode.

These two examples have dealt with "oxide–oxide" rather than with "metal–oxide" redox systems, but in these cases it is very unlikely that the latter would be more reproducible. Thus, manganese metal exists in three modifications and is very hard and brittle; its lower oxide and hydroxide oxidize very readily. Nickel is not quite so unsuitable, but the green lower oxide or hydroxide is nonconducting and tends to change into black oxy-hydroxide. It is clearly not very profitable to try to exploit these transitional metals as a basis for reversible electrodes, but examination of their defects, particularly in relation to the oxide phases, may serve as a guide to the minor transgressions of less ill-behaved systems.

It could be expected that the copper, silver, gold subgroup metals would be more suitable, if only because they are of simple, cubic, close-packed structure, are reasonably soft and easy to obtain in a pure, reproducible state. They also cover a range of "nobilities," and it may illustrate some of the points that have been made to consider them briefly in sequence.

The extreme rapidity with which copper forms an oxide film in air is well known, and may easily be followed by coulometric reduction methods (24). A freshly plated copper electrode, introduced into buffer solutions devoid of copper ions, behaves like a copper–cuprous oxide electrode, responding in the theoretical way to pH within the pH range 4.7 to 8.0. Even electrodes that have been heated in hydrogen, and have been directly introduced into deoxygenated solutions show the same behavior over a more restricted pH range (25). In aerated systems, however, there is a tendency for the electrode potentials to deviate positively from the thermodynamic values, and there is little doubt that some further oxidation of the film proceeds (26), accompanied by a dissolution reaction (27)

$$\tfrac{1}{2}Cu_2O + \tfrac{1}{4}O_2 + 2H^+ = Cu^{2+} + H_2O$$

for which $\Delta G° = -23.7$ kcal. These facts, which are all consistent with the well-known thermodynamic survey of the $Cu–H_2O$ system by Pourbaix (28), show that this electrode system is not a very useful one; copper is not noble enough and the cupric ion in solution is too stable.

These disadvantages might be less marked in the silver–silver oxide system, for the metal is more noble than copper. The lower oxide, Ag_2O, is thermodynamically stable, and shares with Cu_2O the advantage of having a well-defined (if unique) structure which could be formed from that of the parent metal with some expansion only. Consultation of the "potential–pH diagram" for silver (29) in comparison with that of copper (28) clearly shows the reduced intervention of higher-valent states. Thus, the argentic ion does not exist in aqueous solution under normal circumstances

$$E^\circ_{Ag^{2+},Ag^+} = 1.939 \text{ volt at } 25°C$$

$$\text{cf. } E^\circ_{Cu^{2+},Cu^+} = 0.168 \text{ volt at } 25°C$$

but AgO and Ag_2O_3, although of increasing thermodynamic instability, may be produced; indeed the operation of the "silver oxide electrode" in batteries depends upon them. It may be appropriate to indicate the value of the examination of anodic charging curves, obtained by methods such as that developed by Hickling (30) to obtain information about metal–metal oxide systems; valuable correlations with thermodynamic data may be obtained, particularly when steps are taken to eliminate polarization (31). Such methods have shown (31–34) that Ag_2O may be anodically formed upon silver, with a very well-marked potential arrest, before the formation of a higher oxide sets in. It is less favorable that the potential–pH diagrams indicate that Ag_2O has a rather shorter range of stability on the pH scale than Cu_2O. On balance, it turns out that the properties of the system do allow a workable silver–silver oxide reference electrode to be made, just good enough to allow it to receive specific discussion in the following section.

Finally in the sequence, it is found that gold is far too noble. Lower-valent compounds have a very strong tendency to disproportionate, and no Au, Au_2O electrode has been achieved (35) and no potential arrests corresponding with the formation of aurous oxide are found in anodic polarization curves (36). The Au, Au_2O_3 couple has been studied (37) and a value of $E° = 1.363$ volt at 25°C assigned and confirmed (38), but this is lower than that calculated from critically selected thermodynamic data (2, 3). In any event, it lies outside the stability domain of water and could cause oxygen to be evolved at an oxygen electrode ($E° = 1.229$ volt at 25°C).

This introductory survey may indicate that the field of really satisfactory metal–metal oxide reference electrodes is not likely to be very wide.

II. Metal–Metal Oxide Reference Electrodes

A. The Silver–Silver Oxide Electrode

Since the first extensive work by Luther and Pokorny (39), little success has attended rather sporadic attempts (summarized in ref. 40) to secure adequate reproducibility. Electrode potentials tended to be rather erratic and to drift away from their thermodynamic values in a negative direction. This situation has recently been changed by Hamer and Craig (40), and it is interesting to note their methods of preparing the electrodes. The first method, which was not satisfactory, consisted of coating a platinum spiral with a bolus of porous silver (exactly as for a thermal-electrolytic silver–silver chloride electrode; Chap. 4, Section III,B,3). This was immersed in a slurry of silver oxide and the cell solution. Potentials were erratic and fell with time. But if a new silver electrode was introduced into the same half-cell, it would at first record the correct potential before showing a similar decay, which, it may be noted, also involved an inversion of temperature coefficient. This proved that the trouble was associated with the silver, and it was explained in terms of the capacity for silver to take up oxygen at room temperature to form a nonstoichiometric, chemisorbed film with marked passivating tendencies. This sort of phenomenon appears to be an unpredictable difficulty that may be encountered with electrodes of this class.

Satisfactory electrodes were prepared by a method designed to obviate such an effect. An electrode prepared from a 1.5 cm square of platinum gauze, welded to a wire and mounted in the ordinary way, was folded into a V-shaped trough, pasted with moist silver oxide and dried. This treatment was repeated until all of the platinum was encased in dry silver oxide. It was then subjected to very cautious reduction in hydrogen at 60°C, so that the extent of reduction (judged by the gray color) was only fractional. The electrode was then cooled in hydrogen and transferred directly to the cell, without being washed. Potentials which remained steady within 1 mv for 14 to 38 days were attained in about half a day. The emf of the experimental cell,

$$\text{Ag} \mid \text{Ag}_2\text{O} \mid \text{KOH (aq)} \mid \text{HgO} \mid \text{Hg}$$

was 0.2440 ± 0.005 volt at 25°C; temperature coefficients were obtained between 0° and 90°C, the value at 25°C being -0.000198 ± 0.000003 volt deg^{-1}. Emf's were not dependent upon electrolyte concentration, except when this was in the range of 5–30 wt % of caustic alkali. Taking the standard potential of the mercury–mercuric oxide electrode as 0.9258 volt at 25°C, this leads to $E°_{\text{Ag,Ag}_2\text{O,H}^+} = 1.1700$ volt at 25°C. This result was accurate enough to warrant recalculation of the thermodynamic properties of silver oxide. This paper (40) understandably serves as a model for thermodynamic calculations and ingenuity in overcoming a specific experimental difficulty. The authors contemplate extended work, using the hydrogen electrode as the fundamental standard of reference, and it is not yet possible to assess the general usefulness of the silver–silver oxide electrode in its new guise. It may be noted, however, that the solubility product of silver oxide (Ag$_2$O; $K_s = 1.96 \times 10^{-8}$ at 25°C) is rather higher than desirable.

Silver oxide electrodes involving higher valency oxides have recently been reviewed (*41*); they are not serviceable for reference purposes.

B. The Mercury–Mercuric Oxide Electrode

This electrode has the initial advantages of a highly reproducible standard state for the metallic phase and complete freedom from any disturbing effects due to variable valency of oxide. This is because mercurous oxide does not exist (*42*); precipitation reactions in which it, or mercurous hydroxide, might be formed yield only a mixture of mercuric oxide and metallic mercury (*43*). Although mercuric oxide is well known to exist in yellow and red forms which differ in solubility [yellow 51.3, red 48.7 mg liter^{-1} at 25°C (*44*)], it appears probable that the difference is confined to particle size and disappears with due equilibration. No mercuric hydroxide can be isolated, but its formal acidic and basic dissociation constants have been estimated (*33*) and are very small. It is more basic than acidic, and this, coupled with the solubility figures given above, indicate that the usefulness of the mercury–mercuric oxide electrode will be confined to alkaline solutions, although it may be noted that mercuric oxide in aqueous solution is essentially a nonelectrolyte, and, accordingly, the less likely to disturb pH.

The promise of this electrode has, to a limited extent been realized. Thus Brönsted (*45*) found that the cell

$$H_2, Pt \mid KOH \text{ (aq)} \mid HgO \mid Hg$$

had an emf independent of the concentration of the electrolyte, except for small differences attributable to varying water activity; the $E°$ value he obtained at 25°C, recalculated by Lewis and Randall (*46*), was 0.9265 volt. Donnan and Allmand (*47*) confirmed the good behavior of the electrode, finding it to be stable over several days, reproducible to better than ±0.1 mv, and independent in potential of the form of mercuric oxide used (the yellow oxide, however, was somewhat slower to "settle down" than the red).

A more extensive investigation was made by Ming Chow (*48*), with admirable care, leading to an $E°$ value at 25°C of 0.92640 volt; he found the emf's of the hydrogen–mercuric oxide cell to be constant, within a mean deviation of ±0.06 mv for sodium hydroxide molalities between 0.001 and 0.3 mole kg^{-1}. This result was fairly well supported by the value soon afterwards obtained by Mujamoto (*49*), 0.9268 volt and that obtained by interpolation from the measurements of Fried (*50*), 0.9260 volt. All the remaining determinations have been made by a Japanese school (*51–54*) whose results are somewhat lower, but bear the imprint of a high degree of reproducibility and interagreement. The whole of the available data have been assembled and critically assessed by Hamer and Craig (40), whose final conclusions may be noted. Taking the average of all the results that could be corrected to zero concentration, they obtained $E°$ at 25°C equal to 0.92581 ± 0.00036 volt, with a temperature coefficient at 25°C of −0.0002878 volt deg^{-1}. This is in excellent agreement with 0.92575 volt calculated from critically selected thermodynamic data (3), although it is doubtful whether more than four figures can be significant.

It is of interest that all the data agree within ±0.4 mv and the results given in the four later Japanese papers agree to within ±0.1 mv. This indicates that, among metal–metal oxide electrodes, the mercury–mercuric oxide electrode is uniquely well behaved. Its behavior may be further improved by the devices found to be of benefit to the calomel electrode (Chap. 3, Section II,B), such as use of hydrophobic electrode vessels (55), and there appears to be an opportunity for its more precise evaluation. Although it cannot supplant the hydrogen electrode, it has been widely applied as a reference electrode for use in alkaline solutions (e.g., refs. 20, 40). The following fixed potential electrodes have been described by Samuelson and Brown (56). Using a saturated calomel electrode (of potential assumed to be 0.2446 volt at 25°), and an intervening molar potassium chloride bridge, they obtained

$$Hg \mid HgO \mid Ba(OH)_2, \text{satd.} \parallel E = 0.1462 − 0.00060(t − 25) ± 0.0002 \text{ volt}$$

$$Hg \mid HgO \mid Ca(OH)_2, \text{satd.} \parallel E = 0.1923 − 0.00010(t − 25) ± 0.0010 \text{ volt}$$

where t is temperature in °C, and E is potential on the hydrogen scale.

No very special precautions, except those needed to secure components of reasonable purity, seem to be needed in setting up mercury–mercuric oxide electrodes. The mercuric oxide is best prepared by gentle ignition of carefully crystallized mercuric nitrate, and is washed before use, but reagent grade commercial mercuric oxide, thoroughly extracted with water on the steam bath, appears to be satisfactory (40, 56).

Studies have been made of the spontaneous formation of an oxide film on mercury in air (57) and by anodic polarization in alkaline solutions (58). The latter confirm the nonexistence of any oxide other than mercuric oxide.

C. The Antimony Electrode and its Congeners

1. The Antimony Electrode

The use of antimony as a basis for a metal–metal oxide electrode was initiated by Uhl and Kestranek (59) nearly forty years ago; since then it has had a checkered career. Thus, in 1937, Glasstone (*60*) said of it ". . . it is not readily poisoned, and since no special technique is required for measurement of the potential, it is finding increasing application." This is no longer the case, for except in circumstances which have already been mentioned, and for special applications in which small size is obligatory (as for swallowing), it has been very largely replaced by the glass electrode. Another reason for its present-day lack of popularity is its unreliability, which involves the need for frequent reconditioning, and for calibration in buffers. Not only does its $E°$ value vary, but it very often fails to show the theoretical potential/pH slope. Nevertheless, the antimony electrode is by no means completely obsolete; it has certainly formed the subject matter of a very large number of publications, and has recently been reviewed (*61*).

A survey shows that there are at least two functionally different kinds of antimony electrode. There are wild discrepancies between recorded $E°$ values, but there is a clear division between two groups of them. This was brought out in the useful summary made by Mehta and Jatkar (*62*) in 1935, which is suitable for purposes of preliminary discussion. Using the equation

$$E° = E + \frac{2.303RT}{F} \, pH \tag{10}$$

they calculated an $E°$ value for each experimental emf obtained by various workers, and plotted these against pH from 0 to 14. In so far as an electrode behaves theoretically it should provide, in such a diagram, a horizontal line. The closest approach to this was provided by the results of Roberts and Fenwick (*63*) between pH values of 1 and 10; from pH 10 to pH 13, there was a slight droop. Apart from this, the $E°$ value was 0.1445 ± 0.005 volt at 25°C, which is to be regarded as a very satisfactory performance. The others which showed horizontal sections were those of Parks and Beard (*64*), Mehta and Jatkar (*62*), Ball, Schmidt and Bergstresser (*65*) and Kolthoff and Hartong (*66*). The pH ranges of linearity, and the approximate $E°$ values were, in order:

pH 2.5–8, $E° = 0.25$ volt at 25°C;

pH 2.5–8.5, $E° = 0.275$ volt at 25°C;

pH 3.0–8.5, $E° = 0.28$ volt at 20°C;

pH 6–10.5, $E° = 0.34$ volt at 14°C.

Outside these ranges the lines rose, with decreasing pH at the low pH end, and with rising pH at the high pH end, with frequently a subsidiary minimum towards the high pH end before the rise. The general shape might be roughly described as a truncated catenary, with a subsidiary dip displaced to the higher pH side. Some of the curves showed no horizontal section at all (67–69), but all of them were spread around an $E°$ of 0.28 volt with a "band width" of about 0.1 volt.

At this stage it might be thought advisable to consider the Roberts and Fenwick electrode and disregard the rest, but this would not be justifiable without looking at each work individually, since it is $(E - E°)$ which is of primary importance in many connections, rather than $E°$ itself (cf. Chap. 1, Section V), and any electrode which obeys the Nernst relation deserves attention.

Roberts and Fenwick (63) used a cell of the "flowing" type previously mentioned (5, 6), containing antimony and antimony trioxide in powdered form, contact being made by a platinum wire plated with antimony, or conditioned by pretreatment in antimony trifluoride solution. The arrangement is illustrated in Fig. 1 and was used with a flowing liquid junction

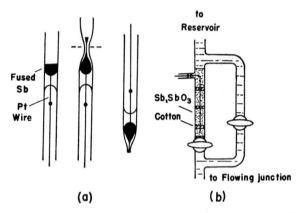

FIG. 1. Antimony electrode designs. (a) Stages in the construction of a Levin semi-micro electrode (104). (b) Powder electrode design for use with flowing junction (63).

and a hydrogen electrode half-cell. Their antimony was prepared in crystalline form by rapid electrolysis of a solution of very pure antimony trioxide in aqueous hydrofluoric acid. Deposited upon a platinum sheet, it was easily removed by flexing the sheet, and was stored under water until used. Their oxide, shown to be entirely free from pentavalent antimony, was made by hydrolyzing distilled antimony trichloride in hot water, washing for some weeks, and drying at 110°C. It was shown by X-rays to be the orthorhombic form, which is higher in free energy content than the alternative cubic modification. The cubic form was accordingly prepared by allowing recrystallization to occur at an elevated temperature (above 570°C). With use of these materials, with solution deaerated with nitrogen, and with the unexplained precaution of pretreating the electrode with a solution of higher pH than that to be used in measurement, Roberts and

Fenwick obtained the admirable results already noted. It is clear that they had taken the greatest pains to establish the components of their electrode system in reproducible standard states. It is worth noting that the ortho-rhombic oxide gave a higher $E°$ value, and that the effect of admitting air was also to raise $E°$ and slightly decrease $dE/d\mathrm{pH}$ below the proper value. Under these conditions, the $E°$ value (0.1504 volt) was in agreement with that determined by Schuhmann (70) from the cell

$$\mathrm{H_2 \mid HClO_4\ (aq) \mid Sb_2O_3 \mid Sb}$$

(0.1524 volt). It is of interest that the critically selected value for this potential recently published in the "potential–pH diagram" of Pourbaix and his co-workers (71) is 0.152 volt for the cubic oxide, and 0.167 volt for the orthorhombic, at 25°C. There is thus no doubt that Roberts and Fen-wick established a close approach to a proper thermodynamic Sb, Sb_2O_3, H^+ system, inconvenient and slow to reach equilibrium though it was. These authors realized, of course, that from acid, through neutral, to alkaline (72) solutions, the predominant form of antimony in solution would change along an overlapping sequence such as Sb^{3+}, $SbOH^{2+}$, SbO^+, $SbO \cdot OH$, SbO_2^-, $Sb(OH)_4^-$, but that this would not be significant, provid-ing that equilibrium continuously existed with the same invariant solid phases, i.e., Sb and Sb_2O_3.

The question therefore arises, what happens at the other antimony electrodes which show so much higher potentials? They are all made of massive antimony, cast in sticks or plated, usually with oxide provided by adventitious, superficial oxidation, which is known to occur in both air (73) and in electrolytic solutions (74). Franke and Willaman (75) and Snyder (76) were among the first to use antimony in systems free from added trioxide. This is now the general practice, although Kolthoff and Hartong (66) claimed that oxide added to the antimony in casting gave an electrode which equilibrated more rapidly. It is certainly not merely the physical form of the electrode which is significant in deciding whether the "low" or the "high" potential is recorded, for cast, plated, and powder electrodes have all given "high" results in the hands of the same worker (77).

Before exploring possible answers to this question, however, it is de-sirable to examine further the status of the cast and plated electrodes and note any of their properties which may be significant in relation to the problem. Firstly, attention is directed to the work of Parks and Beard (64), who used cast electrodes, treated before use by polishing with emery and rinsing with distilled water. They found that it was useless to use these electrodes in conjunction with an ordinary potentiometer, and that an electronic voltmeter was needed to obtain steady readings. This seems to be very understandable for an electrode which depends for its reversibility on an invisible oxide film, and may be very significant. In unstirred solutions exposed to air, steady readings were obtained in one minute, showing no drift except in the more alkaline range of pH values. The response was linear from pH 2–7 with a slope equal, within experimental error, to the theoretical value of 0.05915 volt at 25°C; the reproducibility of measurement was about 2 mv and interagreement between eight electrodes was reasonably good (maximum divergence, 3.5 mv). The $E°$ value was 0.254 volt at 25°. This performance was satisfactory, but the observed potentials were displaced negatively by stirring and positively by bubbling oxygen. Such effects are excluded in the definition of a fully reversible electrode with an adequate exchange current. They appear to be common with antimony electrodes, and may well be responsible for rather large discrepancies between the results of different workers.

Hovorka and Chapman (78) used antimony cast into sticks, mounted in glass tubes with de Khotinsky cement, so that 2 cm of metal protruded for contact with the solution. They used antimony prepared by the method of Hovorka and Schoenfeld (79), which is substantially the same as that used by Roberts and Fenwick (63), and cast it in 7 mm inside-diameter glass tubing under vacuum. A preliminary heating of the moist antimony in air before casting, to give a little superficial oxidation, was found to be advantageous, and it was preferable to arrange for fine crystal grains in the product. The electrodes were given a high polish by use of graded emery and were electrolyzed in sodium carbonate solution and repolished before use in each new solution. It was claimed that pairs of electrodes thus prepared showed bias potentials of less than 0.02 mv. Used in solutions from which air was not excluded, the electrodes recorded potentials which fitted the equation

$$E = 0.2552 - 0.05893\text{pH at } 25°C$$

between pH 2 and 7. Thus, the slope was a little less than theoretical, but the reproducibility was such as to demand attention. As found by Parks and Beard (64), King (80), and other workers mentioned by Mehta and Jatkar (62), potentials tended to rise above the best E–pH line on the higher side of pH 8.

Perley (81) prepared his antimony by a similar electrolytic method, cast it into sticks, and encased the sticks in molded rubber to expose a flush end, which was ground and polished; glass sheaths were rejected because of entry of impurities into annular crevices. The active area of antimony exposed to the solution was found to be important in relation to galvanometer sensitivity, and a circular area of 13 mm diameter was used. Trace impurities in the antimony had a large effect and copper had to be excluded from it, and from the solutions, at all costs. Between pH 3 and 7, in agitated buffer solutions saturated with air, the dE/dpH slope was theoretical at 25°C. There is difficulty in correlating various authors' $E°$ values where different comparison electrodes have been used, particularly in cells involving calomel electrodes with liquid junctions. Perley used a saturated calomel electrode, and, relative to this, his $E°$ was 0.008 volt (Stockholm convention) Hovorka and Chapman (78), converting this to their own (hydrogen) scale, give the result 0.2538 volt, in good agreement with their own.

Not too much reliance can be placed on the coincidence, but three $E°$ values at 25°C have now been collected for the same type of electrode; 0.254, 0.255, and 0.254 volt, and others may be found in the literature which deviate but little from this value. On the other hand there are many ostensibly very carefully determined values which deviate a good deal.

It seems appropriate at this stage to ask whether this potential corresponds with that of any other well-defined couple; thus Fischbeck and Eimer (82) thought that the metal might be acting as a noble substrate for a redox equilibrium in which it was not directly concerned. Mehta and Jatkar (62), considering that Sb_2O_4 is the only stable oxide at the melting point of antimony, suggested that, in the cast sticks, Sb, Sb_2O_4 must be the effective couple. A recalculation of the potentials to be expected on these various possibilities gives the result:

$$Sb, Sb_2O_3, 0.152 \text{ volt}; \qquad Sb, Sb_2O_4, 0.330 \text{ volt};$$

$$Sb_2O_3, Sb_2O_4, 0.861 \text{ volt}$$

It is obvious that the last of these is beyond consideration. Some of the determined $E°$ values approach that of the Sb, Sb_2O_4 couple, notably that of Kolthoff and Hartong (66) — who, it will be recalled, added Sb_2O_3 to the antimony before casting — but most of them fall well below it. Perhaps, for these very thin oxide films, the observation of Simon and Thaler (83), that the oxides of antimony are not stoichiometrically well defined, applies with particular force. On the other hand, both forms of Sb_2O_3, and Sb_2O_4, have structures which have been completely elucidated by X-rays, although it may be relevant that a substance $Sb_3O_6(OH)$ has been confused with Sb_2O_4 (84). A very interesting suggestion has been made about surface oxides on metals of this kind; this will be mentioned later.

It is clear that useful information might be obtained by the anodic polarization technique, and it has been applied to the problem by El Wakkad and Hickling (85). They found that when antimony was anodized in weakly acidic or alkaline solutions, a first step in the potential–time curve corresponded with the formation of Sb_2O_3, which grew to a film no more than nine molecules thick. The potential then rose to a value corresponding with the formation of Sb_2O_5 beneath the original layer. Finally, passivation occurred and the potential rose to the oxygen evolution value. Clearly, Sb_2O_3 is poorly protective, a poor conductor, and further electrolysis proceeded through cracks in the primary film. Only at very low current densities was any arrest attributable to Sb_2O_4 observed. On stopping the anodization, reduction of higher oxide by antimony proceeded rapidly, so that self-discharge was complete in a matter of seconds. It was also interesting that in 0.1 N hydrochloric acid, cathodic polarization did not reverse the oxidation; the potential fell at once to the hydrogen evolution value, and the film either stripped off, or remained loosely attached to the electrode, indifferent to the hydrogen being given off. In strongly acid or alkaline solutions, continuous dissolution of antimony, to form SbO^+ or SbO_2^- [or $Sb(OH)_4^-$] ions, was observed. These illuminating results rather strongly disfavor potential control by a higher oxide. They suggest that only the *limiting* film is effective, and that the loose oxide formed by its decrepitation cannot be considered part of the electrode system at all. They also indicate reasons for failure of the electrode at the extremes of the pH range. One of the authors of this work, however, had previously expressed the view (*86*) that the tendency of antimony electrodes to have rather positive potentials, increasing with time in oxygenated solutions, was due to the presence and further accumulation of higher oxide. Certainly, no such increase occurs in absence of oxygen.

It appears to be true that the electrical potential of these electrodes is not solely determined by the oxygen potential of an invariant metal–oxide or lower–higher oxide system, but is sensitive to the oxygen content of the solution. If an antimony electrode, freed from oxide by reduction in hydrogen, is introduced, without exposure to air, to thoroughly deoxygenated buffer solutions, the potential–pH plot is a remarkable wavy line, with five inflections between pH 1 and 10 (*87*); quite a hopeless situation. Oxygen in solution therefore appears to be an essential component of those electrode systems to which no oxide is added.

There are a number of ways in which this necessary oxygen may be supposed to act. On the evidence already presented, it is perhaps the simplest assumption that only the limiting oxide film on the antimony is functionally significant. But since the antimony is progressively etched in oxygen-containing solutions (*81*), and a detrimental layer of oxide accumulates and needs cleaning off, it is clear that a continuous corrosion process is going on. The operative limiting film, underneath the useless detritus that it throws off, must therefore be continuously self-renewing, so that a supply of oxygen is required. The comparatively satisfactory behavior of such electrodes then depends, not on retaining an oxide film in an equilibrium state, but in a kinetic steady state. This may be attainable either in a still solution, or in a regularly stirred solution (opinions seem to be equally balanced on which is the better), but clearly nothing could be worse than intermittent stirring. This is consistent with the results of systematic studies of stirring effects (*81, 82, 89*). But still a problem remains; if this view of the electrode is accepted, is the potential still to be regarded as controlled by a metal–metal oxide couple? If so, how is it that the electrode potentials, according to conditions of oxygen concentration and stirring, vary by as much as 140 mv from the proper Sb, Sb_2O_3 value? That the cause of this variation might lie in the nature of the oxide phase is not beyond the bounds of possibility; even if the evidence is rather against the antimony passing to a higher valency state, there is still good reason to think that "surface oxides" (or hydroxides, or oxy-hydroxides) may differ markedly from known bulk oxide phases, and may vary considerably in activity. This aspect is more prominent in the case of bismuth, and will be discussed later. But more detailed consideration indicates that a tenfold change in the activity of Sb_2O_3 would only shift the electrode potential by about 10 mv. One is therefore forced to consider that these electrodes come under mixed control, so that more than one redox system determines their potentials. If antimony in a higher valency state is assumed not to be concerned, the only alternative is that oxygen itself participates in the electrode reaction; i.e., the reaction which involves electron transfer and directly controls electrode potential. Since the electrodes consume oxygen, this seems likely. It is very strongly supported by the observation of Kauko and Knappsberg (*88*) that the antimony electrode responds to oxygen pressure, albeit sluggishly, in the manner to be expected of the reversible oxygen electrode (this chapter, Section III,A). Thus, $dE/d \log P_{O_2}$ was found to be 14.5 mv at 25°C, very close to the theoretical value of 14.8 mv. The $E°$ value, 0.29 volt, was, of course, very far removed from that of the oxygen electrode, 1.23 volt. It will be seen later that this result is remarkable and its implications are not easy to accept at their face value. The assumption that the antimony electrode behaves as a somewhat inefficient oxygen electrode does not, in any case, seem adequate to explain all the effects that oxygen produces. When oxygen is first introduced, there is a fairly rapid displacement of potential in a positive direction. Even if this short term effect may be accounted for in this way, there is a long term change in which the potential drift may persist for days; this can only be due to a progressive change in the state of the electrode surface.

Since there is little doubt that the antimony electrode is a corroding system, it is appropriate to apply the principles of well-known corrosion theory to it. This has been done by Gatty and Spooner (*89*). According to these authors, the surface of the antimony electrode is heterogeneous, but may be regarded as made up of two kinds of area. The first is bare metal, at which anodic dissolution of antimony takes place to furnish such ions in solution (Sb^{3+}, SbO^+, etc.) as are proper to the prevailing pH. In the presence of solid Sb_2O_3, these anodic areas will, in the absence of polarization, tend to fix the potential of the whole electrode at the proper Sb, Sb_2O_3 value. The second consists of metal covered with an oxide film, at which, however, electrons can be passed to oxygen molecules. It is therefore a cathodic area and its potential will be determined by the concentration of dissolved oxygen close to the interface, and this will, in turn, also tend to control the potential of the whole electrode. But, in general, the oxygen electrode reaction is strongly hindered (see this chapter, Section III), and there is no question of these areas approaching the oxygen electrode potential (1.229 volt at 25°C); they will, however, tend to move the potential of the electrode in a positive direction, because they support a spontaneous cathodic reaction. Between these two kinds of area on the electrode surface, a local action current flows within the metal, causing, or increasing, a polarization at each of them. The electrode potential of the bulk metal is at any instant determined by (i) the relative magnitudes of the anodic and cathodic areas and (ii) the degree of polarization produced at them by the local action current, or by diffusional transfer of soluble reactants or products (90). In other words, it is a mixed potential arising from the local action which has been regarded as ubiquitous in corrosion processes (91).

If now antimony electrode in still solution is considered, it can be seen that dissolved oxygen reaching it by diffusion will provide the essential reactant for the cathodic reaction. It will therefore produce cathodic depolarization, and in doing so, will cause the oxide film steadily to grow and increase in stability and area. The electrode potential will then come increasingly under oxygen control and will move in a positive direction. At the same time, the ratio of cathodic to anodic areas in the local cell will increase, so that anodic polarization will set in; this also tends to shift the electrode potential positively. This process goes on until the anodic areas are reduced to pores in the oxide film, and it may be imagined that, ultimately, their closure might occur. If this happened, the process would stop and the electrode would be passivated. But, in the case of antimony, the film is neither strong nor stable enough for this to take place, and a final steady state is achieved, but slowly. This is the reason for the positive drift of electrode potential which, after some days, tends to a limiting value corresponding with an $E°$ of 0.29 volt at 25°C. If an electrode in this condition is scraped without being removed from the solution, the "scraping effect" noted by Bodforss and Holmqvist (131) is observed; the anodic area is increased and the cathodic area is reduced, with resulting decrease in anodic polarization and increase in cathodic polarization. The potential is accordingly shifted in a negative direction.

This treatment provides plausible explanations for many other experimental facts. Complex-forming substances, such as tartrates, tend to remove oxide film and favor anodic depolarization by increasing the anodic/cathodic area ratio; they will have a similar effect by incorporating antimony into complex anions, thus directly stimulating anodic dissolution. This is in accord with the negative displacement of potential that these substances produce. Oxidizing substances, on the other hand, will have the opposite effect and cause a positive shift in potential. The addition of neutral salts, such as potassium chloride, shifts the antimony electrode potential markedly in a negative direction (*131*), when the concentrations reach values high enough to reduce the solubility of oxygen to a significant extent, thus increasing cathodic polarization.

The theory deals very well with the otherwise very puzzling effects of stirring. Clearly stirring may have two effects. By bringing oxygen up to cathodic areas, it may increase cathodic depolarization (or reduce cathodic polarization) sending the electrode potential more positive. By sweeping away ions produced by anodic dissolution (occurring at a finite rate) at anodic areas, it may decrease anodic polarization and send the electrode potential more negative. According to circumstances and the state of the electrode surface, either one or the other of these effects may predominate.

Of three otherwise identical antimony electrodes immersed in the same buffer solution (pH 3), one kept stationary will be negative in potential to one which is rotated continuously, and this in turn will be negative with respect to the third which is subjected to oxygen bubbling. In the earlier stages of film growth, it is cathodic depolarization which predominates. On the other hand, if an electrode which has been immersed in oxygenated solution for 24 hr is rotated, the potential becomes more negative, the effect reaching a limit of about 15 mv. When rotation is stopped, the potential returns quite rapidly to its original, more positive value. In the later stages of film growth, it is anodic depolarization which predominates. These two examples deal with electrodes subjected to steady treatment, or which have reached a steady state. In other cases, in which a changing electrode is submitted to intermittent changes of treatment, the operation of both effects can be seen, and can be quite clearly distinguished because the effect of stirring on anodic polarization is understandably faster than that on cathodic polarization. Two examples to illustrate this may be quoted from Gatty and Spooner's work.

An electrode, half an hour after immersion in a still, aerated buffer solution, showed a potential creeping in a positive direction. It was suddenly subjected to stirring, when an immediate negative displacement of potential occurred (attributable to the rapid onset of anodic depolarization). But, under the new conditions of relative movement of electrode and solution, the rate of "positive creep" of the potential was considerably greater (due to the slower onset of cathodic depolarization). When stirring was stopped, the potential quite rapidly assumed a value more positive than before, indeed more positive than the value it would have reached if the electrode had been left alone. This was explained by the more rapid recovery of anodic than cathodic polarization and by the increase in the ratio of cathodic to anodic areas during the operation.

In another experiment, an electrode was placed in a buffer solution through which oxygen was steadily bubbled. Half an hour later, its potential was changing in a positive direction at about 7 mv hr^{-1}. Oxygen bubbling was then stopped, and surprisingly as it seems at first, the potential at once became more positive at an initial rate of 750 mv hr^{-1}, but the rapidity of change soon decreased; the potential passed through a maximum, and then fell to a more negative value than before. Resumption of oxygen bubbling reinstated the positive creep at about its original rate. This effect is to be explained by the rapid onset of anodic polarization, and the much slower buildup of cathodic polarization when bubbling no longer produced motion of the solution around the electrode.

It is very difficult to see how these experiments, and others which the authors describe, can be explained in any other way than on the basis of the local action theory. Their further arguments cannot be followed, but they made the very important point that the temperature coefficient of the antimony electrode potential cannot be properly considered in purely thermodynamic terms. Each electrode, because of the difficulty of reproducing the surface state of a hard, brittle metal, is its own kinetic problem and its potential is what Pourbaix calls "une tension reactionelle." How this potential varies with temperature may well be controlled by one reaction rate or another and is likely to be very variable.

Before discussing temperature coefficients, attention must be given to a somewhat different viewpoint proposed by Tourky and his co-workers (87, 92), which also envisages the antimony electrode as a continuously corroding system. Emphasis is placed upon the difference in properties between an oxide such as Cu_2O, in which permeability to cuprous ions facilitates film growth, and Sb_2O_3 which is impermeable to antimony ions. In one case the metal–metal oxide equilibrium is readily established, but in the other it is not, because of the restriction to oxide film growth. This is suggested to give rise to an "overvoltage" effect; the cathodic process of oxygen reduction is hindered, and oxygen which would otherwise be incorporated continuously in a growing oxide film remains adsorbed upon the oxide surface, where it provides a population of "oxygen doublets." It is these which are supposed to give rise to the positive increment of electrode potential of about 100–150 mv, but why they should do so is not cogently demonstrated. In general support of this idea, it is noted that the effect is not unique to antimony, but, as will be seen, occurs in many cases in which cation transport across an oxide film is restricted, and it always produces about the same potential displacement from the proper metal–metal oxide value.

Measurements of the dependence of the antimony electrode potential on temperature have been mainly confined to the limited range of 10–30°C. The temperature coefficient (which, as usually quoted, includes the effect of temperature on a saturated calomel reference electrode) is reported to change from about -1 mv deg^{-1} at pH 2–4 to about -3 mv deg^{-1} at pH 8–11 (81, 93). The value to be expected for the Sb, Sb$_2$O$_3$ couple is -3.57 mv deg^{-1}, and should not vary with pH at all. A very much smaller dependence of potential on temperature is claimed by other workers (89, 94, 101), so that the whole position is very uncertain. A more recent study by Tourky and Khairy (95) reveals an almost fantastic situation. For electrodes in both aerated and anaerobic systems, $E°$ values were found to decrease gradually for temperatures rising from 20° to 30°C, then to fall to a minimum at 40°C, rise to a sharp maximum at around 50°C and finally fall rapidly again at higher temperatures. Although these results were obtained with three kinds of electrode system, some reserve is necessary in accepting them because they involve extrapolations of potential–pH lines which were not uniformly rectilinear nor, obviously, always of theoretical slope. Nevertheless, the effects are so large, that it is unlikely that they could be adventitious. The authors' arguments to explain them cannot be followed in detail, but it is clear that no simple equilibrium can be involved. It is conceivable that the first effect of rising temperature is, by promoting oxide solubility and increasing reaction rates, to cause an approach to the reversible metal–metal oxide potential (surprisingly enough, actually attained by the deoxygenated electrodes). The generally increased rate of oxide formation might, at still higher temperatures, lead to the substantial completion of a poorly conducting oxide film, on which the proposed "oxygen overvoltage" might become prominent. Further rise of temperature, causing oxygen desorption, could possibly lead to the fairly rapid dissipation of the potential increment which this effect is supposed to cause. No decision can be reached about this rather complicated theory, and it will be suitable to defer any further comment on the mechanism of the antimony electrode until some other electrode systems have been discussed.[1]

Little more need be said about the antimony electrode, other than to

[1] It may be pointed out, however, that a recent suggestion (71) that the antimony electrode is really a kind of hydrogen electrode is untenable; it is based on a mistake in regard to reference electrodes made by the distinguished authors concerned.

summarize information which may be useful in practice. Of the three main types, the limitations of the powder electrodes have already been indicated. Although a simple form has been described by Holmqvist (96), it is unlikely to find much useful application because of the existence of simpler and more satisfactory alternatives; it was, however, applied to quite accurate dissociation constant determinations, in a cell with a flowing junction, by Fenwick and Gilman (97). The same applies to plated electrodes; recommended by Brinkman and Buijtendijk (98) for use in biological systems, and improved by Zhukov and Avseevich (68, 99) by use of electrodeposition on an amalgamated platinum wire from an acetone solution of antimony trichloride, these electrodes are only occasionally well behaved. In general, they are irreproducible (100) and have a very limited useful life (81). This leaves only cast antimony electrodes for serious consideration.

The earliest and most widely used, the cast, or stick electrodes have the advantages of ruggedness and simplicity; the asset of low electrical resistance, however, may be somewhat illusory, for reasons already indicated. Recommendations concerning their preparation and use are very numerous and sometimes contradictory. Ball (101), as a result of a comprehensive review and investigation, concluded that commercially available antimony could be used, without critical control of casting conditions, to obtain electrodes with bias potentials not exceeding 5 mv. On the other hand, Shcherbakov (102) maintains that only electrodes prepared from very pure metal give reproducible results. This agrees with the findings of a number of previous workers, and the antimony is normally purified by electrodeposition, using Hovorka and Schoenfeld's method (79), which has already been outlined. In casting, it is the general practice to use the pure metal without deliberate addition of oxide (66), but, in view of the excellence of Hovorka and Chapman's results (78), it may well be desirable to follow their method, which has also been described.

Very many different forms of stick electrode have been invented, including some with built-in scrubbing brushes (103) for periodical renewal of the electrode surface. Levin (104) describes a semimicro electrode in which only the tip of a column of antimony cast inside quite a narrow glass tube is exposed to the solution; periodical rubbing with fine emery of the flush surface removes glass and antimony together. Three steps in its construction are illustrated in Fig. 1. The electrode is said to be readily prepared and satisfactory in performance (61); it is readily adaptable to an accurate acid-base differential titration technique (105). An even smaller electrode of the same type, shaped like a dental probe, has been used (106). Many other forms of microelectrodes have been devised (61), but it is highly probable that all of them need be used in association with an electronic pH meter.

There is general agreement that electrodes are best prepared for use by polishing with a fine abrasive, and it may well be that such treatment is instrumental in setting up the kind of limiting oxide film which is needed. Since the electrodes deteriorate with use, becoming covered with an inactive corrosion product, this treatment must be repetitive but, after such treatment, a resting period of a few days has been recommended, perhaps to relieve strain in the metal surface (107), or with immersion in water, for surface oxidation to proceed (80). Various other pretreatments have been advocated, including dipping in concentrated nitric acid (108), etching by successive treatments with dilute sulfuric and nitric acids (109), electrolysis in dilute sodium carbonate solution (78), treatment with hot sodium hydroxide solution (99) or keeping for several days in a solution of pH = 11.8 (110). It is somewhat difficult to perceive what might be a common feature of these treatments, unless it be to ensure cleanliness and secure a certain degree of surface oxidation. It may be best for each experimenter to attain these objectives according to his own lights; the present author is unable to adjudicate.

The antimony stick electrodes must be used in aerated solutions and, for pH measurements, must be calibrated by means of buffers; theoretical, or even rectilinear response cannot always be expected. Sensitivity to stirring must be anticipated and therefore steady conditions of one sort or another must be uniformly established. The solution must be free of interfering solutes which include oxidizing or reducing agents (81, 111), salts of acids which form complexes with antimony, such as citric, oxalic, tartaric and phenylacetic acids, certain amino acids, and salts of metals more noble than antimony, notably copper. Nevertheless, even under adverse conditions, the antimony electrode retains a margin of usefulness provided it is used and calibrated under controlled conditions; thus it has been used in solutions containing traces of chlorine, or in presence of sodium sulfite or sulfide. Its field of application has been very wide indeed, extending over industrial pH control (81, 112) in water treatment and the sugar and paper production industries, in biological and medical studies for the determination (somewhat unreliably) of the pH of blood (98), for continuously recording the acidity of stomach contents (113) and in dental and oral studies (106, 114). It has been used for measuring the pH of fresh water (115), sea water (116), brine (117) and liquors associated with dyes and plating baths (94), latex (118), oil (119), soap (120), tanning (121), and paper pulp (122). The widest use of all has been to determine the pH of soils (107, 123–130); a more exhaustive list will be found in a recent review (61), and is impressive. It may be noted, however, that most of the references concerned are more than twenty years old, and that many of the applications would very likely have brought interfering substances into contact with the electrode, but under circumstances in which rapid, *ad hoc*, rough measurements with a robust electrode were of primary interest. In general, it is unsafe to use the antimony electrode to determine the pH of any medium which contains unknown constituents (*131*).

It is, perhaps, worthwhile to make a final assessment of the antimony electrode in the following way.

Setting aside powder and plated electrodes, all the data relating to cast or stick electrodes have been converted to the hydrogen scale, so that they may be as comparable as possible within uncertainties due to reference electrode and liquid junction potentials. The results are collected in Table I. In two cases it has been necessary to select the mean temperature of a quoted range and, where two lines have been used by an author to represent the whole potential–pH dependence, only the one in better accordance with the Nernst relation has been chosen. The calomel electrode potentials used in these calculations are shown in an appendix to Table I.

TABLE I

Collected Data for Antimony Stick Electrodes

Authors	Reference	Temp (°C)	E (hydrogen scale, volts)	pH range
Kolthoff and Hartong	(*66*)	14	0.273–0.0536 pH	1–5
Britton and Robinson	(*67*)	14	0.265–0.053 pH	2–12
Uemura and Sueda	(*132*)	17.5	0.249–0.0538 pH	1–9
Tomiyama	(*93*)	20	0.259–0.0567 pH	2–12
Ball	(*101*)	20	0.261–0.0580 pH	2–7
King	(*80*)	24	0.261–0.0575 pH	3–12
Franke and Willaman	(*75*)	25	0.230–0.054 pH	0–12
Snyder	(*76*)	25	0.231–0.054 pH	4–9
Parks and Beard	(*64*)	25	0.250–0.0591 pH	2–7
Mehta and Jatkar	(*62*)	25	0.274–0.059 pH	2.5–8.5
Bravo	(*133*)	25	0.239–0.059 pH	5–11
Perley	(*81*)	25	0.249–0.059 pH	3–7
Hovorka and Chapman	(*78*)	25	0.255–0.05893 pH	2.2–8
Levin	(*104*)	25	0.241–0.055 pH	2–12
Lava and Hemedes	(*134*)	27.5	0.227–0.057 pH	2–12
Harrison & Vridhachalam	(*107*)	30	0.218–0.0498 pH	4–9
Tourky and Moussa	(*92*)	30	0.244–0.0586 pH	1.9–7.2

Reference electrode	14°	17.5°	20°	24°	25°	27.5°	30°
N calomel	0.283	0.282	0.281	0.280	0.280	0.279	0.279
Saturated calomel	—	—	—	—	0.244	—	0.241

To examine any correlation between the results, obtained at 7 temperatures, by 17 independent workers, a least squares calculation has been applied to the $E°$ values; it leads to the relation

$$E° = 0.245 - 0.00225(t - 25) \text{ volt} \tag{11}$$

where t is temperature in °C. It is interesting that the temperature coefficient which comes out of this calculation, -2.25 mv deg^{-1}, is not far from the mean of the values directly determined by Perley (81), -1.73 mv deg^{-1}, but this is probably coincidental, for the error is large. The sign of the temperature coefficient is often wrongly quoted because of confusion with sign conventions. The probable error in any one $E°$ evaluation works out at ± 8.5 mv. This corresponds to about ± 0.15 pH unit.

Less satisfaction is obtained from a similar calculation applied to the potential–pH slopes. They are best represented by

$$\frac{dE}{d\text{pH}} = 0.0565 + 0.000145(t - 25) \text{ volt} \tag{12}$$

where t is temperature in °C. The proper Nernst relation is

$$\frac{dE}{d\text{pH}} = 0.05915 + 0.000198(t - 25) \text{ volt} \tag{13}$$

The probable error of each slope is ± 0.0047 volt which is large ($> \pm 8\%$). Although for an individual electrode the situation may not be nearly as bad, it is obvious that careful calibration is necessary.

Since the $E°$ value for the antimony electrode at 25°C which comes out of this analysis is identical, within experimental error, with the potential of the saturated calomel electrode at the same temperature, it is tempting to set up an equation for pH, to be used when these electrodes are combined in a cell. This would be

$$\text{pH} = \frac{E - 0.00160(t - 25)}{0.0565 - 0.000145(t - 25)} \tag{14}$$

where E is the measured emf of the cell and t is temperature in °C. This procedure, first suggested by Avseyevich and Zhukov (68), is seen to be very undesirable, involving the possibility of errors as large as half a pH unit.

This survey perhaps puts the antimony electrode in perspective. It appears that it may be finding a new sphere of usefulness in nonaqueous systems (135).

2. The Bismuth Electrode

The bismuth electrode has not been so extensively studied, but it seems to have some potentialities, and to present some features of interest. Mehta and Jatkar (136) studied the properties of pure crystalline bismuth (Merck) which was not polished or pretreated in any way. Unlike antimony, it did not tarnish on keeping in water, and its potential–pH response was examined in buffer solutions, with the use of an electronic voltmeter. Over the limited pH range 5 to 7.4, the potential–pH slope was 0.06011 volt at 30°C, very close to the theoretical value, and outside this range the electrode was found to be serviceable provided it was calibrated. The $E°$ value at 30°C was 0.4737 volt, with a temperature coefficient of -0.0015 volt deg^{-1}; this gives an $E°$ at 25°C of 0.4852 volt. This is not very far from the value to be expected for the Bi, Bi(OH)$_3$ couple (0.4780 volt) at this temperature, calculated from the data recently assembled for the Bi–H$_2$O system by Van Muylder and Pourbaix ([137]).

Dickinson and Rudge ([138]) found that electrodes of bismuth electrodeposited on platinum wire were unsatisfactory, but electrodes made by casting pure, precipitated bismuth (entirely free from traces of platinum or copper) in Pyrex tubes to form rods, 30 mm × 2 mm gave a theoretical response to pH over the range 5 to 8. The rods were highly polished in appearance, and needed preparation for use by exposure to air for several days, or by dipping into bismuth nitrate solution and gently heating in a Bunsen flame. The electrode potentials followed the relation

$$E = 0.468 - 0.058 \text{ pH at } 20°C$$

and had a temperature coefficient of -0.0016 volt deg^{-1}.

Schwabe ([139]), impressed with the possible advantage that bismuth might have over antimony in being more noble and less likely to adopt higher valency states, made a more extensive study, using electrodes prepared by a variety of methods. These included bismuth electrodeposited from perchlorate solutions ([140]) on to graphite sticks, vacuum-cast bismuth sticks, and amalgam electrodes, and they were combined with glass, hydrogen and saturated calomel electrodes in a common intercomparison cell. Initially, the results were promising. The electrodes could cope with micro-amp currents without appreciably polarizing, they were insensitive to stirring or to the gas passed through the solution (O$_2$, N$_2$, H$_2$), they responded quite rapidly to pH changes without hysteresis effects, and were much less sensitive than antimony to the presence of oxidizing or reducing substances. All the emf's (measured with respect to the saturated calomel electrode) obtained by use of 14 bismuth electrodes of three types, in buffer solutions covering the pH range 3–14, fitted the relation

$$E = 0.1462 - 0.05073 \text{ pH at } 20°C$$

but the scatter was rather large, the average deviation being ±5 mv. If the saturated calomel electrode potential at 20°C is taken as 0.2444 volt ([141]), the $E°$ value for the bismuth electrode on the hydrogen scale becomes 0.3910 volt at 20°C. Using the temperature coefficient previously adopted, this leads to an $E°$ value at 25°C of 0.3835 volt, which may be compared with that expected for the Bi, Bi_2O_3 couple, 0.3712 volt (137). It is, however, to be noted that the potential–pH slope was substantially less than the theoretical (0.0582 volt at 20°C), and it was even more unsatisfactory that in unbuffered solutions it declined to a still lower value (0.0464 volt), and the $E°$ fell also, by no less than 52 mv. This increased still further the serious discrepancy with the $E°$ value of Mehta and Jatkar (136), which may, however, be associated with the quite different methods of electrode preparation.

The disappointing behavior of the bismuth electrode in unbuffered solutions suggested the existence of pronounced salt effects, and these have been examined by Schwabe and Philipp (142). The effects are large, mainly dependent on the anion of the added salt, but decrease with rising pH in an approximately linear way, becoming more or less negligible at around pH 6. They always involve a displacement of potential in the negative direction, but the effect is not instantaneous, and there is an "overshoot," i.e., the potential falls when salt is added, passes through a minimum, and then shows a slow, partial recovery. Determinations were made of the solubilities of the basic bismuth salts containing the same anions, and it was shown that the less soluble the basic salt, the greater the potential displacement caused by addition of a corresponding soluble salt. This suggested the occurrence of a slow substitution reaction forming basic salt at the expense of hydroxide; the concomitant release of hydroxyl ions, and their diffusion away from the reaction zone, would then explain the overshoot effect. Since, with increasing alkalinity, the solubility of the hydroxide would be repressed more than that of any basic salt, the effect might be expected to vanish with rise of pH.

But, even in the higher pH range, the potential–pH slope never does attain the theoretical value, and it will be remembered that antimony is also somewhat prone to this defect. The authors make an interesting suggestion about it; although based upon evidence which has since required modification, it is still worthy of serious consideration. Granér and Sillén (143) had presented results indicating that the bismuth ion hydrolyzes to form polymeric entities, held together by oxygen bridges, which could be represented by $Bi_nO_{2n+1}H_{n+2}$. If this can for the moment be accepted, in order to follow Schwabe and Philipp's argument, it is reasonable to suppose that the solubility of this polynuclear oxy-hydroxide will decrease as n increases. With rising hydroxyl ion activity, the solubility of a given species will decrease in accordance with mass action law, but, at the same time, the value of n for optimum stability is likely to decrease. A picture is thus produced of an oxy-hydroxide of varying stoichiometry, prone to ion exchange, and altering in composition along the pH scale. The fact that later work has shown that, in the solution phase, only a hexanuclear complex is formed (144) does not necessarily rob this picture of credibility as far as a surface film, formed at the metal–solution interface is concerned. Schwabe and Philipp certainly entertained this idea, but modified it in terms of a simplified model. Thus, they showed that if the electrode potential is determined by a Nernst equation involving adsorbed hydroxyl ions (no doubt in the form of a surface oxide or oxy-hydroxide), and if these ions are in Langmuir adsorption equilibrium with ions in the bulk solution phase, a linear potential–pH plot with a slope less than theoretical is explicable.

The further work of Schwabe and Philipp, however, showed that whilst the bismuth electrode could be used with reasonable satisfaction for pH determination (with adequate calibration) in neutral or alkaline solutions, and was not sensibly affected by reducing or oxidizing agents (except H_2O_2), it was not really insensitive to dissolved oxygen. Slow and erratic positive displacements of potential over the whole pH range occurred, indicating a tendency to "function as an oxygen electrode." Kriventsova and Shatalov (145) also observed this effect, as well as the undesirable influence of chloride ion, but obtained a somewhat improved performance by pretreatment of the electrode with 20% chromic acid solution.

More recently, Sammour and Moussa (146) have examined the behavior of electrodes made from bismuth reduced in hydrogen and distilled in vacuum, introduced into deoxygenated buffer solutions without exposure to air. The potentials of these electrodes were stable and, plotted against pH, gave a line with four distinguishable sections. These were assigned to potential-determining reactions which can be represented:

$$2Bi + 3H_2O = Bi_2O_3 + 6H^+ + 6e^- \qquad (pH\ 11.5 - 13.0;\ E^\circ_{found} = 0.389\ volt)$$

$$Bi + 2H_2O = BiO \cdot OH + 3H^+ + 3e^- \qquad (pH\ 9.0 - 10.5;\ E^\circ_{found} = 0.366\ volt)$$

$$5Bi + 7H_2O = 2BiO \cdot OH + 3BiO + 12H^+ + 12e^-$$
$$(pH\ 4.0 - 8.0;\ E^\circ_{found} = 0.335\ volt)$$

$$Bi + H_2O + Cl^- = BiOCl + 2H^+ + 3e^- \qquad (pH\ <4.0)$$

All these results relate to 25°C; the slopes of the first three sections were close to the theoretical value of 0.059 volt. The last section was separately investigated with use of pure hydrochloric acid solutions and a linear potential–pH plot of slope 0.020 volt was obtained over the range pH 0.8–2.8, $E^\circ_{found} = 0.160$ volt. This agrees with theoretical requirements, and with earlier work of Noyes and Ming Chow (147); the other E° figures were also shown to be reasonably consistent with known thermodynamic data. In oxygenated systems, potential–pH curves were obtained which showed similar inflected and stepped characteristics, if somewhat smoothed out, but were displaced bodily to more positive potentials. It was supposed that previous workers had overlooked these eccentricities, and by drawing the best straight line through all their points, had obtained slopes substantially less than theoretical. The positive increment of potential produced by oxygenation was discussed in terms of the "oxygen overvoltage" effect, which was suggested to be inhibited by chloride ions in strongly acid solutions.

It is clear that this interesting contribution is controversial. Although thermodynamic properties are assigned to bismuth monoxide, BiO, by Latimer (3), it has been stated that the evidence is that claims made for its existence are erroneous (148), and it is not included in the more recent thermodynamic survey by Pourbaix (137). If, however, it does exist, perhaps as a "surface interaction product" between Bi and Bi_2O_3, it is surprising that it should participate in potential control as much in oxygenated as in deoxygenated systems. It must be admitted, however, that at present there is no means of eliminating all but one of the theories about the behavior of the bismuth electrode.

3. The Arsenic Electrode

Arsenic exists in three modifications; yellow, black and gray, of which only the latter is stable at ordinary temperatures and has metallic properties. Arsenic trioxide, As_2O_3, exists in at least two crystalline forms. Care is therefore necessary in attempting to set up an arsenic–arsenic trioxide couple of reproducible electrochemical properties. This was first achieved by Schuhmann (149), who found it necessary to sublime the arsenic, in a nitrogen atmosphere, on to a surface maintained between 305° and 360°C, in order to get the pure metallic form. It was resublimed on to a platinum spiral, which was kept for some time at 310°C, and then cooled slowly; all these operations were carried out in nitrogen. The arsenic-clad spirals, however, were not satisfactory as electrodes as they stood, but were effectively used as contacts in "powder electrodes." Covered with powdered arsenic at the bottom of a half-cell, they were further submerged beneath a slurry prepared by lengthy equilibration of cell solution (0.22–0.94 M perchloric acid) with powdered arsenic and arsenic trioxide. The oxide had been recrystallized from aqueous hydrochloric acid (150), thoroughly washed, and dried in vacuum. These electrodes, nitrogen-filled and sealed, reached equilibrium in about 36 hours and, against a hydrogen electrode, provided emf's which led to $E° = 0.2340$ volt at 25°C (and 0.2250 volt at 45°C). This is in precise agreement with 0.234 volt at 25°, recently chosen as the best thermodynamic value for the As, As_2O_3 couple by Van Muylder and Pourbaix (151). Similar results have been obtained with powder electrodes by Tourky and Moussa (152), who have also shown that they respond nearly theoretically to pH over the range pH 1–7. Somewhat surprisingly, it was also shown that arsenic-on-platinum electrodes prepared by sublimation of the element in hydrogen, or by thermal decomposition of arsine, when used in rigorously deoxygenated buffer systems, registered potentials in agreement with the same thermodynamic requirements (153).

There appears to be another kind of arsenic electrode, consisting of arsenic, sublimed on platinum, used in aerated solutions. They record potentials about 100 mv positive to the "thermodynamic" ones, but respond linearly to pH over the range pH 3–10 (138, 152). This again recalls the behavior of antimony. It has been discussed in similar terms [local action (154), "tension reactionelle" (151), "overvoltage" (152)], but there are certain differences. Thus, the arsenic electrodes are not appreciably affected by cathodic or anodic pretreatment, reach steady potentials more quickly and do not show "positive creep," and are much less sensitive to oxidizing agents. The fact that aged electrodes are rather less positive in potential than fresh ones supports the other evidence that the increment of potential above the thermodynamic value is not due to the development of higher oxide (152).

There seems to be some possibility of using arsenic electrodes for pH determination. Dickinson and Rudge (138) found them to be stable (if allowed to stand a few days before use) and to follow the relation $E = 0.360 - 0.058$ pH at 20°C (pH 3–10), whilst Mousa (155) finds $E = 0.368 - 0.0590$ pH at the same temperature, and demonstrates their utility in pH titrations. Evidently, calibrations must always be desirable, however, for electrodes of this kind. The arsenic electrode is likely to cause heavy contamination of systems in which it is placed, since the minimum solubility of arsenic trioxide over the pH range is high (150, 156). Data to illustrate this, and to make comparison with antimony and bismuth, are shown in Table II, which contains solubilities for the stable forms of the trioxides, taken from the Pourbaix surveys (71, 137, 151).

It can be seen that the ranges of pH over which these electrodes can be serviceable (e.g., As, 0–9; Sb, 1–11; Bi, >4) correspond with practical experience, but the successful application of the first two depends on the extreme weakness of the acids $HAsO_2$ and $HSbO_2$. Thus, the pK values are 9.21 and 11.00 respectively. In the case of arsenic, the "margin of safety" is small indeed, for the pH of water in equilibrium with As_2O_3 at 25°C is 4.94.

D. Other Serviceable Metal–Metal Oxide Electrodes

1. The Tungsten Electrode

Early experimental work has been summarized by Gatty and Spooner (157) and was stimulated by the desire to find something better than the

TABLE II

CONCENTRATIONS OF SOLUTES IN EQUILIBRIUM WITH STABLE TRIOXIDES AT 25°C[a]

Solute	pH														
	0	1	2	3	4	5	6	7	8	9	10	11	12	13	14
AsO^+	95.5	9.5	1.0	0.1	—	—	—	—	—	—	—	—	—	—	—
$HAsO_2$	209	209	209	209	209	209	209	209	209	209	209	209	209	209	209
AsO_2^-	—	—	—	—	—	—	0.1	1.3	12.9	126	1259	—	—	—	—
Total As	304	218	210	209	209	209	209	210	222	335	1468	—	—	—	—
SbO^+	0.89	0.09	0.01	—	—	—	—	—	—	—	—	—	—	—	—
$HSbO_2$	0.12	0.12	0.12	0.12	0.12	0.12	0.12	0.12	0.12	0.12	0.12	0.12	0.12	0.12	0.12
$Sb(OH)_4^-$	—	—	—	—	—	—	—	—	—	—	0.01	0.12	1.23	12.3	123
Total Sb	1.01	0.21	0.13	0.12	0.12	0.12	0.12	0.12	0.12	0.12	0.13	0.24	1.35	12.4	123
$BiOH^{2+}$	—	—	—	912	9.12	0.09	0.00	—	0.01	0.00	—	—	—	—	—
BiO^+	—	—	—	891	89.1	8.91	0.89	0.09	0.01	0.001	—	—	—	—	—
Total Bi	—	—	—	1803	98.2	9.00	0.89	0.09	0.01	0.001	—	—	—	—	—

[a] Concentrations in millimoles liter^{-1}.

antimony electrode for industrial use, particularly for controlling the pH of liquids in noncirculating flow. Tungsten has the advantage that it is always readily available in the form of wire and can be sealed directly into Pyrex glass. Limited satisfaction was obtained (*158, 159*); each wire required its own calibration, and potential–pH lines were high in slope and nonlinear. This was later confirmed in the systematic investigation of Britton and Dodd (*160*). Rather better results were later obtained by Abichandani and Jatkar (*161*) who obtained a theoretical potential–pH response from pH 2.8 to 9.4, provided the electrode was used in a system swept out with hydrogen, and by Brintzinger and Rost (*162*) who obtained good potential–pH straight lines over the range pH 1–9 (with greater tolerance, up to pH 13). Not many points of general agreement can be found, except that oxidative pretreatment of the tungsten is deleterious; no treatment at all, rubbing with abrasive, or boiling-out with water appear to be effective. The disagreement between reports on the tungsten electrode is itself support for the view that its potential is determined by local action processes depending on very variable surface states (*157*), and this is the view taken by Shatalov and Marshakov (*163*), who find that no single line will cover the potential–pH relation over the whole pH range.

From the thermodynamic point of view, tungsten, apart from the facts that it is hard, brittle and very easily passivated, is unsuitable as a basis for a metal–metal oxide electrode because it is not noble enough in aqueous solutions of any pH (*164*), and certainly in alkaline solutions it tends to decompose water with hydrogen evolution. In practice, however, it is not corroded in acid solutions, presumably because of the formation of an oxide layer, unless these contain complexing anions (fluoride, phosphate, oxalate). Clearly, the existence of a protective oxide film is not a circumstance favorable to thermodynamic reversibility, and neither is the sequence of oxide phases revealed by detailed analysis of the tungsten–oxygen system (*165*), namely, WO_3 (pale yellow); $WO_{2.9(approx.)}$, blue needles; $WO_{2.88} - WO_{2.50}$, reddish-violet needles; WO_2, brown, monoclinic. The stepwise formation of extremely thin layers (1–3 molecules thick) of oxides of increasing valency has been observed upon tungsten as a result of controlled anodic oxidation (*166*). The tendency of tungsten to reduce the higher oxide, WO_3, is seen by the negative creep in potential of "powder electrodes" with time (*166*). It is therefore not very fruitful to attempt any correlation of very variable observed electrode potentials with thermodynamic data. It is, however, worthy of note that a tungsten electrode subjected to cathodic pre-electrolysis in strong alkali hydroxide solution, and used in buffers protected from air, has been found to respond theoretically to pH from pH 1 to 11, and to have an $E°$ value in agreement with that expected for the W, WO_2 couple (*167*).

If the tungsten electrode is to be regarded as serviceable, it is only because of its desirable properties of ruggedness, and its application to pH measurement or control with adequate calibration, or to potentiometric end-point detection.

2. The Molybdenum Electrode

Since molybdenum is so similar to tungsten, it is not surprising to find that its story in relation to electrode potential behavior is approximately the same. Thermodynamic data for the molybdenum-water system have been assembled (168). The metal is non-noble, readily passivates, and forms colored, nonstoichiometric, intermediate oxide phases. It has been studied by most of the workers who examined tungsten, and seems to have a similar degree of usefulness, which, for pH determination, is not very high (169).

3. The Tellurium Electrode

Tellurium is not a metal; it is an intrinsic semiconductor. The element, in its so-called "metallic" form, is isomorphous with gray selenium and consists of long chains of covalently bound atoms. Its electrical conductance is very small, but is greatly increased by the presence of traces of impurities. Early studies of its electrode behavior were made by Kasarnowsky (170) and by Lukas and Jilek (171), but the possibility of applying tellurium electrodes to pH determination was first systematically examined by Tomiček and Poupě (172). It was found that very pure tellurium must be used. Cast into rods, about 8 mm in diameter, and mounted in glass tubes, the tellurium was prepared for use by systematic polishing with fine emery paper, rinsing with distilled water, and wiping with filter paper. Greasy contamination was particularly to be avoided. Such electrodes, in buffer solutions saturated with air (preferably free of carbon dioxide) or oxygen, attained a steady potential within a minute of immersion, and, at 20°C, followed the relation $E = 0.603 - 0.058$ pH reasonably well over the range pH 1–12. But the potential–pH plot in fact deviated considerably from linearity, and specific salt effects attributable to chloride ion were observed. Nevertheless, the electrodes had the great advantage of insensitivity to anions, such as tartrate, which upset the antimony electrode. They could also be used in dilute permanganate solutions, but were disturbed by sulfite. They can even be used in titrations involving chromic acid (173), and it appears that they may be regarded as worthwhile competitors to the antimony electrode. This view is supported by the results of controlled anodic (and cathodic) polarization experiments (174) which showed only one well-marked potential arrest corresponding fairly well with the formation and reduction of the dioxide, TeO_2. The reversible potential for the

Te, TeO_2 couple at pH = 0 given by Latimer (175) is 0.529 volt at 25°C, and an $E°$ value close to this (0.53 volt) has been observed in the pH range 1–5 (176). A more detailed investigation of tellurium electrodes of various types (177) has shown that this standard potential (0.530 volt) is recorded by electrodes that have been reduced in hydrogen and are used in absence of oxygen, and also by powder electrodes. Otherwise, for electrodes in aerated buffer solutions, the $E°$ values are very much higher. It is clear that the effect of oxygen, observed with so many supposed metal–metal oxide electrodes, is again in operation, raising the potentials from the expected thermodynamic values by anything up to 150 mv, and making calibration an essential prerequisite to pH determination.

4. Other Electrodes

The list of metals the potentials of which respond to pH is by no means exhausted by the cases that have been discussed, but at the present time it seems probable that all the examples likely to be of useful application have been covered. For exploration of further possibilities the original literature must be consulted. This task may be aided by reference to standard works already quoted, by a recent admirable compilation of oxidation-reduction potentials (178), and by the numerous publications of Pourbaix and his co-workers which are leading to the establishment of an "Atlas d'Equilibres Electrochimiques." In addition to the examples already quoted, these authors have dealt with Al (179), B (180), Be (181), Cd (182), Cr (183), Co (184), Cu (185), Ge (186), Au (187), Fe (188), Pb (189), Mg (190), Mn (191), Hg (192), Ni (193), Nb (194), Re (195), Se (196), Ta (197), Tc (198), Te (199), Tl (200), Sn (201), Ti (202), U (203), V (204), Zn (205), and Zr (206). General accounts of the methods involved are available (28, 207, 208).

Particular interest is attached to electrodes formed from semiconductors (e.g. Ge) in equilibrium with electrolytic solutions, which may show a hydrogen electrode function without intervention of any oxide layer. Developments in this field are likely to clear up many outstanding problems in relation to the behavior of metal oxides, particularly in the form of thin layers on the parent metal substrate, for all the oxides are, in principle, semiconductors. It is beyond our present scope to follow this; the present state of knowledge has been recently reviewed (209).

III. The Oxygen Electrode

A. General and Thermodynamic Considerations

At a fully reversible oxygen electrode, equilibrium must be established between molecular oxygen and oxide ions in solution. In aqueous solution, the equilibrium constant

$$K = (a_{OH^-})^2/(a_{O^{2-}})(a_{H_2O})$$

has the value 10^{23} at 25°C, so that it is convenient to express the standard oxygen electrode potential in terms of unit fugacity of oxygen gas, unit activity of water and unit activity of hydroxyl (not oxide) ions. But in any aqueous solution hydroxyl ions remain in equilibrium with hydrogen ions and water molecules, so that an alternative standard electrode is one in which oxygen at unit fugacity is in equilibrium with water at unit activity and hydrogen ions at unit activity. In this second case the standard electrode potential is identical with the standard emf of the hydrogen–oxygen cell, which can be evaluated thermodynamically. Thus, the cell reaction per faraday is

$$\tfrac{1}{2}H_2 \text{ (ideal, 1 atm)} + \tfrac{1}{4}O_2 \text{ (ideal, 1 atm)} = \tfrac{1}{2}H_2O \text{ (liq)}$$

for which $\Delta G°$ at 25°C is -28.345 kcal (2), so that

$$E°_{cell} = \frac{-\Delta G°}{nF} = \frac{28.245 \times 4.1840}{96,493} = 1.229 \text{ volt} = E°_{O_2,H^+}$$

If the activity of the water does not depart from its standard value of unity, and if gaseous nonideality is ignored, the potential of the oxygen electrode under nonstandard conditions will clearly be given by

$$E°_{O_2,H^+} = E°_{O_2,H^+} + \frac{RT}{4F} \ln P_{O_2} + \frac{RT}{F} \ln a_{H^+} \tag{15}$$

If the partial pressure of oxygen, P_{O_2}, with which the electrode is supposed to be in equilibrium has the standard value of 1 atm, then at 25°C,

$$E_{O_2,H^+} = 1.229 - 0.05916 \text{ pH} \tag{16}$$

from which it is obvious that the oxygen electrode responds to pH in the same way as the hydrogen electrode.

Since the ionic product of water is defined as $K_w = a_{H^+} \cdot a_{OH^-}$, and the potential of a given electrode is independent of the way in which we choose to regard it, Eq. (15) can be written

$$E_{O_2,H^+} = E_{O_2,OH^-} = E°_{O_2,H^+} + \frac{RT}{4F} \ln P_{O_2} + \frac{RT}{F} \ln K_w - \frac{RT}{F} \ln a_{OH^-}$$

With $K_w = 1.008 \times 10^{-14}$ at 25°C (210), and at unit partial pressure of oxygen, this becomes

$$E_{O_2,OH^-} = 0.401 - 0.05916 \log a_{OH^-} \tag{17}$$

at 25°C, which sets a value to the standard potential of the oxygen potential as usually defined, i.e.,

$$E°_{O_2,OH^-} = 0.401 \text{ volt}$$

The oxygen electrode thus appears to provide no more information about aqueous solutions than does the hydrogen electrode but certain special features of interest, and possibly some practical advantages, are associated with it.

The use of electrodes of various kinds for measuring pH has been discussed at length, and it is generally understood that this function satisfactorily identifies the position of equilibrium which has been attained in the competition for protons between all the acidic (proton donating) and basic (proton accepting) entities which may be present in any aqueous solution. Water itself is amphiprotic (both proton donating and accepting) and participates, with the solutes it may contain, in the over-all, linked system of proton-transfer equilibria. It therefore acts as a standard, and when its own self-ionization equilibrium is exactly balanced, this is the "neutral point" on the acidity scale, or pH 7 on the pH scale at 25°C. But there is another property of aqueous solutions in general which is of almost equally wide application and interest. This is oxidizing or reducing power, and some scale analogous to pH to measure it, and to identify something akin to a "neutral point" is much to be desired. It is attained by using the hydrogen and oxygen electrodes in conjunction with each other in the following way.

Oxidation-reduction reactions are essentially concerned with electron transfer, and an unattackable metal electrode immersed in a solution in which a mobile equilibrium of this kind exists will assume a potential characteristic of the "redox balance" which is attained. A highly reducing system will tend to donate electrons to the metal phase and make its potential more negative; an oxidizing system will have the reverse effect. If it is imagined that the electrode can also catalyze the hydrogen and oxygen electrode reactions, the redox equilibrium system in the aqueous solution must generate and maintain appropriate equilibrium pressures of oxygen and hydrogen. These in turn must be in equilibrium with each other and with the liquid water phase. This equilibrium is thermodynamically defined; thus for the dissociation

$$2H_2O \text{ (liq)} = 2H_2 \text{ (gas)} + O_2 \text{ (gas)}$$

$\Delta G°$ is 113.38 kcal at 25°C. Application of the reaction isotherm then indicates that at equilibrium

$$\log [(P_{H_2})^2 \cdot P_{O_2}] = -83.10 \qquad (18)$$

and this can be symbolized by analogy with the pH convention as

$$2rH + rO = 83.10 \qquad (19)$$

At the "redox neutral point," $P_{H_2} = 2P_{O_2}$, so that $rH = rO - 0.30$, and this is equivalent to $rH = 27.60$ and $rO = 27.90$. Thus the position of what Pourbaix calls "absolute neutrality" in an aqueous solution at 25°C (i.e. such that the dissociation of the solvent into ions, and its tendency to dissociate into elementary gases are precisely the same as in pure water) is characterized by pH = 7.0 and rH = 27.6, or rO = 27.9 (*211*). By use of either of the equations

$$E = 0.02958 \text{ rH} - 0.05916 \text{ pH} \tag{20}$$

$$E = 1.229 - 0.01479 \text{ rO} - 0.05916 \text{ pH} \tag{21}$$

the potential of the hypothetical electrode of versatile reversibility is found to be 0.402 volt at 25°C, at this absolute neutral point.

Clearly, if an aqueous solution contains rather a strong reducing agent, then according to the redox potential and the pH, rH will tend to have a low value. If it falls to zero, this corresponds with an equilibrium pressure of hydrogen of 1 atm, so that, under ordinary ambient conditions, such a system will not be thermodynamically stable; the water will be decomposed with hydrogen evolution. Whether this occurs in practice will depend on the presence, or not, of any barrier opposing the process. At the other extreme, any strongly oxidizing system in solution for which rO = 0 will be on the verge of thermodynamic stability, tending to decompose water with evolution of oxygen. Thus, rH = 0 and rO = 0 mark the limits of the thermodynamic stability of water and in the Pourbaix diagrams (*28, 71, 151, 164, 168, 179–208*) of potential plotted against pH, these values fall on sloping lines which enclose a band within which water is stable.

Attention may now be returned to pH-indicating electrodes. For any solution which is in equilibrium with a hydrogen electrode, rH = 0. Conditions are strongly reducing and the solution cannot be allowed to contain any mobile redox system with rH > 0, otherwise continuous reduction is likely to occur. Examples of the incidence of such troubles have been mentioned (Chap. 2, Section II,B,4) and others have not because they are so obvious; a hydrogen electrode cannot be used in acid solutions of permanganate or dichromate. An oxygen electrode, if adequately reversible, would therefore obviously have a sphere of usefulness different from that of the hydrogen electrode, insofar as it is itself an oxidizing and not a reducing agent. It is, however, a very powerful oxidizing agent with rO = 0.

It is clear that this is but part of a general problem. All the pH indicating electrodes might be labeled with their rH or rO values, except that $E°$ serves the same purpose. The glass electrode is an exception, for it has the unique advantage that it cannot oxidize or reduce anything. This sort of problem is not of very common occurrence in pH determination, since in most cases solutions do not contain oxidizing or reducing agents. Even if they do, there may be no electron-transfer mechanism by which continuous oxidation or reduction can occur in absence of a "potential mediator" (*212*).

In special cases, however, there may be great difficulty which is usually met by recourse to the glass electrode (*213*). But it remains true that the $E°$ (or rH or rO) of a pH indicating electrode is a significant part of its definition, to be taken into account when such electrodes are chosen for use.

A specific comparison of the hydrogen and oxygen electrodes may now be made, in order to assess any possible advantages, or otherwise, of the latter. The over-all electrode reactions, operating in acid or alkaline solutions, respectively, may be represented

$$\text{Hydrogen electrode} \begin{cases} 2H_3O^+ + 2e^- = H_2 + 2H_2O \\ 2H_2O + 2e^- = H_2 + 2OH^- \end{cases}$$

$$\text{Oxygen electrode} \begin{cases} O_2 + 4H_3O^+ + 4e^- = 6H_2O \\ O_2 + 2H_2O + 4e^- = 4OH^- \end{cases}$$

It is seen at once that the reaction at the oxygen electrode involves the transfer of four electrons, twice as many as for the hydrogen electrode reaction. That this transfer should occur in one simple step is unlikely, so it may be expected that the mechanism of the oxygen electrode reaction will be more complicated than that of the hydrogen electrode.

A similar conclusion may be reached by considering what other products of reduction than H_2, or other products of oxidation than O_2, might be formed from the common constituents of aqueous solutions, to complicate the formal reaction equilibria. Neither of these equilibria is established by means of freely occurring electron transfers in homogeneous solution, so that in each case the metallic phase will have to act as a catalyst. This usually involves some quite intimate kind of intervention, so that the physics and chemistry of the metal phase must be taken into consideration.

For the hydrogen electrode, these complications have already been discussed in some detail (Chap. 2, Section I,D) and, in the simplest case are limited to the formation of hydrogen atoms adsorbed upon the metal substrate. For the oxygen electrode, however, the possibilities are much wider. They can be assessed by examining the list to be found, for example in Latimer's book (*214*); thus the following entities might easily participate:

$$O, \ OH, \ H_2O_2, \ HO_2^-, \ HO_2, \ O_2^-$$

variously in "free" or adsorbed states, together with surface oxides, peroxides, hydroxides or oxy-hydroxides derived from the metal phase. Some progress has been made in surveying the domains of thermodynamic stability of hydrogen peroxide and the radicals and ions to which it gives rise (*215*) and in studying the energetics of reactions in which they are concerned (*216*) but complex problems remain to be solved in relation to their electrochemical behavior. Application of the theory of the kinetics of activation-controlled consecutive electrochemical reactions to five possible mechanisms for the anodic evolution of oxygen by Bockris (217) may be quoted as marking notable progress. The diagnostic criteria worked out gave immediate indication of variation of mechanism from one electrode material to another.

The general situation is that a number of electrodes must be grouped together for discussion under the general heading of "the oxygen electrode." In somewhat exaggerated analogy, it could be said that a complicated marshalling yard of reaction routes lies between water molecules or hydroxyl ions on one side and oxygen molecules on the other, with most of the routes passing through a well-defined junction, representing hydrogen peroxide. The existence of this "junction" has long been known; it was found polarographically by Heyrovsky (218) in studying the reduction of dissolved oxygen at the dropping mercury cathode. The hydrogen peroxide wave is so well defined that it affords a sensitive method of analysis for this substance at extreme dilutions (219). Even in this case, the reaction path seems to be anything but simple; according to Frumkin (220) it is to be represented by

$$O_2 \xrightarrow{e^-} O_2^- \xrightarrow{H^+} HO_2 \xrightarrow{e^-} HO_2^- \xrightarrow{H^+} H_2O_2 \xrightarrow{e^-} OH + OH^- \xrightarrow{e^-} 2OH^-$$

Some simplification might be expected at the mercury electrode, for it is one of the few metals which does not catalyze the decomposition of hydrogen peroxide, and trigger off a radical chain reaction. Nevertheless, it appears that there are two electrodes at which well-defined over-all reactions can be established with a greater or less degree of reversibility. These are

$$O_2 + 2H_2O + 4e^- \rightleftharpoons 4OH^-$$

$$O_2 + H_2O + 2e^- \rightleftharpoons HO_2^- + OH^-$$

and the electrodes concerned may, for brevity, be called the oxygen electrode and the oxygen–peroxide electrode. It seems that the reaction

$$H_2O_2 + 2e^- \rightarrow 2OH^-$$

is always irreversible, so that the peroxide electrode does not exist, although this title may be justifiably used in another connection. There are no doubt many other, less well-defined electrodes, subject to mixed potential control, or defective in reversibility, which are important only from one point of view. That is, that we cannot afford to ignore their existence. They are to be encountered at every turn in corrosion studies, and it is sobering to think how many reference electrodes have been used in aerated solutions without due regard to the possibility that dissolved oxygen might exert some electromotive effect. It has been seen that in some cases the effect is far too large to escape attention.

B. The Oxygen Electrode

Many attempts were made to set up a reversible oxygen electrode, but until quite recently, only one succeeded. This, however, involved a fused salt electrolyte, within the temperature range 330° to 1000°C (*221*). All attempts to make the oxygen electrode work in aqueous solutions failed (*222*). Usually, noble metals were employed and the general finding was that although potentials often rose with time, they never attained the proper value, and the electrodes showed great sensitivity to stirring and to polarization. It was as if the proper oxygen electrode reaction, itself not very mobile, was being bypassed by the occurrence of some easier process, perhaps formation of metal oxide. It was significant, however, that traces of hydrogen peroxide were sometimes detected in the half-cell solutions.

The first substantial progress from this unsatisfactory position was made by Hoar (*223*), who carried out both anodic and cathodic polarizations with single-sided platinum electrodes in both acid and alkaline, oxygen-swept solution. He obtained Tafel lines which, on both sides of the zero current point, showed well-developed rectilinear sections; these on extrapolation, intersected at a potential of 1.20 volt, quite close to the known theoretical value, 1.229 volt at 25°C. Resting potentials, however, showed the same erratic characteristics as previously observed; they were then attributed to the self-polarization of an electrode incompletely covered with an unstable oxide film, and the view was expressed that the oxygen electrode reaction can only be expected to occur on an oxide, as distinct from a metal, surface. The importance of this work, however, lay in demonstrating that, however tenuously, the oxygen electrode reaction may become potential-controlling.

With the development of electrochemical techniques, and recognition of the profound effects of very rigorous purification of electrode systems, further progress became possible and was notably achieved by Bockris and Huq (*224*). Interesting and radical changes were found in the behavior of platinum electrodes in aqueous, oxygen-swept sulfuric acid solutions with progressive stages of purification. Initially, the same erratic and indeterminate behavior as encountered by all previous workers was found. Purification by cathodic pre-electrolysis, however, led to the establishment of a potential of 0.840 ± 0.002 volt, at 25°C, at a new platinum electrode, but hydrogen peroxide was detected in the solution; it will later be seen that this coincides closely with the potential of the peroxide electrode. But purification was continued by means of anodic pre-electrolysis, which had the effect that another fresh electrode assumed a potential of 1.24 ± 0.03 volt when introduced to the solution, and showed a sensitivity to oxygen partial pressure in reasonable agreement with the requirements of Eq. (15).

Extrapolated Tafel lines, derived from cathodic and anodic polarization measurements, intersected on the potential axis at 1.225 ± 0.014 volt, very close to the theoretical value. Determinations of Tafel slope and assessments of stoichiometric number (Chap. 2, Section I,D), which were found to approximate to 0.12 volt and 4 respectively, suggested that the rate-limiting step for the oxygen electrode reaction, occurring on a fully de-activated (oxidized) platinum surface, is a single electron transfer from a water molecule (or hydroxyl ion) to form an adsorbed radical, but subsequent rapid steps could not be uniquely identified. For alkaline solutions, Hoar (225) has proposed a different mechanism in which rate-limitation occurs in the formation of hydrogen bonds between adsorbed hydroxyl radicals and ions; the entities so produced undergo rapid dimerization, redistribution of charge, dehydration and final discharge to produce oxygen molecules. It is, however, clear that these problems of mechanism are difficult to solve unambiguously, but uncertainties about them do not obscure the main facts of present interest. These are that the reversible oxygen electrode is now attainable, but only under conditions of rigorous purification; its exchange current is so small that alternative processes readily take over, and do so when limits of impurities (unidentified, except for H_2O_2) exceed about 10^{-11} mole liter^{-1} (224).

In spite of the limitations of the imperfect oxygen electrode, it can act as a sensitive and accurate end-point indicator in direct, or differential, acid-base titrations. Furman (226) found that platinized platinum, supplied with air (or better, oxygen) in the conventional Hildebrand apparatus (227) gave potentials which drifted in a positive direction, initially at 5–10 mv hr^{-1} in acid solutions and at 30–60 mv hr^{-1} in alkaline, but in about 20 minutes became quite steady enough to generate pH titration curves of very nearly "theoretical" shape. The particular virtue was that these curves were unaffected by the presence of oxidizing systems such as chromate–dichromate or permanganate. The electrode therefore earns its keep among the many others available for analytical potentiometric titrations (228).

C. The Oxygen–Peroxide Electrode

In 1943 Berl (229) published the remarkable observation that graphite, carrying on its surface 5 mg cm^{-2} of finely divided active carbon (laid on with a spray-gun in the form of a suspension in toluene-ethanol containing some ethyl cellulose), behaved as an electrode highly reversible to both oxygen and hydrogen peroxide in alkaline solutions. He produced strong evidence that the electrode reaction was

$$O_2 + H_2O + 2e^- \rightleftharpoons HO_2^- + OH^-$$

and agreement with the appropriate Nernst equation was soon confirmed (230), but attempts to extend the reaction to neutral or acid media failed, and no better catalyst than active carbon could be found. These results were of such interest as to initiate investigations too numerous to be reviewed in the present context, and the outstanding fact is that the Berl reaction proceeds with great facility at an activated carbon (not ordinary

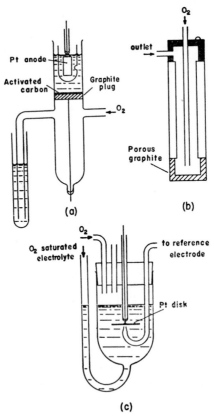

FIG. 2. Oxygen electrode designs. (a) Arrangement for the study of cathodic processes (231). (b) Simple dip-type electrode assembly. (c) Pt disk electrode after Hoar (223).

graphite) surface, providing an electrode with a polarization which is small even at 500 ma cm^{-2} and capable of producing hydrogen peroxide from oxygen with high current efficiency. Two questions which immediately arose have received satisfactory answers.

The first question is, why is the exchange current of the Berl reaction very high, whereas that of the oxygen electrode proper is vanishingly small?

It is probably because the latter involves the breaking of the interatomic bond in molecular oxygen, and this is very strong

$$O_2 \text{ (gas)} \rightarrow 2 \, O \text{ (gas)}; \quad \triangle G^\circ = 110 \text{ kcal}$$

That this breakage does not occur in the Berl reaction has recently been shown (231) by use of isotopically discriminated oxygen; in both anodic and cathodic processes, the unit O—O is exchanged between molecular oxygen and hydrogen peroxide with bond modification but not breakage — there was no exchange with oxygen of H_2O or OH^-. This result placed a limitation on possible mechanisms, and the most probable was thought to be the electrochemical reduction of adsorbed molecular oxygen, perhaps proceeding by two single-electron transfer steps involving adsorbed HO_2 radicals as intermediates.

The second question is why activated carbon is so effective a catalyst for this reaction. The answer probably lies in the tendency of carbon to adsorb oxygen (and other paramagnetic molecules) to form a surface complex, which electron paramagnetic resonance measurements (232) have indicated may be of a peroxide nature. Carbon pretreated by heating to a high temperature in vacuum is very much less effective (233). This fits in very well with the quite simple mechanism already proposed. That the reaction does not occur easily in neutral or acid solutions has been confirmed by Hickling and Wilson (234) in their studies of the anodic decomposition of hydrogen peroxide, but the reason is obscure. It is relevant and interesting that the most effective electrodes are based on porous graphite through which oxygen can be passed, but the maximum gas–solution interaction is achieved by rendering the electrode surface hydrophobic; this is effected (231) by applying the active carbon layer from a suspension in, for example, a benzene solution of gum rubber. Typical electrode arrangements are illustrated in Fig. 2. The special nature of carbon makes comparison with other possibly catalytic materials difficult, but it appears that nickel is inactive; silver, platinum, and palladium have limited activities while spinels ($NiFe_2O_4$) have quite high activities (235).

D. The Peroxide Electrode

It has already been noted that the reaction

$$H_2O_2 + 2e^- \rightarrow 2OH^-$$

does not occur reversibly. It was pointed out by Weiss (236) that it is energetically disfavored because the Franck-Condon principle would require the interoxygen distance to remain unchanged during the act of electron transfer, and the ion-ion repulsion energy of the immediate products would be very high. In any case, a single electron transfer is more probable, so that the alternative reaction

$$H_2O_2 + e^- \rightarrow OH + OH^-$$

is preferred. If the radical produced at the electrode surface acts in the same way as radicals in solution, it is likely to set off the chain reaction,

$$OH + H_2O_2 \rightarrow HO_2 + H_2O$$

$$HO_2 + H_2O_2 \rightarrow OH + H_2O + O_2$$

terminated by

$$OH + HO_2 \rightarrow H_2O + O_2$$

with continuous decomposition of the peroxide. Weiss found that, at platinum, cathodic polarization could cause copious *oxygen* evolution from peroxide solutions; clearly, enhanced cathodic generation of free radicals and consequent proliferation of decomposition chains was responsible.

In view of this situation it is surprising to find that there is an electrode, involving hydrogen peroxide as an essential component, which shows tolerably reversible behavior. It was observed by Flis (237) that a platinum electrode in a solution containing hydrogen peroxide changes its potential linearly with pH and can be used for the titration of acids and bases. It has also been observed that a platinum electrode in oxygenated solutions shows a marked improvement in reversibility after being subjected to cathodic treatment (224, 238). Bockris and Oldfield (239) found that bright platinum and gold electrodes in oxygen-free buffer solutions (purified by pre-electrolysis at a mercury cathode) containing hydrogen peroxide (10^{-6} to 5 molar) gave a linear potential–pH response over the range pH 0–14, according to the relations:

$$\text{Pt,} \ E = 0.835 - 0.059 \ \text{pH}, \qquad \pm 0.005 \ \text{volt at } 25°C$$

$$\text{Au,} \ E = 0.842 - 0.059 \ \text{pH}, \qquad \pm 0.007 \ \text{volt at } 25°C$$

independently of the concentration of peroxide or the presence of molecular oxygen. Such an electrode is unique; its operation depends critically upon the presence of hydrogen peroxide, but not upon its activity; rather less than one part in 10^7 is enough. Molecular oxygen does not participate in the potential controlling reaction, nor do oxide films of normal kind, for those on platinum and gold would lead to potentials more positive, and more different from each other, than those observed. It appears that the only tenable explanation is to be found in the continuous catalytic decomposition of the peroxide, which maintains upon the electrode surface a saturation concentration of adsorbed "free" radicals. Very low concentrations of peroxide in solution are adequate to do this, and no higher concentrations can increase the population of radicals upon the surface above the saturation limit. If the adsorption energy is supposed to be large and independent of electrode potential, this explanation is plausible, but for each metal substrate the "$E°$ value" must depend upon the adsorption energy and would be expected to vary considerably with the surface state of the metal.

It is not yet clear whether these electrodes have a field of useful application and perhaps their main interest lies in demonstrating the existence of a kind of association between oxygenated entities and metal (or oxide) surfaces that needs to be taken into account in wider connections.

E. MIXED ELECTRODES

A possibly misguided attempt has been made to pick out electrodes at which isolated and identifiable reactions are supposed to occur. This was probably justified for the Berl electrode, although even here the potentials are 35–40 mv more positive than the thermodynamic values. In most cases electrodes in oxygenated systems will, if they are not inert, come under mixed potential control; their study then presents the most complex problems and their analytical usefulness declines, except for their importance in furthering the understanding of electrochemical phenomena of possibly wider significance. In order to present a more balanced view without too distant excursions, reference may be made to two recent investigations.

Gerischer and Gerischer (240) have studied the catalytic decomposition of hydrogen peroxide at platinum. Rest potentials were strongly dependent on pH in the general way found by Bockris and Oldfield (239) but, taken rapidly, before steady states had been established, they certainly did not generate a theoretical line. They tended to reflect variations in the character of the metal surface from one electrode to another; they also varied with time, and anomalously with pH, particularly at pH values higher than 8. Cathodic and anodic studies revealed passivation, activation and hysteresis effects, perhaps associated with hydrogen or oxygen films, or oxide layers of a special kind. In the region of the rest potential, however, the measurements gave rise to rectilinear Tafel lines, and extrapolation of these indicated that the exchange current was proportional to hydrogen peroxide concentration, but depended upon pH in a complicated way, which was also reflected in measured rates of oxygen evolution. It was necessary to conclude that the rest potential was mixed, and that to the reactions proposed by Weiss (236) must be added

$$H_2O_2 \rightarrow HO_2 + H^+ + e^-$$

and

$$H_2O_2 + H^+ + e^- \rightarrow OH + H_2O,$$

emphasizing that free radicals are generated by *both* cathodic and anodic electron transfers. This might well indicate how a stationary population of such radicals could be maintained. Oxygen evolution occurred at pH values lower than about 6 by the reaction,

$$HO_2 \rightarrow O_2 + H^+ + e^-$$

but above pH 6 mainly by the chain reaction, the contribution of which increased with hydrogen peroxide concentration and with decreasing electrode activity. At high pH values, it was necessary to envisage the entry of a new decomposition mechanism, probably because of the changing nature of the platinum surface as it becomes covered with an oxide layer varying in structure and thickness. This mechanism might be the same as that originally proposed by Haber (*241*), namely, alternate formation and reduction of metal oxide.

Vielstich (*242*) has made a study of the oxygen electrode reaction in alkaline solutions at porous electrodes of carbon, platinum, nickel, and silver under resting and current-carrying conditions, in the presence of oxygen, hydrogen peroxide, or both. In the latter case the electrodes behaved as if controlled primarily by the Berl reaction, but there was a positive increment of potential as large as 100 mv in the case of silver. The electrodes were therefore under mixed control. In considering what other reaction could intervene, Vielstich reasonably excluded those which are known to be more hindered than the Berl reaction, and came to the conclusion that the catalytic decomposition of hydrogen peroxide must be involved, and this be represented as

$$H_2O_2 + M \rightarrow M-O + H_2O$$

where M—O represents chemisorbed oxygen formed by hydrogen peroxide decomposition, which can take part in the reaction

$$M-O + H_2O + 2e^- \rightleftharpoons M + 2OH^-$$

which occurs with facility. Then the equilibrium potential and exchange current of this reaction, and those of the Berl reaction, were adequate to explain the rest potentials and current–potential curves for all the electrodes examined, and it was possible to set up the general reaction scheme

$$\longrightarrow O_2 + H_2O + 2e^- \rightleftharpoons HO_2^- + OH^-$$
$$HO_2^- + H^+ \rightleftharpoons H_2O_2$$
$$H_2O_2 + M \rightarrow H_2O + M-O$$
$$M-O + H_2O + 2e^- \rightleftharpoons 2OH^- + M$$
$$2M-O \rightarrow O_2 + 2M$$

It is of particular interest that M—O is to be regarded as a metal-oxygen compound of undefined stoichiometry, taking an intermediate place between free atomic oxygen and normal metallic oxides, and not possessing any predictable oxygen potential. The distinction between such "compounds" and normal oxides is illustrated by the case of silver which catalyzes both peroxide decomposition and the Berl reaction. Its catalytic efficiency, however, is decreased when it is covered by a layer of Ag_2O by anodization.

The evidence for the existence of a special kind of oxygen–metal, or perhaps oxygen–oxide, interaction occurring at metal–solution interfaces

TABLE III

SUMMARY OF SOME OXYGEN ELECTRODE REACTIONS

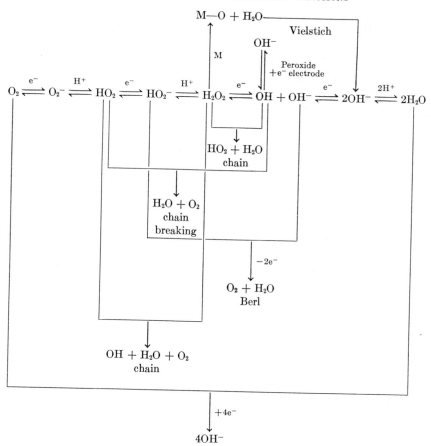

therefore seems to be considerable, even if knowledge about its nature remains scanty. Giner (243), from evidence produced by charging curves, has argued in favor of chemisorbed O_2 entities which, with preformed O—O bonds, could readily produce H_2O_2 on reduction. It seems as if every conceivable suggestion has been made at one time or another, and the over-all picture remains somewhat obscured by unresolved complexities.

An attempt has been made to correlate the reactions that have been discussed and is displayed in Table III. The backbone of this table is the sequence of steps which has been established for the polarographic reduction of oxygen; other reactions which occur under different circumstances to varying degrees are represented, with no implications regarding their mechanisms.

It seems probable that these reactions cannot be ignored for any metal–aqueous-solution–oxygen system in which oxidations or reductions occur. Although the tentative idea (244) that hydrogen peroxide is essentially involved in all anodic oxidations has not been sustained, it is certainly true for cathodic *oxidations* in oxygenated solutions (245). It is important that metals show individual and characteristic behaviors in relation to oxygen reduction. This is well shown in the elegant studies made by Delahay (246), which were carried out as follows.

A metal electrode, contained in a vessel completely filled with a phosphate buffer solution of pH 6.9, initially saturated with air and continuously stirred magnetically, was subjected to cathodic polarization at a constant predetermined potential. Total current was measured as a function of time, and the concentrations of dissolved oxygen (decreasing) and of hydrogen peroxide (increasing) were followed by means of a built-in polarograph. Each metal was studied in this way over a wide range of polarization potentials, and the total current could, over quite short time intervals, be partitioned between 4-electron reduction, 2-electron reduction and any other electrode process such as metal dissolution, oxide film formation, or hydrogen ion discharge. In general, the rate of oxygen consumption increased quite rapidly as the potential was made more negative, and in all cases (Ag, Al, Cu, Fe, Mg, Ni, Pb, Pt, Sn and Zn) both reduction processes occurred concurrently in some potential range or another. The 4-electron reduction, however, always increased in its proportional contribution with increasingly negative polarization, eventually tending to assume complete predominance. But the way in which the ratio of the contributions of the two processes (4/2) increased along the negative potential scale was highly characteristic for each metal. Although these experiments were not diagnostic of reaction mechanism, they showed how widely this must vary from case to case, so that one process or another is differentially catalyzed according to the identity of the metal, its surface state, and polarization potential. Perhaps the most important result was that hydrogen peroxide is *always* formed in the electrolytic reduction of oxygen; for aluminum and zinc in nearly 100% yield at the less negative polarizations, but in very small yield for tin. For platinum and nickel, yields of 60–20% are obtained over a wide range of potentials, but for copper, silver, and iron, catalytic decomposition of hydrogen peroxide prevents the building up of its concentration. In all cases, the rest potentials (zero observable current) of the metals were such as to favor a high yield of peroxide in any localized oxygen reduction. In other words, the self-polarization potentials assumed by these metals when undergoing spontaneous corrosion in oxygenated solutions are such as to make the production of hydrogen peroxide very likely.

This idea is not new (*247*) and hydrogen peroxide has indeed been repeatedly detected in corroding systems, e.g. aluminum in moist air (*248*). Some very old and, at first sight, barely credible observations are of considerable interest in this connection. They have been reviewed by Keenan (*249*) and are to do with various substances which act on photographic plates in the dark. Such substances are magnesium, aluminum, zinc or linseed oil recently exposed to light, and it was Russell (*250*) who suggested that the effect was due to traces of hydrogen peroxide produced by the action of moist air on *freshly-abraded* metal surfaces, or, for the linseed oil, by well-known autoxidation processes. More recently, Grunberg (*251, 252*) has confirmed the reality of the "Russell effect" for a number of metals and has associated it with an observation by Kramer (*253*) that abraded metal surfaces emit electrons at relatively low temperatures; this has also been found for evaporated films of metals, and even of crystalline non-metals (*254*). Grunberg has further shown (*255*) that electrons are ejected from such metal surfaces (abraded, evaporated, sputtered) by visible light at frequencies far below the normal photoelectric thresholds; Al, Mg, and Zn show an emission peak at 4700 Å. These abnormal properties decay in the course of many hours, and the process is greatly hastened by even low pressures of oxygen, in which O_2^- ions have been identified. It therefore seems very likely that fresh metal surfaces, in a state far removed from stability, can generate hydrogen peroxide from water and oxygen by much the same mechanism as ionizing radiations do so (*256*). But in all cases the effect is associated with the tendency of the metal to form an oxide film, and is believed to arise in the oxide and not the underlying metal. Thus, when a metal is abraded, lattice imperfections in the oxide film *already present* lead to the trapping of electrons from the metal phase in anion vacancies; it is to these electrons that the abnormal electron-availability must be attributed.

These results and conclusions can hardly be irrelevant in relation to the usual practice of preparing antimony, bismuth, tungsten and similar electrodes for use by abrading them (this chapter, Sections II, C and D).

Recently Roikh (*257*) has made a comprehensive survey of the formation of hydrogen peroxide in the atmospheric corrosion of metals, and has conducted experiments with, *inter alia*, Mg, Al, Zn, Cd, Ni, Pb, Fe, Sb, Bi, Cu, Ag, Hg, Mo, and Au. Using twelve different reagents for detecting peroxide, he obtained positive indications in all cases, finding Mg, Al, and Zn to be the most productive. In all cases the yield was enhanced by repeated mechanical cleaning of the metal surfaces. There is, therefore, a considerable bulk of evidence (only a small part of which has been marshalled) to support the thesis that oxygen electrode reactions are seldom to be ignored.

This section is concluded by a return to the main theme of useful reference electrodes, in order to describe an electrode which is difficult to classify, but for which remarkable claims have been made. It is the iridium electrode described by Perley and Godshalk (*258*), which, according to patent specifications, gives a near-theoretical response to pH over ranges of pH 0 to 14 and temperatures from $0°$ to $70°C$, in solutions which may contain strong oxidizing agents or dissolved CO_2, SO_2, NH_3, H_2S, Cu^{2+}, Ag^+, but not hydrogen. It is unaffected by stirring, or by the presence of Li^+, Na^+ or K^+ ions, but it does show a definite ionic strength relationship. It should be used in a solution in contact with air but not in one through which oxygen is bubbled, although its potential is insensitive to wide variations of oxygen pressure. Although the electrode is of low impedance, it must be used in conjunction with a high impedance measuring circuit, or in series with a high, current-limiting resistance (10^7 ohms or more), for it cannot deal with more than 10^{-7} amp cm^{-2} without polarizing. For a supposedly reversible electrode this is a surprising disability, but since the authors' claims for this electrode are so outstanding and their reports are not very accessible, it may be in order to describe the preparative methods in some detail.

The choice of base metal, or its method of mounting, is not critical, but it must be cleaned first with soap and water, lightly burnished and cleaned again, finally by cathodic polarization at 0.2 to 0.3 amp cm^{-2} for ten minutes in hot 0.05 M trisodium phosphate solution. It is then thoroughly washed, and stored in distilled water. The iridium plating solution is prepared by adding 15 ml of 95% ethanol to a solution of 1.3 gm of H_2IrCl_6 in 100 ml of water and boiling until the color changes from red to brown to black. The solution is further boiled to expel excess of ethanol, filtered and made up to 100 ml with water; 8.4 ml of concentrated hydrochloric acid are then added to bring the total HCl concentration to 1 M. For the plating, a carbon anode is preferred, prepared by cleaning, soaking in aqua regia for twelve hours, and washing with distilled water. It is carried out for 2–3 hours at room temperature at a current density of 1.5 ma cm^{-2}, with constant stirring. A bright iridium deposit, containing no occluded hydrogen, is obtained in this way. It is essential that it should be nonporous, and thus not allow any contact between the base metal and the solution. To ensure this, it is best to carry out a series of electrodepositions, with cleaning and burnishing operations between. Satisfactory iridium can also be made by high vacuum sputtering or evaporation.

The authors mention that rhodium and perhaps ruthenium and osmium can be used in the same way. It is not obvious how these electrodes work. The Perley and Godshalk electrode has an $E°$ value of about 0.97 volt, somewhat higher than the value given for the Ir, IrO$_2$ couple, 0.93 volt by Latimer (259), which suggests the intervention of some kind of adsorbed oxygen layer which the "air electrode reaction" ($E° = 1.13$ volt) might be able to sustain. The behavior is similar to that of the platinum electrodes of Bockris and Oldfield (239).

IV. Summarizing Comments

A great deal of ground has been covered in the preceding sections of this chapter, and not all of it has been reduced to an orderly state. It may therefore be useful to trace a path, as on a small-scale map, to show the salient landmarks and possible connecting routes between them. Metal–metal oxide electrodes will be the point of departure.

The basic requirements for satisfactory metal–metal oxide electrodes are largely self-evident but somewhat difficult to achieve. Thus nobility of metal and stability of oxide do not run together, and hardness and polymorphism obstruct the attainment of reproducible standard states. Chemical requirements for the oxide are that it should be amphoteric so that it may come into equilibrium with appropriate ions in solution over a wide pH range, but this must not lead to undue solubility at either extreme, nor must enhanced solubility arise from complex ion formation. The solid phase must remain invariant with no tendency for transformation to basic salt or higher oxide. The oxide must be strictly stoichiometric if the metal–oxide couple is to have a reproducible potential, but such oxides are poor conductors of electricity and, by forming passivating layers, are likely to stifle the electrochemical equilibria needed to sustain reversibility of operation. On the other hand, a well-conducting oxide film is usually nonstoichiometric, and all the oxide electrodes capable of passing considerable currents are derived from metals of variable valency. A mechanism then operates for keeping the oxide layer from attaining any one definite valency state, so the electrode potential is variable.

In the face of these difficulties, most of the metal–oxide electrodes used for pH indication are empirically attained compromises, and nearly all of them operate by means of an invisible, limiting oxide film, although excess oxide which is not really part of the electrochemical system at all, may accumulate as an undesirable corrosion product. Whether such invisible films bear any relation in their properties to the bulk-phase oxides (and there is evidence that this is not the case) is in doubt, for most of these electrodes have potentials which are more positive than the thermodynamic values for other reasons. These are associated with their use in oxygen-containing solutions, in which oxygen consumption occurs and corrosion of the metal substrate proceeds. The corrosion may be general, proceeding by ion and electron transfer through a semiconducting oxide film, but, probably in most cases, heterogeneity of metal surfaces favors local action corrosion. In this, oxygen consumption occurs at cathodic, oxide-covered areas, and metal dissolution takes place at localized anodic areas. The electrode then comes under mixed control; its potential is a reaction potential, which varies with time, conditions of oxygenation and stirring, and has a temperature coefficient which constitutes a problem in reaction kinetics rather than in thermodynamics. But there is some doubt whether this local action theory, sound in principle though it is thought to be, is enough. A general reason for this doubt is that all these electrodes are admittedly metal–metal-oxide–oxygen mixed electrodes, and are only likely to be fully understood in the light of all that is known about the mechanistically complicated oxygen electrode. A special reason is that so many of them (As, Sb, Bi, W, Mo, Te, etc.) show about the *same* positive deviation, in aerated solutions, from the proper metal–metal oxide potentials, and this has prompted the suggestion that there is a common explanation, namely the adsorption of oxygen molecules upon oxide layers at which cathodic reduction of oxygen is hindered. No very direct evidence for this exists, and the possibility must be faced that, since these oxides are all, in principle at least, semiconductors, phenomena concerned with special surface states, as yet not fully investigated, may be concerned.

Turning to the oxygen electrode, we find a multiplicity of reaction paths, beset with activation energy barriers which seem to operate in a differential and highly characteristic way for each metal, or metal oxide, surface, but the outstanding fact is that hydrogen peroxide is an ubiquitous intermediate. The catalytic decomposition of this compound is an electrochemical reaction, initiated at an electrode surface by electron transfer in either direction, and is liable to set off reaction chains in which free radicals are involved. There is evidence that these radicals are strongly adsorbed at the surfaces of metals, and probably at those of oxides as well. Other suggestions have been made to the effect that there is a special kind of association between oxygen and metal surfaces; adsorbed atoms which lie in activity between free atoms and those combined in oxide films; adsorbed O_2 entities which easily equilibrate with peroxide in solution. All these suggestions lack more than inferential evidence to support them, no doubt because of the difficulty of examining metal–solution interfaces. Probably in the single case of silver there can be no doubt about the distinction between such a special kind of association and oxide film formation.

It is clear that metal–metal oxide electrodes need to be reconsidered in the light of these facts and theories concerning the oxygen electrode. A very definite link is provided by the demonstrated intervention of hydrogen peroxide in spontaneous corrosion reactions, and by the admitted fact that most of the metal–metal oxide electrodes are corroding systems. Further progress in elucidation of the link is awaited.

V. Metal–Metal Sulfide Electrodes

A. General Consideration

On chemical grounds, considerable differences are to be expected between the electrochemistry of the sulfur system and that of the oxygen system, already discussed. It is, however, somewhat surprising that the reversibility found for the sulfur–sulfide ion electrode in certain fused salt systems (260) extends to aqueous solutions. Thus, Allen and Hickling (261, 262) have reported that an unattackable electrode in an aqueous solution containing sodium hydroxide, sodium sulfide and dissolved sulfur assumes, in absence of air, a reproducible potential consistent with the relation,

$$E = -0.522 + 0.029 \log C_S - 0.058 \log C_{Na_2S}$$

at 25°C, over a wide range of concentrations of sulfur, C_S, and of sulfide, C_{Na_2S}. On polarization, current flow accurately follows a Tafel law consistent with rate-limitation by slow discharge. The whole behavior indicates that only the processes

$$S + S^{2-} \rightleftharpoons S_2^{2-}; \qquad S_2^{2-} + 2e^- \rightleftharpoons 2S^{2-}$$

are involved, except that higher polysulfide ions participate with rising C_S. It appears, however, that the chemical potential of sulfur in the ions S_n^{2-} is nearly independent of n for values between 2 and 4 (263), so that the sulfur behaves just like "dissolved sulfur." This simplicity stands in welcome contrast to the complications of the oxygen electrode. It is not, however, preserved if oxygen is *also* involved, as reference to the "potential–pH diagram of sulfur" indicates (264).

For practical application, interest centers in metal–metal sulfide electrodes which are hoped to respond theoretically to sulfide (or hydrosulfide) ion activity in aqueous solution. How closely real electrodes can be made to approach this ideal will depend largely on the properties of metallic sulfides. There is a wealth of thermodynamic data (mainly determined nonelectrochemically) concerning them because of their importance in large-scale pyrometallurgical processes (265), so that the potential to be expected for any likely metal–metal sulfide couple can readily be calculated. But, in comparison with oxides, the properties of sulfides are not at all favorable to attainment of satisfactory electrode systems of this kind. Thus, the S^{2-} ion is larger and more deformable than O^{2-}, so that metal–sulfur bonds tend to be less ionic in character than the corresponding metal–oxygen bonds. In general, sulfides of metals tend to be covalent and many of them (particularly the sulfides of transitional metals) show a pronounced trend towards metallic bonding. This trend is seen in the occurrence of sequences of phases, such as Co_9S_8, CoS, Co_3S_4, CoS_2, in variability of composition, metallic luster, electrical conductance, and in miscibility with metals and each other. Thus, we are, in general, provided with nonstoichiometric semiconductors for the essential nonmetallic phases of the desired electrode systems, with disadvantages already discussed (this chapter, Section I,D).

It is interesting that many sulfides are well enough conducting to replace altogether the normal metallic phase of a metal–metal ion electrode, and are controlled in potential by the activity of the appropriate metal ions in solution in conformity with a Nernst equation. According to Noddack (266), the solid phase can be regarded as a sort of diluted metal and the sulfur plays no part in the electrode processes. There is, of course, a difference from the normal electrode system in that no extensive process can occur in either direction without an alteration in the composition of the electrode surface. Since variability in composition is a characteristic property of these sulfides, this is no bar to the establishment of a considerable exchange process, ions in solution, for example, popping in and out of cation vacancies (267). The metallic sulfides thus have their own electrochemical series, quite different from that of the parent metals. It might be though that this could be predicted, and dealt with quantitatively, on a straightforward thermodynamic basis, but this appears not to be the case; although some of the assumptions involved may be questionable (e.g. that the sulfur is totally inert electrochemically), it does seem to be demonstrable that the sulfides have their own electrochemical properties which cannot be predicted on any simple basis.

Attempts have nevertheless been made to use reversible cells incorporating metal–metal sulfide electrodes to secure thermodynamic data on sulfides. Thus for silver, cuprous, lead and stannous sulfides, Kapustinsky and Makolkin (268) used cells such as

H$_2$S, 1 atm | Cu$_2$S | HCl, m ⋮ HCl, m | Pt, H$_2$, 1 atm

the two half-cell solutions being maintained in equilibrium, respectively, with hydrogen sulfide and with hydrogen. The cell reaction is

$$2Cu + H_2S = Cu_2S + H_2$$

so that the emf of the cell does not depend on the concentration of electrolyte. Each sulfide electrode had to be prepared by a highly individual method; the cuprous sulfide was obtained as a "convenient molten chunk" after fusion with excess sulfur at 1150°C. It is doubtful whether such a method is suitable for the purpose, and still more whether it was justified to use essentially *sulfide* electrodes of which the parent metal was not a component, for the presence of the metal would appear to be a thermodynamic necessity. The measured emf's, at three different temperatures, showed fluctuations not exceeding 0.006 volt. With later results from the same school (*269, 270*), the data are summarized (for 25°C alone) in Table IV, and compared with values derived from critically selected thermodynamic data (*2*).

TABLE IV

OBSERVED AND CALCULATED POTENTIALS OF M | MS | H$_2$S ELECTRODES

Sulfide	Ag$_2$S	Cu$_2$S	PbS	SnS	CdS	ZnS	HgS
E (observed, volt)	−0.0362	−0.2467	−0.2850	−0.2566	−0.5445	−0.8387	−0.0569
E (calcd, volts at 25°C)	−0.0319	−0.275	−0.3092	−0.256	−0.557	−0.863	−0.0820

Although the basis of comparison cannot be regarded as unassailable, it is evident that, except in two cases, the agreement is rather poor. It is considered that only electrodes based on silver or mercury merit more detailed consideration at the present time.

B. THE SILVER–SILVER SULFIDE ELECTRODE

Silver sulfide exists in two forms, α and β, with a transition temperature at 178°C. The α form, stable at higher temperatures, contains silver ions arranged at random in the interstices of a cubic body-centered lattice of anions. The β-form is an n-type semiconductor, and well-defined amounts of silver can be added to, or removed from it in a cell (*271*),

Ag | AgI | Ag$_2$S | Pt

It has a solubility product of 6.2×10^{-52} at 25°C, and from this it is immediately obvious that if the silver–silver sulfide electrode is to be regarded as an electrode of the second kind, it cannot possibly operate by means of the classical mechanism. It is therefore perhaps unjustifiable, on all counts, to try to anticipate how such electrodes are likely to perform.

It turns out that the silver–silver sulfide electrode is reasonably well-behaved. Noyes and Freed (272) studied the cell

Ag | Ag$_2$S | HCl, m, satd. with H$_2$S, 1 atm ⋮ HCl, m | Pt, H$_2$ 1 atm

using electrodes prepared in various ways. For use in 0.1 M hydrochloric acid, they were made by dipping platinum spirals, coated with porous silver by thermal decomposition of silver oxide paste, into an aqueous solution of hydrogen sulfide. For use in 0.5 M HCl, the wires were coated first with silver iodide, which was converted to sulfide in the same manner. Solid silver sulfide, precipitated from silver nitrate solution, was added to the half-cell solution, through which hydrogen sulfide was bubbled. This gas, required to be adequately pure, was made by heating magnesium hydrosulfide solution. This in turn was prepared by passing ordinary hydrogen sulfide into a cold suspension in water of carbonate-free magnesia. The results for the cell emf are shown in the tabulation.

Temperature (°C)	5°	10°	25°	35°
emf (volts)	0.03805	0.03767	0.03658	0.0357

These results were confirmed within about 0.4 mv by those of Makolkin (270) and Kimura (273), namely, 0.0362 volt and 0.0368 volt respectively at 25°C. Later measurements by Goates, Cole, and Gray (274), who used platinum spirals plated with silver (from 4% silver nitrate solution), then anodized in 1 m sodium sulfide solution, or treated with hydrogen sulfide in solution for several minutes, tended to "cross over" the results of the earlier workers. Their emf values are tabulated below.

Temperature (°C)	5°	25°	45°
emf (volts)	0.0382	0.0362	0.0340

These results gave rise to a temperature coefficient of -1.04×10^{-4} volt deg^{-1} as compared with -0.81×10^{-4} (272) and -0.80×10^{-4} (270) volt deg^{-1} at 25°C. Perhaps the best assessment of this quantity based on nonelectrochemical data is in terms of ΔS for the cell reaction, which is -2.5 cal deg^{-1}, leading to -0.53×10^{-4} volt deg^{-1} for the temperature coefficient of the emf. The correlation is very poor in either case, and perhaps this emphasized that electrodes of this kind must be empirically characterized for useful purposes.

The emf of this cell, of which a mean value of 0.0364 ± 0.00025 volt at 25°C might be adopted, is not of course the standard potential of the silver–silver sulfide electrode. This was determined by the last named workers using the cell

$$\text{Ag} \mid \text{Ag}_2\text{S} \mid \text{Na}_2\text{S}, m \parallel N \text{ calomel}$$

with only four molalities of sodium sulfide. Corrections were applied for the hydrolysis of the sulfide ion, using $K = 1.0 \times 10^{-15}$ for the first dissociation constant of hydrogen sulfide and $K_w = 10^{-14}$ for the ionic product of water. Activities were calculated from analytical concentrations by use of the Debye-Hückel equation. The results lead to

$$E^\circ_{\text{Ag,Ag}_2\text{S,S}^{2-}} = -0.7125 \pm 0.0004 \text{ abs volt at 25°C}$$

A more recent result due to Freyberger and de Bruyn (275), who used silver-plated platinum wires anodized in sodium sulfide solution, is -0.7180 ± 0.0035 volt at 22.5°C. It is somewhat disconcerting that Golding (276) has recently stated the electrode does not follow the proper Nernst relationship; while reproducible enough to determine sulfide ion activities in alkaline solution, it requires calibration and cannot be regarded as thermodynamically reversible. Although it is remarkable that this should have been overlooked by previous workers, the position must be accepted as uncertain.

C. THE MERCURY–MERCURIC SULFIDE ELECTRODE

Mercurous sulfide is obtained in precipitation reactions but at once disproportionates completely, no doubt because of the great insolubility of mercuric sulfide ($K_S = 9 \times 10^{-52}$ at 25°C). The stable couple is therefore mercury–mercuric sulfide. There are, however, two forms of mercuric sulfide; red (cinnabar) and black. The latter has the zinc blende structure, but, because of the tendency of mercury to form two strong covalent bonds, it passes over into the distorted rock-salt structure of cinnabar. Since this is the more stable form (ΔG° equals -11.67 kcal, as compared with -11.05 kcal for the black modification), it should, in principle, be used to prepare electrodes. This was done by Makolkin in the work mentioned previously (270); the mercuric sulfide was obtained by heating at 50–60°C a solution of mercuric chloride which had been treated first with an excess of aqueous ammonia and then, without filtering, an excess of sodium thiosulfate solution. His results for the hydrogen sulfide cell are tabulated below.

Temperature (°C)	15°	25°	35°
emf (volts)	0.0628	0.0569	0.0525

The temperature coefficient appears to vary rapidly over this range and the value at 25°C, -0.00050 volt deg^{-1}, is again greater than that calculated from entropy data, i.e., -0.00039 volt deg^{-1}.

Goates, Cole, and Gray (*277*) studied the same cell using black sulfide generated by the direct action of hydrogen sulfide on mercury and obtained on emf of 0.0504 ± 0.009 abs volt at 25°C, not in good agreement with 0.0685 volt calculated from selected thermodynamic data. It is, however, lower than Makolkin's result for the red sulfide, which is the correct relationship for the relative stabilities.

Experiments were also carried out with the cell

$$\text{Hg} \mid \text{HgS} \mid \text{Na}_2\text{S}, m \parallel N \text{ calomel}$$

Measurements were quite elaborately corrected for hydrolysis and converted to the ideal molality scale by use of activity coefficients from a Debye-Hückel calculation, finally yielding a standard free energy of formation of mercuric sulfide of $\Delta G°$ equals -10.5 ± 0.07 kcal at 25°C. The standard potential of the electrode was not quoted, but may be calculated as

$$E°_{\text{Hg,HgS,S}^{2-}} = -0.661 \pm 0.0015 \text{ volt at } 25°C$$

There is a discrepancy of about 25 mv with the value to be expected from accepted thermodynamic data.

The final comments may be made that metals like silver and mercury, directly attacked by sulfide ions, are likely to show nonthermodynamic reaction potentials in all media containing these ions. In any case, it is unlikely that a significant exchange reaction involving sulfide ion could be supported by any mechanism satisfying thermodynamic requirements, except approximately, because of the extreme insolubility of the sulfides. It is no doubt this property which makes many electrode systems very sensitive to traces of sulfur-containing impurities (*278*).

References*

1. Kobayashi, Y., Akai, N. and Furukawa, S., *J. Sci. Hiroshima Univ.* 5, 57 (1934).
2. Rossini, F. D., Wagman, D. D., Evans, W. H., Levine, S., and Jaffe, I., Selected values of chemical-thermodynamic properties. *Natl. Bur. Standards Circ.* **No. 500** (1952).
3. Latimer, W. M., "Oxidation Potentials," 2nd ed. Prentice-Hall, New York, 1952.

* *Note:* The following abbreviations have been used in this bibliography: *CITCE*, Proceedings of the International Committee of Electrochemical Thermodynamics and Kinetics; *CEBELCOR RT.*, Rapport Technique du Centre Belge pour l'Etude de la Corrosion, Brussels.

4. Perley, G. A., *Ind. Eng. Chem. Anal. Ed.* **11**, 316 (1939).

5. Brönsted, J. N., *Kgl. Danske Videnskab Selskab, Math. fys. Medd.* **3**, No. 9 (1920).

6. Güntelberg, E., *Z. physik. Chem.* **123**, 199 (1926).

7. Evans, U. R., "Metallic Corrosion, Passivity and Protection," 2nd ed. Arnold, London, 1946.

8. Cabrera, N., and Mott, N. F., *Repts. Progr. in Physics* **12**, 163 (1949).

9. Hoar, T. P., in "Modern Aspects of Electrochemistry" (J. O'M. Bockris, ed.), Vol. 2, Chapter 4. Academic Press, New York, 1959.

10. Mott, N. F., *Trans. Faraday Soc.* **43**, 429 (1947).

11. Garner, W. E., Stone, F. S., and Tiley, P. F., *Proc. Roy. Soc.* **A211**, 472 (1952).

12. Grimley, T. B., in "Chemistry of the Solid State," (W. E. Garner, ed.), Chapter 14. Academic Press, New York, 1955.

13. Lynes, W., *J. Electrochem. Soc.* **103**, 467 (1956).

14. Maxwell, K. H., and Thirsk, H. R., *J. Chem. Soc.* 4057 (1955).

15. Brown, D. J., and Liebhafsky, H. A., *J. Am. Chem. Soc.* **52**, 2595 (1930).

16. Maxwell, K. H., and Thirsk, H. R., *J. Chem. Soc.* 4054 (1955).

17. Hills, S., and Vosburgh, W. C., *J. Electrochem. Soc.* **104**, 5 (1957).

18. Vosburgh, W. C., *J. Electrochem. Soc.* **106**, 839 (1959).

19. Kozawa, A., *J. Electrochem. Soc.* **106**, 79 (1959).

20. Briggs, G. W. D., Jones, E., and Wynne-Jones, W. F. K., *Trans. Faraday Soc.* **51**, 1433 (1955).

21. Jones, E., and Wynne-Jones, W. F. K., *Trans. Faraday Soc.* **52**, 1260 (1956).

22. Briggs, G. W. D., and Wynne-Jones, W. F. K., *Trans. Faraday Soc.* **52**, 1272 (1956).

23. Conway, B. E., and Bourgault, F. E., *Can. J. Chem.* **37**, 292 (1959).

24. Tödt, F., Freier, R., and Schwarz, W., *Z. Elektrochem.* **53**, 132 (1949).

25. Tourky, A. R., and El Wakkad, S. E. S., *J. Chem. Soc.* 740 (1948).

26. Tourky, A. R., and Khairy, E. M., *J. Chem. Soc.* 2626 (1952).

27. Rawson, A. E., private communication, 1959.

28. Pourbaix, M. J. N., "Thermodynamics of Dilute Aqueous Systems," p. 53. Arnold, London, 1949.

29. Delahay, P., Pourbaix, M., and Van Rysselberghe, P., *J. Electrochem. Soc.* **98**, 65 (1951); *Proc. 2nd Meeting CITCE, Milan, 1950.*

30. Hickling, A., *Trans. Faraday Soc.* **41**, 333 (1945).

31. Nagel, K., Ohse, R., and Lange, E., *Z. Elektrochem.* **61**, 795 (1957).

32. Hickling, A., and Taylor, D., *Discussions Faraday Soc.* **1**, 277 (1947).

33. Jones, P., Thirsk, H. R., and Wynne-Jones, W. F. K., *Trans. Faraday Soc.* **52**, 1003 (1956).

34. Göhr, H., and Lange, E., *Z. physik. Chem. (Frankfurt)* **17**, 100 (1958).

35. Buehrer, T. F., Wartman, F. S., and Nugent, R. L., *J. Am. Chem. Soc.* **49**, 1271 (1927).

36. Hickling, A., *Trans. Faraday Soc.* **42**, 518 (1946).

37. Gerke, R. H., and Rourke, M. D., *J. Am. Chem. Soc.* **49**, 1855 (1927).

38. Buehrer, T. F., and Roseveare, W. E., *J. Am. Chem. Soc.* **49**, 1989 (1927).

39. Luther, R., and Pokorny, F., *Z. anorg. u. allgem. Chem.* **57**, 290 (1908).

40. Hamer, W. J., and Craig, D. N., *J. Electrochem. Soc.* **104**, 206 (1957).

41. Dirkse, T. P., *J. Electrochem. Soc.* **106**, 453 (1959).

42. Sidgwick, N. V., "The Chemical Elements and Their Compounds," p. 292. Oxford Univ. Press, London and New York, 1950.

43. Fricke, R., and Ackerman, P., *Z. anorg. u. allgem. Chem.* **211**, 233 (1933).

44. Garrett, A. B., and Hirschler, A. E., *J. Am. Chem. Soc.* **60**, 299 (1938).

45. Brönsted, J. N., *Z. physik. Chem.* **65**, 84, 744 (1909).

46. Lewis, G. N., and Randall, M., "Thermodynamics," p. 408. McGraw-Hill, New York, 1923.

47. Donnan, F. G., and Allmand, A. J., *J. Chem. Soc.* **99**, 845 (1911).

48. Ming Chow, *J. Am. Chem. Soc.* **42**, 488 (1920).

49. Mujamoto, S., *Sci. Papers Inst. Phys. Chem. Research (Tokyo)* **1** (4), 31 (1922).

50. Fried, F., *Z. physik. Chem.* **123**, 406 (1926).

51. Ishikawa, F., Kimura, G., Sexagint, Y. Osaka, *Chem. Inst. Dept. Sci. Kyoto Imp. Univ.* 255 (1927).

52. Shibata, F. L. E., and Murata, F., *J. Chem. Soc. (Japan)* **52**, 399 (1931).

53. Shibata, F. L. E., Kobayashi, Y., and Furukawa, S., *J. Chem. Soc. (Japan)* **52**, 404 (1931).

54. Kobayashi, Y., and Wang, H. L., *J. Sci. Hiroshima Univ.* **5A**, 71 (1934).

55. Hills, G. J., private communication, 1957.

56. Samuelson, G. J., and Brown, D. J., *J. Am. Chem. Soc.* **57**, 2711 (1935).

57. El Wakkad, S. E. S., and Salem, T. M., *J. Phys. Chem.* **54**, 1371 (1950).

58. El Wakkad, S. E. S., and Salem, T. M., *J. Phys. Chem.* **56**, 621 (1952).

59. Uhl, A., and Kestranek, W., *Monatsh. Chem.* **44**, 29 (1923).

60. Glasstone, S., "The Electrochemistry of Solutions," 2nd ed., p. 384. Methuen, London, 1937.

61. Stock, J. T., Purdy, W. C., and Garcia, L. M., *Chem. Revs.* **58**, 611 (1958).

62. Mehta, D. N., and Jatkar, S. K. K., *J. Indian Inst. Sci.* **18A**, 85 (1935).

63. Roberts, E. J., and Fenwick, F., *J. Am. Chem. Soc.* **50**, 2125 (1928).

64. Parks, L. R., and Beard, H. C., *J. Am. Chem. Soc.* **54**, 856 (1932).

65. Ball, T. R., Schmidt, W. B., and Bergstresser, K. S., *Ind. Eng. Chem. Anal. Ed.* **6**, 60 (1934).

66. Kolthoff, I. M., and Hartong, B. D., *Rec. trav. chim.* **44**, 113 (1925).

67. Britton, H. T. S., and Robinson, R. A., *J. Chem. Soc.* 458 (1931).

68. Avseevich, G. P., and Zhukov, I. I., *Z. Elektrochem.* **35**, 349 (1929); **37**, 771 (1931).

69. Harrison, W. H., and Vridhachalam, P. N., *Mem. Dept. Agr. India, Chem. Ser.* **10**, 157 (1929).

70. Schuhmann, R., *J. Am. Chem. Soc.* **46**, 52 (1924).

71. Pitman, A. L., Pourbaix, M., and de Zoubov, N., *Proc. 9th Meeting CITCE*, p. 32. Butterworths, London, 1959; *CEBELCOR RT.* 55, Brussels, 1957; *J. Electrochem. Soc.* **104**, 594 (1957).

72. Grube, G., and Schweigardt, F., *Z. Elektrochem.* **29**, 257 (1923).

73. Tammann, G., *Rec. trav. chim.* **44**, 113 (1925).

74. Güntherschulze, A., *Z. Physik.* **36**, 563 (1926).

75. Franke, K. W., and Willaman, J. J., *Ind. Eng. Chem.* **20**, 87 (1928).

76. Snyder, E. F., *Soil Sci.* **26**, 107 (1928).

77. El Wakkad, S. E. S., *J. Chem. Soc.* 2894 (1950).

78. Hovorka, F., and Chapman, G. J., *J. Am. Chem. Soc.* **63**, 955 (1941).

79. Hovorka, F., and Schoenfeld, F. K. (unpublished); Schoenfeld, F. K., Thesis, Western Reserve University, 1937.

80. King, N. J., *Ind. Eng. Chem. Anal. Ed.* **5**, 323 (1933).

81. Perley, C. A., *Ind. Eng. Chem. Anal. Ed.* **11**, 316, 319 (1939).

82. Fischbeck, K., and Eimer, F., *Z. Elektrochem.* **44**, 845 (1938).

83. Simon, A., and Thaler, E., *Z. anorg. u. allgem. Chem.* **162**, 253 (1927).

84. Wells, A. F., "Structural Inorganic Chemistry," p. 502. Oxford Univ. Press, London and New York, 1950.

85. El Wakkad, S. E. S., and Hickling, A., *J. Phys. Chem.* **57**, 203 (1953).

86. El Wakkad, S. E. S., *J. Chem. Soc.* 2894 (1950).

87. Tourky, A. R., and Moussa, A. A., *J. Chem. Soc.* 756 (1948).

88. Gatty, O., and Spooner, E. C. R., "The Electrode Potential Behaviour of Corroding Metals in Aqueous Solutions," p. 331. Oxford Univ. Press, London and New York, 1938.

89. Kauko, Y., and Knappsberg, L., *Z. Elektrochem.* **45**, 760 (1939).

90. Hoar, T. P., *in* "Modern Aspects of Electrochemistry" (J. O'M. Bockris, ed.) Vol. 2, Chapter 4, p. 324. Academic Press, New York, 1959.

91. Wagner, C., and Traud, W., *Z. Elektrochem.* **44**, 391 (1938).

92. Tourky, A. R., and Moussa, A. A., *J. Chem. Soc.* 752 (1948).

93. Tomiyama, T., *J. Biochem. (Japan)* **18**, 285 (1933).

94. Brewer, R. E., and Montillon, G. H., *Trans. Electrochem. Soc.* **55**, 357 (1929).

95. Tourky, A. R., and Khairy, E. M., *J. Chem. Soc.* 2626 (1952).

96. Holmqvist, A., *Svensk. Kem. Tidskr.* **47**, 102 (1935).

97. Fenwick, F., and Gilman, E., *J. Biol. Chem.* **84**, 605 (1929).

98. Brinkman, R., and Buijtendijk, F. J. J., *Biochem. Z.* **199**, 387 (1929).

99. Zhukov, I. I., and Avseevich, G. P., *Z. Elektrochem.* **35**, 349 (1929).

100. Kolthoff, I. M., and Furman, N. H., "Potentiometric Titrations." Wiley, New York, 1926.

101. Ball, T. R., *Trans. Electrochem. Soc.* **72**, 139 (1937).

102. Shcherbakov, A. A., *Zhur. Anal. Khim.* **6**, 157 (1951).

103. Wulff, P., Kordatzki, W., and Ehrenberg, W., *Z. Elektrochem.* **41**, 542 (1935).

104. Levin, I., *Chemist Analyst* **41**, 89 (1952).

105. Stock, J. T., and Purdy, W. C., *Chemist Analyst* **47**, 43 (1958).

106. Thompson, F. C., and Brudevold, F., *J. Dental Research* **33**, 849 (1954).

107. Harrison, W. H., and Vridhachalam, P. N., *Mem. Dept. Agr. India, Chem. Ser.* **10**, 157 (1929).

108. Vogel, J. C., *J. Soc. Chem. Ind.* **49**, 297 (1930).

109. Böttger, W., and Szebellédy, L. V., *Z. Elektrochem.* **38**, 737 (1932).

110. Tomiyama, T., *J. Biochem. (Japan)* **18**, 285 (1933).

111. Britton, H. T. S., "Hydrogen Ions," 4th ed. Chapman and Hall, London, 1955.

112. Greer, W. N., *Trans. Electrochem. Soc.* **72**, 153 (1937).

113. Haggard, H. W., and Greenberg, L. A., *Science*, **93**, 479 (1941).

114. Charlton, C., *Australian Dental J.* 228 (1956).

115. Izmaïlov, N. A., Vail, E. I., Aleksandrova, A. M., and Gurevich, E. L., *Uchenye Zapiski Khark. Univ.* **50**, 11 (1954).

116. Martinez de Murguia, J. A.-T., *An. fis. y quím. (Madrid)* **42**, 189 (1945).

117. Afans'ev, S. K., Portnov, M. A., and Chepelkin, Y. N., *J. Appl. Chem. (U.S.S.R.)*, **10**, 1421 (1937).

118. Deribere, M., *Rev. gén. mat. plastiques* **10**, 197 (1934).

119. Leclerc, E., *Bull. assoc. ing. elec. (Liege)* **10**, 210 (1932).

120. Wulff, P., *Fette u. Seifen* **48**, 388 (1941).

121. Pleass, W. B., *Arch. phys. biol.* **9**, 267 (1932).

122. Smelik, J., and Habinger, H., *Prakt. Chem.* **4**, 130 (1953).

123. Puri, A. N., *Mem. Punjab Irrigation Research Inst.* **4**, 11 (1932).

124. Itano, A., *Ber. Ōhara Inst. landwirtsch. Forsch. Okayama Univ.* **4**, 273 (1929).

125. Schollenberger, C. J., *Soil Sci.* **41**, 123 (1936).

126. Barnes, E. E., and Simon, R. H., *J. Am. Soc. Agron.* **24**, 156 (1932).

127. Best, R. J., *J. Agr. Sci.* **21**, 337 (1931).

128. Du Toit, M. S., *S. African J. Sci.* **27**, 227 (1930).

129. Hock, A., *Bodenk. u. Pflanzenernähr.* **27**, 370 (1942).

130. Lindeman, J., *Meld. Norg. Landbrukshøiskole* **6**, 302 (1926).

131. Bodforss, S., and Holmqvist, A., *Z. physik. Chem.* **A161**, 61 (1932).

132. Uemura, T., and Sueda, H., *Bull. Chem. Soc. Japan* **8**, 1 (1933).

133. Bravo, G. A., *Chim. e ind. (Milan)* **17**, 521 (1935).

134. Lava, V. G., and Hemedes, E. D., *Philippine Agriculturist* **17**, 337 (1928).

135. Stock, J. T., and Purdy, W. C., *Chem. Revs.* **57**, 1159 (1957).

136. Mehta, D. N., and Jatkar, S. K. K., *J. Indian Inst. Sci.* **18A**, 109 (1935).

137. Van Muylder, J., and Pourbaix, M., *Proc. 9th Meeting CITCE, Paris, 1957*, p. 47. Butterworths, London, 1959; *CEBELCOR RT.* 48, 1957.

138. Dickinson, H. O., and Rudge, E. A., *J. Soc. Chem. Ind. (London)* **68**, 101 (1949).

139. Schwabe, v. K., *Z. Elektrochem.* **53**, 125 (1949).

140. Harbaugh, M., and Mathers, F. C., *Trans. Electrochem. Soc.* **64**, 293 (1933).

141. Chateau, H., *J. chim. phys.* **51**, 590 (1954).

142. Schwabe, K., and Philipp, B., *Z. Elektrochem.* **55**, 411 (1951).

143. Granér, F., and Sillén, L. G., *Acta Chem. Scand.* **1**, 631 (1947).

144. Sillén, L. G., *Quart. Revs. (London)* **13**, 146 (1959).

145. Kriventsova, B. A., and Shatalov, A. Y., *Zhur. Fiz. Khim.* **27**, 1476 (1953).

146. Sammour, H. M., and Moussa, A. A., *J. Chem. Soc.* 1762 (1958).

147. Noyes, A. A., and Ming Chow, *J. Am. Chem. Soc.* **40**, 739 (1918).

148. Sidgwick, N. V., "The Chemical Elements and Their Compounds," p. 803. Oxford Univ. Press, London and New York, 1950.

149. Schuhmann, R., *J. Am. Chem. Soc.* **46**, 1444 (1924).

150. Anderson, E., and Story, L. G., *J. Am. Chem. Soc.* **45**, 1102 (1923).

151. Van Muylder, J., and Pourbaix, M., *CITCE IX, Paris, 1957;* Butterworths, London, 1959, p. 20; *CEBELCOR RT.* 46, 1957.

152. Tourky, A. R., and Moussa, A. A., *J. Chem. Soc.* 1297 (1949).

153. Tourky, A. R., and Moussa, A. A., *J. Chem. Soc.* 1302 (1949).

154. Gatty, O., and Spooner, E. C. R., "The Electrode Potential Behavior of Corroding Metals in Aqueous Solutions," p. 367. Oxford Univ. Press, London and New York, 1938.

155. Moussa, A. A., *Analyst* **76**, 96 (1951).

156. Tourky, A. R., and Moussa, A. A., *J. Chem. Soc.* 1305 (1949).

157. Gatty, O., and Spooner, E. R. C., "The Electrode Potential Behavior of Corroding Metals in Aqueous Solutions," p. 371. Oxford Univ. Press, London and New York, 1938.

158. Baylis, J. R., *Ind. Eng. Chem.* **15**, 852 (1923).

159. Holven, A. L., *Ind. Eng. Chem.* **21**, 965 (1929).

160. Britton, H. T. S., and Dodd, E. N., *J. Chem. Soc.* 829 (1931).

161. Abichandani, C. T., and Jatkar, S. K. K., *J. Indian Inst. Sci.* **21A**, 345 (1938).

162. Brintzinger, H., and Rost, B., *Z. anal. Chem.* **120**, 161 (1940).

163. Shatalov, A. Y., and Marshakov, I. A., *Zhur. Fiz. Khim.* **28**, 42 (1954).

164. Deltombe, E., de Zoubov, N., and Pourbaix, M., *CITCE VIII*, p. 250, Madrid, 1956, Butterworths, London, 1958; *CEBELCOR RT.* 32, 1956.

165. Wells, A. F., "Structural Inorganic Chemistry," p. 367. Oxford Univ. Press, London and New York, 1950.

166. El Wakkad, S. E. S., Rizk, H. A., and Ebaid, J. G., *J. Phys. Chem.* **59**, 1005 (1955).

167. El Wakkad, S. E. S., Salem, T. M., Rizk, H. A., and Ebaid, J. G., *J. Chem. Soc.* p. 3776 (1957).

168. Deltombe, E., de Zoubov, N., and Pourbaix, M., CITCE VIII, Madrid, 1956, Butterworths, London, 1958, p. 238; *CEBELCOR RT.* 35, 1956.

169. Issa, I. M., and Khalifa, H., *Anal. Chim. Acta* **10**, 567 (1954).

170. Kasarnowsky, J., Z. *physik. Chem.* **109**, 287 (1924).

171. Lukas, J., and Jilek, A., *Chem. listy* **20**, 396 (1926).

172. Tomiček, O., and Poupě, F., *Collection Czechoslov. Chem. Commun.* **8**, 520 (1936).

173. De Brouwer, St., *Bull. soc. chim. Belges* **48**, 158 (1939).

174. Khalifa, H., and Issa, I. M., *J. Indian Chem. Soc.* **34**, 87 (1957).

175. Latimer, W. M., "Oxidation Potentials," 2nd ed. p. 89. Prentice-Hall, New York, 1952.

176. Tourky, A. R., Issa, I. M., and Awad, S. A., *Chim. Anal.* **37**, 367 (1955).

177. Issa, I. M., Khalifa, H., and Awad, S. A., *J. Indian Chem. Soc.* **34**, 275 (1957).

178. Charlot, G., Bézier, D., and Courtot, J., "Tables de Constantes et Données Numeriques," 8: Constantes sélectionnées potentiels d'oxydo-réduction. Pergamon, New York, 1958.

179. Deltombe, E., and Pourbaix, M., *Proc. 9th Meeting CITCE*, p. 117. Butterworths, London, 1959; *CEBELCOR RT.* 42 (1956).

180. Deltombe, E., de Zoubov, N., and Pourbaix, M., *Proc. 9th Meeting CITCE*, p. 102. Butterworths, London, 1959.

181. Delahay, P., Pourbaix, M., and Van Rysselberghe, P., *CITCE III*, p. 15. Manfredi, Milan, 1951.

182. Deltombe, E., and Pourbaix, M., *Proc. 6th Meeting CITCE*, p. 133. Butterworths, London, 1954; *CEBELCOR RT.* 3 (1953).

183. Deltombe, E., de Zoubov, N., and Pourbaix, M., *CEBELCOR RT.* 41, 1956; Pourbaix, M. J. N., "Thermodynamics of Dilute Aqueous Systems," p. 96. Arnold & Co., London, 1949.

184. Deltombe, E., and Pourbaix, M., *Proc. 6th Meeting, CITCE*, p. 153. Butterworths, London, 1954; *CEBELCOR RT.* 6 (1954).

185. Pourbaix, M., Thesis, Delft, Beranger, Paris, 1945; Ref. 28, p. 53.

186. de Zoubov, N., Deltombe, E., and Pourbaix, M., *CEBELCOR RT.* 27 (1955).

187. Delahay, P., Pourbaix, M., and Van Rysselberghe, P., *Proc. 3rd Meeting CITCE*, p. 51. Manfredi, Milan, 1951.

188. Deltombe, E., and Pourbaix, M., *Proc. 6th Meeting CITCE*, p. 118. Butterworths, London, 1954; *CEBELCOR RT.* 7, 19 (1954).

189. Delahay, P., Pourbaix, M., and Van Rysselberghe, P., *Proc. 2nd Meeting CITCE*, p. 15. Tamburini, Milan, 1950; *CEBELCOR RT.* 13 (1954).

190. Van Muylder, J., and Pourbaix, M., *Proc. 8th Meeting CITCE*, p. 218. Butterworths, London, 1958; *CEBELCOR RT.* 39 (1956).

191. Moussard, A. M., Brenet, J., Jolas, F., Pourbaix, M., and Van Muylder, J., *Proc. 6th Meeting CITCE*, p. 190. Butterworths, London, 1954; *CEBELCOR RT.* 18 (1954).

192. Delahay, P., Pourbaix, M., and Van Rysselberghe, P., *Proc. 3rd Meeting CITCE*, p. 15. Manfredi, Milan, 1951.

193. Deltombe, E., de Zoubov, N., and Pourbaix, M., *Proc. 7th Meeting CITCE*, p. 193. Butterworths, London, 1955; *CEBELCOR RT.* 23, 1955.

194. Van Muylder, J., de Zoubov, N., and Pourbaix, M., *Proc. 7th Meeting CITCE*, p. 193. Butterworths, London, 1955; *CEBELCOR RT.* 23 (1955).

195. de Zoubov, N., and Pourbaix, M., *Proc. 9th Meeting CITCE*, p. 66. Butterworths, London, 1959; *CEBELCOR RT*. 51 (1957).

196. Delahay, P., Pourbaix, M., and Van Rysselberghe, P., *Proc. 3rd Meeting CITCE*, p. 15. Manfredi, Milan, 1951.

197. Van Muylder, J., and Pourbaix, M., *Proc. 9th Meeting CITCE* p., 84. Butterworths, London, 1959; *CEBELCOR RT*. 52 (1957).

198. de Zoubov, N., and Pourbaix, M., *Proc. 9th Meeting CITCE*, p. 57. Butterworths, London, 1959; *CEBELCOR RT*. 50 (1957).

199. Deltombe, E., de Zoubov, N., and Pourbaix, M., *CEBELCOR RT*. 33 (1956).

200. Delahay, P., Pourbaix, M., and Van Rysselberghe, P., *Proc. 3rd Meeting CITCE*, p. 15. Manfredi, Milan, 1951.

201. Deltombe, E., de Zoubov, N., and Pourbaix, M., *Proc. 7th Meeting CITCE*, p. 216. Butterworths, London, 1955; *CEBELCOR RT*. 25, 1955.

202. Schmets, J., and Pourbaix, M., *Proc. 6th Meeting CITCE*, p. 167. Butterworths, London, 1954; *CEBELCOR RT*. 4 (1953).

203. Deltombe, E., de Zoubov, N., and Pourbaix, M., *Proc. 8th Meeting CITCE*, p. 258. Butterworths, London, 1958; *CEBELCOR RT*. 31 (1956).

204. Deltombe, E., de Zoubov, N., and Pourbaix, M., *CEBELCOR RT*. 29 (1956).

205. Delahay, P., Pourbaix, M., and Van Rysselberghe, P., *Proc. 2nd Meeting CITCE*, p. 34. Tamburini, Milan, 1950.

206. Maraghini, M., Van Rysselberghe, P., Deltombe, E., de Zoubov, N., and Pourbaix, M., *Proc. 9th Meeting CITCE*, p. 92. Butterworths, London, 1959; *CEBELCOR RT*. 45, 1957.

207. Delahay, P., Van Rysselberghe, P., Deltombe, E., de Zoubov, N., and Pourbaix, M., *J. Chem. Educ.* **27**, 683 (1950).

208. Pourbaix, M., *Ossature metal*. Nos. 1 and 2 (1953).

209. Green, M., in "Modern Aspects of Electrochemistry" (J. O'M. Bockris, ed.) Vol. 2, Chapter 5. Academic Press, New York, 1959.

210. Harned, H. S., and Robinson, R. A., *Trans. Faraday Soc.* **36**, 973 (1940).

211. Pourbaix, M. J. N., "Thermodynamics of Dilute Aqueous Systems," p. 38. Arnold, London, 1949.

212. Glasstone, S., "An Introduction to Electrochemistry," pp. 275, 287, 289. Van Nostrand, New York, 1942.

213. Covington, A. K., and Prue, J. E., *J. Chem. Soc.*, 3696, 3701 (1955); 1567 (1957).

214. Latimer, W. M., "Oxidation Potentials," 2nd ed., p. 39. Prentice-Hall, New York, 1952.

215. Delahay, P., Pourbaix, M., and Van Rysselberghe, P., *Proc. 2nd Meeting CITCE*, p. 42. Tamburini, Milan, 1950.

216. Evans, M. G., Hush, N. S., and Uri, N., *Quart. Revs. (London)* **6**, 186 (1952).

217. Bockris, J. O'M., *J. Chem. Phys.* **24**, 817 (1956).

218. Heyrovsky, J., *Trans. Faraday Soc.* **19**, 785 (1924).

219. Kolthoff, I. M., and Lingane, J. J., "Polarography," p. 557. Interscience, New York, 1952.

220. Frumkin, A. N., *Akad Nauk S.S.S.R.* 402 (1955).

221. Haber, F., *Z. anorg. Chem.* **51**, 245 (1906).

222. Glasstone, S., "The Electrochemistry of Solutions," 2nd ed., p. 335. Methuen, London, 1937.

223. Hoar, T. P., *Proc. Roy. Soc.* **A142**, 628 (1933).

224. Bockris, J. O'M., and Huq, A. K. M. S., *Proc. Roy. Soc.* **A237**, 277 (1956).

225. Hoar, T. P., *Proc. 8th Meeting CITCE*, p. 439. Butterworths, London, 1958.

226. Furman, N. H., *J. Am. Chem. Soc.* **44**, 2685 (1922).

227. Hildebrand, J. H., *J. Am. Chem. Soc.* **35**, 847 (1913).

228. Furman, N. H., *Ind. Eng. Chem. Anal. Ed.* **14**, 367 (1942).

229. Berl, W. G., *Trans. Electrochem. Soc.* **83**, 253 (1943).

230. Weisz, R. S., and Jaffe, S. S., *Trans. Electrochem. Soc.* **93**, 128 (1948).

231. Davies, M. O., Clark, M., Yeager, E., and Hovorka, F., *J. Electrochem. Soc.* **106**, 56 (1959).

232. Austen, D. E. G., Ingram, D. J. E., and Tapley, J. G., *Trans. Faraday Soc.* **54**, 400 (1958).

233. Moussa, A. A., Embaby, H. K., and Sammour, H. M., *J. Chem. Soc.* 2481 (1958).

234. Hickling, A., and Wilson, W. H., *J. Electrochem. Soc.* **98**, 425 (1951).

235. Humphreys, R. A., *Dissertation Abstr.* **16**, 669 (1956).

236. Weiss, J., *Trans. Faraday Soc.* **31**, 1547 (1935).

237. Flis, I. E., *Zhur. Anal. Khim.* **10**, 38 (1954).

238. Winkelman, D., *Z. Elektrochem.* **60**, 731 (1956).

239. Bockris, J. O'M., and Oldfield, L. F., *Trans. Faraday Soc.* **51**, 249 (1955).

240. Gerischer, R., and Gerischer, H., *Z. physik. Chem. (Frankfurt)* **6**, 178 (1956).

241. Haber, F., and Grinberg, S., *Z. anorg. Chem.* **18**, 37 (1898); Haber, F., *Z. physik. Chem.* **34**, 513 (1900); *Z. Elektrochem.* **7**, 44 (1901).

242. Vielstich, W., *Z. physik. Chem. (Frankfurt)* **15**, 409 (1958).

243. Giner, V. J., *Z. Elektrochem.* **63**, 386 (1959).

244. Glasstone, S., and Hickling, A., *Chem. Revs.* **25**, 407 (1939).

245. Haissinsky, M., *Discussions Faraday Soc.* **1**, 254 (1947).

246. Delahay, P., *J. Elektrochem. Soc.* **97**, 198 (1950).

247. Dunstan, W. R., Jowett, H. A. D., and Goulding, E., *J. Chem. Soc.* **87**, 1548 (1905).

248. Churchill, J. R., *Trans. Electrochem. Soc.* **76**, 341 (1939).

249. Keenan, G. L., *Chem. Revs.* **3**, 95 (1926).

250. Russell, W. J., *Proc. Roy. Soc.* **61**, 424 (1897).

251. Grunberg, L., and Wright, K. H. R., *Nature* **170**, 456 (1952).

252. Grunberg, L., *Proc. Phys. Soc.* **B66**, 153 (1953).

253. Kramer, J., *Z. Physik.* **128**, 538; **129**, 34 (1951).

254. Gobrecht, H., and Barsch, G., *Z. Physik.* **132**, 129 (1952).

255. Grunberg, L., *Research* **8**, 210 (1955); *Brit. J. Appl. Phys.* **9**, 95 (1958).

256. Haissinsky, M., *Discussions Faraday Soc.* **12**, 133 (1952).

257. Roikh, I. L., *Zhur. Fiz. Khim.* **32**, 1136 (1958).

258. Perley, G. A., and Godshalk, J. B., U. S. Patent No. 2, 416, 949; British Patent No. 567, 722, June 10, 1942.

259. Latimer, W. M., "Oxidation Potentials," 2nd ed., p. 218. Prentice-Hall, New York, 1952.

260. Rose, B. A., Davis, G. J., and Ellingham, H. J. T., *Discussions Faraday Soc.* **4**, 161 (1948).

261. Allen, P. L., and Hickling, A., *Chem. & Ind. (London)* 1558 (1954).

262. Allen, P. L., and Hickling, A., *Trans. Faraday Soc.* **53**, 1626 (1957).

263. Latimer, W. M., "Oxidation Potentials," 2nd ed., p. 72. Prentice-Hall, New York, 1952.

264. Valensi, G., *Proc. 2nd Meeting CITCE*, p. 51. Tamburini, Milan, 1951.

265. Hopkins, D. W., "Physical Chemistry and Metal Extraction." J. Garnet Miller, Ltd., London, 1954.

266. Noddack, W., Wrabetz, K., and Herbst, W., *Z. Elektrochem.* **59**, 752 (1955).

267. Wrabetz, K. E., *Z. Elektrochem.* **60**, 722 (1956).

268. Kapustinsky, A., and Makolkin, I. A., *Acta Physicochim. U.R.S.S.* **10**, 245 (1939).

269. Makolkin, I. A., *Zhur. fiz. Khim.* **14**, 429 (1940).

270. Makolkin, I. A., *Zhur. fiz. Khim.* **16**, 18 (1942).

271. Miyatani, S., *J. Phys. Soc. Japan* **10**, 786 (1955).

272. Noyes, A. A., and Freed, E. S., *J. Am. Chem. Soc.* **42**, 476 (1920).

273. Kimura, G., *Bull. Inst. Phys. Chem. Research (Tokyo)* **14**, 94 (1935).

274. Goates, R. J., Cole, A. G., Gray, E. L., and Faux, N. D., *J. Am. Chem. Soc.* **73**, 707 (1951).

275. Freyberger, W. L., and de Bruyn, P. L., *J. Phys. Chem.* **61**, 586 (1957).

276. Golding, R. M., *J. Chem. Soc.* 1838 (1959).

277. Goates, R. J., Cole, A. G., and Gray, E. L., *J. Am. Chem. Soc.* **73**, 3596 (1951).

278. Shreir, L. L., and Smith, J. W., *J. Electrochem. Soc.* **98**, 193 (1951).

Chapter Eight

Electrodes Reversible to Sulfate Ions

D. J. G. Ives and F. R. Smith

I. Introduction

In order to set up an electrode of the second kind reversible to sulfate ions, a metal must be found which is sufficiently noble and which forms a stable, unhydrolyzed, anhydrous sulfate of low solubility. That the choice is very limited is shown by Table I, which contains relevant data for the only four metals with properties at all suitable for the purpose.

TABLE I

STANDARD METAL–METAL ION POTENTIALS AND SOLUBILITIES OF METAL SULFATES

M, M^{n+}	$E^{\circ}_{M,M^{n+}}$ (1) (int volts)	Stable sulfate phase	Molality of satd soln of sulfate (2)	
Ag, Ag^+	0.799	Ag_2SO_4	0.0268	(25°C)
Hg, Hg_2^{2+}	0.798	Hg_2SO_4	0.00117	(25°C)
Pb, Pb^{2+}	−0.126	$PbSO_4$	0.000149	(25°C)
Tl, Tl^+	−0.335	Tl_2SO_4	0.0535	(20°C)

Clearly, silver and thallous sulfates are more soluble than could be desired, and this restricts electrodes based upon them to two limited applications. In the first of these, the half-cell solution is in equilibrium with the solid salt, but contains no foreign sulfate; the electrode is then no longer one of the second kind, but a reference electrode of fixed potential. It has an advantage in allowing a "common ion liquid junction" (Chapter 1, Section VI) to be formed with a solution containing a soluble sulfate, as in the cell

393

$$\text{Ag} \mid \text{Ag}_2\text{SO}_4 \text{ (s)} \mid \text{Ag}_2\text{SO}_4 \text{ (satd)} \vdots \text{K}_2\text{SO}_4 \text{ (}m\text{)} \mid \text{Hg}_2\text{SO}_4 \mid \text{Hg}$$

studied by Ishikawa and Hagisawa (*3*).

In the second application, in which the half-cell solution does contain a second, soluble, sulfate, the solution must unavoidably be treated as a mixed electrolyte and again a liquid junction will be involved. The silver–silver sulfate electrode, in direct equilibrium with dilute sulfuric acid solutions, has been used at temperatures up to 250°C (*4*), and there is good reason to suppose that it may be superior to others for operation under such extreme conditions (*5*). It may be noted that its selenium analog,

$$\text{Ag} \mid \text{Ag}_2\text{SeO}_4 \mid \text{H}_2\text{SeO}_4$$

has been used to good effect (*6*). A thallium amalgam–thallous sulfate electrode has been described (*7*) and its standard potential at 25°C (-0.4360 int volt) has been included in a compilation of electrode potentials by Gerke (*8*). These electrodes, however, are not of sufficient general utility to merit further discussion.

The solubility of mercurous sulfate causes inconvenience when sulfuric acid or sulfate solutions more dilute than about 0.05 molal are used (*9*). The solubility of lead sulfate is usually negligible even in the most dilute solutions, but it increases with rise of temperature, particularly in moderately concentrated sulfuric acid solutions (*10*).

Mercurous sulfate has a tendency to hydrolyze which has, however, been overemphasized (*11, 12*). This tendency increases with rise of temperature (*9*) and is perhaps enhanced by the disproportionation reaction which is favored by the weakness of the Hg—Hg bond (*13*). Continued washing with water at room temperature produces a greenish-yellow basic salt, $\text{Hg}_2\text{O} \cdot \text{Hg}_2\text{SO}_4 \cdot \text{H}_2\text{O}$ (*9*), but sulfuric acid of molality exceeding 0.0013 mole kg^{-1} will maintain Hg_2SO_4 as the stable solid phase (*14*).

Although it is stated in the older literature (*15*) that lead sulfate is extensively hydrolyzed by water, this reaction does not appear to be troublesome in practice. Disproportionation in the sense

$$2\text{PbSO}_4 + 2\text{H}_2\text{O} = \text{Pb} + \text{PbO}_2 + 2\text{H}_2\text{SO}_4$$

is not thermodynamically favored, since $\Delta G°$ for this reaction at 25°C is 94.14 kcal (*16*).

It can be seen from Table I that lead, and still more thallium, is less noble than mercury and might be expected to dissolve in acid solutions, with liberation of hydrogen. From recorded data (*16*) it can be shown that the reaction

$$\text{Pb} + \text{H}_2\text{SO}_4 \text{ (ideal aq soln, } m = 1\text{)} = \text{PbSO}_4 + \text{H}_2 \text{ (1 atm)}$$

is accompanied by standard free energy and entropy changes of

$$\Delta G^\circ = -16.55 \text{ kcal}$$

and

$$\Delta S^\circ = 46.80 \text{ cal deg}^{-1}$$

It is therefore thermodynamically favored and will become more so as the temperature rises. The irreversible dissolution of lead in sulfuric acid solutions is, however, hindered by the high overpotential for the hydrogen evolution reaction at the lead electrode (cf. Chapter 2, Section I,D). This hindrance will, however, depend critically upon purity and freedom from depolarization, e.g., by dissolved oxygen. It is known that lead of 99.99% purity is much less vulnerable to attack than metal only 99.9% pure (*17*). This difficulty is often minimized by the use of two-phase amalgams (cf. thallium), which also offers the advantage of reproducibility of surface properties, but is bound to be accentuated by rising temperature.

It is clear that only lead–lead sulfate and mercury–mercurous sulfate electrodes are likely to be generally serviceable, but they are supplemented by the lead dioxide–lead sulfate electrode, which may be represented

$$\text{Pt} \mid \text{PbO}_2 \mid \text{PbSO}_4 \mid \text{SO}_4^{2-}$$

since platinum is normally used for an unattackable metallic phase. This electrode operates quite differently from the sulfate-reversible electrodes of the second kind and must be briefly considered.

Lead dioxide, in contact with a solution containing plumbous ions and hydrogen ions, forms a reversible electrode, of which the standard potential has been determined; it has the value $E^\circ = 1.467$ int volt at 25°C (*18*). It may be regarded as a plumbic–plumbous oxidation-reduction electrode, but the activity of the plumbic ions must be proportional to the fourth power of the activity of hydrogen ions, in virtue of the presence of solid lead dioxide and of the linked equilibria

$$\text{PbO}_2 \rightleftharpoons \text{Pb}^{4+} + 2\text{O}^{2-}$$

$$2\text{O}^{2-} + 2\text{H}_2\text{O} \rightleftharpoons 4\text{OH}^-$$

$$4\text{OH}^- + 4\text{H}^+ \rightleftharpoons 4\text{H}_2\text{O}$$

The electrode reaction is

$$\text{PbO}_2 + 4\text{H}^+ + 2e^- = \text{Pb}^{2+} + 2\text{H}_2\text{O}$$

If, in addition, the activity of plumbous ions is reciprocally linked to the activity of sulfate ions by the presence of solid lead sulfate, the electrode reaction becomes

$$\text{PbO}_2 + 4\text{H}^+ + \text{SO}_4^{2-} + 2e^- = \text{PbSO}_4 \text{ (s)} + 2\text{H}_2\text{O}$$

The expression for the electrode potential is then

$$E = E^\circ + \frac{RT}{2F} \ln \frac{(a_{H^+})^4 \cdot a_{SO_4^{2-}}}{(a_{H_2O})^2} \tag{1}$$

which stands in contrast to the expression for sulfate-reversible electrodes of the second kind, which is

$$E = E^\circ - \frac{RT}{2F} \ln a_{SO_4^{2-}} \tag{2}$$

II. The Lead–Lead Sulfate Electrode

Lewis and Brighton (19) reported unfavorably on this electrode, which they found to operate erratically in dilute sulfuric acid solutions, whether a lead or an amalgam base was used and whether air was excluded or not. The trouble, which they assigned to irreversible attack of the acid on the lead, certainly did not reside in the metal phase, for lead electrodes prepared from glass-scraped metal, or by electrodeposition, were well behaved in lead perchlorate solutions. They also gave satisfactory lead–lead halide electrodes. Horsch (20) also found the lead–lead sulfate electrode to be unsatisfactory, giving, when based upon a 1% amalgam, a potential which changed with time. It had, however, already been shown (21) that it was desirable to use amalgams containing between 1.8% and 66% of lead, for over this range electrode potentials are independent of total composition because of the coexistence of two metallic phases (22). Thus, Henderson and Stegeman (23) used amalgams containing 2.5% to 6% of lead, prepared by electrolyzing 10% lead nitrate solution at a mercury cathode, as the basis of a standard cell

$$\text{Pb(Hg)} \mid \text{PbSO}_4 \mid \text{Na}_2\text{SO}_4 \cdot 10\text{H}_2\text{O} \mid \text{Na}_2\text{SO}_4 \text{ (satd)} \mid \text{Hg}_2\text{SO}_4 \mid \text{Hg}$$

which was reproducible in emf (0.96464 int volt at 25°C) to ±0.02 mv. That this cell works extremely well is shown by the good interagreement of other determinations of its emf at 25°C, namely 0.96466 (24), 0.96463 (25), 0.96462 (26) and 0.96471 (27) int volt.

Bray (28) made a statement of the conditions necessary for satisfactory operation of the lead amalgam–lead sulfate electrode. They were the use of a two-phase amalgam, the use of a "definite form" of lead sulfate, preequilibration of the solution with lead sulfate and exclusion of oxygen. He used these electrodes successfully, in conjunction with zinc amalgam electrodes, to study the activity coefficients of zinc sulfate in aqueous solution. This work has been extended by Cowperthwaite and La Mer (29) with results accurate enough, between 0° and 50°C, to provide substantial support for the Gronwall, La Mer, and Sandved extension of the Debye-Hückel theory (*30*). Similar work by La Mer and Parks (*31*) concerned with cadmium sulfate solutions was also successful; lead amalgam electrodes, prepared by electrodeposition from lead nitrate solution and covered with precipitated lead sulfate, were found to be reproducible in potential to within 0.06 mv.

The preparation of the amalgam may be briefly described. The electrolytic cell consisted of two beakers and an inverted Y-tube which could be used to make solution connection between them. One contained, as cathode, a pool of mercury which had been stirred under dilute nitric acid for 24 hr and then twice distilled in a current of dry air by Hulett's method (*32*); it was covered with a solution of thrice-recrystallized lead nitrate. This compartment was provided with a stirrer. The other contained a platinum wire anode in 1 N nitric acid. Electrolysis, at a current of 0.2 amp, was continued until the mercury contained about 6% of electrodeposited lead. Concentration of solution and current density appear not to be critical, for no details were given. The amalgam was washed, dried, heated until homogeneous and then was passed through a capillary tube into an evacuated receiver which could subsequently be filled with dry nitrogen. The receiver was also used as a dispenser, being equipped with a tap and a delivery tube at the bottom, and with a jacket which could be filled with boiling water in order to render the amalgam homogeneous before delivery into an electrode compartment. A suitable preparation of lead sulfate is described later in relation to the lead dioxide–lead sulfate electrode.

In spite of the good behavior of lead amalgam–lead sulfate electrodes in neutral, or nearly neutral solutions, they have not been widely used in acid solutions. This may be because of the entry of an additional experimental difficulty, for which a reason has been suggested, or because cells containing sulfuric acid are restricted in application on account of the incomplete dissociation of the acid. The first accurate measurements using the cell

$$Pb(Hg), \text{2 phase amalgam} \mid PbSO_4 \mid H_2SO_4 \ (m) \mid Pt, H_2 \ (1 \text{ atm}) \quad (A)$$

were made by Baumstark (*33, 34*), followed by Shrawder and Cowperthwaite (*35*), who used the same electrolytic method for preparing their amalgam as the previous workers in the same school. It is of interest that advantage was found in covering the amalgam with a film of *dry* lead sulfate before the introduction of the oxygen-free solution.

According to the Stockholm Convention (Chapter 1, Section IV), the emf of cell (A) is negative, and the reaction

$$PbSO_4 \ (s) + H_2 \ (1 \text{ atm}) = Pb(Hg) + 2H^+ \ (aq) + SO_4^{2-} \ (aq)$$

is accompanied by an increase in Gibbs free energy which may be represented

$$\Delta G = \Delta G^{\circ} + 2RT \ln m_{H^+}\gamma_{H^+} + RT \ln m_{SO_4^{2-}}\gamma_{SO_4^{2-}}$$
$$= \Delta G^{\circ} + 2RT \ln m\gamma_{H^+} + RT \ln m\ \gamma_{SO_4^{2-}} \tag{3}$$

where m is the molality of sulfuric acid in the cell solution and where, in making this substitution, the activity coefficients have become, without change of notation, stoichiometric activity coefficients, taking incomplete dissociation into account. It follows that

$$\Delta G = \Delta G^{\circ} + 3RT \ln 4^{1/3} \cdot m\gamma_{\pm} \tag{4}$$

and hence the emf of the cell becomes

$$E = E^{\circ} - \frac{3RT}{2F} \ln 4^{1/3} \cdot m\gamma_{\pm} \tag{5}$$

Use of the Hitchcock extrapolation method (allowing for incomplete dissociation in computing ionic strength) led to the standard emf values shown in the second line of Table II.

TABLE II

STANDARD POTENTIALS OF LEAD AMALGAM–LEAD SULFATE AND
LEAD–LEAD SULFATE ELECTRODES

Temp (°C)	0°	12.5°	25°	37.5°	50°
$E^{\circ}_{Pb(Hg),PbSO_4}$ (int volts)	−0.3281	−0.3392	−0.3505	−0.3619	−0.3738
$E^{\circ}_{Pb,PbSO_4}$ (int volts)	−0.3335	−0.3448	−0.3563	−0.3680	−0.3802
	−0.3310	−0.3430	−0.3553	−0.3678	−0.3806

These figures may be identified with the standard potentials of the two-phase lead amalgam–lead sulfate electrode. There is, however, a difference of chemical potential between lead in the amalgam and in the pure metal. This has been studied by Bates, Edelstein, and Acree (36), with results in agreement with earlier findings (37, 38). Their results have been used to calculate, from Shrawder and Cowperthwaite's data, the standard potentials of the lead–lead sulfate electrode shown in the third line of Table II. The value at 25°C is in fair agreement with −0.3557 int volt, derived from the standard emf of the lead accumulator cell (39) and the standard potential of the lead dioxide–lead sulfate electrode (40). The last line of figures in Table II are calculated from Harned and Hamer's equation (26) for the standard emf of the hydrogen–lead sulfate cell, namely,

$$E^{\circ} = 0.33096 + 9.5244 \times 10^{-4}t + 8.069 \times 10^{-7}t^2$$

where t is temperature in °C, derived indirectly. Signs have been adjusted to conform with the Stockholm Convention. The discrepancies are obvious.

The present position appears to be that the lead–lead sulfate electrode has fallen into disfavor, in spite of its earlier promise. Shrawder and Cowperthwaite's activity coefficients for sulfuric acid solutions were not in good agreement with later determinations (41) and Harned and Hamer (26) formed an adverse opinion of the reliability of this electrode in acid solutions. No doubt these factors, coupled with the availability of alternative electrodes, have contributed to the obsolescence of the lead–lead sulfate electrode. There seems to be no immediate prospect of preparing a convenient electrode of this type by an electrolytic method similar to that used for the silver–silver chloride electrode. Although lead is soft and self-annealing (42, 43), its electrochemical properties vary greatly according to the state of its surface and electrodeposition seems to offer no advantages (36). Anodization in sulfuric acid leads to the formation of passivating films of lead sulfate in various forms. This is accompanied by a sudden rise of potential to values at which oxide formation begins underneath the sulfate layer (44, 45). Lead sulfate films, for reasons perhaps associated with lack of good electrical contact, are sometimes not cathodically reduced with high current efficiency (46). Difficulties of this kind remain obstacles to the preparation of electrolytic lead–lead sulfate electrodes.

III. The Lead Dioxide–Lead Sulfate Electrode

This electrode was chosen in preference to others for study of the thermodynamic properties of sulfuric acid solutions by Harned and Hamer (9). The emf's of the cell

$$\text{H}_2 \text{ (1 atm), Pt} \mid \text{H}_2\text{SO}_4 \text{ (}m\text{)} \mid \text{PbSO}_4 \mid \text{PbO}_2 \mid \text{Pt} \qquad \text{(B)}$$

were determined by Hamer (47) for values of m, the molality of sulfuric acid, between 0.0005 and 7.0 mole kg^{-1}, for temperatures between 0° and 60°C. This work involved a close study of methods for preparing the lead dioxide in a suitably stable form. In general, commercial samples were unsatisfactory, no matter how they were treated before use. Neither were the products of the oxidation of alkaline plumbite solutions by chlorine, bromine or hydrogen peroxide serviceable. The best procedure was found to be the electrolysis of 3 liters of an aqueous solution containing 100 gm of lead nitrate and 400 ml of concentrated nitric acid, maintained at 93°C, with use of a platinum gauze anode supplied with a current density of 2.5 amp cm^{-2}. A platinum wire cathode, surrounded by a porous cup, was used and the solution was continuously stirred. In agreement with a previous observation (48), it was found to be essential to digest the black powder so formed on the steam bath with 3 M sulfuric acid for a week. This no doubt helped to bring the dioxide to its most stable form and to remove any lower oxide by conversion to sulfate. The product was stored under 0.1% sulfuric acid.

Lead sulfate was prepared by simultaneous, dropwise addition of 500 ml of 0.5 M solution of twice recrystallized lead nitrate and 500 ml of 0.5 M sulfuric acid to 2 liters of boiling 0.1 M sulfuric acid, with constant stirring. After it had been washed, the precipitate was digested on the steam bath for 24 hr with 2 M sulfuric acid, and was stored under 0.1% sulfuric acid.

Although, in the preparation of the electrode, the proportions of the dioxide and sulfate could be varied, it was best to use approximately equal amounts. After being dried on a Gooch filter, the solids were shaken with the cell electrolyte for 15 to 30 minutes in a glass-stoppered vessel, and introduced as a paste into a cell compartment containing a sealed-in platinum wire. Air-free electrolyte was introduced into the cell after evacuation. Except at 0°C, only two hours were needed for equilibrium to be attained. It was satisfactory, even desirable, to use the electrode pastes repeatedly, with suitable intervening re-equilibrations with the appropriate cell solutions. It should be noted that lead dioxide precipitated by adding a solution of electrolytic, or chemically precipitated, lead dioxide in hot, concentrated sodium hydroxide solution to a large volume of hot conductance water gave identical results.

For solutions more dilute than 0.01 m, a correction for the solubility of lead sulfate was applied. Two methods of extrapolation for the determination of the standard emf values were used. One was a semiempirical, "stoichiometric" method in which incomplete dissociation looked after itself. The other was a more rigorous method in which it was taken into account, and in which the limiting Debye-Hückel law could be incorporated (40). It would not be appropriate to give details of these methods, but it must be indicated that, since the cell reaction is

$$\text{H}_2 \text{ (1 atm)} + \text{PbO}_2 + \text{H}_2\text{SO}_4 \ (m) = \text{PbSO}_4 + 2\text{H}_2\text{O}$$

both must be based on the thermodynamic relationship

$$E = E° + \frac{RT}{2F} \ln (m_{\text{H}^+})^2 m_{\text{SO}_4^{2-}} + \frac{RT}{2F} \ln (\gamma_{\pm})^3 - \frac{RT}{2F} \ln (a_{\text{H}_2\text{O}})^2 \quad (6)$$

where $a_{\text{H}_2\text{O}}$ is the activity of water in the cell solution. For the dilute solutions involved in the extrapolation, the last term in the equation tends to zero.

The results from the more rigorous treatment were expressed to within ±0.05 mv by the equation

$$E° = 1.67699 + 2.85 \times 10^{-4}t + 1.2467 \times 10^{-6}t^2 \quad (7)$$

where t is temperature in °C and the potential is in int volt. The best selected values are displayed in Table III.

TABLE III

Standard Potentials of the Lead Dioxide–Lead Sulfate Electrode (47)

Temp (°C)	$E^{\circ}_{Pt,PbO_2,PbSO_4}$ (int volts)	Temp (°C)	$E^{\circ}_{Pt,PbO_2,PbSO_4}$ (int volts)
0	1.67694	35	1.68847
5	1.67846	40	1.69036
10	1.67998	45	1.69231
15	1.68159	50	1.69436
20	1.68322	55	1.69649
25	1.68488	60	1.69861
30	1.68671		

The results obtained in this work, coupled with those of Harned and Hamer from the hydrogen–mercurous sulfate cell (9) gave values for the activities of sulfuric acid, and of water in the stronger solutions, which did not agree as precisely as could be expected with data obtained by other methods (49, 50). It has been suggested (51) that this might be due to the irreversible attack of sulfuric acid at higher concentrations upon lead dioxide, leading to loss of oxygen. However, Beck, Singh, and Wynne-Jones (52) carried out measurements of the emf's of cell (B) over temperature and molality ranges of 5° to 55°C and 0.1 to 8 mole kg^{-1} respectively, with results that lead them to express the view that Hamer's data are in error. Certainly the temperature coefficients of the new emf values give results for ΔH° for the cell reaction which are in much better agreement with calorimetric data (53). The new measurements did not lend themselves to extrapolation, but an E° value at 25°C was derived from the equation

$$E^{\circ} = E - \frac{RT}{2F} \ln 4m^3\gamma_{\pm}^3/(a_{H_2O})^2 \tag{8}$$

where stoichiometric mean activity coefficients for sulfuric acid and activities of water were taken from Stokes's critically selected data (54). The mean of 17 such solutions to Eq. (8) covering the whole molality range was 1.6870 ± 0.0001 int volt, which is seen to differ by about 2 mv from the corresponding figure in Table III. The occurrence of this discrepancy, which seems to have an experimental source, is surprising, for almost the same methods were used in the later as in the earlier work. The only identifiable differences are that, in the later work, the cells were not evacuated before filling, that a lower current density was used in the electrolytic preparation of the lead dioxide (two preparations, made at 1.5 and 0.25 amp cm^{-2} were electromotively identical) and that a warning was given against grinding, crushing, or even unduly mechanically disturbing the oxide before use.

It may be relevant that lead dioxide is not a strictly stoichiometric compound. Although its composition is not very variable (*55*), it is an electronic conductor and may be appreciably deficient in oxygen (PbO $_{\measuredangle 1.95}$).

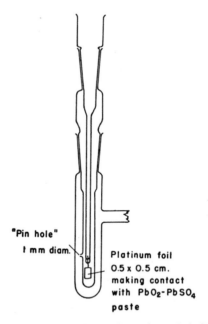

"Pin hole"
1 mm diam.

Platinum foil
0.5 x 0.5 cm.
making contact
with PbO$_2$-PbSO$_4$
paste

FIG. 1. Lead dioxide–lead sulfate electrode half-cell.

Perhaps more significant is the remarkable fact that until quite recently only a tetragonal form was known. It is that produced electrolytically under conditions of low pH and has been designated the β-form. Another, an orthorhombic α-form, is now known (*56*) to be generated from plumbite, lead acetate and neutral lead nitrate solutions, and its presence has been identified in the positive plate of the lead accumulator (*57*). The massive lead dioxide electrodes described by Sugino (*58*), electrodeposited from neutral lead nitrate solutions, no doubt consist of the α-form. Whilst it is to be expected that the α- and β-PbO$_2$ electrode potentials should differ, there is at present no agreement about the magnitude, and even the sign, of the difference (*59*). It has, furthermore, recently been shown in tracer studies of the exchange between β-lead dioxide and plumbous ions (*60*) that disordered material in the region of lattice dislocations is appreciably above the stable ground state in energy content. Under these circumstances, it is seen to be probable that the electrode potential discrepancies are but another example of the difficulties associated with bringing solid materials into reproducible standard states.

The half-cell used by Beck, Singh, and Wynne-Jones (52) seems admirably suited to electrodes at which sparingly soluble crystalline or powdered materials are involved, and is therefore illustrated in Fig. 1.

The cell

$$Pb \mid PbSO_4 \mid H_2SO_4 \text{ (aq)} \mid PbSO_4 \mid PbO_2 \mid Pt \qquad (C)$$

is the thermodynamic analogue of the lead accumulator, which has been the subject of a vast bulk of research. Although this does not fall within the scope of the present work, it may be mentioned that there is strong evidence that, under reversible conditions (39), and under those of slow discharge (61), the cell reaction is strictly

$$Pb + PbSO_4 + 2H_2SO_4 = 2PbSO_4 + 2H_2O$$

as long ago proposed by Gladstone and Tribe (62). This is not to suggest that all the problems associated with the lead accumulator have been solved.

IV. The Mercury–Mercurous Sulfate Electrode

Comment has already been made on the disadvantageous properties of mercurous sulfate, its tendency to hydrolyze and its rather high solubility. That its solubility is appreciable has the compensating advantage of promoting extremely efficient depolarization and this, coupled with the virtues of mercury, places the mercury–mercurous sulfate electrode almost alongside the hydrogen electrode in being capable of outstanding reproducibility. This is no doubt why it has been used in the standard cells which provide the experimental emf scales, including the obsolete Clark cell and the now universally adopted Weston cell. It stands in sharp contrast to the calomel electrode (see Chapter 3) in calling for no very special preparative techniques and, in all probability, in operating by no special mechanism distinct from that suggested by thermodynamics. As with other electrodes based on mercury, however, benefit may be derived from the use of hydrophobic electrode vessels (63).

In spite of these intrinsic advantages, much of the earlier work with this electrode seems to have been affected by serious errors. Thus, Randall and Cushman (64) found the hydrogen–mercurous sulfate cell to be reproducible in emf and obtained results which were, in the main, concordant with earlier work of Brönsted (65) and of Lewis and Lacey (66). These results were used by Lewis and Randall (67), in conjunction with freezing point and vapor pressure data, to calculate activity coefficients for sulfuric acid solutions. Yet Randall and Cushman's $E°$ value at 25°C, 0.6213 int volt, is now known to be more than 6 mv high. The value adopted by Randall and Langford (68) was even higher. It may be that insufficient attention was paid to hydrolysis, the effects of which were pointed out by Harned and Sturgis (69) and by Akerlöf (70), who also emphasized the need for washing the mercurous sulfate repeatedly with the cell solution, and of ensuring that the platinum wire making contact with the mercury remains unwetted with the solution. Although mercury is known to dissolve in aerated dilute sulfuric acid, Randall and Stone (71) alleged that the electrode was not appreciably disturbed by dissolved air, but this may be a reflection of somewhat tolerant standards; Vosburgh and Craig (48), on the other hand, recommended the exclusion of air.

A remarkable advance was made by Harned and Hamer (26) in the use of the hydrogen–mercurous sulfate cell. They found that cells containing dilute solutions were not sufficiently reproducible in behavior to allow the standard emf values to be determined by extrapolation, so they computed them by use of activity coefficients determined by means of cells with lead dioxide–lead sulfate electrodes. Their results are shown in Table IV.

TABLE IV

STANDARD POTENTIALS OF THE MERCURY–MERCUROUS SULFATE ELECTRODE (26)

Temp (°C)	$E°_{Hg,Hg_2SO_4}$ (int volts)	Temp (°C)	$E°_{Hg,Hg_2SO_4}$ (int volts)
0	0.63495	35	0.60701
5	0.63097	40	0.60305
10	0.62704	45	0.59900
15	0.62307	50	0.59487
20	0.61930	55	0.59051
25	0.61515	60	0.58659
30	0.61107		

They are represented to within ±0.05 mv by the expression

$$E° = 0.63495 - 781.44 \times 10^{-6}t - 426.89 \times 10^{-9}t^2$$

where t is temperature in °C and potentials are in int volts.

Recently Beck, Dobson, and Wynne-Jones (71a) re-examined this cell over the temperature range 5° to 55°C for sulfuric acid molalities between 0.1 and 8 mole kg^{-1}. Their electrode systems were of the kind shown in Fig. 1 and were incorporated into a multicompartment cell lending itself to tests of reproducibility; this was found to be better than ±0.05 mv. A layer of about 0.1 inch thickness of mercurous sulfate (prepared by the flowing anode method) was placed upon a small pool of mercury in the inner vessel of each half-cell compartment, and this was flushed out five times with the sulfuric acid to be used as the cell electrolyte. It was then allowed to stand overnight in fresh sulfuric acid of the same molality. Values of the standard emf, computed by Eq. (5) with use of activities interpolated from Stokes's data (54) were remarkably constant for the whole molality range, leading to an average of 0.61560 ± 0.00005 abs volt at 25°C. This exceeds by 0.25 mv the value of Harned and Hamer (26), 0.61535 abs volt on the same scale. Temperature coefficients of the emf's led to heats of reaction in excellent conformity with calorimetric data (53), which was not the case for the earlier work. It is thus possible that the figures recorded in Table IV may need adjustment.

In this work, and in most other published work in which the mercury–mercurous sulfate electrode has been used, the mercurous sulfate has been prepared by electrolytic methods devised by Hulett (72). These are illus-

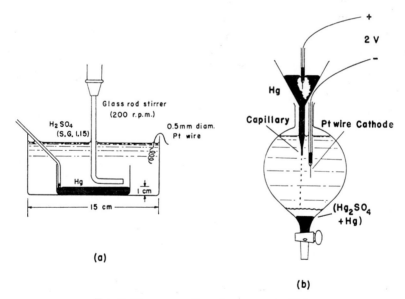

(a)

(b)

Fig. 2. The preparation of mercurous sulfate.

trated in Fig. 2, which is largely self-explanatory. In one of these methods [Fig. 2 (a)], a mercury pool anode is used. The electrolyte is made by adding one volume of concentrated sulfuric acid to six volumes of water and electrolysis is carried out with a current of 2 amp. Since the mercurous sulfate must not be allowed to collect upon the mercury anode, the stirrer, which should not unduly agitate the mercury, is arranged to keep the sulfate in suspension and swirl it into the outer vessel. The process of transfer is assisted if the motion of the solution in the outer vessel is damped by means of glass plates. The product is gray because of the presence of finely divided mercury and 50 to 60 gm may be produced in each run. In the second method [Fig. 2 (b)] a flowing anode is used, with sulfuric acid of the same concentration.

In either case, the product is a gray powder which should be stored under sulfuric acid not more dilute than unimolal and should be protected from the action of light.

Much work devoted to the study of mercurous sulfate for use in Weston cells unfortunately led to differences of opinion; one, in relation to hydrolysis, has already been mentioned. Another relates to particle size. Vosburgh and Eppley (73) said that the mercurous sulfate should be large grained, and should be digested with boiling dilute sulfuric acid to bring it to this state. This is in agreement with Elliott and Hulett (74), who recommended washing with sulfurous acid to reduce finely divided material to mercury. Summers and Gardiner (75), on the other hand, found that well crystallized mercurous sulfate was unsatisfactory and more susceptible to the effects of hydrolysis. It seems justifiable to conclude that this earlier work, directed to a particular purpose, hardly calls for close attention in a more general context.

The mercury–mercurous sulfate electrode has been very widely used. It was first applied, in cells with and without liquid junctions, to determine transport numbers by Ferguson and France (76). Earlier determinations of metal–metal ion standard potentials depended upon it (77) and studies have been made, with its use, of activity coefficients of sulfuric acid in solutions containing ammonium sulfate (78), zinc sulfate (79), acetic acid (80), methanol (81), ethanol (82), isopropanol (83), and ethylene glycol (84). It is probable that the considerable reduction in solubility of mercurous sulfate, and perhaps of its tendency to hydrolyze, which accompanies a transfer from water to a partially aqueous or nonaqueous medium (27) is beneficial. The electrode has been used in anhydrous ethanol (85). Particular interest attaches to the measurements of Kanning and Bowman (86) on sulfuric acid in anhydrous methanol. Their mercurous sulfate was prepared by dissolving the C.P. product in concentrated sulfuric acid, in the presence of mercury. This solution, added dropwise to a large excess of absolute methanol, gave a white mercurous sulfate which, after washing twenty times by decantation, afforded electrode potentials reproducible to ±0.3 mv. The standard potentials in this solvent were found to be 0.5443, 0.5392, 0.5351, and 0.5318 int volt at 20°, 25°, 30°, and 35°C, respectively. Activity coefficients determined in this work approached conformity with the Debye-Hückel limiting law on the basis of the behavior of the sulfuric acid as a uni-univalent electrolyte.

V. General Comments

Comparison can be made between the most probable experimental values of the standard potentials of the three main sulfate-reversible electrodes and those calculated from the critically selected standard free energies of formation published by the National Bureau of Standards (12). Such a comparison, for the single temperature of 25°C, is made in Table V.

TABLE V

EXPERIMENTAL AND THERMODYNAMIC ELECTRODE POTENTIALS[a]

	Pb, PbSO$_4$	Pb, PbO$_2$, PbSO$_4$	Hg, Hg$_2$SO$_4$
E°_{emf} (int volts)	−0.3563	1.6849	0.61515
$E^{\circ}_{ex\Delta G^{\circ}}$ (abs volts)	−0.3588	1.6823	0.6119

[a] At 25°C.

It is seen that in no case is the agreement very good. One set of figures comes directly from emf measurements concerned with individual cells. The other may be regarded as derived from a system of interrelated thermodynamic data to which many different kinds of measurement have contributed. It is salutory to realize that these, and most other, standard electrode potentials cannot be regarded as having absolute significance within a few mv. This is underlined by a comparison of the electrochemical and third law entropies of mercurous sulfate recently published by Brackett, Hornung, and Hopkins (87). Bearing in mind that 1 mv corresponds with only 0.023 kcal (gm equiv)$^{-1}$, this is not surprising, and there is nothing to prevent the standard potentials being used in a comparative way (as in the determination of activity coefficients) as quantities known within much closer limits. The imposing scheme of equations, valid from 0° to 60°C, showing nine standard emf values of related cells as functions of temperature, all mutually consistent within ±0.1 mv, published by Harned and Hamer (26) bear witness to this. In each individual case, however, the full number of significant figures quoted cannot be considered to have absolute significance.

REFERENCES

1. Conway, B. E., "Electrochemical Data," p. 289. Elsevier, London, 1952.
2. Seidell, A., "Solubilities of Inorganic and Metal-Organic Compounds," 3rd ed. Van Nostrand, New York, 1940.

3. Ishikawa, F., and Hagisawa, H., *Bull. Inst. Phys. Chem. Research (Tokyo)* **14**, 1205 (1935).

4. Lietzke, M. H., and Stoughton, R. W., *J. Am. Chem. Soc.* **75**, 5226 (1953).

5. Lietzke, M. H., and Stoughton, R. W., *J. Am. Chem. Soc.* **78**, 3023 (1956).

6. Gelbach, R. W., and King, G. B., *J. Am. Chem. Soc.* **64**, 1054 (1942).

7. Ishikawa, F., *J. Chem. Soc. Japan* **43**, 560 (1922).

8. Gerke, R. H., *Chem. Revs.* **1**, 377 (1925).

9. Harned, H. S., and Hamer, W. J., *J. Am. Chem. Soc.* **57**, 27 (1935).

10. Craig, D. N., and Vinal, G. W., *J. Research Natl. Bur. Standards* **22**, 55 (1939).

11. Gardiner, W. C., and Hulett, G. A., *Trans. Amer. Electrochem. Soc.* **56**, 111 (1929).

12. Hager, O. B., and Hulett, G. A., *J. Phys. Chem.* **36**, 2095 (1932).

13. Gurney, R. W., *J. Chem. Phys.* **6**, 499 (1938).

14. Craig, D. N., Vinal, G. W., and Vinal, F. E., *J. Research Natl. Bur. Standards* **17**, 709 (1936).

15. Mellor, J. W., "A Comprehensive Treatise on Inorganic and Theoretical Chemistry," Vol. VII, p. 809. Longmans, Green, New York, 1927.

16. Rossini, F. D., Wagman, D. D., Evans, W. H., Levine, S., and Jaffe, I., Selected values of chemical thermodynamic properties. *Natl. Bur. Standards Circ.* **No. 500** (1952).

17. Schikorr, G., and Schaller, I. E., *Metallwirtschaft* **20**, 1135 (1941).

18. Brown, D. J., and Zimmer, J. C., *J. Am. Chem. Soc.* **52**, 1 (1930).

19. Lewis, G. N., and Brighton, T. B., *J. Am. Chem. Soc.* **39**, 1906 (1917).

20. Horsch, W. G., *J. Am. Chem. Soc.* **41**, 1787 (1919).

21. Puschin, N. A., *Z. anorg. Chem.* **36**, 207 (1903).

22. Fay, H., and North, E., *Am. Chem. J.* **25**, 216 (1901).

23. Henderson, W. E., and Stegeman, G., *J. Am. Chem. Soc.* **40**, 84 (1918).

24. Mellon, M. G., and Henderson, W. E., *J. Am. Chem. Soc.* **42**, 676 (1920).

25. Ishikawa, F., and Hagisawa, H., *Bull. Inst. Phys. Chem. Research (Tokyo)* **13**, 1019 (1934).

26. Harned, H. S., and Hamer, W. J., *J. Am. Chem. Soc.* **57**, 33 (1935).

27. La Mer, V. K., and Carpenter, E. L., *J. Phys. Chem.* **40**, 287 (1936).

28. Bray, U. B., *J. Am. Chem. Soc.* **49**, 2372 (1927).

29. Cowperthwaite, I. A., and La Mer, V. K., *J. Am. Chem. Soc.* **53**, 4333 (1931).

30. Harned, H. S., and Owen, B. B., "The Physical Chemistry of Electrolytic Solutions," 3rd ed., p. 562. Reinhold, New York, 1958.

31. La Mer, V. K., and Parks, W. G., *J. Am. Chem. Soc.* **53**, 2040 (1931); **55**, 4343 (1933).

32. Hulett, G. A., *Phys. Rev.* **21**, 288 (1905); **33**, 307 (1911).

33. Baumstark, G., Dissertation, Catholic University of America, Washington, D.C., 1932.

34. MacInnes, D. A., "Principles of Electrochemistry," p. 191. Reinhold, New York, 1939.

35. Shrawder, J., and Cowperthwaite, I. A., *J. Am. Chem. Soc.* **56**, 2340 (1934).

36. Bates, R. G., Edelstein, M., and Acree, S. F., *J. Research Natl. Bur. Standards* **36**, 159 (1946).

37. Gerke, R. H., *J. Am. Chem. Soc.* **44**, 1686 (1922).

38. Carmody, W. R., *J. Am. Chem. Soc.* **51**, 2905 (1929).

39. Beck, W. H., and Wynne-Jones, W. F. K., *Trans. Faraday Soc.* **50**, 136 (1954).

40. Harned, H. S., and Owen, B. B., "The Physical Chemistry of Electrolytic Solutions," 3rd ed., p. 570. Reinhold, New York, 1958.

41. Harned, H. S., and Owen, B. B., "The Physical Chemistry of Electrolytic Solutions," 3rd ed., p. 574. Reinhold, New York, 1958.
42. Norbury, A. L., *Trans. Faraday Soc.* **19**, 140 (1923).
43. Rose, T. K., *J. Inst. Metals* **8**, 123 (1912).
44. Fleischmann, M., and Thirsk, H. R., *Trans. Faraday Soc.* **51**, 71 (1955).
45. Lander, J. J., *J. Electrochem. Soc.* **98**, 213 (1951); **103**, 1 (1956).
46. Smith, F. R., unpublished data, 1960.
47. Hamer, W. J., *J. Am. Chem. Soc.* **57**, 9 (1935).
48. Vosburgh, W. C., and Craig, D. N., *J. Am. Chem. Soc.* **51**, 2009 (1929).
49. Shankman, S., and Gordon, A. R., *J. Am. Chem. Soc.* **61**, 2370 (1939).
50. Stokes, R. H., *J. Am. Chem. Soc.* **69**, 1291 (1947).
51. Hamer, W. J., *Natl. Bur. Standards Circ.* **No. 524**, p. 184 (1953).
52. Beck, W. H., Singh, K. P., and Wynne-Jones, W. F. K., *Trans. Faraday Soc.* **55**, 331 (1959).
53. Craig, D. N., and Vinal, G. W., *J. Research Natl. Bur. Standards* **24**, 482 (1940).
54. Stokes, R. H., *Trans. Faraday Soc.* **44**, 295 (1948).
55. Byström, A., *Arkiv Kemi Miner Geol.* **20A**, No. 11 (1945).
56. Zaslavskii, A. E., Kondrashov, U. D., and Tolkachev, S. S., *Doklady Akad. Nauk S.S.S.R.* **75**, 559 (1950).
57. Bode, H., and Voss, E., *Z. Elektrochem.* **60**, 1053 (1956).
58. Sugino, K., *Bull. Chem. Soc. Japan* **23**, 115 (1950).
59. Fleischmann, M., and Liler, M., *Trans. Faraday Soc.* **54**, 1270 (1958).
60. Bone, S. J., Fleischmann, M., and Wynne-Jones, W. F. K., *Trans. Faraday Soc.* **56**, 111 (1960).
61. Beck, W. H., Lind, R., and Wynne-Jones, W. F. K., *Trans. Faraday Soc.* **50**, 147 (1954).
62. Gladstone, J. H., and Tribe, A., *Nature,* **25**, 221, 461; **26**, 251, 342, 603 (1882); **27**, 583 (1883).
63. Hills, G. J., private communication, 1960.
64. Randall, M., and Cushman, O. E., *J. Am. Chem. Soc.* **40**, 393 (1918).
65. Brönsted, J. N., *Z. physik. Chem.* **68**, 693 (1910).
66. Lewis, G. N., and Lacey, W. N., *J. Am. Chem. Soc.* **36**, 804 (1914).
67. Lewis, G. N., and Randall, M., "Thermodynamics." McGraw-Hill, New York, 1923.
68. Randall, M., and Langford, C. T., *J. Am. Chem. Soc.* **49**, 1445 (1927).
69. Harned, H. S., and Sturgis, R. D., *J. Am. Chem. Soc.* **47**, 945 (1925).
70. Akerlöf, G., *J. Am. Chem. Soc.* **48**, 1160 (1926).
71. Randall, M., and Stone, H. A., *J. Am. Chem. Soc.* **51**, 1752 (1929).
71a. Beck, W. H., Dobson, J. V., and Wynne-Jones, W. F. K., *Trans. Faraday Soc.* **56** (1960).
72. Hulett, G. A., *Phys. Rev.* **32**, 257 (1911).
73. Vosburgh, W. C., and Eppley, H., *J. Am. Chem. Soc.* **46**, 104 (1924).
74. Elliott, R. B., and Hulett, G. A., *J. Phys. Chem.* **36**, 2083 (1932).
75. Summers, D. B., and Gardiner, W. C., *Trans. Am. Electrochem. Soc.* **56**, 144 (1929).
76. Ferguson, A. L., and France, W. G., *J. Am. Chem. Soc.* **43**, 2150 (1921).
77. MacInnes, D. A., "Principles of Electrochemistry," p. 195. Reinhold, New York, 1939.
78. Crockford, H. D., and Simmons, N. L., *J. Am. Chem. Soc.* **56**, 1437 (1934).
79. Tartar, H. V., Newschwander, W. W., and Ness, A. T., *J. Am. Chem. Soc.* **63**, 28 (1941).
80. MacDougall, F. H., and Blumer, D. R., *J. Am. Chem. Soc.* **55**, 2236 (1933).

81. Shibata, F. L. E., and Oda, S., *J. Chem. Soc. Japan* **52**, 590 (1931).

82. Crockford, H. D., and Wideman, S. A., *J. Phys. Chem.* **50**, 418 (1946).

83. Land, J. E., and Crockford, H. D., *J. Am. Chem. Soc.* **72**, 1895 (1950).

84. French, C. M., and Hussain, C. F., *J. Chem. Soc.* 2211 (1955).

85. Scholl, A. W., Hutchison, A. W., and Chandlee, G. C., *J. Am. Chem. Soc.* **57**, 2542 (1935).

86. Kanning, E. W., and Bowman, M. G., *J. Am. Chem. Soc.* **68**, 2043 (1946).

87. Brackett, T. E., Hornung, E. W., and Hopkins, T. E., *J. Am. Chem. Soc.* **82**, 4155 (1960).

Chapter Nine

Membrane Electrodes

G. J. Hills

I. Introduction

The term "membrane electrode" is applied to a system in which a selective membrane separates two electrolyte solutions and at which an electrical potential difference is established characteristic of the difference in activity of a common ion constituent on either side. This membrane potential responds in a reproducible manner to changes in the activity difference of one kind of ion so that if one of the two solutions is of fixed and known composition, then the observed membrane potential is indicative of the composition of the other. For various membranes used under suitably restricted conditions this result can be achieved for almost any ionic species. The glass electrode may be regarded as a special example of membrane electrode and whilst none of the other membrane electrodes discussed below has so high a degree of specificity, they have the advantage of being more general in application and conform more closely to theoretically predicted behavior. They may be used to measure the ionic activities of any electrolyte chemically compatible with them and, even further, they allow a closer approach to be made, with fewer restrictive assumptions, to the study of individual ionic activities, ultimately inaccessible as these may be.

Many membrane electrodes function ideally only in dilute solutions, i.e. $<0.01\ m$, but even in concentrated solutions $(>1\ m)$, the departures from ideality are a smooth function of concentration and are sufficiently well understood for the electrode to be "calibrated" i.e., for the deviations from ideal behavior to be allowed for. Most of the membranes which are discussed below can be made perfectly selective for either cations or for anions but remain unselective in the sense that they will not discriminate between one cation species and another, or between one anion species and another. There are signs, however, that even this limitation may be overcome and that the way may be open for the gradual development of membrane electrodes specifically reversible to many of the ions for which no conventional reference electrodes exist.

All of the membranes described below are prepared from clays or from natural or synthetic polymer materials and much of their development has been carried out by colloid chemists, polymer chemists, and biochemists. The analytical uses of membranes, e.g., as membrane electrodes, represents only one of several aims of this development work and certainly the principal goal has been the imitation and understanding of the controlled selectivity of the natural membranes of biological systems.

The practical application of membrane electrodes to analytical purposes requires not only directions for the preparation and use of the membranes but, very particularly, an appreciation of the theory of membrane potentials. A knowledge of the factors governing the selectivities and degree of nonideality of membranes is essential both to the development and use of membrane electrodes and to the interpretation of the emf values of cells containing them.

II. The Development of Membrane Electrodes

The development of membrane electrodes has followed the steady refinement of the measurement of membrane potentials. Their possible uses were first recognized by Haber (1–3) after Nernst and Riesenfeld (4) had shown that any interface supporting a concentration gradient and allowing the reversible transfer of only a single ionic species from one solution to the other, gives rise to a potential difference and acts electromotively in a manner analogous to that of a conventional reference electrode reversible to that ionic species. The theory of membrane potentials was further developed by Donnan (5), by Horovitz (6, 7), by Teorell (8, 9), by Meyer and Sievers (10), by Tendeloo (11), by Marshall (12), and by Scatchard (13), the last two authors dealing especially with membrane electrodes.

The most significant advance was the practical realization of the systems idealized in these theoretical treatments. Michaelis (14, 15) was the first to describe the successful application of membranes of high ionic selectivity but the two most important developments were due to Marshall (12, 16–22), who was responsible for developing zeolite and clay membranes, and, especially, to Sollner and Gregor (23–30) whose collodion-based membranes remain the simplest and often the most suitable membrane electrodes for the potentiometric determination of ionic activities.

The years following 1945 also saw the increasing use of synthetic ion exchange resins. Their selectivity towards different ionic species is governed by the same factors which control the ionic permeability of membranes and several research workers, notably Kressman (*31, 32*), and Wyllie and Patnode (*33*), showed how membranes of ion exchange materials also functioned reproducibly and selectively as membrane electrodes over a wide range of concentrations of individual ionic species. This type of membrane can be prepared in two ways: (i) as a homogeneous sheet or film of porous cross-linked polymer material, the pores of which are charged with fixed carboxylic or sulfonic acid groups (cation-selective membranes) or amino groups in the -onium form (anion-selective membranes) (*31, 32, 34–46*), and which are accessible to all but the largest ions; or (ii) as a heterogeneous membrane which can be made by impregnating a porous polymer material with adsorbable polyelectrolyte (*47–49*), or, more usually, by incorporating particles or beads of ion exchange resin into an inert plastic matrix by molding the beads and plastic binder in a suitable press (*33, 50, 51*). This last type of membrane is tough and flexible, and is available in large sheets (e.g., of several square feet) from the manufacturers of ion exchange materials.[1]

More recently still, Gregor and his co-workers (*52*) have begun the development of an entirely different type of membrane especially for use as membrane electrodes of high specificity. These are termed "multilayer membrane electrodes" and are built up by successive layering of, for example, calcium stearate monolayers into a thin strip. The potential difference across the strip responds ideally to the difference in concentration of calcium ions on either side of the strip, even, it is suggested, in the presence of other cations. The subject of specific-ion membrane electrodes is discussed further in Section VI, but none of the other examples quoted there show quite the same promise as do these multilayer electrodes.

III. The Theory of Membrane Electrode Potentials

The simplest concept of an ion selective membrane is that due to Teorell (*8, 9, 53–55*) and to Meyer and Sievers (*10*). The membrane is regarded as a porous diaphragm throughout which there is an even distribution, along the pore walls, of one particular species of fixed ionized or ionizable groups and which is permeated by the solution in which it is

---

[1] For example, from The Permutit Co., Ltd., Gunnersbury Avenue, London, W.4; Ionics, Inc., 152 Sixth Street, Cambridge, Massachusetts; Rohm and Haas Co., Washington Square, Philadelphia 5, Pennsylvania.

immersed (as, for example, in Fig. 1). Assuming that the pH of the imbibed solution is such that all of the groups are ionized, their concentration ($\bar{X}$ gm equivalent $kg_{H_2O}^{-1}$) is virtually constant, being subject only to the relatively minor changes in the degree of swelling of the membrane. This concentration is the most important characteristic of the membrane and, provided that there are no large or uncharged pores through which elec-

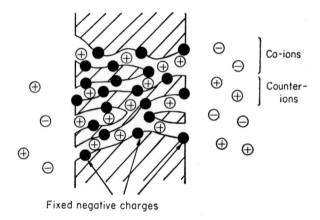

Fixed negative charges

FIG. 1. Diagrammatic representation of a perm-selective membrane.

trolyte can "leak," it will determine the efficiency, or selectivity, of the membrane.

The concentration of these ions within the membrane can be calculated (40) by an application of the Donnan equilibrium in the following way.

Since the membrane must, as a whole, remain electrically neutral, the concentration of fixed charges which it contains, $\bar{X}$, must be balanced by an equal net concentration of opposite charge provided by diffusible ions. These are the counter-ions, i, of opposite sign of charge, and the co-ions, j, of the same sign of charge. Thus,

$$\bar{X} + \bar{m}_j = \bar{m}_i$$

and $$\bar{a}_i/\bar{\gamma}_i = \bar{X} + (\bar{a}_j/\bar{\gamma}_j)$$

where concentrations of diffusible species have been expressed in terms of molal activities and activity coefficients, and all terms relating to the membrane phase are "barred."

But thermodynamic equilibrium between the membrane and the solution outside must be preserved, so that

$$\bar{a}_i \cdot \bar{a}_j = a_i \cdot a_j$$

Then

$$\frac{\bar{a}_i}{\bar{\gamma}_i} = \bar{X} + \frac{a_i \cdot a_j}{\bar{a}_i \cdot \bar{\gamma}_j}$$

$$\therefore \left\{\frac{\bar{a}_i}{\bar{\gamma}_i}\right\}^2 = \frac{\bar{X} \cdot \bar{a}_i}{\bar{\gamma}_i} + \frac{a_i \cdot a_j}{\bar{\gamma}_i \cdot \bar{\gamma}_j}$$

which can be solved as a quadratic in $\overline{m}_i = \dfrac{\bar{a}_i}{\bar{\gamma}_i}$ to yield

$$\overline{m}_i = \frac{\bar{X}}{2} + \left\{\frac{\bar{X}^2}{4} + \frac{m_\pm{}^2 \gamma_\pm{}^2}{\bar{\gamma}_\pm{}^2}\right\}^{\frac{1}{2}} \tag{1a}$$

and similarly,

$$\overline{m}_j = -\frac{\bar{X}}{2} + \left\{\frac{\bar{X}^2}{4} + \frac{m_\pm{}^2 \gamma_\pm{}^2}{\bar{\gamma}_\pm{}^2}\right\}^{\frac{1}{2}} \tag{1b}$$

where $m_\pm \gamma_\pm$ represents the mean molal activity, $a_\pm$, of a single (1:1) electrolyte, ij, in equilibrium with the membrane and $\bar{\gamma}_\pm$ is the corresponding mean molal ionic activity coefficient inside the membrane phase. From these equations it is seen that for small values of $(m_\pm \gamma_\pm / \bar{X}\bar{\gamma}_\pm)$, $\overline{m}_i \to \bar{X}$ and $\overline{m}_j \to 0$. Since $\bar{X}$ is invariably large, 1 to 5 m, this condition is not difficult to fulfill and, when this is so, the counter-ions are the only significant diffusible species in the membrane, i.e., their transport number is unity, and the membrane is said to be perfectly perm-selective for that species.

The unequal distribution of diffusible ions at the interface is accompanied by a potential difference, the Donnan potential, π, given by the general and self-evident equation, for counter-ions of any valency z_i (including sign),

$$\pi = \frac{RT}{z_i F} \ln \frac{a_i}{\bar{a}_i} \tag{2}$$

This phase boundary potential is indeterminate, but if the membrane separates two solutions of different composition, there will be two unequal Donnan potentials, π_{I} and π_{II} which, together with the intramembrane diffusion potential, give rise to a (Volta) potential difference across the membrane which is, approximately at least, easily measurable. The sum of the Donnan potential differences is given by

$$\pi_{\mathrm{I}} + \pi_{\mathrm{II}} = \frac{RT}{z_i F} \ln \left[\left(\frac{a_i}{\bar{a}_i}\right)_{\mathrm{I}} \middle/ \left(\frac{a_i}{\bar{a}_i}\right)_{\mathrm{II}}\right] \tag{3}$$

Since $\bar{a}_i = \overline{m}_i \cdot \bar{\gamma}_i$ and $\overline{m}_i$ is given by Eq. (1a), this sum may be written for (1:1) electrolytes

$$\pi_{\mathrm{I}} + \pi_{\mathrm{II}} = \frac{RT}{z_i F} \ln \frac{(a_i)_{\mathrm{I}}}{(a_i)_{\mathrm{II}}} \cdot \frac{[\bar{X}_{\mathrm{II}}^2(\bar{\gamma}_i)_{\mathrm{II}}^2 + 4(a_\pm)_{\mathrm{II}}^2(\bar{\gamma}_i/\bar{\gamma}_j)_{\mathrm{II}}]^{\frac{1}{2}} + \bar{X}_{\mathrm{II}}(\bar{\gamma}_i)_{\mathrm{II}}}{[\bar{X}_{\mathrm{I}}^2(\bar{\gamma}_i)_{\mathrm{I}}^2 + 4(a_\pm)_{\mathrm{I}}^2(\bar{\gamma}_i/\bar{\gamma}_j)_{\mathrm{I}}]^{\frac{1}{2}} + \bar{X}_{\mathrm{I}}(\bar{\gamma}_i)_{\mathrm{I}}} \tag{4}$$

which, it may be noted, takes into account the separate values of $\bar{X}$, $\bar{\gamma}_i$ and $\bar{\gamma}_j$ appropriate to each interface.

But the total potential difference across the membrane includes a diffusion potential arising from the spontaneous transfer of diffusible entities across it from one solution to the other. In all the theories of membrane potentials, it is equated to that of a "constrained liquid junction," i.e.,

$$\phi_{\text{diffusion}} = -\frac{RT}{F} \int_{\text{I}}^{\text{II}} \sum \frac{\bar{t}_i}{z_i} \, d \ln \bar{a}_i \tag{5}$$

where $\bar{t}_i$, $\bar{t}_j$, etc., are the transport numbers of the diffusible species in the membrane phase. This equation is not integrable unless certain assumptions are made about the appropriate ionic distributions and about single ion activity coefficients. Planck assumed that the total ionic *concentration* varied linearly through the diffusion zone and this assumption, together with equation of the relevant activity coefficients to unity, is the usual basis for evaluating the membrane diffusion potential. No integration of the flux equations in terms of activities has yet been given, although the difficulties involved have been emphasized by Schlögl and Helfferich (*56*) and a general integration for ions of different valencies (but again restricted to ideal systems) has been performed by Schlögl (*57*). The Planck assumption, used by Teorell, leads to the expression for $\phi_{\text{diffusion}}$, for a single (1:1) electrolyte,

$$\phi_{\text{diffusion}} = \frac{RT}{z_i F} \cdot \frac{\bar{U}_i - \bar{U}_j}{\bar{U}_i + \bar{U}_j} \cdot \ln \left[\frac{\bar{U}_i(\bar{m}_i)_{\text{I}} + \bar{U}_j(\bar{m}_j)_{\text{I}}}{\bar{U}_i(\bar{m}_i)_{\text{II}} + \bar{U}_j(\bar{m}_j)_{\text{II}}} \right] \tag{6}$$

where $\bar{U}_i$ and $\bar{U}_j$ are the counter-ion and co-ion mobilities (assumed to be constant) within the membrane phase.

The total membrane potential is therefore given by

$$\Delta E = \pi_{\text{I}} + \pi_{\text{II}} + \phi_{\text{diffusion}}$$

$$= \frac{RT}{z_i F} \ln \frac{(a_i)_{\text{I}}}{(a_i)_{\text{II}}} \cdot \left[\frac{\bar{X}_{\text{II}}(\bar{\gamma}_i)_{\text{II}} \{1 + (1 + \xi_{\text{II}}^2)^{\frac{1}{2}}\}}{\bar{X}_{\text{I}}(\bar{\gamma}_i)_{\text{I}} \{1 + (1 + \xi_{\text{I}}^2)^{\frac{1}{2}}\}} \right]$$

$$+ \frac{\bar{U} \cdot RT}{z_i F} \cdot \ln \left[\frac{\bar{X}_{\text{II}} \{\bar{U} + (1 + \xi_{\text{II}}^2)^{\frac{1}{2}}\}}{\bar{X}_{\text{I}} \{\bar{U} + (1 + \xi_{\text{I}}^2)^{\frac{1}{2}}\}} \right] \tag{7}$$

where

$$\bar{U} = \frac{\bar{U}_i - \bar{U}_j}{\bar{U}_i + \bar{U}_j} \quad \text{and} \quad \xi = 2a_{\pm}/(\bar{X} \cdot \bar{\gamma}_{\pm})$$

This equation for membrane potential is still deficient in two respects. Firstly, it takes no account of differential swelling across the membrane, i.e., the effect on $\bar{\gamma}_{\pm}$ of a swelling-pressure gradient. This, however, is not likely to be a large factor and can be avoided by suitable design of membrane. Secondly, the equation neglects the contribution to the diffusion potential arising from the transport of solvent. This could lead to an appreciable error and, although the transport of water can also be minimized by suitable choice of membrane, its effects can seldom be neglected; it is considered further below.

The equation as it stands can take two extreme forms:

(1) When external concentrations are large compared with the fixed ion concentration, i.e., $a_\pm \gg \overline{X}$, it reduces to that for a normal diffusion potential,

$$E_J = -\frac{RT}{F}\left[\left(\frac{\overline{U}_+}{\overline{U}_+ + \overline{U}_-}\right) \ln \frac{(a_+)_{\text{II}}}{(a_+)_{\text{I}}} - \left(\frac{\overline{U}_-}{\overline{U}_+ + \overline{U}_-}\right) \ln \frac{(a_-)_{\text{II}}}{(a_-)_{\text{I}}}\right] \quad (8)$$

(2) When $a_\pm \ll \overline{X}$, the equation reduces even further to

$$\Delta E = -\frac{RT}{z_i F} \ln \frac{(a_i)_{\text{II}}}{(a_i)_{\text{I}}} \quad (9)$$

which is true for counter-ions of any valency. The last condition is the one most closely approached in practice. It is equivalent to the total exclusion of the co-ion species when the membrane is perfectly perm-selective towards the counter-ions. Under these conditions, the membrane potential has its maximum value and is frequently designated ΔE_{max}. It is this equation which is most commonly used to express membrane potentials and to evaluate the results from membrane electrode measurements.

The extent to which Eq. (9) can be used to study ionic activities depends, of course, on the precision required from the measurements. It is applicable, within experimental error, to many of the membranes described below in contact with solutions of molality up to 0.05 mole kg^{-1}, and, in two instances, up to 1 mole kg^{-1}. Above 0.05 m, and very often even above 0.01 m, many membranes show significant deviations from the ideality expressed by Eq. (9) and then a more complete expression, e.g., Eq. (7), must be used. Equation (7), however, contains two inaccessible quantities a_i and $\bar{\gamma}_i$. The former can be eliminated using appropriate reference electrodes reversible to the counter-ion or co-ion species (see Section IV, A, 1) and the measured emf of the combination,

reference electrode	solution of ij, $(a_\pm)_{\text{I}}$	membrane	solution of ij, $(a_\pm)_{\text{II}}$	reference electrode

would thus reveal $d \ln \bar{\gamma}_i$. Alternatively, since the variation of $\bar{\gamma}_\pm$ is determined almost entirely by the corresponding variation in $\bar{\gamma}_i$ ($\bar{\gamma}_j \sim$ constant), the ratio $(\bar{\gamma}_i)_{\text{II}}/(\bar{\gamma}_i)_{\text{I}}$ could reasonably be equated to $(\bar{\gamma}_\pm)_{\text{II}}/(\bar{\gamma}_\pm)_{\text{I}}$ and on this assumption, the observed value of the membrane potential would lead to $d \ln a_i$.

This approach, however, is not a very fruitful one in practice, not just because it neglects the transport of solvent but also because the term, $\overline{U}$, though accessible in principle, is not easily evaluated. It is therefore simpler to use the quasi-thermodynamic treatment of Scatchard (*13*). In this, the membrane is regarded wholly as a liquid junction separating two homogeneous solutions. The membrane potential is thus given by an appropriate form of Eq. (5), i.e.,

$$\Delta E = -\frac{RT}{F} \int_{\mathrm{I}}^{\mathrm{II}} \left[\frac{\bar{t}_i}{z_i} d \ln a_i - \frac{\bar{t}_j}{z_j} d \ln a_j + \bar{t}_w \, d \ln a_w \right] \tag{10}$$

where $\bar{t}_i$, $\bar{t}_j$ and $\bar{t}_w$ are the transport numbers of counter-ions, co-ions and solvent (water) *in the membrane phase*, and a_i, a_j and a_w are the corresponding activities in the *external* solution.[2]

This is a useful equation because it shows clearly, by comparison with Eq. (9), the two sources of deviation from the perm-selectivity equivalent to ΔE_{max}, which are here expressed by the last terms on the right hand side of Eq. (10). It is also not integrable without making the assumptions which lead to Eq. (7). In this case, these amount to assuming that the transport numbers are constant. This is not strictly true, and becomes less so as the value of $d \ln a_{\pm}$ increases. Nevertheless, an approximation to the truth can be made by taking an average value of each transport number, here designated $\bar{t}'_i$, $\bar{t}'_j$ and $\bar{t}'_w$, such that

$$\Delta E = -\frac{RT}{F} \left[\frac{\bar{t}'_i}{z_i} \ln \frac{(a_i)_{\mathrm{II}}}{(a_i)_{\mathrm{I}}} - \frac{\bar{t}'_j}{z_j} \ln \frac{(a_j)_{\mathrm{II}}}{(a_j)_{\mathrm{I}}} + \bar{t}'_w \ln \frac{(a_w)_{\mathrm{II}}}{(a_w)_{\mathrm{I}}} \right] \tag{11}$$

or, by eliminating a_w in terms of the Gibbs-Duhem relation,

$$\Delta E = -\frac{RT}{F} \left[\frac{\bar{t}'_i}{z_i} \ln \frac{(a_i)_{\mathrm{II}}}{(a_i)_{\mathrm{I}}} - \frac{\bar{t}'_j}{z_j} \ln \frac{(a_j)_{\mathrm{II}}}{(a_j)_{\mathrm{I}}} - \bar{t}_w \left(0.018 \, a'_{ij} \ln \frac{(a_i a_j)_{\mathrm{II}}}{(a_i a_j)_{\mathrm{I}}} \right) \right] \tag{12}$$

where a'_{ij} is the *average* external molal activity. These average transport numbers are not accessible from first principles. It is possible that they may be obtainable from separate Hittorf experiments, although this has not been confirmed, and it is not certain that the near-equilibrium conditions under which membrane potentials are measured are at all close to those obtaining during ionic and electro-osmotic transport.

It must therefore be concluded that none of the existing theories of membrane potentials allows an unambiguous evaluation of nonideal membrane potentials to be made. This does not mean, however, that membrane electrodes cannot usefully be used in solutions in which they are not perfectly selective, i.e., when $\Delta E < \Delta E_{max}$. In the next section, dealing with the measurement of membrane potentials, it will be seen that the emf of a

---

[2] It is desirable, in this and other connections, to adopt the definition of transport numbers due to Scatchard (*13*), i.e., "The transport number of a given species is the net number of gram-formula-weights of that species which crosses an imaginary plane in the solution, in the direction of positive current, when one faraday of electricity passes across that plane." (Cf. Spiro, reference *58*.)

membrane cell can be expressed in terms of a single deviation term which is a smooth function of external ionic activity. From a prior calibration experiment, a membrane electrode can therefore be used quite precisely, albeit empirically, as a measure of differences in ionic activity, even in concentrated solutions.

Before considering this aspect, mention must be made of two other complicating circumstances that are met in relation to membrane potentials. The theoretical treatment presented so far has dealt only with homo-ionic potentials, arising at a membrane separating two solutions of the same salt. If, instead, the membrane separates solutions of different salts, the resultant potential, a so-called bi-ionic potential (B.I.P.) is more difficult to determine and much more difficult to describe theoretically (59–62). If only the co-ion species differ, i.e., the two solutions have a common counter-ion, the extra complication may well be negligible since the role of the co-ion is small. When the counter-ion species differ, no simple theory is applicable and in the use of membrane electrodes, this situation is avoided.

The above treatment is also inapplicable to systems containing more than one diffusible counter-ion species in the external solutions. Whilst membranes can easily be made to exclude either cations or anions, they cannot normally be made appreciably selective towards one ionic species out of several of the same charge. This is the most serious limitation of existing membrane electrodes and the few but important attempts to prepare membranes which do show ion specificity will be considered in detail in Section VI.

IV. The Measurement of Membrane Potentials

A. PRINCIPLES

Homo-ionic membrane potentials can be usefully measured in a number of ways.

1. Use of Reference Electrodes Reversible to the Counter-ions or Co-ions

If on either side of the membrane reference electrodes reversible to either the counter-ions or the co-ions are used, the cell emf is

$$E = \Delta E + \frac{RT}{z_i F} \ln \frac{(a_i)_{\text{II}}}{(a_i)_{\text{I}}} \tag{13a}$$

or

$$= \Delta E + \frac{RT}{z_j F} \ln \frac{(a_j)_{\text{II}}}{(a_j)_{\text{I}}} \tag{13b}$$

The values corresponding to ideal selectivity, i.e., ΔE_{max}, are therefore respectively

$$E_{max} = 0 \tag{14}$$

and

$$E_{max} = \frac{RT}{F} \cdot \frac{\nu}{\nu_j z_j} \cdot \ln \frac{(a_\pm)_{II}}{(a_\pm)_I} \tag{15}$$

where ν and ν_j are, respectively, the total number of ions and the number of co-ions (in gram-ions) produced per mole of salt.

For conditions of nonideality, Eq. (12) can be simplified by substituting $(1 - |\bar{t}'_j|)$ for $\bar{t}'_i$ and $|\bar{t}'_w|$ for $\bar{t}'_w$, the modulus signs being required because both transport numbers can be either positive or negative. The emf of the membrane cell containing electrodes reversible to the co-ions becomes

$$E = -\frac{RT}{F} \left[\frac{(1 - |\bar{t}'_j|)}{z_i} \ln \frac{(a_i)_{II}}{(a_i)_I} + \frac{|\bar{t}'_j|}{z_j} \ln \frac{(a_j)_{II}}{(a_j)_I} \right.$$
$$\left. - |\bar{t}'_w| \left(0.018 \, a'_{ij} \ln \frac{(a_{ij})_{II}}{(a_{ij})_I} \right) - \frac{1}{z_j} \ln \frac{(a_j)_{II}}{(a_j)_I} \right] \tag{16}$$

which, by rearrangement, becomes

$$E = \frac{RT}{z_j F} \cdot \frac{\nu}{\nu_j} \left[1 - |\bar{t}'_j| - 0.018 \, a'_{ij} \, |\bar{t}'_w| \right] \ln \frac{(a_\pm)_{II}}{(a_\pm)_I} \tag{17}$$

The deviation from ideality, $E_{max} - E$, is thus expressed by the bracketed terms, which are singly and collectively smooth functions of external ionic activity, $a_\pm$. Although, therefore, the individual terms may be independently inaccessible, the relation between E and $a_\pm$ is quite suitable as a basis for calibration and interpolation. This may be illustrated from some accurate measurements made by Lakshminaryaniah and co-workers (63) on the cell

$$\text{Pt, H}_2 \left| \begin{array}{c} \text{KOH (aq)} \\ (a_\pm)_I \end{array} \right| \begin{array}{c} \text{polymethacrylate} \\ \text{membrane} \end{array} \left| \begin{array}{c} \text{KOH (aq)} \\ (a_\pm)_{II} \end{array} \right| \text{H}_2, \text{Pt}$$

They determined the cell emf over a wide range of KOH molalities, although $(a_\pm)_{II}/(a_\pm)_I$ never exceeded 10. Their results can be summed so as to show the variation of cell emf with $(a_\pm)_{II}$ for a fixed value of $(a_\pm)_I = 0.00108$ m. This variation is shown in Fig. 2 together with the linear relation predicted by Eq. (15). The observed values are, as is to be expected, significantly lower than those calculated on the basis of complete permselectivity, but are close to those calculated from Eq. (7), assuming all intra-membrane activity coefficients to be unity but taking the water transport term into account. This agreement must be regarded as fortuitous since the intra-membrane environment is far removed from the ideal ionic state. In order to use Eq. (7) more realistically, measurements were made of the mean ionic activity coefficients in the membrane phase and, by equating $(\bar{\gamma}_i)_{\mathrm{II}}/(\bar{\gamma}_i)_{\mathrm{I}}$ to $(\bar{\gamma}_\pm)_{\mathrm{II}}/(\bar{\gamma}_\pm)_{\mathrm{I}}$ corresponding emf values could be calculated since values of $\overline{U}$ were available from other sources (64). This procedure, however, considerably worsened the agreement.

The same authors also determined the transport numbers of co-ions and solvent, corresponding approximately to t'_j and t'_w terms in Eq. (17). The cell emf values calculated from these data are also shown in Fig. 2;

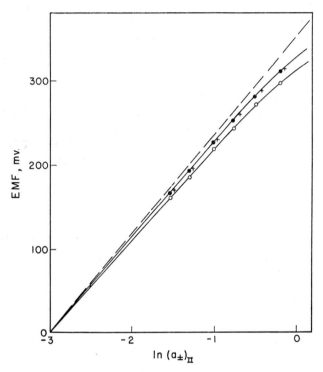

Fig. 2. Observed and calculated emf's of the membrane cell

Pt, H₂ | KOH, $(a_\pm)_{\mathrm{I}}$ = 0.00108 | membrane | KOH $(a_\pm)_{\mathrm{II}}$ | H₂, Pt

as a function of activity gradient. KEY: – – –, E_{max}; – + – + –, observed emf; –●–●–, calculated ideal emf including water transport term; –O–O–, emf calculated using observed transport numbers.

the agreement between observed and calculated data is also not good. Ironically, therefore, the refined treatments of membrane potential are apparently less satisfactory than the simple, ideal theory, notwithstanding the fact that they require much ancillary information to be used at all. It may be concluded therefore that for most membrane systems operating under conditions of only partial selectivity, it is simpler and as accurate experimentally to determine the form of the appropriate $dE/d\ln(a_{\pm})_{II}$ relation and to interpolate graphically or algebraically from this.

2. Use of Reference Electrodes of Fixed Potential

A more general method of measuring membrane potentials and one most frequently used employs two standard half-cells as reference electrodes, e.g.,

saturated calomel electrode	salt bridge	standard solution of counter-ion salt	mem- brane	test solu- tion	salt bridge	saturated calomel electrode

Neglecting any asymmetry potential difference between the two liquid junctions, the emf of this membrane cell is equal to the Volta potential difference across the membrane as described by Eq. (9) or, more generally, by Eq. (12). On either basis, the ratio $(a_i)_{II}/(a_i)_I$ is directly obtainable. Further, the single ion activity, $(a_i)_{II}$, in the test solution can be evaluated in terms of whatever assumption is made in resolving the known $(a_{\pm})_I$ value of the standard solution.

3. The Null Method

The third method of using membranes is equally applicable to conditions of perfect or partial selectivity, irrespective of the properties of the membrane and of the particular values of $\bar{t}_i$, $\bar{t}_j$, $\bar{t}_w$, etc. It is the null, or titration method. Initially, the membrane separates the test solution of unknown composition and a very dilute solution of a corresponding salt (or even just water). A standard solution of this salt is then run in until the emf of the membrane cell, as indicated by reference electrodes or by standard half-cells, is zero. The "null" composition of the standard solution corresponds in the first case to identical $a_{\pm}$ values and, in the second, to identical a_i values.

B. The Technique of Measurement

The measurement of membrane electrode potentials is a straightforward procedure. The membranes are usually of low ohmic resistivity and, with one or two exceptions, there is no need for the special equipment generally associated with the glass electrode. Some aspects of the use of membrane electrodes call for special comment.

1. Mounting of the Membrane

The form in which the electrode is mounted and used depends on the nature of the membrane material (the preparation of the main varieties of membrane is described below). The "homogeneous" membrane, consisting of a thin sheet of ion exchange material (i.e., either a carefully cut slice of zeolite or clay film, or a cast film of synthetic resin), is normally fragile and requires careful support. It can be cemented on to the ground end of a glass tube [Fig. 3(a)] or held in rubber gaskets between glass flanges (the flanged joints of industrial glass piping, when ground flat, are particularly useful for this purpose, Fig. 3(b)).

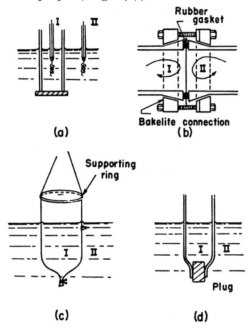

FIG. 3. Some common types of membrane electrode.

The collodion-based membranes of Sollner and Gregor (*30*) are cast over test tubes. This procedure results in thin ($\sim 50\mu$) transparent "bag" membranes which are supported on glass rings and tied, if necessary, at their lower ends with linen thread [Fig. 3(c)]. Even stronger membranes can be made by supporting the ion exchange material either in a rigid matrix, such as a porous glass disc (*65, 66*), as a molded plug of resin beads in a thermoplastic binder (*33*) [Fig. 3(d)] or as a rubbery sheet of resin-impregnated plastic material (*67*) which can also be mounted between flanges.

2. Stirring of the Solutions Adjacent to the Membrane

The concentration gradient across a membrane which is responsible for the membrane potential also gives rise to steady flux of electrolyte in one direction and a steady flux of solvent in the other. The principal effect of these fluxes is to create concentration gradients on both sides of the membrane and to lower the concentration gradient within the membrane itself. This situation is immediately evident when the membrane potential is observed to fall slowly and asymptotically with time to a lower value. If the external solutions are then stirred, the value at once rises again, and, with increasingly efficient stirring of the solutions adjacent to the membrane, rises further to a limiting value.

The magnitude of the initial fall, i.e., the difference between the unstirred value and the stirred, depends on three factors: the over-all concentration gradient, the absolute concentrations of electrolyte involved, and the porosity or permeability of the membrane. With homogeneous membranes the effect of stirring is significant even at the lowest concentrations. The collodion-based membranes are not so porous; not only is the effect of stirring less marked but the deviation term l'_w is also much smaller and on both accounts the membranes show a closer approach to ideal behavior under comparable conditions. The heterogeneous membranes are even less permeable to ions and solvent. Their porosity and permeability can be progressively decreased by increasing the content of plastic binder, by increasing the molding pressure and by filling any gaps between the ion exchange particles and the matrix with a hydrophobic fluid such as silicone oil (68). All of these treatments increase the resistivity of the membrane, but not to an inconvenient extent and, in certain cases, e.g., with resin plug electrodes (33), the effects of diffusion become negligibly small.

With other membranes, such as those available commercially, the effect of stirring is significant when either or both of the solutions is more concentrated than 0.1 m. Even with the most efficient stirring, however, some residual Nernst diffusion layer remains (62, 69–71), the effect of which in lowering the membrane potential will increase with the diffusive flux. The magnitude of this contribution to the nonideality is not known. It is probably not large and is certainly reproducible enough, for a particular membrane electrode arrangement, to be included in the initial calibration.

C. Preparation of Membranes

1. Zeolite and Clay Membranes

The Marshall-type membranes were initially single crystals of chabazite or apophyllite, cut and ground to thin plates, but later, films of colloidal clays of the montmorillonite and beidellite groups were found to be much better. They are easy to prepare, are durable and have proved very useful in the measurement of ionic activities especially in soils and other colloidal systems.

Wyllie and Patnode (33) showed how the clay particles can be more usefully incorporated into a plastic matrix and the development of clay membranes has followed along this line. In recent work of this kind, Barrer and James (*68*) have described the preparation of membranes of, for example, synthetic faujasite and synthetic sodium analcite embedded in polystyrene, polythene or polymerized methyl methacrylate. The membranes were prepared by mixing together finely ground zeolite with powdered thermoplastic and pressure-molding them into discs at 150°C. The water-permeability of these membranes was further reduced by presoaking them in silicone fluid and several such membranes showed a very high degree of selectivity (*68*).

All such zeolite membranes are cation-selective.

2. Collodion-Based Membranes

The preparation of this type of membrane has been described in several publications and was summarized by Sollner and Gregor in 1954 (*30*). The cation-selective membranes are prepared by casting successive films (generally two) of collodion cotton from a 4% solution in 1:1 ether-alcohol solution using a test tube as former. After most of the solvent has evaporated, the film is coagulated in water, oxidized (to produce carboxylic acid groups) by immersion in N sodium hydroxide solution containing dissolved air, and then dried (irreversibly) to the desired degree of thickness and porosity.

The electropositive anion-selective membranes are prepared by soaking the highly porous coagulated film in a 2% solution of protamine sulfate at pH 10.5 for several days. This membrane can then be dried as before.

The ordinary cation-selective collodion membrane suffers the disadvantages of being readily hydrolyzed in acid solutions and also in being unresponsive to the alkaline earth ions, for example, which combine chemically with the carboxylate groups. This type of membrane has, however, been greatly improved by Neihof (*48*). He has shown that the carboxylic acid groups may be replaced by the much more effective sulfonic acid groups. This is achieved by dissolving polystyrene sulfonic acid in the initial casting solution, or by soaking the coagulated film in aqueous sodium polysulfonate solution.

Although collodion-based membranes have been shown to be highly satisfactory in many solutions and are stable for several days, they are more sensitive to deterioration than membranes based on synthetic ion exchange resins, which are described next.

3. Synthetic Resin Membranes

Cation-selective membranes have been prepared from cross-linked polymethacrylic acid (*40*), sulfonated phenol-formaldehyde (*32, 58*) and sulfonated polystyrene (*41–45*). The first variety is prepared by polymerizing a solution of methacrylic acid and a cross-linking agent, contained between two glass plates. The other membranes are cast from sulfonated monomer. Homogeneous anion-selective membranes can be prepared by the polymerization of ethyleneimine cross-linked with epichlorhydrin (*38*).

These membranes, once considered desirable because of their transparency and apparent homogeneity, are nevertheless too brittle and too porous for use as membrane electrodes and would not normally be recommended for use as such.

They can, however, be easily modified in such a way as to eliminate these defects whilst still retaining the stability and high fixed charge concentration which are characteristic of these ion exchange materials. This is done in several ways. As indicated previously, the membranes can be supported by casting them on a gauze backing or in a fritted disk (*65, 66*). They can be grafted onto a tougher porous backing such as polythene by the "graft polymer" technique (*72*) of chemically bonding two separate polymers by irradiating an intimate mixture of them with an intense cobalt source. To make a membrane, a porous polythene sheet is coated with a thin layer of polystyrene, irradiated and then sulfonated in the usual way. The unbonded material (a small fraction of the total) is removed at this stage, leaving a flexible membrane of high ionic selectivity (*72*). But, more usually, the ion exchange material, i.e., sulfonated or aminated polystyrene, is mixed thoroughly with a plastic binder and molded under pressure into a flexible sheet. This type of membrane is much less porous and permeable than the parent resin material; it therefore shows a closer approach to the function of an ideal membrane electrode. It is the type which is available commercially (see footnote 1 on page *413*) and although not as elastic or rugged as it might be, is nevertheless easily handled, clamped, and mounted as a membrane electrode.

4. Multilayer Membrane Electrodes

This recent development (*52*) involves different preparative techniques. The aim is to build up successive parallel layers of an insoluble salt such as calcium stearate, and then to mount these between two electrolyte solutions in such a way that the transport of the potential-determining calcium ions is in a direction at right angles to the axis of orientation of the molecules in the monolayers. The experimental procedure is an intricate one and the original papers should be consulted for full details. Briefly, successive monolayers of the stearate are taken up from the surface of a Langmuir trough onto the virginal edges of a freshly broken microscope slide. Adhesion to these edges is first ensured by rubbing on to them a layer of ferric stearate and then, after ∼50 layers of the appropriate alkaline earth stearate have been superimposed, the fitting edges of both halves of the slide are carefully pressed back into place and immediately cemented to a supporting face plate [Fig. 4(a)]. The final membrane, illustrated diagrammatically in Fig. 4(b), has a high ohmic resistivity ($\ll 50$ megohms)

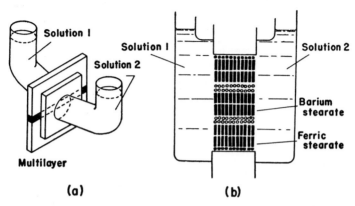

Fig. 4. (a) Multilayer membrane cell. (b) Diagrammatic representation of a multilayer membrane.

and a sensitive electronic voltmeter is required to measure the membrane potentials.

V. Applications of Membrane Electrodes

The recorded applications fall into two categories. The first has been concerned with the investigation of membrane performance, i.e., with the measurement of membrane potential between two solutions of known composition. The observed value, ΔE, is compared with the ideal value, ΔE_{max}, and in terms of some arbitrary precision, a limit is set to the usefulness of Eq. (9). Many such studies have been recorded and it is not easy to summarize them. The generalization may be made that the limit of ideality is a property of the membrane but is seldom dependent on the species of counter-ion. Thus a particular membrane will show similar selectivity to all the alkali metal ions and similar selectivity also towards alkaline earth ions and other divalent ions such as zinc, cadmium, manganese, and copper. Numerous individual studies have been recorded (73–81) and have recently been summarized (81–85). The limits of ideal behavior of some typical membranes are shown in Table I; the limit in each case referring to the maximum concentration below which $\Delta E/\Delta E_{max}$ is not less than 0.99.

Special uses of membrane electrodes, e.g., in liquid ammonia (66) and as low temperature protodes (i.e., sources of hydrogen ions) (86), have also been described.

TABLE I

LIMITS OF IDEAL PERFORMANCE OF SOME TYPICAL MEMBRANES[a]

Membrane	Conservative estimate of limit	Reference
Homogeneous membranes of pure ion exchange resin	0.01 m	58, 65
Homogeneous membranes of zeolite sheet	0.1 m	16
Homogeneous membranes based on collodion	0.05 m	46–49
Heterogeneous membrane of plastic-bonded resin	0.02 m	42–44
Heterogeneous membrane of plastic-bonded resin plug	1 m	33
Heterogeneous membrane of plastic-bonded zeolite	1 m	68

[a] $\Delta E/\Delta E_{max}$ is not less than 0.99.

Within the limits of ideality discussed above, there have been a number of applications of membrane electrodes to the determination of ionic activities and ionic concentrations in solutions of unknown composition. Nearly all of these measurements have been directed towards the determination of alkali and alkaline earth ion activities in suspensions of clays, although there have also been similar measurements in solutions of soaps, of polymeric ions and of proteins (87–91). The latter type of measurements have used the collodion-based membranes, particularly the modification of them described by Neihof (48). Ostacoli and Saini (91) also checked their membrane potential measurements of sodium ion activity against a sodium amalgam electrode; the agreement was excellent.

VI. The Development of Specific Membrane Electrodes

It was pointed out earlier in this chapter that a serious limitation of membrane electrodes is their lack of specificity towards particular ionic species of the same charge. Thus, in solutions containing more than one electrolyte, the membrane potential responds to the total cationic or the total anionic concentration. The reservation must be made that if one of the diffusible ions has unusual properties such as high mobility (H^+ ion) or large size (macro-ion), then some distinction can often be made between its contribution to the total membrane potential and that of others. This, however, is an unsatisfactory basis for the use of membrane electrodes in ordinary systems and will not be considered further.

The development of membrane electrodes which will respond electromotively, as does the glass electrode, to only *one* species of ion is still in its early stages, but sufficient success has been achieved to merit some discussion of its essential features. Two types of specificity are possible, one physical and the other chemical.

Although ions in solution do not differ greatly in their sizes, some discrimination by the membrane is possible, particularly if the membrane pores are small and inelastic. This type of channel is commonly found in zeolitic materials. Thus, Marshall's montmorillonite membranes, pretreated at 490°C, became insensitive to divalent cations and could be used for the determination of alkali ion concentrations in the presence of calcium and barium ions. Further refinemc_t of this ion sieve property is obviously possible. Barrer and Sammon (*92, 93*) have shown that, under certain conditions, synthetic analcite will quantitatively take up sodium and potassium ions but totally exclude cesium ions, which evidently cannot penetrate the windows of the successive cages of this zeolite. Barrer and James (*68*) therefore prepared membranes of this material by molding it into a plastic binder and attempted to demonstrate that such a membrane would respond only to sodium or potassium, but not to cesium ions or other large ions such as R_4N^+. This specific selectivity was not achieved, almost certainly because of "leaks" i.e., additional, uncharged paths, between the zeolite particles and the binder. The filling of this space with an inert fluid, such as silicone fluid, certainly improved the efficiency of the membrane, and membranes of this type were cation selective over a wide concentration range (0–2 *m*). Whilst therefore the specificity of such membranes is still incomplete, they are clearly a good basis for further improvement.

Chemical specificity has been sought by incorporating into the membrane, a reagent which reacts specifically (by complex formation or precipitation) with the ion in question. Thus Waermann *et al.* (*94*) prepared membranes from an ion exchange material developed by Skogseid (*95*) which, because of its similarity to dipicrylamine, showed a marked preference for potassium over sodium ions. Bi-ionic membrane potentials were observed which were indicative of this preferential selectivity but not to the extent of conferring on this membrane the status of a potassium electrode.

The idea of incorporating into the membrane some insoluble form of the ion being studied has been implemented in other ways. Tendeloo and Krips (*96*), for example, prepared membranes of paraffin wax supported on a gauze and containing a suspension of calcium oxalate. Although these membranes were not subjected to a thorough test, they gave a specific and theoretical response to the calcium ion concentration which was independent of the pH and of the presence of potassium ions. Several applications of this calcium electrode to the study of calcium binding in protein solutions were described. Similar, but less satisfactory, applications of the same principle have been noted by Hirsh-Ayalon (*97*) and by Babcock (*98*). In both cases, a membrane impregnated with barium sulfate was used.

The corresponding membrane potential was sensitive to barium and to sulfate ions but, whilst these membranes could be used as indicator electrodes in titrations, they could hardly be described as membrane reference electrodes.

Finally, there are the multilayer membranes of Gregor and Schonhorn (52). These stearate membranes, described above, show excellent cationic selectivity (cf. Table II) which is comparable with that of the Wyllie and Patnode and of the Barrer and James electrodes. Gregor and Schonhorn state the membranes are also ion selective, i.e., specifically selective to the ionic species incorporated in them, and although confirmatory results are not available as yet, this appears to be a highly promising type of membrane electrode.

TABLE II

MEMBRANE POTENTIALS OBSERVED WITH MULTILAYER MEMBRANE
ELECTRODES IN THE CELL

Ag	AgCl	calcium chloride solution (I)	calcium membrane	calcium chloride solution (II)	AgCl	Ag

Molality of solution (I)	Molality of solution (II)	Cell emf (mv)	
		Observed E	Calculated E_{max}
0.001	0.0001	85.4	86.0
0.002	0.001	25.4	25.05
0.020	0.010	23.9	23.20
0.025	0.0125	23.8	24.05
0.05	0.025	22.7	22.20
0.20	0.100	23.7	23.60
1.00	0.500	29.5	30.80
5.00	2.500	94.5	93.25
5.00	0.500	190	188

REFERENCES

1. Haber, F., and Beutner, R., *Ann. Physik* [4] **26**, 327 (1908).
2. Haber, F., *Ann. Physik* [4] **26**, 927 (1908).
3. Haber, F., and Klemensiewicz, Z., *Z. physik. Chem.* **67**, 385 (1909).
4. Nernst, W., and Riesenfeld, E. H., *Ann. Physik* [4] **8**, 600 (1902).
5. Donnan, F. G., *Chem. Revs.* **1**, 73 (1925).
6. Horovitz, K., *Z. Physik* **15**, 369 (1923).
7. Horovitz, K., *Z. physik. Chem.* **115**, 424 (1925).
8. Teorell, T., *Proc. Soc. Exptl. Biol. Med.* **33**, 282 (1935).
9. Teorell, T., *Proc. Natl. Acad. Sci.* **21**, 152 (1935).

10. Meyer, K. H., and Sievers, J.-F., *Helv. Chim. Acta* **19**, 649, 665, 987 (1936).

11. Tendeloo, H. J. C., *J. Biol. Chem.* **113**, 333 (1936).

12. Marshall, C. E., *J. Phys. Chem.* **43**, 1155 (1939); **48**, 67 (1944); **52**, 1284 (1948).

13. Scatchard, G., *J. Am. Chem. Soc.* **75**, 2883 (1953).

14. Michaelis, L., *Colloid Symposium Monograph* **5**, 135 (1927).

15. Michaelis, L., *Kolloid Z.* **62**, 2 (1933).

16. Marshall, C. E., and Bergman, W. E., *J. Am. Chem. Soc.* **63**, 1911 (1941).

17. Marshall, C. E., and Bergman, W. E., *J. Phys. Chem.* **46**, 52, 325 (1942).

18. Marshall, C. E., and Krinbill, C. A., *J. Am. Chem. Soc.* **64**, 1814 (1942).

19. Marshall, C. E., and Krinbill, C. A., *J. Phys. Chem.* **46**, 1077 (1942).

20. Marshall, C. E., and Ayers, A. D., *J. Am. Chem. Soc.* **70**, 1207 (1948).

21. Marshall, C. E., and Eime, L. O., *J. Am. Chem. Soc.* **70**, 1302 (1948).

22. Chatterjee, B., and Marshall, C. E., *J. Phys. Chem.* **54**, 671 (1950).

23. Carr, C. W., and Sollner, K., *J. Gen. Physiol.* **28**, 119 (1944).

24. Carr, C. W., Gregor, H. P., and Sollner, K., *J. Gen. Physiol.* **28**, 179 (1945).

25. Sollner, K., *J. Am. Chem. Soc.* **65**, 2260 (1943); **68**, 409 (1954).

26. Sollner, K., and Gregor, H. P., *J. Am. Chem. Soc.* **67**, 346 (1945).

27. Sollner, K., *J. Phys. Chem.* **49**, 47, 171, 265 (1945).

28. Sollner, K., and Gregor, H. P., *J. Phys. Chem.* **50**, 470 (1946); **51**, 299 (1947); **54**, 325, 330 (1950).

29. Sollner, K., and Gregor, H. P., *J. Colloid Sci.* **6**, 557 (1951); **7**, 37 (1952).

30. Gregor, H. P., and Sollner, K., *J. Phys. Chem.* **50**, 53, 88 (1946); **58**, 409 (1954).

31. Kressman, T. R. E., *Nature* **165**, 568 (1950).

32. Kressman, T. R. E., *J. Appl. Chem.* **4**, 123 (1954).

33. Wyllie, M. R. J., and Patnode, H. W., *J. Phys. Chem.* **54**, 204 (1950).

34. Juda, W., and McRae, W. A., *J. Am. Chem. Soc.* **72**, 1044 (1950).

35. Manecke, G., and Bonhoeffer, K. F., *Z. Elektrochem.* **55**, 475 (1951).

36. Manecke, G., *Z. Elektrochem.* **55**, 672 (1951).

37. Manecke, G., *Z. physik. Chem. (Leipzig)* **201**, 193 (1952).

38. Bonhoeffer, K. F., Miller, L., and Schinderwolf, U., *Z. physik. Chem. (Leipzig)* **198**, 270 (1951).

39. Schlögl, R., *Z. Elektrochem.* **57**, 195 (1953).

40. Hills, G. J., Kitchener, J. A., and Ovenden, P. J., *Trans. Faraday Soc.* **51**, 719 (1955).

41. Graydon, W. F., and Stewart, R. J., *J. Phys. Chem.* **59**, 86 (1955).

42. Gregor, H. P., Jacobson, H., Shair, R. C., and Wetstone, D. M., *J. Phys. Chem.* **61**, 141 (1957).

43. Gregor, H. P., and Wetstone, D. M., *J. Phys. Chem.* **61**, 147, 151 (1957).

44. Gregor, H. P., and Wetstone, D. M., *Discussions Faraday Soc.* **21**, 162 (1956).

45. Rosenberg, N. W., George, J. H. B., and Potter, W. D., *J. Electrochem. Soc.* **104**, 111 (1957).

46. Sollner, K., *J. Phys. Chem.* **61**, 156 (1957).

47. Sollner, K., and Neihof, R., *Arch. Biochem. Biophys.* **33**, 166 (1951).

48. Neihof, R., *J. Phys. Chem.* **58**, 916 (1954).

49. Gottlieb, M. H., Neihof, R., and Sollner, K., *J. Phys. Chem.* **61**, 154 (1957).

50. Wyllie, M. R. J., and Kanaan, S. L., *J. Phys. Chem.* **58**, 73 (1954).

51. Winger, A. G., Bodamer, G. W., and Kunin, R., *J. Electrochem. Soc.* **100**, 178 (1953).

52. Gregor, H. P., and Schonhorn, H. *J. Am. Chem. Soc.* **79**, 1507 (1957); **81**, 3911 (1959).

53. Teorell, T., *Z. Elektrochem.* **55**, 460 (1951).

54. Teorell, T., *Progr. in Biophys. Biophys. Chem.* **3**, 305 (1953).

55. Teorell, T., *Discussions Faraday Soc.* **21**, 9 (1956).

56. Schlögl, R., and Helfferich, F., *Z. Elektrochem.* **56**, 644 (1952).

57. Schlögl, R., *Z. Elektrochem.* **57**, 195 (1953).

58. Spiro, M., *J. Chem. Educ.* **33**, 464 (1956).

59. Sollner, K., *J. Phys. Chem.* **53**, 1211, 1226 (1949).

60. Wyllie, M. R. J., *J. Phys. Chem.* **58**, 67, 73 (1954).

61. Bergsma, F., and Staverman, A. J., *Discussions Faraday Soc.* **21**, 61 (1956).

62. Helfferich, F., *Discussions Faraday Soc.* **21**, 83 (1956).

63. Lakshminaryaniah, N., Thesis (London), 1956; Lakshminaryaniah, N., Hills, G. J., and Jacobs, P. W. M., in course of publication.

64. Despić, A., and Hills, G. J., *Trans. Faraday Soc.* **51**, 1260 (1955).

65. Brun, T. S., Special Publication No. 15, University of Bergen, 1954.

66. Bergin, M. J., and Heyn, A. H. A., *J. Am. Chem. Soc.* **76**, 4765 (1954).

67. Kressman, T. R. E., and Tye, F. L., *Discussions Faraday Soc.* **21**, 185 (1956).

68. Barrer, R. M., and James, S. D., *J. Phys. Chem.* **64**, 417, 421 (1960).

69. Helfferich, F., *Z. physik. Chem. (Frankfurt)* **4**, 386 (1955).

70. Partridge, S. M., and Peers, A. M., *J. Appl. Chem.* **8**, 49 (1958).

71. Mackay, D., and Meares, P., *Kolloid Z.* **167**, 31 (1959).

72. Chen, W. K. W., Mesrobian, R. B., Ballantine, D. S., Metz, D. J., and Gilnes, A., *J. Polymer Sci.* **23**, 903 (1957).

73. Sinha, S. K., *J. Indian Chem. Soc.* **31**, 572 (1954); **32**, 35 (1955).

74. Basu, A. S., and Sinha, S. K., *J. Indian Chem. Soc.* **32**, 399 (1955).

75. Mitra, D. K., and Chatterjee, B., *J. Indian Chem. Soc.* **32**, 751 (1955).

76. Hutchings, D., and Williams, R. J. P., *Discussions Faraday Soc.* **21**, 192 (1956).

77. Basu, A. S., *Sci. and Culture (Calcutta)* **21**, 447 (1956).

78. Basu, A. S., *J. Indian Chem. Soc.* **35**, 451 (1958).

79. Kahlweit, M., *Z. physik. Chem. (Frankfurt)* **6**, 45 (1956).

80. Chaussidon, J., *Compt. rend. acad. sci.* **244**, 2798 (1957).

81. Parsons, J. S., *Anal. Chem.* **30**, 1262 (1958).

82. Argersinger, W. J., *Ann. Rev. Phys. Chem.* **9**, 157 (1958).

83. Krishnaswamy, N., *J. Sci. Ind. Research (India)* **17A**, 328 (1958).

84. Sollner, K., *Svensk Kem. Tidskr.* **6–7**, 267 (1958).

85. See also numerous other contributions in the *Discussions Faraday Soc.* **21** (1956).

86. Eigen, M., and De Maeyer, L., *Proc. Roy. Soc.* **A247**, 505 (1958).

87. Carr, C. W., Johnson, W. F., and Kolthoff, I. M., *J. Phys. Chem.* **51**, 636 (1947).

88. Chandler, R. C., and McBain, J. W., *J. Phys. Chem.* **53**, 930 (1949).

89. Carr, C. W., and Topol, L., *J. Phys. Chem.* **54**, 176 (1950).

90. Carr, C. W., *Arch. Biochem. Biophys.* **40**, 286 (1952); **43**, 147 (1953); **46**, 417, 424 (1953).

91. Ostacoli, G., and Saini, G., *Ann. chim. (Rome)* **46**, 614 (1956).

92. Barrer, R. M., and Sammon, D. C., *J. Chem. Soc.* 675 (1956).

93. Barrer, R. M., *J. Chem. Soc.* 2342 (1950).

94. Waermann, D., Bonhoeffer, K. F., and Helfferich, F., *Z. physik. Chem. (Frankfurt)* **8**, 265 (1956).

95. Skogseid, A., Thesis, University of Oslo, Norway, 1948.

96. Tendeloo, H. J. C., and Krips, A., *Rec. trav. chim.* **76**, 703, 994 (1957); **77**, 406, 678 (1958).

97. Hirsch-Ayalon, P., *J. Polymer Sci.* **23**, 697 (1957).

98. Babcock, R. F., *Dissertation Abstr.* **19**, 428 (1958).

Chapter Ten

Reference Electrodes in Nonaqueous Solutions

G. J. Hills

I. Introduction

From the time of the earliest potentiometric measurements in aqueous solutions, there has followed a similar but more limited and less co-ordinated development of electrodes, cells and potentiometric devices for use in nonaqueous solutions. Each nonaqueous solvent system is open to a range of measurements comparable in extent with the range of potentiometric measurements in aqueous solutions and the total field of interest is therefore considerable. There is an extensive if somewhat sporadic literature on the subject which illustrates a wide variety of purposes (as well as variation in quality) and which is difficult to classify. The number of deliberate attempts to study electrode potentials, as such, in nonaqueous solutions is not large but there have been numerous accounts of, for example, polarographic measurements involving reference electrodes and even more numerous accounts of potentiometric titrations in nonaqueous media which have often, although not always, involved the use of reference electrodes.

This chapter will be concerned to describe such electrode systems, operating in anhydrous media, as have been shown to be reversible, reproducible, and suitable for use as reference electrodes. It will not deal with electrodes such as bare wires, retarded (gebremste) electrodes and other indicator electrodes of simple construction which are often sufficient to indicate precisely enough equivalence points in titrations, but which are neither associated with a known electrode reaction nor subject to the Nernst relation. Neither will the chapter be concerned with the numerous applications of potentiometric measurements in nonaqueous solutions. The variation of standard emf values, or the free energy of transfer of solutes from one solvent to another, the effects of changing dielectric constant and solvation energy on acidity or degree of electrolytic dissociation are subjects of great potential interest, but they are not sufficiently advanced to warrant attempting a general review and do not fall strictly within the present limited terms of reference.

The ground to be covered is further restricted by the fact that there is no need to discuss the relatively precise measurements of emf values and electrode potentials which have been made in relation to solutions in the aliphatic alcohols, in mixtures of these with water and in partly aqueous mixtures involving other simple organic solvents such as acetone and dioxane. These measurements have formed a natural and straightforward extension of the corresponding measurements in aqueous solutions and have been included in the material of the preceding chapters. Excellent accounts of this particular aspect as a whole can be found in standard texts (1, 2) and in additional summaries (3–7). In this connection, it is interesting to note that almost all of the common reference electrodes considered in previous chapters are applicable to alcoholic media, as well as to electrolyte solutions in some other inert organic solvents. There is invariably some loss of reproducibility as compared with their performance in aqueous solutions but only the glass electrode loses its useful function altogether in completely anhydrous media.

Reference electrodes in the other nonaqueous solutions will be considered in terms of each solvent system in turn, rather than in terms of the range of applicability of each electrode. This is a natural classification which emphasizes the fact that the practical and theoretical problems encountered in this field are, almost always, peculiar to the particular solvent employed. The intending investigator must have its properties and special requirements foremost in his mind, rather than those of any one kind of electrode. A given electrode must be adaptable to the system it is desired to study. The separate consideration of each solvent is preceded by a section of general comments relevant to the whole field of study of nonaqueous electrolyte solutions.

II. General Considerations Relating to Nonaqueous Systems

A. EXPERIMENTAL TECHNIQUES

Most of the potentiometric measurements in nonaqueous solutions have been carried out at room temperature, and the electrodes and cells have been similar in design and construction to those used in aqueous solutions. The first additional problem is presented by the preparation and purification of the solvent. These operations are less easily accomplished than is the case for water mainly because they are much less liberally available. "Conductance stills" which reject large proportions of solvent are impracticable, and resort must be had to standard methods such as repeated fractional distillation or crystallization; these must normally be preceded by chemical purifications peculiar to each solvent. Additional difficulties are often encountered from the great susceptibility of many nonaqueous solvents to adventitious contamination. Fortunately, with a single exception, most of the residual impurities left by normal purification techniques will not be electrochemically active. The exception is the ubiquitous impurity, water, which will always be a probable contaminant from the surrounding atmosphere. The presence of even small concentrations of water is likely to have a marked effect on the properties of an electrolyte in nonaqueous solution, not only because of its low molecular weight, but also because of the preferred solvation of the ions by water molecules, leading to an increase in ionization. Water may, however, be a *necessary* contaminant in some cases, e.g., to facilitate the functioning of the glass electrode. For completely anhydrous systems, especially for those which readily react with water, an enclosed apparatus is essential. This is useful also if the solvent vapor is obnoxious and we have found that a glass envelope of the type shown in Fig. 1(a) is the basis of a useful general purpose apparatus for electrochemical measurements in closed systems; ancillary equipment is shown in Fig. 1(b). It has flanged joints, flexible ball-and-socket connections and large and small syringe attachments which allow for the greatest degree of movement and adaptability even for systems under vacuum or an inert atmosphere.

Very often, the measurement of electrode potential is the easiest part of the procedure and the greatest degree of uncertainty is attached to the value of the electrolyte concentration. The composition of the nonaqueous solution may be determined externally by the normal preparative and analytical methods. On the other hand, it may be more convenient to prepare the solution *in situ*, and to determine its composition by sampling or by conductance measurement. As a further alternative, a particular electrolyte can often be generated coulometrically, in precise quantity, by, for example, anodic dissolution of a metal. This is a very convenient way of altering ionic concentrations in an enclosed system.

B. The Range of Electrolyte Solutions

The most serious limitation of electrochemical studies of nonaqueous solutions is the comparatively small range of solutes available. Most non-aqueous solvents have a dielectric constant appreciably lower than that

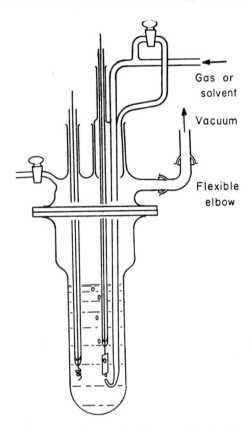

Fig. 1a. Vacuum-tight envelope for use with closed systems.

of water and, in consequence, show a markedly lower capacity to dissolve inorganic electrolytes. They also give rise to solutions in which the degrees of ionization and dissociation of electrolytes are much lower than in aqueous solutions. Even when the dielectric constant is not small, it does not follow that a solvent will give rise to solubilities and degrees of ioniza-tion comparable with those in water. The size of the solvent molecule and the availability of the dipole are also important factors; thus nitrobenzene, for example, whilst having a dielectric constant of 34.8 at 25°C, is not a good ionizing solvent.

Some solutes have intrinsically higher solubilities than others, irrespective of the solvent. Those having large ions, such as alkylammonium cations, iodide, phenolate, benzenesulfonate, and picrate anions, generally show appreciable solubility even in solvents of very low dielectric constant. Silver salts are also often more soluble than others. Solvents which undergo auto-ionization often preferentially dissolve solutes containing an ion in common with the products of auto-ionization. Thus, sulfites are soluble in liquid sulfur dioxide and acetates in acetic anhydride, although an important exception to this generalization is found with liquid ammonia, in which amides are even less soluble than are oxides and hydroxides in water. In inorganic solvents, the range of solubilities may well be quite different from that instinctively remembered for aqueous solutions. Taking liquid

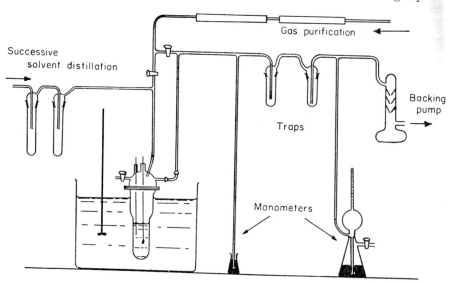

FIG. 1b. Ancillary equipment for use with a closed system.

ammonia again as an example, silver and mercurous salts are readily soluble in it, whereas all sulfates, even ammonium sulfate, are insoluble. The basis of these generalizations is to be found in the extensive studies, principally by Kraus and his co-workers, of the conductivities of a wide variety of nonaqueous solutions. They have led to an accurate description of the properties of nonaqueous electrolyte solutions in terms of the degree of ionization or dissociation of the solutes dissolved in them. These conductance studies have been reviewed from time to time (8–12) and are necessary reading before corresponding emf measurements can be undertaken or interpreted.

C. The Range of Electrodes

With the single exception of the "electron electrode," there are no new electrodes, unique to nonaqueous solutions. Potentiometric studies of nonaqueous systems have therefore been mainly concerned with the application of electrodes of value proven in aqueous solutions, although some electrodes not generally serviceable in aqueous systems may come into their own in other solvents because of favorable changes in solubility relationships. In general, the range of application of a given electrode is somewhat restricted and there has hitherto been much less emphasis on the finer details of electrode preparation and electrode reproducibility. Indeed the level of accuracy of most potentiometric measurements in anhydrous solutions has been insufficient to warrant any distinction between alternative methods of preparing electrodes. Only in the case of the hydrogen electrode has it been customary to describe in detail its preparation and performance. This chapter therefore differs from those preceding it in that its main concern is to indicate the solvents in which most of the significant emf measurements have been made and to indicate which electrodes function reversibly and reproducibly in them. The causes of the residual uncertainties in electrode potential have generally not been known and there is every reason to suppose that the electrodes which obviously function well could in many cases be refined to a much higher level of performance.

Where metal salts do dissolve and ionize, the normal potential-determining charge-transfer processes occur at the appropriate metal or metal-amalgam electrodes and give rise to potentials governed by the Nernst relation,

$$E = E^\circ + \frac{RT}{nF} \ln \alpha\, m\, \gamma \qquad (1)$$

where m is the molality of the potential-determining electrolyte, α its degree of ionization, and γ the molal ionic activity coefficient. Electrodes of the second kind can also be devised although they are not always based on the same sparingly soluble salts (e.g., of silver or mercury) as those familiar from aqueous systems. Where such electrodes are available, they can be combined with other electrodes in cells without liquid junction, which can be made the basis of thermodynamic measurements of the kind described in Chapter 1 and elsewhere, although, so far, this rewarding approach has received little attention in relation to anhydrous nonhydroxylic solvents.

Indeed, the number of electrochemical measurements of precise thermodynamic significance in solvents of this type is very small.

Two types of cell without liquid junction which have been used are (1) the silver halide–mercurous halide cell exemplified by

$$\text{Ag} \ \Big| \ \text{AgCl} \ \Big| \ \begin{array}{c} \text{chloride solution} \\ \text{in anhydrous solvent} \end{array} \ \Big| \ \text{Hg}_2\text{Cl}_2 \ \Big| \ \text{Hg},$$

and (2) the amalgam cell exemplified by

$$\begin{array}{c} \text{Hg, M} \\ (N_1) \end{array} \ \Big| \ \begin{array}{c} \text{metal salt solution} \\ \text{in anhydrous solvent} \end{array} \ \Big| \ \begin{array}{c} \text{Hg, M} \\ (N_2) \end{array}$$

where N_1 and N_2 represent different mole fractions of the metal M in the two amalgams. Neither type of cell gives any thermodynamic information concerning the nonaqueous electrolyte system because the emf values of both cells are, theoretically, independent of the solution phase separating the electrodes. This, however, has the advantage that the theoretical emf values can be calculated from independent data and can be used therefore to check the observed values as well as the reproducibility and reversibility of each electrode combination. The use of cells with liquid junctions makes a smaller demand on the range of reference electrodes available in any one solvent but is hampered by the absence of transport numbers corresponding to these systems.

Mention must be made at this stage that by far the commonest reference electrode that has been used in nonaqueous systems is the ordinary *aqueous* calomel electrode. This is connected to the nonaqueous solution *via* a salt bridge, the junction being made through a sintered disc or asbestos plug, or through the ground glass sleeve of the dip-type calomel electrode. Although the junction so formed involves the intermixing or interdiffusion of different solvents, the liquid junction potential is evidently sufficiently constant in many cases for electrode potentials in the nonaqueous solution to be measured with a precision of a few millivolts. This rather unsatisfactory practice will not be discussed. In most cases, there are suitable alternative reference electrodes which involve only the solvent in question; they avoid the possibility of large and unknown junction potentials and also the possibility of contaminating the nonaqueous system with water. There is no theoretical advantage to be gained by referring emf measurements in a variety of solvent systems to a particular half-cell potential in another. Similar remarks can be made about the glass electrode which also has been used widely for potentiometric titrations in nonaqueous media. Here, the risk of contamination is negligible but there is little evidence that this electrode functions satisfactorily in completely anhydrous media.

Even for measurements in glacial acetic acid where, it is claimed, it can be used "for several titrations" (*13*), marked deterioration sets in which can be only partly remedied by replacement of the internal aqueous solution. It seems clear that the ordinary glass electrode responds only to *hydrated* hydrogen ions and attempts, for example, to use the glass electrode with the same nonaqueous solution inside and out have been unsuccessful (*14*) except at elevated temperatures in molten salt systems where the glass functions simply as a membrane permeable only to alkali metal ions (*15*). The use of synthetic resin membranes as selective diaphragms in anhydrous media is possible (*16*) but there has been little development along these lines as yet.

As well as these two reference electrodes, ill-suited to transfer from their proper sphere, simple wire electrodes of platinum, gold, molybdenum, and other metals have been used in potentiometric titrations. They show a partial pH response even in anhydrous solutions and serve to indicate end-points in acid-base titrations. This aspect has been well covered in a number of recent reviews (*11, 17–22*), all of which contain extensive bibliographies.

D. Standards of Electrode Potential

All of the measurements of emf in nonaqueous solutions can be considered on the thermodynamic basis given in Chapter 1; the choice of standard states and the departures from ideality are dealt with in the same way. The individual electrode potentials in any solvent are referred, wherever possible, to that of the standard hydrogen electrode in the same solvent. Fortunately, this electrode is widely applicable to nonaqueous systems and combinations of other electrodes with the hydrogen electrode, sometimes involving the uncertainties of a liquid-junction potential, can generally be made. Where this is not the case an alternative working standard can usually be found. Standard potentials are obtained by the usual extrapolation methods based on the Debye-Hückel theory, care being taken to define the concentration scale, since in solvents other than water, the molar and molal scales give very different values for the standard electrode potential.

III. Reference Electrodes in Individual Solvent Systems

The solvent systems will be considered in order of decreasing similarity with aqueous solutions. Thus, the "inert" organic solvents which resemble the alcohols as electrolyte media are considered first. These are followed by the more unusual organic solvents, the "super-acid" liquid fatty acids and the highly ionizing liquid aliphatic amides. Next, liquid ammonia, hydrazine, and related solvents are considered and these are followed by the less commonly used inorganic solvents. Several of the reviews mentioned above have classified similar data in terms of electrodes. Cruse (22), in particular, briefly reviews the whole range of application of the hydrogen, quinhydrone, and glass electrodes to nonaqueous systems. A similar review of other electrodes, particularly of the antimony electrode, is included in the paper of Deal and Wyld (23).

A. "INERT" ORGANIC SOLVENTS

1. Hydrocarbons

Extensive studies of indicator electrodes and potentiometric titrations in hydrocarbon and related solvents have been made, principally to determine directly the degree of acidity in fuel oils and lubricating oils. The work that has been summarized (11, 19, 24–26) has been based, almost exclusively, on a combination of indicator electrode and aqueous reference electrode and contains many instances where the addition of some other solvent, such as alcohol, was necessary before satisfactory results could be obtained. Some isolated examples exist of more deliberate attempts to utilize reference electrodes and the Nernst relation. Thus, the use of the silver–silver picrate electrode (27) and the copper–copper oleate electrode (28) has been reported but these electrodes, which were immersed directly in hydrocarbon solutions or solutions in anhydrous dioxane, gave measurements of only semiquantitative significance.

Many of the difficulties of making emf measurements in solvents of very low dielectric constant are evident from the work of La Mer and Downes (29). They successfully attempted the titration of trichloracetic acid with diethylamine in benzene solution using two quinhydrone electrodes in a cell with liquid junction, as shown below.

Pt	quinhydrone		quinhydrone		Pt
	diethylamine, 0.0413 m		diethylamine (x)		
	tetraisoamylammonium iodide (satd)		tetraisoamylammonium iodide (satd)		
	trichloracetic acid, 0.165 m		trichloracetic acid, 0.165 m		

in benzene solution

To obtain reproducibility, they were obliged to use two large smooth platinum electrodes which were pressed on either side of the filter paper which supported the liquid junction (Fig. 2). Both solutions were saturated with tetraisoamylammonium iodide to minimize the liquid-junction potential and to decrease the ohmic resistance of the solution. Even so the resistance was still too high for any ordinary galvanometer to be used, notwithstanding the proximity of both large electrodes; lacking, apparently, an electronic voltmeter, they measured the cell emf by charging a condenser to

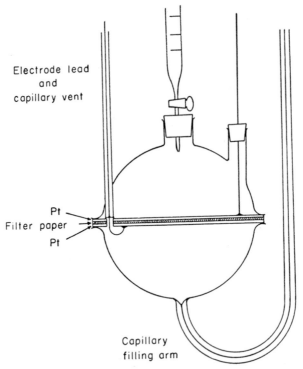

Electrode lead
and
capillary vent

Pt
Filter paper
Pt

Capillary
filling arm

Fig. 2. The cell of La Mer and Downes for acid-base titrations in benzene solution.

the cell voltage then discharging it through a ballistic galvanometer. In this way, they were able to measure emf's to ±0.1 mv and obtained excellent titration curves with sharp inflections.

2. Acetone

While a number of accurate measurements of electrode potentials have been made using electrolyte solutions in aqueous acetone (3, 30) very few corresponding studies have been made in anhydrous acetone. The work on aqueous acetone solutions indicates that the hydrogen, quinhydrone, and silver–silver chloride electrodes all function satisfactorily in the presence of acetone, although some difficulty has been experienced with the slow hydrogenation of acetone at platinum surfaces.

In anhydrous acetone, however, the situation is not so clear. Ulich and Spiegel (*31*) showed that whilst cells of the type

$$\text{Na, Hg} \left.\begin{array}{c} \\ (N_1) \end{array}\right| \begin{array}{c} \text{NaI in} \\ \text{acetone} \end{array} \left|\begin{array}{c} \text{Na, Hg} \\ (N_2) \end{array}\right.$$

gave reproducible emf's, the cell

$$\text{Ag} \mid \text{AgCl} \mid \text{chloride solution in acetone} \mid \text{Hg}_2\text{Cl}_2 \mid \text{Hg}$$

did not. The irreproducibility was attributed mainly to the calomel electrode and, in particular, to the disproportionation reaction of the mercurous ion. The silver–silver chloride electrode was also thought to be affected by the formation of complex argento-chloride ions. Although some complex formation does take place, for the solubility of both calomel and silver chloride in acetone is significantly increased by the addition of lithium chloride, the silver–silver chloride electrode is not sufficiently affected for its reproducibility or usefulness to be impaired. Everett and Rasmussen (*32*) used it quite successfully to study the degree of dissociation of hydrogen chloride in acetone solution using the cell,

$$\text{Pt, H}_2 \mid \text{HCl in anhydrous acetone} \mid \text{AgCl} \mid \text{Ag}$$

The silver–silver chloride electrodes consisted of an intimate mixture of precipitated silver and silver chloride as recommended by Güntelberg (*33*). The hydrogen electrodes were constructed from platinum foil, and were black-platinized. No reduction of the acetone was detectable even after hydrogen had been bubbled through the system for 24 hr, and over the entire range, the cell emf's were reproducible to ± 0.1 mv. Because of the high cell resistance, an electronic voltmeter was required. The cell emf is given by the expression

$$E = E^\circ - \frac{2RT}{F} \ln \alpha \, m_{\text{HCl}} \, \gamma_\pm \tag{2}$$

and since the dissociation constant of the acid is defined by

$$K = m_{\text{HCl}} \frac{\alpha^2}{(1-\alpha)} \frac{\gamma_\pm^2}{\gamma_{\text{HCl}}} \tag{3}$$

Eq. (2) becomes

$$E = E^\circ - \frac{RT}{F} \ln m_{\text{HCl}} - \frac{RT}{F} \ln K - \frac{RT}{F} \ln (1-\alpha) - \frac{RT}{F} \ln \gamma_{\text{HCl}} \tag{4}$$

Since K is small ($\sim 10^{-8}$), $(1-\alpha)$ may safely be equated to unity, whence

$$E + \frac{RT}{F} \ln m_{\text{HCl}} = E^\circ - \frac{RT}{F} \ln K - \frac{RT}{F} \ln \gamma_{\text{HCl}} \tag{5}$$

The left-hand side of Eq. (5) was found to be a linear function of m_{HCl} and, on extrapolation to zero molality gave, as intercept, the value of $[E° - RT/F \ln K]$. Unfortunately, considerable uncertainty exists as to the value of K but taking it as 10^{-8} mole kg^{-1}, gives a value of $E_m°$ at $25°$ equal to 0.53 abs volt.

In spite of the reported failure of the calomel electrode to function satisfactorily in anhydrous acetone, the mercury–mercurous iodide electrode apparently works fairly well. Yoshida (34) made a series of measurements on the cell,

$$\text{Cd, Hg} \mid \text{CdI}_2, \text{ saturated solution in acetone} \mid \text{Hg}_2\text{I}_2 \mid \text{Hg}$$

using solutions of cadmium iodide in acetone (as well as in several alcohols and water). The emf of the cell became constant after 2–3 days and thereafter its reproducibility was better than ± 0.5 mv, the mean value of several cells being, within a few hundredths of a millivolt, the same as the theoretical value. The mercurous iodide was prepared by rubbing together mercury and iodine in the presence of a little alcohol which was later evaporated off. No mention was made of any attempt to dry the acetone.

3. Diethyl Ether

Solvent ether is widely used as a medium for organic reactions and the potentiometric measurements in this solvent have all been designed to illuminate some feature of preparative organic chemistry. Thus, the measurements of Berglund and Sillén (35) were directed towards the understanding of the Grignard reaction. They initially studied the calomel and silver chloride reference electrodes using the cells,

$$\text{Ag} \mid \text{AgCl} \mid \text{LiCl} + \text{LiClO}_4, \text{ anhydrous ether} \mid \text{Hg}_2\text{Cl}_2 \mid \text{Hg}$$

and

$$\text{Ag} \mid \text{AgCl} \mid \underbrace{\text{LiCl}(c_1), N \text{ LiClO}_4 \parallel \text{LiCl}(c_2), N \text{ LiClO}_4}_{\text{anhydrous ether}} \mid \text{Hg}_2\text{Cl}_2 \mid \text{Hg}$$

Both cells functioned satisfactorily, the first giving a constant emf (unfortunately not quoted), and the second an emf which responded to variations in the ratio (c_1/c_2) of the lithium chloride concentrations in the manner predicted by the simple Nernst relation,

$$E = \text{constant} + \frac{RT}{F} \ln \frac{c_1}{c_2} \qquad (6)$$

The large excess of lithium perchlorate swamped any difference of activity coefficient in the two solutions, and also any liquid-junction potential.

They then proceeded to show that the electrode system,

$$\text{Hg, Mg} \mid \text{Mg(ClO}_4)_2 \text{ in anhydrous ether} \ldots$$

is also reversible and that its potential varies in the expected manner with the concentration of magnesium perchlorate. This is in accord with some earlier measurements, by Scherer and Newton (36) on the cell,

$$\begin{array}{c|c|c|c}
\text{Mg} & \text{MgBr}_2 \cdot 2(\text{C}_2\text{H}_5)_2\text{O} & & \\
\text{(solid rod)} & \text{saturated solution} & \text{Hg}_2\text{Br}_2 & \text{Hg} \\
& \text{in anhydrous ether} & &
\end{array}$$

The emf of this cell was also reproducible and was equal to 1.561 ± 0.004 int volts at 25°C. Earlier still, Bent and Gilfillan (37) had measured the emf of the cell

$$\begin{array}{c|c|c}
\text{K, Hg} & \text{potassium triphenyl} & \text{K, Hg} \\
(N_1) & \text{in anhydrous ether} & (N_2)
\end{array}$$

Its emf was reproducible to better than ±0.1 mv and was in precise agreement with the theoretical value.

4. Acetonitrile

Several sets of emf measurements have been made with this solvent and the present status of the common reference electrodes is similar to that obtaining in acetone. The earliest measurements were those of Ulich and Spiegel (31) who examined the reproducibility of the cell,

$$\text{Ag} \mid \text{AgCl} \mid \text{chloride solutions in acetonitrile} \mid \text{Hg}_2\text{Cl}_2 \mid \text{Hg}$$

They found it to be quite unsatisfactory and concluded that the calomel electrode was behaving irreproducibly. The silver–silver chloride electrode, on the other hand, was reproducible to ±0.2 mv and the cell

$$\text{Hg, Tl} \mid \text{TlCl in acetonitrile} \mid \text{AgCl} \mid \text{Ag}$$

gave an emf in excellent agreement with that calculated from standard free energy data. The defectiveness of the mercury–mercurous halide electrodes (chloride, bromide, and iodide), was confirmed in a later, thorough investigation of the mercurous halide–silver halide cell by Cruse and coworkers (38). They studied solutions of alkali halides and alkylammonium halides in acetonitrile and found deviations of up to ±50 mv from the theoretical values. Similar deviations were also noted in a parallel investigation of chloride solutions in other anhydrous solvents, and these authors concluded that the mercurous halide electrodes were unusually sensitive to the disproportionation reaction of mercurous ions which was accentuated by the marked solubility of mercuric halides (as complex ions) in halide solutions in acetonitrile. Silver chloride also forms soluble complex ions in acetonitrile (*39*) but to a smaller degree than does mercuric chloride. The stability of the silver–silver chloride electrode is such that it was later incorporated into the reference half-cell

$$\text{Ag} \mid \text{AgCl} \mid \begin{array}{c} \text{Me}_3\text{EtNCl, saturated} \\ \text{solution in acetonitrile} \end{array} \mid \cdots \cdots$$

for use in acetonitrile solutions (*40*). Another reference half-cell for use in this system was proposed by Pleskov (*41*), i.e.,

$$\text{Ag} \mid \begin{array}{c} \text{AgNO}_3, 0.01 \ N \text{ solution} \\ \text{in acetonitrile} \end{array} \mid \cdots \cdots$$

Its potential was shown to be reproducible and is, presumably, less sensitive to variations in temperature than that of the preceding electrode. Some measurements have also been made with the glass electrode in this solvent (*24, 42*) and the most recent of these, by Römberg and Cruse (*42*), suggests that it is satisfactory, at least in potentiometric titrations. These authors also used the hydrogen electrode and the silver–silver bromide electrode as reference electrodes in titrations, and the pH curves they present for the titration of weak acids with weak bases are, in most cases, very good. However, no values of emf's are recorded in their paper from which to judge the degree of reversibility and reproducibility of the hydrogen and glass electrodes in this solvent. The hydrogen electrode is almost certainly not sufficiently stable and reproducible for equilibrium emf values to be measured, in spite of claims to the contrary (*41*). Janz and Taniguchi (*42a*) and Strehlow (*42b*) found that the electrode was rapidly poisoned in acetonitrile solutions. No attempt has been made to refer the potentials of the various other electrodes to the hydrogen scale.

5. Nitrobenzene

The number of potentiometric measurements made on nitrobenzene solutions is limited to two studies (*43, 44*) of acid-base titrations. The hydrogen electrode cannot be used because of the ready reduction of nitrobenzene but the quinhydrone electrode is evidently satisfactory. Its potential is sensitive to the surface condition of the platinum electrode and Schaal (*43*) recommends that a foil electrode should first be flamed, then lightly platinized, washed and dried, and stored in nitrobenzene before use.

Similar electrodes immersed in a nitrobenzene solution of (say) acetic acid, which had been saturated with quinhydrone, gave potentials which agreed to within ±5 mv. In the titrations, two such electrodes were used, one being partially enclosed and therefore retarded.

B. Acidic Organic Solvents

These solvents are of particular interest because of their "super-acid function." Thus, in water, the ion H_3O^+ is the strongest acid conceivable, and water as a solvent does not discriminate between very strong acids such as $HClO_4$, HNO_3, HBr, etc. In other words, H_2O is a strong enough base to remove the proton entirely from such acidic solutes so that they are completely dissociated in aqueous solution and water is therefore a "leveling solvent" (45, 46). This is not the case for solutions in, for example, glacial acetic acid, for CH_3CO_2H is a weaker base than H_2O and $CH_3CO_2H_2^+$ is a stronger acid than H_3O^+. In this solvent, $HClO_4$, HNO_3, and HBr are no longer acidic to the same degree; the solvent is therefore a "differentiating solvent" (47). For similar reasons, bases which are feebly dissociated in water are strongly dissociated in acetic acid, and can be titrated to sharp end-points (17, 18). The preoccupation with acidity relationships has led to a somewhat restricted range of potentiometric measurements in these solvents and most of them involve the hydrogen electrode, the quinhydrone electrode, or a modification of the latter based on the reversible redox system, tetrachlorbenzoquinone $\rightleftharpoons$ tetrachlorhydroquinone, i.e., the chloranil electrode.

1. Acetic Acid

Hutchison and Chandlee (48) made measurements on the cell

$$Pt, H_2 \mid H_2SO_4 \text{ in anhydrous acetic acid} \mid Hg_2SO_4 \mid Hg$$

at 25°C. The simplest form of H-cell was used, the electrodes being prepared in the conventional way, and the range of sulfuric acid concentrations extending from 0.9 molal down to 0.0025 molal. The measurements were reproducible to at least ±1 mv and led to an apparent $E_m°$ value for the mercury–mercurous sulfate electrode of +0.181 int volt. This evaluation was later criticized and was repeated (49) using the Gronwall-La Mer-Sandved extension of the Debye-Hückel theory together with the assumptions that sulfuric acid is a (1:1) electrolyte in anhydrous acetic acid. From these calculations, based on a distance of closest ionic approach equal to 11 Å, an entirely different value of $E_m°$ for the mercurous sulfate electrode was obtained, +0.338 int volt, which is now the accepted value.

Much more recently, Mukherjee (*50*) has studied the cell

$$\text{Ag} \mid \text{AgCl} \mid \text{HCl in anhydrous acetic acid} \mid \text{H}_2, \text{Pt}$$

at 35°C. The hydrogen electrodes were of platinum foil, black-platinized in the usual way, and the silver–silver chloride electrodes were prepared by the method of Noyes and Ellis (*51*). Hydrochloric acid concentrations from 0.005 to 0.0009 molar were used and the emf's were reproducible to ±0.1 mv. The measurements were extrapolated to infinite dilution, account being taken of the known values of the degree of dissociation of HCl in this solvent (*52*). The standard potentials of the silver–silver chloride electrode were evaluated both on the molar and the molal scale, i.e.,

$$\left.\begin{array}{l} E_c^\circ = -0.6180 \text{ abs volt} \\ E_m^\circ = -0.6241 \text{ abs volt} \end{array}\right\} \text{ at 35°C}$$

Although the hydrogen electrode functions well in this solvent, it has frequently been found convenient to use two alternatives, the quinhydrone and chloranil electrodes. This last electrode was introduced and first applied to acetic acid solutions by Conant *et al.* (*53*). Since tetrachlorbenzoquinone and the corresponding quinol do not form a semiquinone, it is necessary to use solutions saturated with both of these compounds; a gold or platinum electrode immersed in such solutions then responds quantitatively to the prevailing hydrogen ion activity. Platinum electrodes are prepared by first igniting them and then standing them in a solution containing the chloranil mixtures. They are washed with fresh acetic acid prior to immersion in the cell solution. To ensure its saturation, this solution may be warmed to ~50°C and then cooled to room temperature. The interagreement between different electrodes was better than ±1 mv (*54–56*).

The standard potential of the chloranil electrode was first determined by Heston and Hall (*57*) from measurements on the cell,

$$\text{Ag} \mid \text{AgCl} \mid \text{HCl, chloranil, in anhydrous acetic acid} \mid \text{Pt}$$

The standard molal emf of this cell at 25°C was evaluated by the method of La Mer and Eichelberger (*49*), using the same value for the distance of closest ionic approach. It was found to be +1.045 int volt which led to a value of +0.680 int volt for the standard molal potential at 25°C for a chloranil electrode. This value differs from the E° values found in other solvents, which is an unexpected feature if it is considered to be determined by the reaction,

$$\underset{(solid)}{\text{tetrachlorbenzoquinone}} + \underset{(gas)}{\text{H}_2} \rightleftharpoons \underset{(solid)}{\text{tetrachlorhydroquinone}}$$

the free energy change of which is independent of the solvent used to dissolve these components. However, it is known (58) that in anhydrous acetic acid tetrachlorhydroquinone forms the *solid* solvate $C_6Cl_4(OH)_2 \cdot 2CH_3CO_2H$ and the corresponding $E°$ value is therefore peculiar to this solvent system.

Several types of standard reference half-cell have also been used in acetic acid solutions. For the early studies, an aqueous calomel electrode was used, and was joined to the acetic acid system by means of a saturated solution of lithium chloride in acetic acid (53–55). Later, half-cells involving only acetic acid were developed. An equivalent version of the calomel electrode was used by Bruckenstein and Kolthoff (59), i.e.,

$$Hg \mid Hg_2Cl_2 \mid \begin{matrix} NaCl, NaClO_4 \text{ saturated solution} \\ \text{of both in acetic acid} \end{matrix} \mid \ldots \ldots$$

The solubility of sodium chloride in anhydrous acetic acid at 25° is only 0.0125 molar and the much more soluble sodium perchlorate is added to minimize the liquid-junction potential and to act as the salt bridge. Assuming that any liquid-junction potential does not vary greatly with the test solution, a standard emf may be assigned to this half-cell in combination with another reference electrode. Thus, at 25°C, the standard emf of the cell,

$$\begin{matrix} \text{saturated calomel electrode} \\ \text{in acetic acid} \end{matrix} \mid \begin{matrix} \text{chloranil} \\ \text{in acetic acid} \end{matrix} \mid Pt$$

was found to be $+0.9095 \pm 0.0002_5$ abs volt on the molar scale, and that of the cell,

$$\begin{matrix} \text{saturated calomel electrode} \\ \text{in acetic acid} \end{matrix} \mid \begin{matrix} \text{chloride solution} \\ \text{in acetic acid} \end{matrix} \mid AgCl \mid Ag$$

$-0.3928 \pm 0.0002_5$ abs volt also on the molar scale. The silver–silver chloride electrode has also been used in a reference half-cell (60, 61) and a robust form of the cell,

$$Ag \mid AgCl \mid KCl, \text{ saturated solution in acetic acid} \mid \ldots \ldots$$

has been described by Glenn (62) and is illustrated in Fig. 3.

Use has been made of the mercury–mercurous acetate electrode (63) in the cell

$$Pb, Hg \mid \underbrace{Pb(OAc)_2 \cdot \tfrac{1}{2}HOAc \mid\mid Pb(OAc)_2 \cdot \tfrac{1}{2}HOAc}_{\text{saturated solutions in acetic acid}} \mid Hg_2(OAc)_2 \mid Hg$$

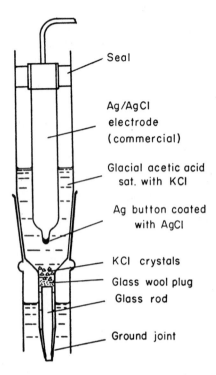

Seal

Ag/AgCl
electrode
(commercial)

Glacial acetic acid
sat. with KCl

Ag button coated
with AgCl

KCl crystals

Glass wool plug

Glass rod

Ground joint

Fig. 3. Silver–silver chloride half-cell for use in glacial acetic acid solutions.

The emf of this combination was reproducible to ±0.1 mv and was constant for several months and equal to 0.7290 int volt.

The Russian school of research led by Izmaïlov and Shkodin has made extensive studies of electrode potentials and potentiometric titrations in nonaqueous solutions, particularly in anhydrous acetic and formic acids. They have used mainly the quinhydrone electrode, often in conjunction with the aqueous calomel electrode and the lithium chloride–acetic acid salt bridge (64, 65). They have also made a careful study of the applicability of the glass electrode to this solvent (13, 65). They showed that it was initially quite satisfactory for potentiometric titrations irrespective of whether it was stored in acetic acid or aqueous solutions. However, after several titrations with the same electrode, its potential became erratic and wandered with time. Its reproducibility could apparently be restored by replenishing the internal (aqueous) solution but each time this was done, its potential in a particular solution was significantly changed.

Tomiček and Heyrovsky (66, 67) also used the glass electrode in anhydrous acetic acid solutions. With a sufficiently sensitive electronic volt-meter, they were able to detect sharp equivalence points in potentiometric acid-base and redox titrations, but they considered this electrode, together with the antimony and tellurium electrodes, to be much inferior to the palladized–gold hydrogen electrode in this solvent. For most of their titrations, they also used an aqueous calomel electrode, the junction between the aqueous and acetic acid solutions being made at an asbestos diaphragm. They also used the lithium chloride–acetic acid salt bridge.

Potentiometric measurements have also been made on electrolyte solutions in monochloracetic acid (68) and in dichloracetic acid (43); in both cases, the chloranil electrode was used. This electrode and the hydrogen electrode have also been successfully used in mixtures of acetic acid and acetic anhydride (69, 70); in this mixture, the standard molal potential of the chloranil electrode was also +0.680 int volt. The hydrogen and glass electrodes have also been used in solutions of pyridine in acetic acid (71).

The electrochemistry of acetic acid solutions has been reviewed recently by Jander and Klaus (72).

2. Formic Acid Solutions

Fewer potentiometric measurements have been made on electrolyte solutions in anhydrous formic acid, but the results are very similar to those for acetic acid. The thermodynamic studies of Mukherjee (50) included measurements with this solvent and he determined the emf of the cell,

$$\text{Ag} \mid \text{AgCl} \mid \text{HCl in anhydrous formic acid} \mid \text{H}_2, \text{Pt}$$

also at 35°C but over the much wider concentration range 0.00033–0.017 molar. Using earlier data for the degree of dissociation of HCl in this solvent (73), he was able to extrapolate his measurements to infinite dilution and to obtain the standard potentials of the silver–silver chloride electrode,

$$\left. \begin{array}{l} E_c{}^\circ = -0.1199_5 \pm 0.0001 \text{ abs volt} \\ E_m{}^\circ = -0.1302 \pm 0.0001 \text{ abs volt} \end{array} \right\} \text{ at } 35°C$$

The earliest potentiometric measurements in this solvent were those of Hammett and Dietz (74) who found that the quinhydrone electrode functioned well in formic acid. They found the electrode easy to prepare and readily reproducible using gold but not platinum electrodes, since platinum catalytically decomposes formic acid. However, Pinfold and Sebba (75) found otherwise and concluded that platinum electrodes could be used. They investigated the cell,

$$\text{Hg} \mid \text{Hg}_2\text{Cl}_2 \mid \begin{array}{c} \text{saturated potassium} \\ \text{chloride in formic acid} \end{array} \parallel \begin{array}{c} \text{quinhydrone, } 0.05 \ M, \\ \text{sodium formate,} \\ 0.25 \ M \text{ in formic acid} \end{array} \mid \text{Pt}$$

The concentration of quinhydrone used had the arbitrary value of 0.05 M, variations in this quantity having no significant effect on the cell emf. The sodium formate was added simply to decrease the cell resistance and also had a negligible effect on the cell emf, since the quinhydrone electrode in this solvent exhibits very little salt effect. The emf of the cell at 25°C was $+0.5384 \pm 0.0005$ abs volt. Pinfold and Sebba recommended the quinhydrone electrode as a polarographic reference electrode. They concluded that this electrode is reversible, reproducible and nonpolarizable in anhydrous formic acid, irrespective of whether nitrogen is used to agitate the solution or not; its potential, moreover, is unaffected by the presence of small traces of water.

The quinhydrone electrode has also been used for acid-base titrations in formic acid by Tomiček and Vidner (76) and Izmaĭlov et al. (65). The last named workers also investigated the performance of the glass electrode in this solvent and found it to be similar to that in acetic acid, i.e., satisfactory for individual titrations, but eventually exhibiting potentials which varied with time.

C. ALIPHATIC AMIDES

The liquid or molten aliphatic amides all have high dielectric constants and dissolve a wide range of electrolytes to form strongly ionized solutions. Numerous conductance and polarographic measurements have been made on such solutions, but so far, only a few studies of electrode potentials in them have been recorded. Fortunately, one of them, that of Pavlopoulos and Strehlow (77) is a thorough and extensive one which indicates the main features and the considerable possibilities of potentiometric measurements in this type of solvent.

1. Formamide

Their measurements were confined to solutions of hydrogen chloride and various ionic metal chlorides in formamide, $HCONH_2$. They first of all investigated the reproducibility of the silver chloride and calomel electrodes in these solutions. They found both electrodes to be unsatisfactory and concluded that the solvent was oxidized by both mercurous and silver ions. Instead, they used the cadmium–cadmium chloride electrode as a reference electrode of the second kind, reversible to chloride ions and giving rise to a negligible concentration of cadmium ions in solution. This electrode was combined with the hydrogen electrode in the cell,

$$Cd \mid CdCl_2 \text{ (solid)} \mid HCl \text{ in anhydrous formamide} \mid H_2, Pt$$

The emf of this cell was reproducible to at least ± 1 mv and, on the basis of a rough extrapolation to infinite dilution, gave the standard potential at 25°C, $E^\circ_{CdCl_2} = -0.617 \pm 0.004$ abs volt on the molar scale. The cadmium chloride electrode was then combined with several other electrode systems, such as

K, Hg | KCl in anhydrous formamide | CdCl$_2$ | Cd

the standard potentials of which could therefore also be evaluated (cf. Table I).

TABLE I

STANDARD MOLAR ELECTRODE POTENTIALS IN FORMAMIDE[a,b]

Electrode system	Standard potential (volts)
K	-2.872 ± 0.005
Rb	-2.855 ± 0.005
Zn	-0.757 ± 0.008
Cd/CdCl$_2$	-0.617 ± 0.004
Cd/CdCl$_2$/KCl[c]	-0.608 ± 0.006
Cd	-0.408 ± 0.009
Tl	-0.344 ± 0.014
Pb	-0.193 ± 0.012
Cu/Cu^{2+}	$+0.279 \pm 0.012$

[a] At 25°C, $E^\circ_H = 0$.
[b] Pavlopoulos and Strehlow (77).
[c] Saturated solution in formamide

In spite of the apparent instability of the silver–silver chloride electrode in formamide, some measurements with it have nevertheless recently been made. Thus, Mandel and Decroly (78), in a brief paper describe successful measurements on the cell

Pt, H$_2$ | HCl in anhydrous formamide | AgCl | Ag

at 25°C. Their measurements were reproducible to at least ± 1 mv, and, by extrapolation, they found the standard molal potential, E°_{AgCl}, equal to $+0.204 \pm 0.002$ abs volt. These authors have recently extended these measurements to temperatures between 15° and 45°C, and have applied the above cell to determine dissociation constants of weak acids in this solvent (78a).

2. Other Amides

The number of potentiometric measurements in the other aliphatic amides is almost negligible. The chloranil electrode has been used to follow the neutralization, with aqueous potassium hydroxide, of organic acids in dimethylformamide (79), and some acid-base titrations have been made in molten acetamide (80) using a molybdenum rod electrode which, because of its oxide layer, is said to function in a manner similar to that of the antimony electrode (80, 81).

D. Liquid Ammonia

Liquid ammonia is an especially interesting nonaqueous solvent. It resembles water in consisting of small polar molecules by which ions are readily solvated. It therefore dissolves a wide range of inorganic and organic electrolytes, although because its dielectric constant is low ($\epsilon = 22$ at $-33°C$), there is a much more marked tendency to ion-pair formation and incomplete dissociation than is found in aqueous solutions. Otherwise, of all the nonaqueous solvents discussed here, its properties differ most from those of water and a knowledge of its chemical reactivity and of the range of electrolyte solutions which it can form is an essential prerequisite to further investigations. Attention must therefore be drawn to the monograph by Franklin (82), now somewhat ancient, to the relevant chapter in Yost and Russell's "Systematic Inorganic Chemistry of the Fifth and Sixth Groups of the Non-metallic Elements" (83) and to the classical conductance paper of Hnizda and Kraus (84).

The experimental techniques involved in measurements with liquid ammonia solutions differ considerably from those adopted with most other electrolyte systems. Whilst measurements can be made, under pressure, at room temperature, it is normally safer and more convenient to work at $-33°C$ or below. This involves the use of a low-temperature thermostat, and, fortunately, continuously refrigerated units are available commercially. A closed system is essential and that shown in Fig. 1 is based on an apparatus now in use for electrochemical measurements at low temperatures.

Several of the commoner electrode systems are straightforwardly applicable to liquid ammonia solutions. Thus, the potential of the hydrogen electrode is reproducible to a few microvolts (85, 86) although the absolute value is unduly sensitive to the variable partial pressure of hydrogen which is difficult to control near the boiling point of the solvent. The quinhydrone electrode is claimed to be reproducible in liquid ammonia (87), but this is certainly not the case for the glass electrode. Heyn and Bergin (14) made a thorough study of cells of the type

$$\text{Pb} \left| \begin{array}{c} \text{Pb(NO}_3)_2, \\ 0.1\ M \end{array} \text{NH}_4\text{NO}_3,\ c \right| \begin{array}{c} \text{glass} \\ \text{membrane} \end{array} \left| \begin{array}{cc} \text{NH}_4\text{NO}_3, & \text{Pb(NO}_3)_2 \\ 0.1\ M & 0.1\ M \end{array} \right| \text{Pb}$$

all in liquid ammonia solution

but never obtained any response to the differences in ammonium nitrate concentration even when the glass was deliberately "ammoniated" by pre-electrolysis in molten ammonium salts.

The stumbling block to the systematic study of electrode potentials and cell emf values in liquid ammonia is the absence of a satisfactory reference electrode of the second kind. None of the electrodes based on silver or mercurous salts can be used, since all such salts either react or dissolve. Most metal sulfates are insoluble but so also is ammonium sulfate. Only thallous chloride has so far approached the necessary requirements. It is sparingly soluble in ammonia and the thallium amalgam/solid thallous chloride electrode is certainly reversible to chloride ions. On this basis, some of the earliest emf measurements on liquid ammonia systems were made by Elliot and Yost (88) and, later extended by Garner and associates (89), to the cell

$$\text{Pt, H}_2 \mid \text{NH}_4\text{Cl, in liquid ammonia} \mid \text{TlCl (solid)} \mid \text{Tl, Hg}$$

The emf measurements were reproducible to better than 1 mv, but, unfortunately, the corresponding standard emf of the thallous chloride electrode was not obtained in the usual way, by extrapolation of the measurements to infinite dilution. Instead, it was evaluated from measurements at finite concentrations using values for the activity coefficients of dissolved ammonium chloride obtained from vapor pressure measurements (90). The interpretation of the vapor pressure measurements, however, was not unambiguous, and hinged on the nature of the state of solid ammonium chloride in equilibrium with liquid ammonia solution, i.e., whether it is solvated or not. The argument between Yost and Hunt was not resolved and later recalculations by Ritchey and Hunt (91) of the standard potential of the thallous chloride and other electrodes gave results greatly different from those of Garner, Green, and Yost. Nevertheless, the results of the last named authors seem to be preferred (11) and are those quoted here, i.e.,

$$E^\circ_{\text{Tl/TlCl(molar)}} = 0.10_0 \text{ int volt at 25°C}$$

More accurate and more significant measurements were made on cells of the type,

$$\text{Zn, Hg} \mid \underbrace{\begin{array}{c} \text{ZnCl}_2 \cdot 6\text{NH}_3, \text{ NH}_4\text{Cl} \\ \text{(solid)} \end{array} \mid \begin{array}{c} \text{TlCl} \\ \text{(solid)} \end{array}}_{\text{in liquid ammonia}} \mid \text{Tl, Hg}$$

the emf's of which were constant to ±0.1 mv and independent of the electrolyte composition. The standard potentials, i.e., on the hydrogen scale, derived from such measurements, however, still carry the uncertainties of the initial standardization of the thallium–thallous chloride electrode, e.g.,

$$\left.\begin{array}{l} E^\circ_{\text{Zn}} \mid \underset{\text{solid}}{\text{ZnCl}_2 \cdot 6\text{NH}_3} \mid \underset{\text{(molar scale)}}{\text{chloride solution}} = -0.72_9 \text{ int volt} \\[2ex] E^\circ_{\text{Cd}} \mid \underset{\text{solid}}{\text{CdCl}_2 \cdot 6\text{NH}_3} \mid \underset{\text{(molar scale)}}{\text{chloride solution}} = -0.36_9 \text{ int volt} \end{array}\right\} \text{ at } 25°\text{C}$$

The single electrode unique to nonaqueous solutions is the "electron electrode". It arises from the solubility of alkali metals in liquid ammonia, where, in dilute solution at least, the metal ionizes and the solution has an intense blue color associated with the free, solvated electrons, i.e.,

$$\text{Na}° \rightleftharpoons \underbrace{\text{Na}^+ + e^-}_{\text{both solvated}}$$

An inert metal electrode immersed in such a solution adopts a redox potential characteristic of the coupled equilibrium reactions,

$$\text{Na}° \rightleftharpoons \text{Na}^+ + \text{solvated electrons}$$

and

$$\text{solvated electrons} \rightleftharpoons \text{metallic electrons} \quad (92–94)$$

This potential may be studied with cells such as

$$\underset{\substack{\text{dilute unreactive} \\ \text{amalgam}}}{\text{Na, Hg}} \mid \text{NaI} \parallel \underset{\substack{\text{in liquid} \\ \text{ammonia}}}{\text{Na}°} \mid \text{Pt or W}$$

and, assuming the liquid-junction potential may be calculated in terms of the Henderson equation the standard potential of the electron electrode with respect to the sodium electrode was found to be −0.10 volt at −50°C.

For potentiometric titrations in liquid ammonia, several reference electrodes have been investigated by Watt and his co-workers (95). The most promising appears to be the mercury–mercuric chloride electrode and the standard half-cell,

$$\text{Hg} \mid \text{HgCl}_2, \text{ saturated solution in liquid ammonia} \mid \ldots\ldots$$

is recommended for use in this solvent (95). It is similar in principal to the lead–lead nitrate reference electrode,

$$Pb \mid Pb(NO_3)_2, 0.1 \ N \text{ in liquid } NH_3 \mid \ldots \ldots$$

used in earlier, Russian work on amalgam cells on this solvent (96–100). The activity coefficients of sodium chloride and potassium chloride in liquid ammonia were determined from other measurements on amalgam cells (101).

E. Anhydrous Hydrazine

This solvent resembles liquid ammonia in many of its properties. It is, however, a liquid over much the same temperature range as water and is therefore easier to study than liquid ammonia. Notwithstanding this, only two investigations of electrode potentials in this solvent have been reported. The first, by Anderson (102) involved measurements on the amalgam cell,

$$\begin{array}{c|c|c} \text{Ba, Hg} & \text{BaCl}_2 \text{ in hydrazine} & \text{Ba, Hg} \\ (N_1) & & (N_2) \end{array}$$

The emf of this type of cell was evidently highly reproducible, i.e., to at least ±0.01 mv, and gave accurate thermodynamic data concerning the amalgam phases. A more comprehensive investigation was later made by Ulich and Biostoch (103). These authors found that the electrodes,

$$\left.\begin{array}{l} \text{Cd, Hg} \mid \text{CdSO}_4 \text{ solid} \mid \text{sulfate solution} \\ \text{Zn, Hg} \mid \text{ZnSO}_4 \text{ solid} \mid \text{sulfate solution} \end{array}\right\} \text{ in anhydrous hydrazine}$$

were both reproducible and, because both solid sulfates were effectively insoluble, functioned well as sulfate electrodes of the second kind. Using the zinc–zinc sulfate electrode, they made measurements, at 0°C, of the emf of the cell,

$$\text{Zn, Hg} \mid \text{ZnSO}_4 \mid \text{H}_2\text{SO}_4 \cdot \text{N}_2\text{H}_4 \text{ in anhydrous hydrazine} \mid \text{Pt, H}_2$$

for a range of hydrazonium sulfate concentrations. Using the limiting Debye-Hückel equation, they extrapolated their measurements to infinite dilution to obtain for the standard molar potential of the zinc–zinc sulfate electrode,

$$E^{\circ}_{\text{Zn,ZnSO}_4} = -0.7100 \text{ int volt at } 0°\text{C}$$

F. Pyridine and Organic Amines

The simpler organic derivatives of ammonia are all effective solvents and give rise to electrolyte solutions. Few potentiometric studies in such media have been carried out and almost all of these have been concerned with amalgam electrodes and amalgam cells. Measurements of this type, on ethylamine (104–107) and on pyridine solutions (108–113), are amongst the earliest emf measurements in nonaqueous solutions.

Other measurements in pyridine solution have been made, with the hydrogen electrode (60, 114), the silver–silver chloride and calomel electrodes (31), and the silver–silver nitrate reference electrode (115, 116), all of which appear to function satisfactorily, though with no great degree of precision. The hydrogen electrode was studied using the cell,

$$\text{Pt, H}_2 \mid \text{pyridine solution} \parallel \text{LiCl } 0.88 \ N \text{ in pyridine} \mid \text{AgCl} \mid \text{Ag}$$

A platinized wire, half immersed, was used and although the measurements were initially satisfactory, they quickly deteriorated and, within an hour, the cell became useless (60).

Gupta (115) also used the hydrogen electrode to standardize, approximately at least, the potential of the silver–silver nitrate electrode which he found to be a more convenient working reference electrode in pyridine solutions. He used a normal platinized platinum foil electrode and commented on the need to use freshly platinized electrodes since "their efficiency fell rapidly with time." Using the silver–silver nitrate electrode, he also studied the copper electrode, which is reversible, the degree of complex formation of copper compounds (115), and also quinone-quinol redox potentials in pyridine solution (116).

Potentiometric acid-base titrations in anhydrous ethylene diamine have been described by Moss and co-workers (116); they used the hydrogen electrode, in conjunction with an aqueous calomel reference electrode. Various phenols and weak carboxylic acids were titrated with ethylene diamine solutions of sodium amino-ethoxide which is an even stronger base than the solvent itself. The hydrogen electrodes were of gold-plated platinum, platinized in the usual way, although it was found that stainless steel tubes, closed at their lower ends by a porous disc of sintered steel, through which hydrogen was bubbled into the solution, were equally effective. It was concluded, however, that the antimony electrode was probably the best pH-sensitive electrode in this solvent. This was also the conclusion of Schaal (43) who states that the glass, quinhydrone, and chloranil electrodes all fail to function satisfactorily in this solvent. It is difficult to assess the preciseness of the measurements of Moss, Elliott, and Hall since their data are presented only in the form of titration curves. However, these authors comment on the fact that the accuracy they obtained was by no means the result of exhaustive effort and could probably very easily be bettered.

G. INORGANIC SOLVENTS

1. Sulfur Dioxide

Liquid sulfur dioxide dissolves a sufficiently wide range of electrolytes to have warranted several conductimetric studies and at least two potentiometric studies. Wickert (117) made some preliminary measurements on the oxygen electrode and on the mercurous bromide electrode. A similar investigation was made soon after by Cruse (118), who demonstrated that the silver–silver chloride electrode was quite reversible and reproducible, and the silver–silver bromide electrode less so, whereas the silver–silver iodide electrode gave a potential which drifted steadily with time. He also showed that the hydrogen electrode was highly reproducible and some measurements were made on the cells,

$$\text{Pt, H}_2 \mid \text{HCl in liquid sulfur dioxide} \mid \text{AgCl} \mid \text{Ag}$$

and

$$\text{Pt, H}_2 \mid \text{HBr in liquid sulfur dioxide} \mid \text{AgBr} \mid \text{Ag}$$

The observed emf's were apparently "too high" but it is not clear on what basis this assertion by the author was made.

2. Hydrogen Fluoride

Some emf measurements have also been made on solutions in anhydrous hydrogen fluoride. The mercury–mercurous fluoride electrode is reversible and measurements on cells of the type

$$\text{M} \mid \text{MF}_2, \text{HF}, \text{NaF} \mid \text{Hg}_2\text{F}_2 \mid \text{Hg}$$
$$\text{liquid hydrogen fluoride}$$

were successfully carried out with various metal–metal fluoride (M/MF_2) systems, including copper, cadmium, silver, and lead. The authors of this work, Koerber and De Vries (119), also report some previous work (120) on the cell

$$\text{Pt, H}_2 \mid \text{HF, KF} \mid \text{F}_2, \text{Pt}$$

but the details are not available.

IV. Conclusions

This chapter has collected together almost all of the significant measurements of electrode potentials in anhydrous nonhydroxylic solutions. If it lacks a coherent theme, it is because the basis for one does not yet exist. Most of the reported emf measurements were incidental to other studies, principally of acidity, and in relatively few cases has any attempt been made to study the electrodes for their own sake. The establishment of the reversibility and reproducibility of a particular electrode system is only the beginning of such a study. Where a metal and its ions in solution can co-exist or where a reversible redox reaction in the solvent is known to occur, then a corresponding reversible electrode potential can reasonably be expected, since charge transfer processes in solution are normally fast. The exact description of the electrode system is a more difficult task; to establish the nature of the potential-determining species, the manner in which their activities vary with the composition of the solution, and the specific rate constant or exchange current of each electrode reaction would, most likely, require a lengthy investigation. Nevertheless, investigations such as this are necessary if the basis of generalizations concerning the properties of electrodes in different solvents are to be made.

Each study is likely to be rewarding in its own right, and, collectively, they represent a considerable body of exciting research yet to be carried out.

REFERENCES

1. MacInnes, D. A., "Principles of Electrochemistry." Reinhold, New York, 1939.
2. Harned, H. S., and Owen, B. B., "The Physical Chemistry of Electrolyte Solutions." Reinhold, New York, 1958.
3. Feakins, D., and French, C. M., J. Chem. Soc. 3168 (1956); 2284, 2581 (1957).
4. Izmaïlov, N. A., Zhur. Fiz. Khim. 23, 639, 647 (1949).
5. Strehlow, H., Z. Elektrochem. 56, 827 (1952).
6. Pavlopoulos, T., and Strehlow, H., Z. physik. Chem. (Leipzig) 202, 474 (1954).
7. Pleskov, V. A., Uspekhi Khim. 16, 254 (1947).
8. Walden, P., Trav. congr. Jubilaire Mendeléev 1, 493 (1936).
9. Kraus, C. A., J. Franklin Inst. 225, 687 (1938).
10. Kraus, C. A., Science 90, 281 (1939).
11. Fischer, L., Winkler, G., and Jander, G., Z. Elektrochem. 62, 1 (1958).
12. Robinson, R. A., and Stokes, R. H., "Electrolyte Solutions." Butterworths, London, 1959.
13. Izmaïlov, N. A., and Aleksandrova, A. M., Zhur. Obshcheĭ Khim. 19, 1403 (1949); 20, 2127 (1950).
14. Heyn, A. H. A., and Bergin, M. J., J. Am. Chem. Soc. 75, 5120 (1953).
15. Bockris, J. O'M., Hills, G. J., Inman, D., and Young, L., J. Sci. Instr. 33, 438 (1956).
16. Bergin, M. J., and Heyn, A. H. A., J. Am. Chem. Soc. 76, 4765 (1954).

17. Fritz, J. S., "Acid-Base Titrations in Non-Aqueous Solvents." G. Frederick Smith Chemical Company, Columbus, Ohio, 1952.

18. Beckett, A. H., and Tinley, E. H., "Titration in Non-Aqueous Solvents," 2nd ed. The British Drug Houses Ltd., Poole, England, 1957.

19. Stock, J. T., and Purdy, W. C., *Chem. Revs.* **57**, 1159 (1957).

20. Palit, S. R., Das, M. N., and Somayajulu, G. R., "Non-Aqueous Titration" (A monograph on acid-base titrations in organic solvents). Indian Association for Cultivation of Science, Calcutta, India, 1954.

21. Riddick, J. A., *Anal. Chem.* **28**, 679 (1956).

22. Cruse, K., *Arch. tech. Messen Lfg.* **248**, 203 (1956); *Lfg.* **249**, 217 (1956).

23. Deal, V. Z., and Wyld, G. E. A., *Anal. Chem.* **27**, 47 (1955).

24. van der Heijde, H. B., and Dahmen, E. A. M. F., *Anal. Chim. Acta* **16**, 378, 392 (1957).

25. Lykken, L., Porter, P., Ruliffson, H. D., and Tuemmler, F. C., *Ind. Eng. Chem. Anal. Ed.* **16**, 219 (1944).

26. Gemant, A., *J. Chem. Phys.* **12**, 79 (1944).

27. Gemant, A., *J. Chem. Phys.* **10**, 723 (1942).

28. Gemant, A., *Trans. Electrochem. Soc.* **78**, 49 (1940).

29. La Mer, V. K., and Downes, H. C., *J. Am. Chem. Soc.* **53**, 888 (1931); **55**, 1840 (1933).

30. Izmaïlov, N. A., and Zabara, I. F., *Zhur. Fiz. Khim.* **20**, 165 (1946).

31. Ulich, H., and Spiegel, G., *Z. physik. Chem.* **177**, 103 (1936).

32. Everett, D. H., and Rasmussen, S. E., *J. Chem. Soc.* p. 2812 (1954).

33. Güntelberg, E., *Z. physik. Chem.* **123**, 199 (1926).

34. Yoshida, T., *Sci. Repts. Tohoku Univ.* **17**, 1279 (1928).

35. Berglund, U., and Sillén, L. G., *Acta Chem. Scand.* **2**, 116 (1948).

36. Scherer, G. A., and Newton, R. F., *J. Am. Chem. Soc.* **56**, 18 (1934).

37. Bent, H. E., and Gilfillan, E. S., Jr., *J. Am. Chem. Soc.* **55**, 247 (1933).

38. Cruse, K., Goertz, E. P., and Petermoeller, H., *Z. Elektrochem.* **55**, 405 (1951).

39. Janz, G. J., and Taniguchi, H., *Chem. Revs.* **53**, 397 (1953).

40. Popov, A. I., and Geske, D. H., *J. Am. Chem. Soc.* **79**, 2074 (1957).

41. Pleskov, V. A., *Zhur. Fiz. Khim.* **22**, 351 (1948).

42. Römberg, E., and Cruse, K., *Z. Elektrochem.* **63**, 404 (1959).

42a. Janz G. J. and Taniguchi, H., unpublished, 1954.

42b. Strehlow, H., private communication to G. J. Janz, 1954.

43. Schaal, R., *J. chim. phys.* **52**, 719 (1955).

44. Wolf, J.-P., *Ann. chim. (Paris)* **8**, 201 (1953).

45. Hantzch, A., *Ber. deut. chem. Ges.* **58**, 612 (1925).

46. Hantzch, A., *Z. physik. Chem.* **134**, 406 (1928).

47. Walden, P., and Birr, E. J., *Z. physik. Chem.* **163**, 263 (1933).

48. Hutchison, A. W., and Chandlee, G. C., *J. Am. Chem. Soc.* **53**, 2881 (1931).

49. La Mer, V. K., and Eichelberger, W. C., *J. Am. Chem. Soc.* **54**, 2763 (1932).

50. Mukherjee, L. M., *J. Am. Chem. Soc.* **79**, 4040 (1957).

51. Noyes, A. A., and Ellis, J. H., *J. Am. Chem. Soc.* **39**, 2532 (1917).

52. Kolthoff, I. M., and Willman, A., *J. Am. Chem. Soc.* **56**, 1007 (1934).

53. Conant, J. B., Small, L. F., and Taylor, B. S., *J. Am. Chem. Soc.* **47**, 1959 (1925).

54. Hall, N. F., and Conant, J. B., *J. Am. Chem. Soc.* **49**, 3047 (1927).

55. Conant, J. B., and Hall, N. F., *J. Am. Chem. Soc.* **49**, 3062 (1927).

56. Hall, N. F., and Werner, T. H., *J. Am. Chem. Soc.* **50**, 2367 (1928).

57. Heston, B. O., and Hall, N. F., *J. Am. Chem. Soc.* **55**, 4729 (1933); **56**, 1462 (1934).

58. König, W., *J. prakt. Chem.* **70**, 33 (1904).
59. Bruckenstein, S., and Kolthoff, I. M., *J. Am. Chem. Soc.* **78**, 2974 (1956).
60. Yvernault, T., Moré, J., and Durand, M., *Bull. soc. chim. Belgrade* **16**, 542 (1949).
61. Mniczewski, J., and Lada, Z., *Roczniki Chem.* **29**, 919 (1955).
62. Glenn, R. A., *Anal. Chem.* **25**, 1916 (1953).
63. Tarbutton, G., and Vosburgh, W. C., *J. Am. Chem. Soc.* **55**, 618 (1933).
64. Shkodin, A. M., Izmaĭlov, N. A., *Zhur Obshcheĭ Khim.* **20**, 39 (1950).
65. Shkodin, A. M., Izmaĭlov, N. A., and Dzyuba, N. P., *Zhur. Obshcheĭ Khim.* **20**, 1999 (1950); **23**, 27 (1953).
66. Tomiček, O., and Heyrovsky, A., *Collection Czech. Chem. Commun.* **15**, 984, 997 (1950).
67. Tomiček, O., *Collection Czech Chem. Commun.* **13**, 116 (1948).
68. Prytz, M., *Acta Chem. Scand.* **1**, 507 (1947).
69. Russell, J., and Cameron, A. E., *J. Am. Chem. Soc.* **60**, 1345 (1938).
70. Isgarischev, N., and Chandlee, G. C., *Z. Elektrochem.* **36**, 457 (1930).
71. Tutundzić, P. S., and Putanov, P., *Bull. soc. chim. Belgrade* **20**, 157 (1955).
72. Jander, G., and Klaus, H., *J. Inorg. & Nuclear Chem.* **1**, 228 (1955).
73. Schlesinger, H. I., and Martin, A. W., *J. Am. Chem. Soc.* **36**, 1589 (1914).
74. Hammett, L. P., and Dietz, N., *J. Am. Chem. Soc.* **52**, 4795 (1930).
75. Pinfold, T. A., and Sebba, F., *J. Am. Chem. Soc.* **78**, 2095, 5193 (1956).
76. Tomiček, O., and Vidner, P., *Chem. listy* **47**, 576 (1953).
77. Pavlopoulos, T., and Strehlow, H., *Z. physik. Chem. (Frankfurt)* **2**, 89 (1954).
78. Mandel, M., and Decroly, P., *Nature* **182**, 794 (1958).
78a. Mandel, M., and Decroly, P., *Trans. Faraday Soc.* **56**, 29 (1960).
79. Kirrmann, A., and Daune-Dubois, N., *Compt. rend. acad. sci.* **236**, 1361 (1953).
80. Jander, G., and Winkler, G., *J. Inorg. & Nuclear Chem.* **19**, 32 (1959).
81. El Wakkad, S. E. S., Rizk, H. A., and Ebaid, J. G., *J. Phys. Chem.* **59**, 1004 (1958).
82. Franklin, E. C., "The Nitrogen System of Compounds." Reinhold, New York, 1935.
83. Yost, D. M., and Russell, H., "Systematic Inorganic Chemistry of the Fifth and Sixth Groups of the Non-Metallic Elements." Prentice-Hall, New York, 1944.
84. Hnizda, V. F., and Kraus, C. A., *J. Am. Chem. Soc.* **59**, 466 (1955).
85. Pleskov, V. A., and Monossohn, A., *J. Phys. Chem. (U.S.S.R.)* **6**, 1299 (1935).
86. Payne, R., and Hills, G. J., Unpublished results.
87. Zintl, E., and Neumayr, S., *Ber. deut. chem. Ges.* **63B**, 237 (1930).
88. Elliott, N., and Yost, D. M., *J. Am. Chem. Soc.* **56**, 1057 (1934).
89. Garner, C. S., Green, E. W., and Yost, D. M., *J. Am. Chem. Soc.* **57**, 2055 (1935).
90. Hunt, H., and Larsen, W. E., *J. Phys. Chem.* **38**, 801 (1934).
91. Ritchey, H. W., and Hunt, H., *J. Phys. Chem.* **43**, 407 (1939).
92. Russell, J. B., and Sienko, M. J., *J. Am. Chem. Soc.* **79**, 4057 (1957).
93. Kraus, C. A., *J. Am. Chem. Soc.* **36**, 864 (1914).
94. Laitinen, H. A., and Nyman, C., *J. Am. Chem. Soc.* **70**, 3002 (1948).
95. Watt, G. W., and Sowards, D. M., *J. Electrochem. Soc.* **102**, 545 (1955).
96. Pleskov, V. A., and Monossohn, A. M., *J. Phys. Chem. (U.S.S.R.)* **4**, 696 (1933).
97. Monossohn, A. M., and Pleskov, V. A., *J. Phys. Chem. (U.S.S.R.)* **3**, 221 (1932).
98. Pleskov, V. A., and Monossohn, A. M., *Acta Physicochim. U.R.S.S.* **2**, 621 (1935).
99. Pleskov, V. A., *J. Phys. Chem. (U.S.S.R.)* **20**, 163 (1946).
100. Pleskov, V. A., *Acta Physicochim. U.R.S.S.* **21**, 235 (1946).
101. Sedlet, J., and De Vries, T., *J. Am. Chem. Soc.* **73**, 5808 (1951).
102. Anderson, P. A., *J. Am. Chem. Soc.* **48**, 2285 (1926).

103. Ulich, H., and Biostoch, K., *Z. physik. Chem.* **178**, 306 (1937).

104. Lewis, G. N., and Kraus, C. A., *J. Am. Chem. Soc.* **32**, 1459 (1910).

105. Lewis, G. N., and Keyes, F. G., *J. Am. Chem. Soc.* **34**, 119 (1912); **35**, 340 (1913).

106. Lewis, G. N., and Argo, W. L., *J. Am. Chem. Soc.* **37**, 1983 (1915).

107. Tamele, M., *J. Phys. Chem.* **28**, 502 (1924).

108. Cady, H. P., *J. Phys. Chem.* **2**, 551 (1898).

109. Richards, T. W., and Garrod-Thomas, R. N., *Z. physik. Chem.* **72**, 165 (1910).

110. Müller, R., and Knaus, W., *Z. anorg. Chem.* **130**, 173 (1923).

111. Müller, R., *Z. Elektrochem.* **35**, 240 (1929).

112. Müller, R., *Monatsh. Chem.* **53**, 215 (1929).

113. Müller, R., and Schmidt, H. J., *Monatsh. Chem.* **53**, 224 (1929).

114. Gupta, A. K., *J. Chem. Soc.* 3473, 3479 (1952).

115. Bertocci, U., *Z. Elektrochem.* **61**, 434, 440 (1957).

116. Moss, M. L., Elliott, J. H., and Hall, R. T., *Anal. Chem.* **20**, 784 (1948).

117. Wickert, K., *Z. Elektrochem.* **44**, 410 (1938).

118. Cruse, K., *Z. Elektrochem.* **46**, 571 (1940).

119. Koerber, G. G., and De Vries, T., *J. Am. Chem. Soc.* **74**, 5008 (1952).

120. Krefft, O. T., Inaug. Diss., Greifswald Inst. für Phys. Chem., Greifswald, Germany, 1939.

Chapter Eleven

Microelectrodes and Electrodes Used in Biology

D. B. Cater and I. A. Silver

I. Introduction

A. The Relationship of Electrochemistry to Biological Problems

Living organisms have to perform chemical, mechanical, osmotic, and electrical tasks. The necessary energy is usually obtained by the *oxidation* of foodstuffs — complex compounds rich in carbon and hydrogen. Our early training in chemistry and biology tends to instill into our minds the concept that oxygen provides the driving force of many chemical reactions and indeed of life itself. From the standpoint of thermodynamics, this is unfortunate because when we compare "the engine of life" to the thermodynamics of Carnot's cycle, we see that the foodstuffs are carbon- and hydrogen-rich substances of high potential energy and therefore able to donate electrons to oxygen which acts as an electron acceptor or low energy sink — in fact the condenser of the engine. In the economy of nature the radiant energy of sunlight is built into high-energy (electron-rich) compounds in plants. This "fuel," which has an oxidation-reduction potential close to zero, is fed into a series of chemical engines, some of which are thermodynamically reversible and allow the energy from that particular oxidation-reduction system to be used for the chemical, mechanical, osmotic or electrical work of life. Some energy may be stored in "accumulators" (high-energy bonds, concentration cells, or polarized membranes) to be available for quick action. In the final act of degradation of the "fuel," hydrogen or electrons are donated to oxygen ($E^\circ_{O_2,H^+} = 1.23$ volt at 25°C) — the low energy sink of the Carnot cycle. There are at least two devices which can be made into a thermodynamically reversible engine; one is the semipermeable membrane, the other is the galvanic cell. In the body, both are used.

B. Types of Electrodes Used in Biology

As the living cell is a chemical engine using electrons or hydrogen as its working medium, the biologist is forced to use electrochemical methods to study certain of the phenomena of life. The interior of a living cell shows a potential difference with respect to the surrounding extracellular fluid. The cell wall is charged and is in a state of polarization maintained by a double ionic layer. This standing potential can be measured with microelectrodes. It is possible to stimulate muscle and nerve cells to activity by breaking down the polarization of their cell walls. This may be done, very conveniently, by imposing small currents from externally applied electrodes. Associated with the passage of an impulse along a nerve fiber, or with the contraction of a muscle fiber, there is a propagated "action potential" which is the basis of much research in neurophysiology and cardiology.

Returning to the fundamental problem of elucidating the energy-providing mechanisms of living cells, the biochemist may study the individual oxidation-reduction systems by potential measurements and the biologist may attempt to study the oxidation-reduction potentials of living cells or tissues. The biologist is faced with many difficulties, some technical, some inherent in the complex system he wishes to study. A noble metal electrode will not only show a potential change in response to a change of oxidation-reduction potential, but may also respond to changes of pH. It will therefore be necessary to measure pH independently. An additional complication is the presence of various amounts of oxygen in all but the simplest bacterial or protozoal preparations. A method of determining oxygen tension is therefore of supreme importance to the biologist; hence his interest in the oxygen cathode, which in spite of all its imperfections offers him some hope of making measurements of oxygen tension *in vivo*.

To summarize, the biologist requires to measure by means of suitable electrode combinations, pH, oxidation-reduction potentials, oxygen tensions, carbon dioxide tensions, and membrane potentials. It is usually most convenient, and in the latter case essential, to establish a solution path between the cell contents (or the extracellular fluid) and *exterior* electrodes, these can be large electrodes of well-established macro-design.

C. Difficulties — Theoretical and Technical

The living cell is of extreme complexity with a multiplicity of oxidation-reduction systems interacting; many of these systems are attached to semirigid cytoplasmic structures and show a high degree of spatial organization. Therefore it will not be possible to measure a true equilibrium (which would be independent of the precise mechanism which is operative) but only a steady state, and this is dependent upon the mechanism of reaction and will involve a time factor and structural factors. This problem is fundamental and must be considered. Although the whole concept of equilibrium measurements and velocity constants based upon the theory of ideal solutions appears to break down when applied to the study of the living cell, yet these powerful tools can be used to analyze the biochemistry of the cell because it is always possible, either in theory or in practice, to bring a measuring system into equilibrium with a specific part of the intracellular mechanism. Fortunately it is possible to measure spectroscopically the state of reduction of the cytochromes *in vitro* and *in vivo* and thus obtain independent data to compare with electrode measurements. How far a reaction between two oxidation-reduction systems can proceed when equilibrium is reached will be given by their characteristic potentials. Thus, this data supplies a fundamental basis for relating many of the dynamic processes in the living cell. See Hill (1) for a discussion of this subject.

The high degree of organization of living matter means that conditions can vary greatly within very small spatial limits. At the cellular level, an electrode advancing 5 μ may first penetrate the cell wall, pass through the cytoplasm and enter the nucleus of a cell. At the tissue level, the movement of an electrode a few microns nearer to a capillary carrying oxygenated blood may result in a much higher reading of oxygen tension. There is therefore a great emphasis on making very small electrodes to probe this structural and biochemical complexity. Measurements with small electrodes mean complex electronic problems; the high resistance of the electrode necessitates very high input impedance of the amplifier and carries a train of insulation problems. There are also troubles with capacitance, "pickup," and "noise."

II. Capillary Microelectrodes for Measuring Resting Potentials

A. DESIGN

Microelectrodes inserted into single cells are usually required, in most physiological investigations, to record both the resting intracellular potential, which is a membrane potential, and also action potentials which are due to rapid alteration of the membrane potential. However, as special problems are involved in measuring rapid changes of potential these will be dealt with separately in Section III. The tip of the electrode must be smaller than 1 μ in order to penetrate the cell wall easily without undue damage to the surface. A larger wound of the cell surface results in leakage of cell contents into the extracellular space and leads to a rapid depolarization of the cell membrane. A small wound seems to seal or allows only a minimal leakage of cell sap. The electrode must give a stable potential. A fine metal electrode is found to have an unstable potential because it becomes polarized and is sensitive to oxidation-reduction potentials, pH changes, etc. The only satisfactory alternative is a fine glass capillary filled with electrolyte acting as a convenient salt bridge between the interior of the cell and a silver–silver chloride electrode [Figs. 1(a) and (b)]. The capillary should have a fine taper with a gradient of $\frac{1}{60}$ to $\frac{1}{10}$ to avoid unnecessary damage to the cell wall, but too fine a taper means an excessively high resistance of the thin column of electrolyte in the microcapillary.

The next problem of design concerns the electrolyte in the electrode. There are three points to be considered: (i) the liquid-junction potential must be as small as possible; (ii) the resistance of the electrode must be as low as possible; and (iii) the diffusion of electrolyte into the cell must be less than that which will damage the cell. Liquid-junction potentials are

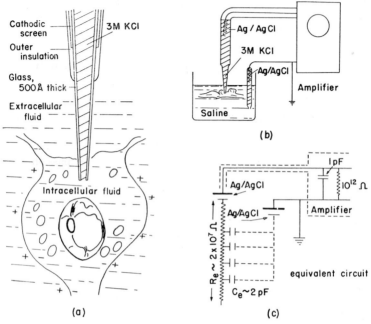

Fig. 1. Capillary microelectrode. (a) Detail of microelectrode inserted into a nerve cell, (b) general arrangement of reference electrodes, and (c) the resistance and capacity of the electrode and amplifier.

nearly ten times greater when sodium chloride is used instead of potassium chloride as the "half-bridge" electrolyte, and this is to be expected (cf. Chapter 1, Section VI). Potassium chloride is therefore almost universally used for the purpose, since the liquid-junction potential due to a tenfold concentration difference of this salt is only ~0.4 mv. When Curtis and Cole (2) introduced 40 μ diameter capillary electrodes 15 mm down the giant nerve fibers of the squid, they filled their electrodes with potassium chloride solution isotonic with sea water. But the giant nerve fiber of the squid is a special case and will tolerate electrodes 60 μ or more in diameter (3). When Nastuk and Hodgkin (4) inserted 0.5 μ diameter microelectrodes into single muscle fibers of the frog, they found it advisable to fill the electrode with 3 M KCl. Their electrodes had a resistance of 20 megohms. An electrode filled with isotonic KCl would have a resistance about eight times this value. An electrode filled with 3 M KCl when immersed in Ringer solution establishes a steady diffusion from the tip of 6×10^{-14} mole sec^{-1}, which is not sufficient to poison the muscle fiber with K$^+$. From the standpoint of physiology the ideal would be a mixture of electrolytes identical with those in the cell sap. The composition of this is not known exactly, but it contains a relatively high concentration of K^+ and phosphate and a low concentration of Na^+ and Cl^- — in contrast to the extracellular fluid which is rich in Na^+ and Cl^- and low in K^+ and phosphate. An electrode filled with intracellular fluid would have too high a resistance and would create a problem at the silver–silver chloride electrode. Perhaps the 3 M KCl is not such a bad compromise; damaged cells tend to leak K^+, so perhaps some K^+ diffusing from the electrode may help to balance loss through the puncture wound. Cells differ greatly in their tolerance to puncture by electrodes. A wound in the cell membrane which depolarizes small cells may not appreciably affect large ones. Ling and Gerard (5) inserted electrodes with a 0.5 μ diameter tip and a taper of $\frac{1}{60}$ into single muscle fibers of frog in order to minimize damage, but such a fine taper makes the resistance of the electrode very high. A taper of $\frac{1}{10}$ is satisfactory for most purposes. Some microelectrodes with very small tips have been shown to develop a potential of > 30 mv when immersed in Ringer solution instead of the calculated value of ~ 3 mv [Nastuk (6), Del Castillo and Katz (7), and Adrian (8)]. This may have been due to blocking of the tip with organic matter so that the electrode became semipermeable to certain ions; another possibility is that it behaved as a glass electrode or was showing rectifying action. Such effects indicate that it is not advisable to have the tip less than 0.5 μ in outside diameter. Brock and associates (9) have shown that traces of detergent may also cause blocking.

For accurate measurement of resting potential difference, the input impedance of the amplifier must be high compared with the resistance of the electrode. As the latter may be of the order of 10^7 to 10^8 ohms, the input impedance of the amplifier should be 10^{11} to 10^{12} ohms. A convenient method of measuring the resistance of the electrode is to use a highly insulated switch in the amplifier to shunt the input to earth through a known high stability resistor of 10^8 ohms and to observe the new value of the potential (10). The circuit must be arranged so that all stray potential differences are balanced or reduced to the absolute minimum.

Since in this kind of measurement two silver–silver chloride electrodes are used in opposition at the same temperature, the bias potential between them should be minimized by placing them in the same 3 M potassium chloride solution and shorting them together for some hours before use. All metal junction and switch metal junction potential differences should be paired. There should be adequate screening of input leads to avoid capacitance, coupling, and rectification of 50 cycle hum through the high resistance circuit. There should be high insulation to prevent lowering of the potential difference due to small leaks to earth.

B. Techniques for Making Capillary Microelectrodes

1. Methods for Making the Glass Capillaries

Borosilicate glass (Pyrex or Phoenix) should be used because of its good mechanical and thermal qualities. It also has other desirable properties such as low solubility of its alkali in water, a high volume resistivity, high breakdown voltage, high dielectric strength, and low surface conductivity. The microcapillary may be drawn out by hand from 1 to 2 mm diameter (lumen ⅔ outside diameter) tubing, heated to red heat with an oxygen–gas microburner. The capillary may with advantage be made in two stages (4). It is first reduced to 0.3 mm in outside diameter and then, with use of a very small flame, the narrow section is heated and pulled apart very rapidly. Many methods have been used to avoid the uncertainties of drawing by hand and to obtain a more uniform product. A simple practical method is that described by Weale (11, 12). The glass tube is surrounded by an electrically heated coil of wire and a weight is used for traction. The details are shown in Fig. 2. Brock, Coombs and Eccles (9) pulled down by hand

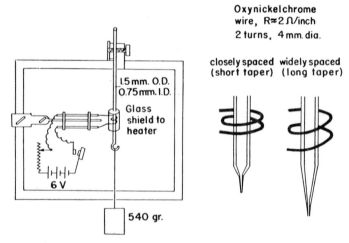

Fig. 2. Simple apparatus for making microcapillaries [after Weale (11)].

Pyrex tube 4.5 mm in outside diameter in a small gas flame to 0.15 mm diameter. A small terminal bead was made by fusion and short lengths were put into a de Fonbrume microforge (13) and pulled down under visual control to 50 μ by a weight of 300 mg. Then, using very localized heating and a weight of 30 mg, the electrodes were pulled down so that the tips were 0.5 to 1 μ outside diameter, and the diameter 20 μ from the tip was

5 μ. Various mechanical contrivances for pulling capillary tubes have been described, using sliding bars, cogs or scissor-like mechanisms, and operated by elastic bands or springs [for details see Kennard (14)]. Alexander and Nastuk (15) described a machine for making microcapillaries in which a two-stage draw by a solenoid and the heating of the glass by a 3 mm diameter platinum helix 3 mm in axial length are both automatically controlled but can be varied by preset controls. A 2 mm diameter Pyrex tube is threaded through the heater coil and clamped in position. The heater current is turned on and the solenoid exerts a small tractive force. The glass softens and extends, and at a preset degree of extension the heater current is automatically cut off and, at another quite independent predetermined point, the pull of the solenoid is greatly increased. At another point the solenoid current is switched off.

2. Filling the Electrodes with 3 M KCl

This should be done as soon as possible after they have been made, to prevent dust and moisture entering the capillary. The classical method of filling them by boiling for 30 minutes in 3 M KCl is apt to damage the tips and it is better to fill them by boiling under reduced pressure. Tasaki et al. (16) boiled the electrodes under reduced pressure in absolute alcohol for up to 20 minutes for the bubbles to disappear and then placed them in distilled water for 2½ minutes and finally in 3 M KCl. This sounds complicated but is quick and effective. Caldwell and Downing (17) immersed the electrode tips in 3 M KCl immediately after preparation. Within 30 minutes, 0.5 mm of the tip was filled by capillarity. The stem of the wider part was then filled with distilled water which gradually distilled over into the 3 M KCl filling the tapering part of the electrode in 40 to 60 hr. The distilled water was then removed and replaced with 3 M KCl using a fine pipette and the electrode was immersed in 3 M KCl for several hours to equilibrate. Because of the difficulty of filling fine capillaries Kao (18) described a method of prefilling the tube with electrolyte before it was drawn. During the heating the electrolyte was expelled from the tube into reservoirs at either end, but when the tube cooled the capillary refilled. About 40% showed small bubbles which disappeared in a few days.

The useful life of capillary microelectrodes is about one week because molds and bacteria grow in them and deposits appear. Storing in alcohol or boiled distilled water in the dark in a refrigerator may prolong the useful life. The addition of small quantities of antibiotics or antiseptic substances such as methylene blue has been advocated. Electrodes are examined under a water immersion lens at a magnification of $\times 800$ and those suitable for use are selected. Electrodes should be handled as little as possible to avoid breakage.

III. Capillary Microelectrodes for Detection of Action Potentials

A. PROBLEMS OF DESIGN

The action potential from a nerve or muscle fiber may last 500 to 1000 μsec. The potential swings from -40 or -50 mv to $+40$ or $+50$ mv and back to the resting level. The impedance and the capacitance of the electrode must be reduced as much as possible if high frequency potential changes are to be followed accurately. The glass wall of the capillary is 500 Å thick near the tip and acts as the dielectric of a very small condenser, the conducting plates of which are the electrolyte inside and outside the capillary. The thickness of the wall is proportional to the outside diameter, but although the thickness of the glass increases with increasing distance from the tip, so also does the area per μ of length. Figure 1(c) shows that the electrode is a series of resistances shunted by small capacities. For practical purposes these can be regarded as replaced by one value for R_e and another for C_e [where R_e is the total resistance of the solution path from the capillary tip to the reversible electrode, and C_e is the total distributed capacity across the capillary walls (19)]. Nastuk and Hodgkin (4) found that the capacitance of the electrode $\sim$1 $\mu\mu$f per mm of length. The effect of the capacitance of the electrode is that its effective impedance is lowered as the frequency increases. Kennard (14) illustrates in graphical form the data of Tasaki (20). As the frequency increases to 5 kc sec^{-1} the impedance falls to less than $\frac{1}{10}$ of its dc resistance. This means, in effect, that the action potential has to fill the shunt capacitance of this tiny condenser and this distorts the form of the wave seen in the oscilloscope. If a step signal with an infinitely fast rise of potential is applied to the tip of the microelectrode, the time required for the exponential rise to reach 63% of the final value is the time constant, and this is given in μsec by the product of the resistance in megohms and the capacity in $\mu\mu$f. The time taken to reach 98% full value will be 4 $\times$ time constant. The total time constant of the recording system will also include capacitance between input grid and the other electrodes of the input pentode, and capacitance between input lead and ground. The various methods which have been used to reduce or abolish the effect of this time constant may be discussed under three headings: (1) reduction of resistance of electrode, (2) reduction of capacitance of electrode and input leads, (3) graphical or electronic correction of signal.

1. Methods Used to Reduce the Resistance of Electrode

The resistance of the electrode, R_e, may be reduced by having the diameter of the tip as large as possible, the narrow capillary portion as short as possible, and the taper behind the tip as wide as possible, consistent with minimal damage to the cell. The use of 3 M KCl as electrolyte will reduce the resistance about eight-fold compared with isotonic saline. Hodgkin and Katz (*21*) inserted a 20 μ diameter bright silver wire between a point 1.5 mm from the tip and a point near the silver–silver chloride electrode. At high frequencies this acted as a low impedance conductor, but for dc potentials the electrode functioned as though entirely filled with electrolyte. Tomita and Funaishi (*22*) used 40 μ diameter silver wire fined down by electropolishing in 10% nitric acid, using a 2 volt battery and making the silver the anode. This enabled them to have the silver wire at the tip of the capillary. Glass microcapillaries entirely filled with metal were used by Gray and Svaetichin (*23, 24*). Silver solder was melted in 1 cm diameter soda glass tube and then pulled out in an oxygen–gas flame. Lengths of 0.5 mm diameter tubing filled with silver alloy were obtained. Then, with a microflame, the metal-filled glass was pulled out to a fine point with a tip 1 μ diameter. The final drawing can be done under microscopic control, using an electrically heated platinum loop. The electrode tip was a capillary containing no metal and was filled by electrodeposition of rhodium which was covered with platinum black by electrolysis in 1% platinum chloride using 1 to 20 μa for 5 minutes. A hemispherical end was produced.

2. Reduction of Effective Capacitance of Electrode

Hodgkin and Huxley (*3*), Huxley and Stämpfli (*25*), Nastuk and Hodgkin (*4*), and Fatt and Katz (*26*) used a cathode follower with the screening of the input lead connected to the cathode. This arrangement, illustrated in Fig. 3, reduces the grid to earth capacity by the metal shield. The grid to cathode capacity is increased by the shield, but this is small because the cathode potential changes to nearly the same extent as the grid potential. Care must be taken to use a reasonably low cathode resistance and to avoid unnecessary capacity between cathode and earth. The response of the system was tested by applying a rectangular voltage step to the tip of the microelectrode. It was found that the recorded potential reached its final value without overshoot in an approximately exponential manner. Nastuk and Hodgkin (*4*) found a time constant of $\sim$35 μsec for an electrode with an impedance of 22 megohms. The capacity of the wall of the electrode when immersed in Ringer was found by passing the electrode through a drop of Ringer in a silver ring connected to earth. It was $\sim$1 $\mu\mu$f per mm of length. The total capacity of input plus electrode was 3.2 $\mu\mu$f, giving a time constant of 70 μsec.

To reduce the capacity of the electrode it may be covered with a deposit of Pt [(*27, 28*) see also Chapter 1, Section VIII,B] which is connected with

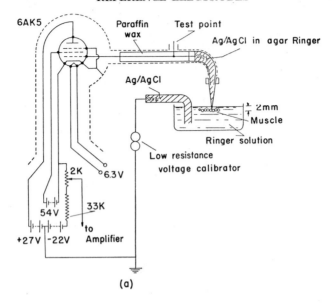

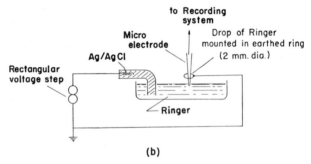

Fig. 3. (a) Electrode with cathode-follower and screened input lead; (b) method of calibration. [After Nastuk and Hodgkin (4)].

the cathode screening [Figs. 1(a), 4]. This deposit will of course have to be insulated from the fluid in the bath by coats of Araldite or varnish. Figure 4 shows the arrangement used by Frank and Fuortes (28). They used a negative-capacitance feed-back preamplifier developed by McNichol and Wagner (29). For best results the feedback of negative capacitance was adjusted by use of a dummy resistance and capacitor corresponding approximately to those of the microelectrode. Solms and co-workers (30) used the principle of positive feedback in order to neutralize the effect of grid to plate capacitance in the input pentode. They also used two cascaded cathode followers in order to reduce to a minimum the effect of stray capacities. With an electrode of 9 megohms resistance they achieved an over-all time constant of 7.8 μsec. Haapanen and Ottoson (*31*) also give a circuit utilizing positive feedback. Woodbury (*32*) built an electrometer valve input stage which reduced the *total* effective input capacitance to less than 1 μμf, regardless of the electrode capacitance. Thus a 30 megohm electrode would have a time constant of 30 μsec which would reproduce

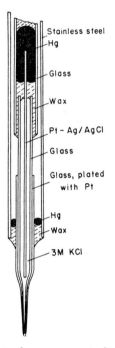

Stainless steel
Hg

Glass

Wax

Pt – Ag/AgCl

Glass

Glass, plated
with Pt

Hg
Wax

3M KCl

FIG. 4. Capillary microelectrode arrangement after Frank and Fuortes (*28*).

accurately all but the fastest potential changes. Nastuk (*6*) considered that a time constant of 30 μsec is needed for faithful reproduction of the action potentials of single muscle fibers.

3. Graphical and Electronic Method of Correction for the Distortion of the Action Potential Wave due to the Time Constant

Burch (*33*), Lucas (*34*) and Rushton (*35*) gave methods for correction of the distortion introduced by the time constant, but these involve considerable labor. Woodbury (*19*) used an electronic circuit to make the correction. The electrode is a series of resistances with shunting capacities but this can be reduced to a single equivalent resistance R_e and a single capacity C_e [see Fig. 1(c)]. The current produced by the action potential

V_a through R_e is $(V_a - V_0)/R_e$ where V_0 is the measured potential. The current through C_e is $C_e \cdot dV_0/dt$.

Then:

$$V_a = (R_e C_e dV_0/dt) + V_0 \qquad (1)$$

The solution of this equation can be performed electronically. The output from the dc amplifier was differentiated, amplified, and added to the direct amplifier output in a mixer stage.

B. RECORDING OF ACTION POTENTIALS BY EXTRACELLULAR ELECTRODES

The virtue of extracellular electrodes is that they do not damage the cell. They can be introduced by a blind technique into the depth of the tissues. Capillary glass, or metal electrodes made by electropolishing stainless steel, insulated with Araldite or Insulex can be used for this purpose, see Green (36). The stainless steel electrode in extracellular fluid is used in conjunction with a stainless steel indifferent electrode to reduce standing potentials to a minimum. The disadvantage of the extracellular electrode is the very low action potential, usually < 1 mv. Lorent de Nó (37) states that this is the second derivative of the tissue membrane potential and is due to the transverse membrane current. The signal may therefore be near to the thermal noise level. Tomita and Funaishi (22) studied the retina of bull frog with 20 μ diameter electrodes containing silver wire and found that saline in the capillary reduced the noise level. An increase of noise level was noticed when the electrodes entered the retinal layer because of increased resistance of this layer. The thermal noise level is given by the expression

$$E^2 = 4 \times 10^{-7} kT(f_1 - f_2)R \qquad (2)$$

where k is Boltzmann's constant, T is the absolute temperature, and $(f_1 - f_2)$ the frequency band. At room temperature and for a frequency band up to 20 kc sec^{-1}

$E^2 = 3.3 \times 10^{-16}R$, or 20 μvolt for a 1 megohm resistance

IV. Design of Electrodes for Stimulation

Much work on the investigation of cell function has depended upon stimulation of the cell by some means and the recording of its reactions. Nerve and muscle cells show the most obvious responses to chemical and electrical stimuli and the majority of the work done with stimulation/ recording techniques has involved one or other of these two tissues.

The chief problem with electrodes for stimulating tissues lies in the prevention or minimizing of polarization of the electrode surface. When a cell is stimulated electrically the production of an action potential by the cell depends upon the stimulus being above the threshold for that particular cell, but the threshold may alter under differing conditions, e.g., a change in the concentration of calcium ions in the extracellular fluid. When a cell is being excited by rapidly repeated monophasic shocks over a period of time it is essential that the stimulus reaching the cell should be of known strength so that any tendency for the cell to become more or less responsive to a given stimulus can be noted. But if under such conditions the stimulating electrode becomes progressively polarized, then the current passing at each shock will fall and the stimulus to the cell will diminish.

Two methods are currently used to overcome the effects of electrode polarization. Either the stimulating circuit can be designed so that it will pass a given current regardless of the resistance of the circuit, or some form of "nonpolarizable" electrode can be used with a constant voltage stimulator. The so-called "nonpolarizable" electrodes generally favored for stimulation experiments are useful only over a limited range of current density. The common forms of electrode are as follows.

a. Platinum (with or without a coating of platinum black): owing to the generally low overvoltage at platinum it can often be used as bare metal in conditions where the current density is low, but MacIlwain (*38*) showed that platinum appeared to catalyze the oxidation of glucose when he used 3 volts ac stimulation of brain slices *in vitro*.

b. Silver–silver chloride: The commonest "nonpolarizable" electrode is the silver–silver chloride system which can be used either in direct contact with the tissues, or through a nylon or cotton wick soaked in the appropriate Ringer's solution. The current-carrying capacity of this electrode is suitable for most biological purposes.

c. Zinc–zinc sulfate: Under conditions which would polarize a silver–silver chloride electrode, a metal in contact with a more soluble salt than silver chloride is necessary, and the zinc–zinc sulfate electrode is frequently used. The zinc is prepared in the form of a rod coated with mercury giving a surface amalgam, as this behaves more like a "pure" zinc surface than the surface of commercially available zinc rods which contain many impurities liable to give rise to small galvanic cells on the surface of the metal. The zinc amalgam rod is immersed in saturated zinc sulfate solution and connected through a porous barrier to a wick soaked in Ringer's solution which makes contact with the tissues. Zinc ions are very toxic to living cells and must not be allowed to come into contact with tissues. For details of electrode preparation see Silver (*39*).

V. Electrodes for Measuring Oxidation–Reduction Potentials

A. Theory

A noble metal electrode placed in a solution containing a reversible oxidation-reduction system will gain or lose electrons until it is in equilibrium with the system and will therefore take up a steady potential (see Chapter 7). A highly reducing system will tend to donate electrons to the metal phase and make its potential more negative, an oxidizing system will have the reverse effect. In living tissues oxidation-reduction systems may conveniently be divided into two types: (a) those in which the oxidized and reduced forms differ solely in the number of electrons, e.g., in which a change of valency of an element has occurred; and (b) those in which "hydrogen transfer" occurs (i.e., either simultaneous or consecutive transfer of both protons and electrons).

a. In an oxidation-reduction system in which the reaction takes place by electron transfer according to the formula

$$\text{Reductant} \rightleftharpoons \text{Oxidant} + n e^- \tag{3}$$

a noble metal electrode placed in such a solution will develop a potential compared with the standard hydrogen electrode

$$E_h = E_h{}^\circ - \frac{RT}{nF} \ln \frac{(a_{\text{Reductant}})}{(a_{\text{Oxidant}})} \tag{4}[1]$$

b. If, however, the oxidation-reduction system is one in which a change of hydrogen occurs it *may* be expressed by, e.g.,

$$A\,H_n \rightleftharpoons A + n H \tag{5}$$

Such a system may be in equilibrium with an electrode so that

$$A\,H_n \rightleftharpoons A + n H^+ + n e^- \tag{6}$$

Hence the appropriate form of Eq. (4) is

$$E_h = E^\circ - \frac{RT}{nF} \ln \frac{a_{AH_n}}{a_A \cdot (a_{H^+})^n} \tag{7}$$

$$= E^\circ - \frac{RT}{nF} \ln \frac{a_{AH_n}}{a_A} - \frac{RT}{F}\,\text{pH} \tag{8}$$

[It was shown by Dixon (40) that either an electron transfer reaction or a gain or loss of H would yield identical equations.] Such a system can also be regarded as being in equilibrium with hydrogen gas of pressure P according to the equation

[1] The symbol E_h is commonly used in biochemical texts and is equivalent to E used elsewhere in this book.

$$\frac{n}{2} H_2 \rightleftharpoons nH \rightleftharpoons nH^+ + ne^- \qquad (9)$$

The fundamental Nernst equation for the hydrogen electrode

$$E_h = \frac{RT}{F} \ln \frac{(H^+)}{(P)^{\frac{1}{2}}} \qquad (10)$$

will apply to this hypothetical pressure of hydrogen gas. These alternative thermodynamic viewpoints are equally valid, but carry no implications with regard to the mechanisms of the chemical reactions concerned. Clark and Cohen (40a) introduced the term rH defined as the logarithm of the reciprocal of the hydrogen pressure (see Chapter 7, Section III,A).

$$rH = \log \frac{1}{P} \qquad (11)$$

and using the value of P given by Eqs. 6 and 9

$$rH = -\log K - \log \frac{(a_{AH_2})}{(a_A)} \qquad (12)$$

This is analogous to the titration curve for an acid in which

$$pH = -\log K_a - \log \frac{(a_{AH})}{(a_{A-})} \qquad (13)$$

In the oxidation-reduction systems found in living tissues, and other systems of unknown constitution and incompletely studied properties, the relation between E_h and pH may not be known. Hewitt (41) suggested that to express electrode potential measurements in terms of rH made the tacit assumption that there was a known simple relationship between the E_h and pH of the system. He therefore considered that oxidation-reduction data of *in vivo* systems should not be described in terms of rH. Dixon (42), however, pointed out the great advantages of the rH notation for describing biochemical systems. Both viewpoints must be considered. When an electrode is placed in relation to living cells or into bacterial cultures, etc., a potential is obtained. If at the same time the pH is measured it will be possible to record the observation on an E_h, pH plot. The precise biochemical system with which the electrode is in equilibrium may be unknown. It therefore seems desirable to record *in vivo* observations on a diagram such as Fig. 5 which has both the advantages of an E_h/pH plot and of an rH/pH diagram. In Fig. 5 the ordinate is E_h in millivolts and the pH is plotted along the abscissa, also in millivolts. The scale is chosen for 30°C when 1 pH unit ≡ 60 mv. The plot for the hydrogen electrode rH = 0 will fall at an angle of 45° to the horizontal, and parallel lines for rH = 10, rH = 20, etc., can be drawn, and for the oxygen electrode at rH = 41. A similar plot at any temperature would still produce the rH lines at 45° —

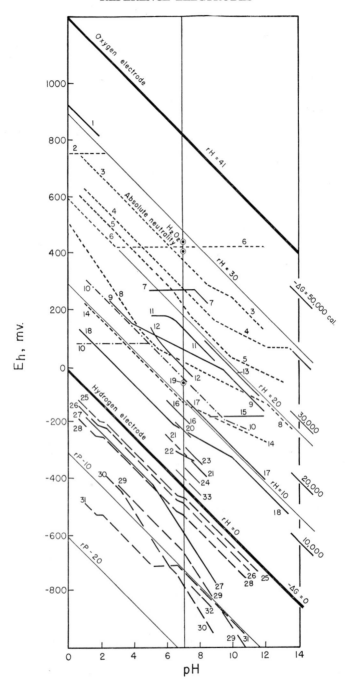

a lower temperature would place the pH lines closer together as one pH unit would be <60 mv, and at higher temperatures the pH lines would be wider apart. On Fig. 5, it is possible to plot directly data taken from E_h, pH measurements. If the diagram is then turned through an angle of 45° so that the rH lines become horizontal, it is possible to gather all the important information which would be seen on an rH/pH plot. The neutrality line through pH 7 is at 45° to the vertical, but the slopes of the pH and rH curves will still give perfectly valid information. For instance, the ferro-ferricyanide system on the E_h/pH plot falls 60 mv for each unit increase of pH from 0 to 3 pH, and then becomes horizontal. On the rH plot this is seen as a constant rH value of 20 from pH = 0 to pH = 3, and then a rise of 2 rH units for each increase of one pH unit from pH = 3 to pH = 12. This is due to dissociation of ferricyanide in alkaline solutions. A number of chemical oxidation-reduction systems are shown on the diagram in dotted lines and biochemical systems in solid lines. An E_h, pH measurement in a living tissue can now be plotted on the diagram and its position relative to important known systems will at once be apparent.

In an oxidation-reduction system such as might be under biochemical investigation the rH will depend on the following four factors.

1. The Nature of the System

A strong reducing agent will have a low rH, and a weak reducing system will have a high rH (low equivalent partial pressure of hydrogen).

FIG. 5. E_h, pH, rH, rP, and $-\Delta G$ data of chemical and biological systems. The nature of the systems is indicated by the curves as follows: - - -, chemical systems; ——, biological systems; —·—·—, pyocyanin, which shows semiquinone formation; — — —, phosphorylation reactions (no direct potential measurements obtainable; data gained by indirect and thermodynamic methods). The specific systems are: 1, adrenaline; 2, Fe^{+2}/Fe^{+3}; 3, catechol; 4, quinhydrone; 5, indophenol; 6, ferro-ferricyanide; 7, cytochrome c; 8, methylene blue; 9, ascorbic-dehydroascorbic; 10, pyocyanin; 11, hemoglobin-methemoglobin; 12, succinic-fumaric; 13, pyridine-hemochromagen; 14, indigo; 15, cyanide hemochromagen; 16, lactic-pyruvic; 17, haem; 18, riboflavin; 19, flavoprotein; 20, alcohol-aldehyde; 21, triose phosphate + phosphate diphosphoglyceric; 22, cozymase; 23, acetoacetic-β-hydroxybutyric; 24, xanthene-uric acid; 25, glycerol-glycerol phosphate; 26, glucose-6-phosphate; 27, aldehyde-acetic; 28, glucose-1-phosphate; 29, ADP-ATP; 30, monophospho-diphosphoglyceric; 31, creatine phosphate; 32, pyruvic-phosphopyruvic; 33, triosphosphate + ADP + coenzyme I $\rightleftharpoons$ phosphoglyceric acid + ATP + reduced coenzyme. The most recent data would put the rP at pH 7 of ADP-ATP, 29, at a level of -6.5 instead of -8 as drawn. This would also raise the positions of the curves 30, 31, 32 a corresponding amount as the positions of these curves are calculated from equilibria with ATP. (We are grateful to Dr. M. Dixon (42) for data and advice.)

2. *The Degree of Reduction of the System*

At the point of 50% reduction

$$rH = rH° = -\log K$$

from which can be obtained the dissociation constant of the reaction

$$AH_2 \rightleftharpoons A + H_2$$

In a simple system, $rH°$ will be independent of dilution (disregarding second order effects).

If the ratio of $(AH_2)/A$ is $\frac{1}{10}$, the rH will be 2 units higher than if it is $\frac{10}{1}$, if the number of equivalents n for the reaction is equal to 2. If $n = 1$, the same increase of the ratio of the reduced to the oxidized form will move the rH through 4 units. When $n = 2$, any tenfold change of $(AH_2)/A$ changes the rH by one unit. When $n = 1$, the displacement is 2 units.

3. *Effect of pH*

If the state of oxidation or reduction of the system affects the degree of ionization, the rH will vary with pH. When the rH of the half-reduced system, $rH°$, is plotted against pH, if the plot lies parallel with the rH lines, the state of oxidation or reduction does not affect the degree of ionization, but if the oxidized form has one more positive (or one less negative) charge than the reduced form, there is an increase of 1 rH unit for each pH unit; if two more positive charges, then rH increases by two for each pH unit (in the ferro-ferricyanide system the rH increases by 10 as pH increases from 3 to 8). The reason for this change of rH with pH arises from the fact that when a component of a system ionizes, this alters the amount of the undissociated substance in the equilibrium. For example, in the case of quinhydrone the oxidized form does not ionize, so the "total oxidant" $= Q$. The reduced form does not ionize below pH 8, but above pH 8 first one phenolic group and then the second ionize as an acid. Hence:

$$\text{total reductant} = QH_2 + QH^- + Q^{2-} \tag{14}$$

When K_1, and K_2 are the first and second dissociation constants

$$\text{total reductant} = QH_2\left[1 + \frac{K_1}{(a_{H^+})} + \frac{K_1K_2}{(a_{H^+})^2}\right] \tag{15}$$

then

$$rH = rH° - \log\frac{(\text{total reductant})}{(\text{total oxidant})} + \log\left[1 + \frac{K_1}{(a_{H^+})} + \frac{K_1K_2}{(a_{H^+})^2}\right] \tag{16}$$

The last term represents the effect of dissociation.

If the rH of the half-reduced, ionized system is plotted against pH the curve is seen to bend at pH 9 and 12 corresponding to the pK values of K_1

and K_2. Dixon (42) states that any bend in the curve which has its concave side upwards represents a dissociation of the reduced form, and every bend with its convex side upwards represents a dissociation of the oxidized form. The dissociation may be either acidic or basic; the rH data will not distinguish between the two possibilities.

4. rH Varies with the Absolute Temperature

a. rH and the Free Energy of Reactions. An important feature of expressing data in terms of rH is that we can read off directly the free energy, $-\Delta G$, of the reaction of any system with H_2. At 30°C, each rH unit corresponds to 1380 calories per mole of A when $n = 2$, or per 2 moles of A when $n = 1$. A scale of $-\Delta G$ is given on the right-hand side of Fig. 5. The energy liberated when a system reacts with oxygen is

$$-\Delta G_{O_2} = 1380(41 - rH) \tag{17}$$

If one oxidation-reduction system reacts with another, the free energy liberated is

$$-\Delta G = 1380\Delta rH \tag{18}$$

where ΔrH is the difference between the rH values of the systems irrespective of their percentage reduction. If all the reactants are at unit activity the standard free energy, $-\Delta G°$, liberated when the two systems react is

$$-\Delta G° = 1380\Delta rH° \tag{19}$$

But $\Delta G°$ is related to the equilibrium constant of a reaction by

$$-\Delta G° = 2.3RT \log K \tag{20}$$

$$\therefore \log K = \Delta rH° \tag{21}$$

The number of rH units between two systems, each at 50% reduction, is equal to the logarithm of the equilibrium constant of the reaction between them. Thus, the way in which two or more oxidation-reduction systems will react when mixed can be seen from Fig. 5.

b. The Notation rP. Dixon (42) pointed out that reactions in which phosphorylation occurred could be treated in a similar fashion to rH by using the notation rP to represent the logarithm of the reciprocal of the phosphate concentration.[2] In most of the systems of physiological interest the concentration of phosphate at equilibrium would be greater than 1 molar, so that these systems, when rP° is plotted against pH, lie below the hydrogen electrode. Unfortunately we have no phosphate electrode but the equilibrium data determined by indirect methods are shown in Fig. 5.[2]

---

[2] Strictly total activity of orthophosphate. rP data are shown by — — — lines in Fig. 5.

When this diagram is twisted so that the rP lines are horizontal, note that the curve for adenosine diphosphate-triphosphate has a negative slope of -1 rP for each increase of 1 unit of pH for values of pH > 7. In this type of diagram the ΔrP or ΔrH units per pH unit should be read from the graph and not judged by the slope.

B. Difficulties of Applying Oxidation-Reduction Potential Measurements to Biological Systems

1. Complexity of System

The noble metal electrode inserted into tissues or cells will be in equilibrium with a complex of linked oxidation-reduction systems which have rH° values at different levels between that of the substrates near rH $= 0$ and oxygen at rH $= 41$. Some of these systems may be fast, balanced reactions which are in continuous equilibrium, but others are not, since there is a net steady progress of vital chemical and physical change. In any case, only some of these reactions are electrochemically reversible in the sense that they can maintain an exchange current at a probe electrode adequate to confer upon the electrode a potential which is characteristic of the system itself. Even if this is the case it is doubtful whether the potential can be regarded as an equilibrium potential in the ordinary sense, for the living system is not in equilibrium. The recorded potentials, therefore, even at a fully reversible electrode, must be looked upon as steady state potentials. The potential shown by the electrode may indicate the mean equilibrium of all the systems, or one system might determine the level because of a long time constant.

2. Spatial Differences in Organization

Biological systems not only show great biochemical complexity, they also have a complex spatial organization. The easiest systems to investigate are bacterial cultures in which there are $< 10^9$ organisms per milliliter (each organism is ~ 1 μ^3 or $\sim 1 \times 3$ μ cylinder) in equilibrium with the surrounding culture medium. It is comparatively simple to measure the E_h and pH of the medium and to note the changes which occur with time or with the growth of the organism, but to extrapolate from the conditions in the medium to the conditions inside the bacterial cell is beset with many difficulties. Electrodes inserted into the tissues of animals will be in extracellular fluid and will be in equilibrium with a larger or smaller number of cells which may differ the one from the other in properties. The metal surface of the electrode might then act as a conducting bridge between two zones at different potentials. A current flowing through the electrode would tend to polarize both zones and the recorded potential of the electrode would be a mean and not representative of either zone. The smaller the electrode the less likely is this to happen; Cater, Phillips, and Silver (43) found that the smaller the electrode the more rapid the response *in vivo* to changes induced by injections of hormones. Microelectrodes of <1 μ could be inserted into single cells, but the inside of the cell is also complex — how complex the electron microscope is only just beginning to reveal — but at the very least we should expect to find big differences between the cytoplasm and the nucleus of a cell.

3. Polarization of Microelectrodes

In early experiments (44–48), comparatively large electrodes and usually commercial pH meters were used as the means for measuring the potential. Cater and Phillips (49) used small electrodes with a surface area of ~ 0.1 mm^2 and a modified DuBridge-Brown (50) electrometer valve circuit (10) with an input impedance of 5×10^{11} ohms. Cater, Phillips, and Silver (10) used electrodes of the same size and an electrometer valve amplifier with an input impedance of 10^{12} ohms. If this was reduced to 10^8 ohms the electrodes were so polarized as to record only about half their true equilibrium potential values. The circuit, as normally operative, would therefore have polarized the electrodes only by a fraction of a millivolt. A microelectrode suitable for insertion into a single cell could have a tip 1 μ diameter $\times$ 3 μ long, i.e., a surface area of ~ 10 μ^2 or 10^{-4} the area of the electrodes used by Cater *et al.* A microelectrode of this dimension would need an amplifier with an input impedance of 10^{16} ohms. A vibrating reed electrometer would be suitable in this respect, but may have a capacity of ~ 30 $\mu\mu$f which might effectively polarize the electrode — or the cell (if the electrochemical capacity of the cell is <30 $\mu\mu$f).

4. Poisoning of Electrodes

Even noble metal electrodes are slowly attacked by substances present in biological systems. The instability of the noble metal–oxygen complex makes oxide films unlikely, but gold and platinum may complex with sulfur compounds and this would alter the observed oxidation-reduction potentials. This matter will be discussed in Section VI.

5. The Presence of Interfering Substances

In biological systems O_2, H_2, CH_4, CO, or H_2S may be present, in larger or smaller amounts, and may seriously interfere with the measurement of oxidation-reduction potentials. Thus Okuyama (44), Uchimura (47), and Cater and Phillips (49), noted that platinum electrodes in tissues showed a fall of potential when the tissues were irradiated. This was thought to be an effect of radiation on the tissue metabolism until Cater, Phillips, and

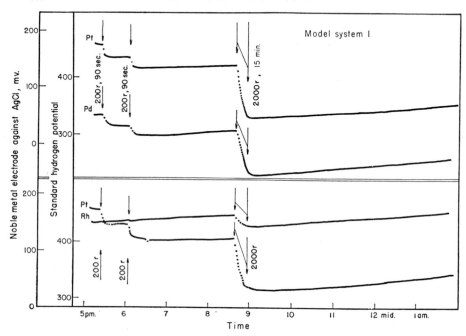

FIG. 6. Effect of 220 KVp X-rays on electrode potentials in unbuffered saline-agar gel. Model System No. 1; 2.5% agar gel in normal saline (Cater and Silver, unpublished).

Silver (*51*) found that radiation did not affect the potential of a gold electrode. They found that the potential fell when Pt, Rh, or Pd electrodes were irradiated in a model system with no redox buffer (Fig. 6). When quinhydrone, $3.4 \times 10^{-3}M$, was present in the system, all the electrodes came to identical potentials and 12,000 r was required to cause a fall of 10 mv (Fig. 7). When $3.4 \times 10^{-6}M$ quinhydrone was used as the buffer, a small dose of radiation had a much bigger effect (Fig. 7). Feates (*52*) has found similar effects. *In vivo* Pt, Pd, and Rh electrodes showed a rapid fall of 400 to 600 mv when the animal breathed hydrogen for two minutes, but the potential of the gold electrode fell only 15 mv, which was comparable with what happened when the animal breathed N_2. It was obvious that the occlusive noble metals were very sensitive to the presence of H_2 and that the nonocclusive metal, Au, was unaffected. It was concluded that the radiation effect was due to the radiochemical production of H_2, or something behaving like H_2, which was occluded by the electrode and affected its potential. Carbon monoxide was found to have a similar but less dramatic effect than H_2 on the potentials of Pt, Pd, and Ir electrodes. It is therefore wise to monitor any biological system with both Pt and Au electrodes. In

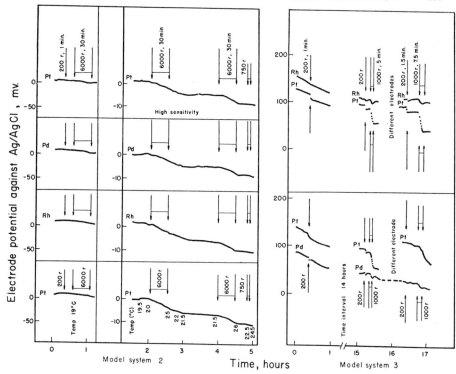

Fig. 7. Effect of 220 KVp X-rays on electrode potentials in saline-agar gel buffered to pH 7.4. Model System No. 2; 2.5% agar gel; NaCl, 0.6%; phosphate buffer, pH 7.4; quinhydrone, 3.4×10^{-3} molar. Model System No. 3, 2.5% agar gel; NaCl, 0.6%; phosphate buffer, pH 7.4; quinhydrone, 3.4×10^{-6} molar (Cater and Silver, unpublished).

bacterial cultures in particular, H_2, CO, CH_4, and H_2S may be readily produced. The action of oxygen is more difficult to assess. When an animal breathed pure oxygen, the electrode potentials of Pt, Ir, Pd, Rh, Au, and Hg became more positive and this was thought to be due to a real physiological and biochemical alteration of the oxidation-reduction potential level. Sometimes the effect was quite small (15 mv ≡ 0.5 rH units); usually it was ∼30 mv or one rH unit, but occasionally it might be as great as 4 rH units. There was always a small change of pH amounting to +2 or 3 mv, or 0.05 fall in pH value. The opposite effects were seen when the animal breathed N_2.

C. Observations on Oxidation-Reduction Potentials *in vivo*

The reader might well pause to ask what is the use of trying to measure these potentials in such complex systems? Yet in spite of all the difficulties, some useful information has come from redox measurements *in vivo*. Gillespie (*53*) used a platinum electrode and a capillary mercury electrode to measure the oxidation-reduction potentials of bacterial cultures. When suitable precautions were taken, constant potentials were obtained for *B. coli* and for mixed cultures of soil organisms grown in deep layers. Measurements with anaerobes showed increased reduction with lapse of time. When soils were water-logged they became highly reducing. This work opened up a new field of investigation into the biochemistry of bacteria. When bacteria enter a new culture medium, in nature or in the laboratory, they first condition their new environment before they multiply. During the lag-phase of growth, the cells increase in volume, the oxidation-reduction potentials fall to low levels; then the cells begin to divide and enter the logarithmic growth phase. A few bacteria require oxygen and are true aerobes. Most bacteria flourish in highly reducing conditions and are anaerobes or facultative anaerobes. The true anaerobes require the absence of oxygen and highly reducing conditions in order to grow. See Hewitt (*41*) for a review of the subject.

The growth requirements of bacteria make the determination of E_h of some importance in the science of food preservation. Barnes and Ingram (*54*) followed the changes with time after killing of the E_h and pH of meat and the relationship to the growth of bacteria. When the E_h was below -44 mv, anaerobes increased and the final E_h of -300 mv was due to bacterial activity. Knight and Fildes (*55*) found germination of tetanus spores inhibited by E_h more positive than $+110$ mv. The E_h/pH conditions of the microflora in the rumen of sheep have been investigated *in vitro* and *in vivo* by Broberg (*56, 57*). The best conditions for preservation of fruit and vegetables is also a field for E_h measurements, and these have also been made to determine the optimal conditions for the sterilization of food by radiation.

The earliest work in cells and animals was done by microinjection of rH and pH indicator dyes (*58–62*). Electrode measurements of E_h have been made in the eye (*62*), in circulating blood (*46*), in the blood of patients (*48*), in plasma (*63–65*), in frog muscle (*44, 47*), in tissue culture (*66*), in rat tumors, muscle, brain, mammary gland, liver and subcutaneous tissue and the tumors of patients (*10, 43, 49, 51, 67, 68*). From these investigations certain fundamental findings have emerged. The electrodes take up a steady potential *in vivo*. The general level of E_h is near to $E°$ of cytochrome c or cytochrome b. There is evidence of redox-buffering or "poise" of the system, because if the levels are disturbed by the animal breathing pure O_2, N_2, or H_2, or by injections of hormones, thiol compounds, or redox drugs, etc., the potentials return after a longer or shorter period to their former levels. The potentials shown by small electrodes in active tissues will respond in quite characteristic ways when the animal is injected with small doses of certain drugs. Cater, Phillips, and Silver (*43, 51, 67, 68*) found that injection of "Synkavit," a vitamin K substitute which is metabolized in the body to a naphthohydroquinone, caused a marked fall of E_h in brain, mammary gland, muscle, and tumor of rats. An injection into the arterial blood supply of a patient's tumor of 1 mg caused a fall of 10 mv (*69*). It was calculated that the quantity of Synkavit in 1 mm³ of tissue in relation to the electrode surface would be $\sim 2 \times 10^{-14}$ mole, so the oxidation-reduction potential must be rather sensitive to its presence. By comparison of the effect of radiation in the model systems (Figs. 6 and 7) and *in vivo*, the quantity of the redox buffers present in tissues must be rather small. The rapidity with which the electrodes become polarized when known currents are allowed to flow could, we believe, be made the basis of a practical means of measuring the quantity of redox buffer present *in vivo*. The potential of electrodes in actively metabolizing tissues fell rapidly after injection of glutathione, cysteine or cysteinamine into the animal and recovered slowly. The effect was seen with Pt, Au, and Hg electrodes.

Some possible interpretations of the significance of E_h determinations *in vivo* have been mentioned in Section V,B,2. It is possible that the oxidized-reduced thiol equilibrium is a slow reaction which might therefore play a big part in determining the potential level of an electrode *in vivo*. This must now be considered.

D. THIOL ELECTRODES

The sulfhydryl compounds are of great importance in biology and many attempts have been made to measure the —SH/—SS— ratio by potentiometric methods. The reaction

$$2RSH \rightleftharpoons RSSR + 2H^+ + 2e^- \tag{22}$$

would give

$$E_h = E^\circ + \frac{RT}{F} \ln (H^+) - \frac{RT}{F} \ln \frac{(RSH)}{(RSSR)^{1/2}} \tag{23}$$

But Dixon and Quastel (*70*) found that the titration curve of cysteine was logarithmic and not sigmoid in shape. Addition of cystine did not alter the potential. The results fitted the equation

$$E_h = E^\circ + \frac{RT}{F} \ln (H^+) - \frac{RT}{F} \ln (RSH) \tag{24}$$

They used solid gold electrodes, but later Dixon (*40*) found the potential of a cysteine solution was 200 mv more negative with a mercury electrode. Michaelis (*71*) found that given sufficient time the potential of Pt, Au, and Hg electrodes all fell to the same level in a solution of cysteine, but that the Hg electrodes fell much more rapidly to the equilibrium level.

Michaelis and Flexner (72) stressed the importance of the rigid exclusion of air and found the potential of cysteine at 38°C was given by the expression

$$E_h = -0.001 + 0.0617 \log (H^+) - 0.0617 \log (\text{cysteine}) \qquad (25)$$

which fits the Dixon and Quastel formula exactly. Also, at unit concentrations, the potential would be that of the hydrogen electrode within the limits of experimental error. An equation of this same form can be derived from Eq. 10 for the hydrogen electrode. It would therefore appear that Dixon's suggestion that 2 RSH yields RSSR + 2H to form a hydrogen atom pressure which can build up on mercury (as the 2H → H$_2$ reaction is very slow at a mercury surface) fits the experimental results, and accords with the finding that bright platinum was poor and black platinum useless as a thiol electrode.[3] On the other hand, from electrochemical evidence, to be potential-controlling H atoms must take part in the reaction

$$H \rightleftharpoons H^+ + e^- \qquad (26)$$

and this does not occur at a mercury electrode. An alternative theory, which would also fit the experimental findings is that RSSR is specifically absorbed on the mercury electrode and that there is a complete monolayer. All that is needed is a surface compound.

$$[Hg(RSSR)] + 2H^+ + 2e^- \rightleftharpoons Hg + 2RSH \qquad (27)$$

cf.

$$HgO + 2H^+ + 2e^- \rightleftharpoons Hg + H_2O \qquad (28)$$

Under these circumstances (RSSR) would be constant and formulas (23), (24), and (25) would all be valid.

On the other hand, Williams and Drissen (73), in potentiometric titration of cysteine with oxidizing agents, found sigmoid curves obeying formula (23), but they obtained different values of $E°$ for different oxidizing agents used as titrants. For the titration of thiourea to formamidine disulfide,

$$2 \begin{bmatrix} NH_2 \\ | \\ C-SH \\ || \\ NH \end{bmatrix} \rightleftharpoons \overset{NH_3^+}{\underset{NH}{\overset{|}{\underset{||}{C}}}} - S - S - \overset{NH_3^+}{\underset{NH}{\overset{|}{\underset{||}{C}}}} + 2e^- \qquad (29)$$

for which

$$2RSH \rightleftharpoons R-S-S-R + 2H^+ + 2e^- \qquad (30)$$

Preisler and Berger (74) found in the pH range studied

$$E_h = E^{°\prime} - \frac{RT}{2F} \ln \frac{(RSH)^2}{(RSSR)} \qquad (31)$$

---

[3] Heyrovsky's views on the catalytic hydrogen waves in polarography support Dixon's suggestion (72a).

Potentiometric titration was performed in the absence of oxygen at 30° using bright platinum electrodes. The curves were sigmoid in type, but asymmetrical and steeper on the side where the relative concentration of oxidant was higher. The concentration altered the position of the curve; $E°$ became 120 mv more positive on dilution of a molar solution to $10^{-3}M$. This is 8 rH units. Preisler and Bateman (75) studied the oxidation of dithiobiuret to the —S—S— form.

$$\underset{\text{Dithiobiuret}}{\overset{\overset{\displaystyle HS}{|} \quad \overset{\displaystyle SH}{|}}{HN=C-\underset{\underset{\displaystyle H}{|}}{N}-C=NH}} \rightleftharpoons \underset{\substack{\text{3,5-Diimino-}\\\text{1,2,4-dithioazoline}}}{\overset{\overset{\displaystyle S\text{——}S}{| \qquad |}}{HN=C-\underset{\underset{\displaystyle H}{|}}{N}-C=NH}} + 2H^+ + 2e^- \qquad (32)$$

They obtained sigmoid curves and the $E°$ was independent of concentration. Formamidine disulfide oxidized dithiobiuret giving theoretical potentials, and this showed that thiol systems can react rapidly and reversibly with one another. Freedman and Corwin (76) used boron carbide electrodes, Cecil and McPhee (77) used silver-thiol electrodes for potentiometric titration, and Cecil (78) found mercury on gold very satisfactory for this purpose. Cater and Wilson (68) in a search for a thiol electrode suitable for use *in vivo* compared four different electrodes in each model experiment. Various concentrations of glutathione in phosphate buffer were added under anaerobic conditions, and the effect of low concentrations of oxygen was followed. The apparatus which was used is shown in Fig. 8. The potentials were measured by an electrometer-valve circuit with an input impedance of 10^{12} ohms, so that the polarization current was very small. Platinum electrodes equilibrated very slowly, gold more rapidly, and mercury on gold very rapidly, when glutathione was added to the buffer solution. The addition of 2% of O_2 in the bubbling gas raised the potential of the Hg electrode in 2 minutes by more than 100 mv, although analysis showed that bubbling with 20% O_2 took 18 hours to convert 84% of the glutathione to the oxidized form. Silver electrodes behaved in a similar fashion to mercury electrodes. The E_h of mercury electrodes *in vivo* fell rapidly after injections of glutathione or Synkavit into the animal, and rose rapidly when the animal breathed pure oxygen. A true thiol electrode has not been found, but the finding of reversible —SH ⇌ —S—S— reactions *in vitro* and *in vivo* and the behavior of the Hg electrode are grounds for hope that the problem can be solved.

E. Technique of Making Electrodes

Pure Pt (30 S.W.G., 0.315 mm diameter) or pure assay Au wire was straightened, freed from grease with alcohol and ether, and dipped in

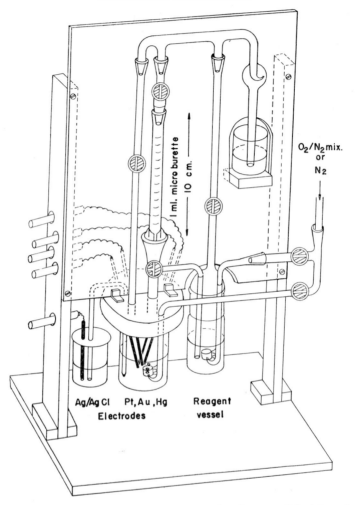

FIG. 8. Apparatus and arrangement for measuring the potential of four electrodes under various concentrations of glutathione and oxygen/nitrogen mixtures.

Araldite 985 E, suitably thinned to avoid forming beads along the electrode. Eight coats were applied, each baked in the oven at 200°C for 10 minutes and the final coat cured for 30 minutes. The tip was either scraped free of Araldite and sharpened to a pencil point 0.3 mm long by means of a glass knife or was clamped in a "Tufnol" [3a] block and ground flat by means of a small piece of very fine hone stone, which had been cleaned by cutting a fresh surface on the stone with a glass slide. The electrodes were boiled in

[3a] A tough plastic laminate.

distilled water before use. A perfectly fresh metallic surface was thus prepared for each experiment. Mercury electrodes were made by dipping the ends of gold electrodes into purified mercury for 1 minute. Microelectrodes were prepared by fusing 50 or 25 μ diameter Pt (80%) Ir (20%) alloy wire into fine glass capillary tubing so that the end of the wire just protruded from the glass or could be ground off flush with the glass. Smaller electrodes than these could conveniently be made by the technique of Gray and Svaetichin (23, 24), in which silver solder is drawn out in glass capillaries, the 1 μ tip rhodium-plated, and then plated with gold. A further alternative is the method of Cater and Silver using gold-plated, stainless steel microelectrodes (see Fig. 11(h), and Chapter 11, Section VII,A,3).

The reference electrode was made by insulating 1 mm diameter pure Ag wire with Araldite, then baring 10 mm of the wire with a glass knife and chloridizing electrolytically in 0.1 N HCl for 10 minutes at 1 ma in the dark. The electrode was then rinsed in distilled water and placed in 0.6% sodium chloride solution, which corresponds to the chloride content of mammalian extracellular fluid. The reference electrode was always inserted into the subcutaneous tissues of the animal. Great uncertainty arises if the reference electrode is placed on the skin or on a saline pad because of the membrane potentials of the skin and its variable pH. The skin may be as acid as pH 4 compared with the pH 7 of the tissues. The authors always inserted the silver–silver chloride reference electrode subcutaneously and this was held at earth potential. The animal was very carefully insulated from earth because the skin was not at earth potential. Any injections or manipulations were made with rubber-gloved hands to avoid short circuiting the animal to earth. Touching the animal with the bare hand had a noticeable polarization effect on the electrode potentials.

VI. Electrodes for Measurement of pH

The measurement of pH in tissues poses a number of problems of technique that are not normally encountered during measurements in purely physical systems. The biological complex of cells, fibers, and extracellular fluids found in animal tissues contains a wide variety of chemical substances. An electrode measuring pH in tissue must therefore be sensitive only to changes of pH and must not respond to alterations of redox potential or oxygen tension, or to the presence of metallic ions such as those of sodium, potassium or calcium, which are normally found in tissue fluids. Proteins are always present to a greater or lesser extent in biological systems and the electrode must be able to tolerate the presence of these and other large molecules, at least for periods of some hours. Owing to the heterogeneous nature of animal bodies, a pH electrode must be small enough to be embedded completely and solely in the particular tissue in which a measurement is to be made. This consideration is particularly important when tissues or organs of widely differing biological activity are anatomically closely related; entirely false information may be obtained if the electrode is embedded partly in one organ and partly in another. For this reason, the smaller an electrode can be made, the more useful it becomes for *in vivo* work. This does not of course apply to the measurement of pH in biological fluids such as urine, saliva or blood which are available in relatively large amounts. Within a given tissue, there will also be abrupt changes of pH conditions depending on whether measurements are being made in extracellular fluid or inside the cell membrane, in cell sap. A further difficulty in relation to making measurements in tissues is that the electrode must be strong enough and of suitable shape to be forced into a solid or semisolid medium, and in practice this usually sets a limit to the kinds of tissue that can be studied. For instance, dense fibrous fascia and bone are obviously difficult substances in which to make pH determinations, although it would be very interesting to know the pH conditions existing at ossification sites, and in fibrous tumors.

The insertion of electrodes of any size into tissue is sure to cause some damage; the larger the electrode the greater the damage, and this will result in bleeding from small blood vessels and the escape of the contents from ruptured cells. Such damage may alter the pH considerably from that normally present in the intact tissue.

The buffering mechanism of the animal body rests largely on a bicarbonate system. Exposure of tissue to the air allows escape of carbon dioxide from the surface of the organ and this may alter the pH of the tissue; precautions must therefore be taken not to allow escape of carbon dioxide from an operation site. Finally, it should be pointed out that any interference with an organ may cause changes in its blood supply. The insertion of a glass electrode may cause reflex dilatation or constriction of blood vessels both in its immediate vicinity and in other parts of the organ. The resulting change of blood flow is likely to affect the pH of the tissue concerned and may give rise to errors in the estimation of resting pH levels. This is particularly important in situations where small changes of pH are expected to follow the administration of some external stimulus such as a drug.

The great advantage of the glass electrode for pH measurement in tissues, as in other situations, is that it responds solely to pH changes. (See Chapter 5 for a discussion of the limitations of the glass electrode response.) Protein is the tissue constituent that is most likely to affect adversely the performance of glass electrodes, but fortunately it is normally in very low concentrations in extracellular fluids, except in the case of blood. Nevertheless, glass electrodes can be used quite satisfactorily in blood, provided that the surface of the electrode is sufficiently smooth to discourage the adherence of blood platelets and the deposition of fibrin. Prolonged, continuous-flow recording of blood pH is inevitably associated with the slow coating of the electrode with plasma protein, which reduces sensitivity, so that frequent cleaning of the electrode is essential if full performance is to be maintained. There are proprietary silicone preparations available for giving glass electrodes a "nonwettable" finish which greatly reduces the rate of deposition of protein from blood. It is claimed that this silicone layer allows the electrode to retain its full sensitivity but it is difficult to reconcile this with the idea of an "hydrated glass" surface on the electrode. It may well be, however, that the improvement obtained through siliconing glass electrodes for use in protein-laden fluids will offset any small decrease in over-all sensitivity that may result from a hydrophobic surface on the electrode.

The fragility of the glass electrode constitutes a major disadvantage to its use for making pH measurements in tissues. In biological investigations, observations of rapid changes of pH are frequently of as much, or more, interest than those of absolute resting levels and, for this reason, thick-walled electrodes with slow response to pH change are of little value. Furthermore, the standard "bulb-ended" electrode is most unsuitable for measurements either in or on the surface of tissues. In the main, two forms of glass electrode have been developed for use *in vivo*; the capillary glass electrode of Voegtlin and co-workers (*79*) for insertion, and the plane membrane electrode for use on tissue surfaces. Recently, plane membrane electrodes have been used in conjunction with gas-permeable membranes in order to make continuous records of P_{CO_2} in tissues or biological fluids (*80–83*). This method is of particular value in biological work owing to the great importance of the bicarbonate buffering system in animal tissue. The combination of glass electrode and CO_2-permeable membrane depends for its usefulness on the finding that CO_2 in physical solution changes the pH of an aqueous medium proportionally to log P_{CO_2} of the solution (*84*). Such electrodes give near-linear response for log P_{CO_2} over the range of P_{CO_2} found in living tissue.

A. The Capillary Glass Electrode

Most glass electrodes used for insertion into tissue are derived from the capillary electrode of Voegtlin *et al.* (*79*). These authors prepared their electrodes as follows:

Corning 015 glass tubing of 7 mm outside diameter and 5 mm inside diameter was melted down to a thick-walled capillary, which was cut and a 3 mm diameter bulb was blown at the end of it. The bulb was heated in a cool flame and drawn out to a fine-pointed capillary. The end was sealed extremely carefully to give a very smooth, sharp point. The lower part of the shank down to the thin-walled area was insulated with a water-repellent cement, as this was found to give greater stability to the electrode. The tube was partly filled with phosphate buffer and connected to a vacuum pump with the electrode upright, in order to extract air from the capillary tip and replace it with buffer. When the air had disappeared from the tip, the shank was filled almost to the top with buffer. Contact was made from inside the shank through a potassium chloride–agar bridge to a calomel half-cell. The electrodes were calibrated before and after use in tissues.

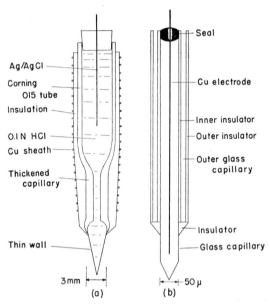

Fig. 9. Capillary glass electrodes. (a) Capillary glass electrode after Voegtlin *et al.* (*79*); (b) microcapillary glass electrode after Caldwell (*86*).

This is an essential check against damage during insertion. Electrodes of this type have a dc impedance of 100–200 megohms at 25°C. At 37°C, they give about 60 mv per pH unit and show no drift after the first minute or two in buffer solution. It is essential to calibrate under the same conditions of temperature as those pertaining during measurement in tissue, i.e., the shank at room temperature and the tip in buffer at 37°C. This type of electrode is strong enough to be forced into soft tissues but it is necessary to incise overlying fascia of organs such as muscle before attempting to insert the electrode, otherwise it may be damaged. After insertion into tissues it is usually found that the reading of the electrode drifts slowly for 20 to 30 minutes towards a more acid pH. This is the result of tissue damage producing a more acid tissue environment and is not a fault in the electrode. Sonnenschein, Walker, and Stein (*85*) modified this electrode for measuring pH in small blocks of tissue. They used either a pure silver wire inner electrode in a saturated solution of silver acetate in 50% acetic acid, or a silver–silver chloride electrode in 0.1 N hydrochloric acid. They boiled their electrodes for 2 hours after half filling them with electrolyte to ensure as rapid an equilibration of the asymmetry potentials as possible. The impedance of their electrodes was of the order of 400 megohms. Like Voegtlin *et al.* (*79*), they took care to insulate the electrode with a water-repellent covering except at the extreme tip (Fig. 9a).

Caldwell (*86*) made a capillary electrode suitable for insertion into very large cells, such as the giant nerve fibers of some cephalopods. He used a low resistance glass of 0.5 cm outside diameter, which was drawn down to a capillary of about 50 μ outside diameter. This was insulated with shellac to within 15 mm of the tip and placed inside a larger capillary of about 80 μ inside diameter. The inner tube projected beyond the outer for the distance that it was uninsulated. The two tubes were then bonded together with resin and the outer tube coated with picein wax. The inner tube was filled with 0.1 N hydrochloric acid and the tip sealed carefully in a microflame. The inner electrode was a 25 μ copper wire dipping into the hydrochloric acid, and was sealed in position with resin. It is very difficult to see the tip of such an electrode but this may be overcome by coloring the tip with some form of marker such as a spot of picein wax (Fig. 9b). Naturally a glass electrode of this size, if it is to be at all robust, will have an extremely high resistance. Caldwell (*86*) rejected those with a resistance greater than 1000 megohms and those which gave a sensitivity of less than 50 mv per pH unit at calibration. Electrodes of such high impedance require very careful screening and very sensitive instrumentation. Caldwell (*86*) used an electrometer impedance converter (*87*). Modern, commercial, vibrating-capacitor electrometers such as the Vibron electrometer (Electronic Instruments Co., Richmond, England) are very suitable for use with these microelectrodes.

Insulation of microcapillary pH electrodes is a difficult technical problem. It is essential that the insulation immediately above the active point should be extremely good so that, when the pointed tip is embedded in a tissue or a cell, the electrode should measure only the pH at its tip and there must be no interference through the shaft of the electrode.

B. The P_{CO_2} Electrode

1. Theory

The glass pH electrode was first used for measuring P_{CO_2} in biological fluids by Stow *et al.* (*80*), who covered a plane glass electrode with a fluid-saturated cellophane membrane which was in turn covered by a thin rubber film, permeable to carbon dioxide but not to ions. The carbon dioxide from fluid under investigation diffused through the rubber membrane, dissolved in fluid held in the cellophane sheet and altered its pH. The change of pH was read from the glass electrode.

The "sensitivity," S, of a P_{CO_2} electrode is defined by Severinghaus and Bradley (82) as

$$S = \Delta pH / \Delta \log P_{CO_2} \tag{33}$$

The interaction of CO_2 and aqueous sodium bicarbonate can be shown as

$$\alpha P_{CO_2} = (H_2CO_3) = \frac{(a_{H^+})^2 + (a_{H^+})(a_{Na^+}) - K_w}{K_1\{1 + [2K_2/(a_{H^+})]\}} \tag{34}$$

Where K_w is the ionic product of water, K_1 and K_2 are the first and second dissociation constants of H_2CO_3, and α is a constant denoting proportionality of $P_{CO_2}:H_2CO_3$ concentration in water.

In water without bicarbonate, Eq. (34) approximates to

$$\alpha P_{CO_2} = (a_{H^+})^2/K_1 \tag{35}$$

Substituting in Eq. 35 for two values of P_{CO_2} and (a_{H^+}), dividing and taking the negative logarithm.

$$-\log \frac{P'_{CO_2}}{P''_{CO_2}} = -\log \frac{(a'_{H^+})^2}{(a''_{H^+})^2} \tag{36}$$

or

$$\log P''_{CO_2} - \log P'_{CO_2} = 2(pH' - pH'') \tag{37}$$

$$S = \Delta pH/\Delta \log P_{CO_2} = 0.5 \tag{38}$$

If $NaHCO_3$ is added, the second term in Eq. (34) becomes dominant above 1 mM Na, so the equation will approximate to

$$\alpha P_{CO_2} = [(a_{H^+})(a_{Na^+})]/K_1 \tag{39}$$

Again taking two values as in (36), we have the sensitivity

$$S = \Delta pH/\Delta \log P_{CO_2} = 1 \tag{40}$$

Thus a low concentration of bicarbonate ion doubles the sensitivity of the electrode.

Severinghaus and Bradley (82) made a careful study of the P_{CO_2} electrode and found that its performance agreed well with theory in dilute solutions of bicarbonate but at higher concentrations the sensitivity was below the calculated value. Also, the equilibrium time was unduly prolonged above a concentration of 0.02 M. Both these phenomena may be due to the increasing amount of CO_3^{2-} present at high concentrations, with the consequent increase in CO_2 exchange necessary to produce measurable effects. Using 0.1 mM sodium bicarbonate, the theoretical sensitivity varies with the carbon dioxide concentration, being 0.98 at 1.8%, 0.96 at 4.8%, and 0.95 at 7% carbon dioxide in the effluent gas. The linearity is rather better if 5 mM sodium bicarbonate is used, but in any case no marked change of sensitivity occurs over the range of P_{CO_2} likely to be found in biological systems.

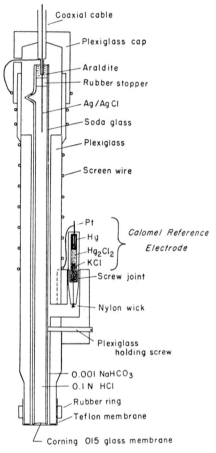

Coaxial cable

Plexiglass cap

Araldite

Rubber stopper

Ag/AgCl

Soda glass

Plexiglass

Screen wire

Pt

Hg

Hg$_2$Cl$_2$

KCl

Calomel Reference Electrode

Screw joint

Nylon wick

Plexiglass holding screw

0.001 NaHCO$_3$

0.1 N HCl

Rubber ring

Teflon membrane

Corning 015 glass membrane

FIG. 10. The P_{CO_2} electrode after Hertz and Siesjö (83).

The P_{CO_2} electrodes of Stow et al. (80), Severinghaus and Bradley (82), and Gertz and Loeschke (81) are large and unsuitable for use in tissues, but are valuable for measurements in biological fluids such as blood. A recent development by Hertz and Siesjö (83) has produced an electrode of suitable shape and size for use at least on the surface of tissues and possibly within them. This electrode also has a shorter equilibration time than those previously described, so that it can follow relatively rapid changes of P_{CO_2}. The response time to 90% equilibrium in 0.1 mM sodium bicarbonate is 25 to 30 seconds, and about 2 minutes in 1 mM.

This electrode, or developments from it, will undoubtedly yield much valuable information on conditions obtaining inside tissues. The P_{CO_2} electrode of Hertz and Siesjö is constructed as follows (Fig. 10).

2. Construction

The assembly consists of a plexiglass housing containing a glass electrode made from a soda glass tube 6.5 mm outside diameter, across one end of which a plane membrane of Corning 015 glass has been fused by the method of MacInnes and Dole (88). Although described as "plane" the glass membrane is in fact very slightly concave when viewed from outside the tube, but the greater the radius of curvature of the concavity, the faster will be the electrode response.

A polytetrafluorethylene (Teflon) membrane, 6 μ in thickness, is stretched across the open end of the plexiglass housing and secured by a rubber ring. The gap between the Teflon and the glass membrane should be about 100 μ. This gap does not contain a cellophane sheet which was present in the original design of P_{CO_2} electrode of Stow et al. (80). A side extension to the plexiglass housing contains a small calomel reference electrode made from a hollowed plexiglass rod. The plexiglass housing is partly filled with 0.001 or 0.0001 M sodium bicarbonate solution to 2 cm above the lower end of the calomel electrode. It is necessary to ensure that the space between the glass and Teflon membranes is filled with this solution; such an arrangement limits the use of this electrode to the upright position. The glass electrode is filled with 0.1 M hydrochloric acid and contact is made through a silver–silver chloride wire sealed into the top of the tube with insulating resin. A screening lead is taken from the calomel electrode round the plexiglass housing to the screen of a coaxial cable, the inner wire of which is soldered to the silver–silver chloride electrode.

Hertz and Siesjö (83) used a calomel half-cell as a reference electrode because Stow et al. (80) found that their silver–silver chloride electrodes were rather unstable. The design of this calomel cell is of interest to the biologist, as it can be used in any position, is very stable and is small and easy to make and handle (Fig. 10).

One disadvantage of this electrode is that, when very dilute solutions of sodium bicarbonate are used within the housing to give short response times, a slow drift of pH is observed in the direction of alkalinity. This is ascribed to slow solution of the very alkaline Corning 015 glass in the small volume of fluid trapped between the Corning glass and the Teflon membrane. No such drift was observed when higher concentrations of sodium bicarbonate were used. Ingvar, Siesjö and Hertz (89) have used this electrode for measuring P_{CO_2} on the surface of the brain of anaesthetized cats and found that the response time was rapid enough to show changes of P_{CO_2} at the brain surface within a few seconds of making the animal breathe increased carbon dioxide in the inspired air. Some of the delay could obviously be accounted for in terms of blood circulation time. It should be pointed out, however, that the membrane P_{CO_2} electrode responds more quickly to increases in P_{CO_2} than to decreases.

3. Measurements of P_{CO_2} and pH in Blood

It is of considerable importance to be able to monitor blood gases and pH both experimentally and clinically during surgery. Much ingenuity has been displayed in design and production of special electrodes for this purpose and a recent symposium has collected the latest ideas on the subject [see Severinghaus (90), Wright (91) and Astrup (92)].

The conventional arrangement for measuring blood pH consists of some form of chamber which is carefully maintained at body temperature if measurements are being made continuously in vivo, and which contains some form of glass electrode, and a reference electrode. Precautions must be taken not to cause clotting of the blood in the chamber or on the electrode. It is also important to avoid any escape of gas from the blood or changes of pressure in the chamber during the measurement of pH, otherwise the pH will be altered. A simple method for taking repeated, small samples of blood for estimation uses an all-glass hypodermic syringe in which the plunger is a glass electrode. This syringe is produced commercially by Electronic Instruments Ltd., and is particularly well suited to taking blood samples anaerobically. An ingenious microcapillary electrode has been described by Wright (91) for making rapid pH measurements on very small quantities of blood. The sample under test is passed through a small capillary made of low resistance glass surrounded by 0.1 N hydrochloric acid. The HCl is connected through silver–silver chloride and the reference electrode is a calomel half-cell.

C. Oxide Electrodes

Although glass electrodes are the first choice on account of their insensitivity to factors other than pH, their fragility has always been a disadvantage for in vivo work. Many workers have used a wide variety of substances to try to measure pH in biological fluids and tissues but have met with only limited success owing to the complex nature of living systems.

Antimony has been used by the majority of investigators in biological work involving metal, pH-sensitive, electrodes and a number of different types of electrode have been devised. These are usually in the form of antimony rod, the surface of which is abraded before use, or of wire of some other metal onto which antimony is electroplated. Freshly prepared antimony electrodes must be "aged" before use, but the process of oxidation must not be allowed to proceed too far or the electrode will lose some sensitivity to pH changes. Antimony microelectrodes can be made by melting antimony within a glass tube and then drawing the tube down to a capillary with an antimony core (93).

Unfortunately, antimony electrodes require frequent calibration and the $E°$ value is variable. Within the range of pH found in tissues the response of antimony is quite good, but the performance falls off beyond pH 3 and pH 8.5. A more serious difficulty is the variation in response of antimony that is found with changes of oxygen tension (94, 95), as variation of P_{O_2} is a characteristic of most living systems. The response of the antimony electrode to temperature changes is also somewhat irregular over the usual biological range of 0 to 45°C (96). Other factors which are likely to affect adversely the performance of pH electrodes made of antimony are oxidizing or reducing agents, carboxylic acids and amino acids, all of which are present in tissues. Some metal ions interact with antimony, but these are not normally found in tissue fluids. However, in cases of poisoning or under some pathological conditions such ions may be present in saliva or urine, e.g., copper.

It is therefore obvious that there are the most severe limitations to the usefulness of antimony electrodes for *in vivo* pH measurements, and as a result they are now used only in situations where it is unwise to use a glass electrode. If the major requirement for an electrode is that it should be robust, and the required degree of accuracy of measurement is not high, then the antimony electrode may be used. For instance, during an investigation of dental caries, antimony electrodes in the form of dental probes were used by Thompson and Brudevold (97) and Charlton (98). In situations where the breakage of a glass electrode might prove dangerous, the metal–metal oxide system is obviously safer, e.g., in stomach (99). Capillary antimony electrodes of the type described by Davies and Rémond (93) and by Levin (100) have the advantage of lower impedance over all-glass electrodes of similar size and can therefore be used with less complex pH meters.

Other metal–metal oxide systems have been used in biological work for making pH measurements in tissues, e.g., bismuth and tungsten. Bismuth is sensitive to changes of P_{O_2}, but is rather less affected by changes of redox potential than antimony. In general, however, it is too variable in performance for use in unknown conditions such as those found in tissue. Caldwell (86) described a microelectrode made of tungsten for pH investigations in cells, but he found it was sensitive to a wide range of chemical substances; in particular, thiol groups, oxidizing agents and also calcium ions affected the responses of the tungsten. The sensitivity to calcium is particularly unfortunate because it is a normal tissue constituent. On the other hand, tungsten has the advantage of great mechanical strength, it can be sealed into glass, and it can be electropolished to points less than $0.5\,\mu$ for use as a microelectrode. These advantages are of little value, however, if the metal gives unreliable information when used as a pH electrode.

The iridium-plated electrode is said to give a near-theoretical response over the range pH 0 to 14 from 0° to 70°C. It is not affected by carbon dioxide, sulfur dioxide, ammonia or hydrogen sulfide, but it will be affected by hydrogen. It is also insensitive to copper, silver, lithium, sodium, and potassium ions and to oxidizing agents and oxygen (101). It has excellent mechanical properties, but is easily polarized and therefore a resistance of at least 10 megohms must be used in series with it. (See Chapter 7 for details of preparation.) The authors have not used this electrode for pH measurements *in vivo* but it appears to have many useful features for this application.

VII. The Oxygen Cathode

Three physical measurements, oxygen tension, oxidation-reduction potentials, and pH are important for the understanding of oxidation in biological systems. The biochemist often measures the metabolic activity of tissue slices in 95% O_2, 5% CO_2, and 95% N_2, 5% CO_2 mixtures, but the conditions *in vivo* are different. A knowledge of the levels of oxygen tension in various tissues would greatly facilitate the correct interpretation of biochemical data (102–105). The physiologist is vitally interested in the oxygen tension in lungs, blood, brain, muscle, and viscera and the changes which occur with activity. The new techniques in cardiac surgery require oxygen tension measurements for diagnosis and for monitoring extracorporal circulation. The radiotherapist needs data on oxygen tension because oxygen is an important radiosensitizer (106, 107). The methods available for measuring oxygen tension include: (i) Tonometry — equilibrating small gas bubbles with the tissues (108–111); (ii) chemical analysis of samples of withdrawn blood; (iii) oximetry — the spectroscopic analysis of the degree of association of hemoglobin and oxygen (112–120); and (iv) the oxygen cathode method. Tonometry and chemical analysis are slow and laborious, the oximeter can measure only the blood oxygen tension and that within a limited range. The oxygen cathode technique can be used for measuring oxygen tension in blood and tissues, it is not limited in its range, can follow rapid changes, and is of wide application, but calibration presents serious problems, which have been discussed by Inch (121) and Cater (68).

A. Types of Electrode

Danneel (122), working in Nernst's laboratory, discovered that the electrolysis current between platinum electrodes at a potential of 0.02 volt was approximately proportional to the concentration of dissolved oxygen. Blinks and Skow (123) applied the method to the study of oxygen exchange in plants, and Davies and Brink (124) used recessed platinum electrodes to make quantitative measurements of oxygen tension in animal tissues.

1. The Recessed Electrode

Platinum wire, 0.17 mm diameter, was degassed by heating to white heat in a hydrogen flame and then carefully sealed with a microflame into tubes of soft glass of comparable diameter which extended beyond the end of the wire to form a recess 0.6 to 1.6 mm in length [Davies and Brink (124)]. This recess should be a uniform cylinder whose axis coincides with that of the Pt wire. The electrodes were then annealed to 425°C to prevent the formation of circular cracks in the glass. Electrodes 25 μ in diameter were also made in this way but an electrically heated Pt loop was used for sealing the fine wire into the glass [see Fig. 11(a) and (b)].

The recessed electrode obeys the laws of linear diffusion until the oxygen diffusion gradient reaches the mouth of the recess. The current at time t secs after applying the potential is given by

$$i_t = nFCA(D/\pi t)^{\frac{1}{2}} \tag{41}$$

where n = number of electrons per M of O_2 electrolyzed,[4] C = initial concentration of oxygen, A = area of Pt surface in cm^2, D = diffusion coefficient of oxygen in cm^{2}sec^{-1}. The advantages of the recessed electrode are that no oxygen is taken from the tissues during the time of the actual observation, and the current is not dependent on the diffusion coefficient for oxygen in the tissues. The current–voltage curve shows a good plateau between 0.3 and 0.8 volt. The disadvantages of the recessed electrode are (1) that the current must be measured at a precise interval after applying the potential, (2) observations cannot be made at intervals less than 5 minutes. In our experience, the equilibration time may be 20 to 30 minutes, and it is therefore impossible to follow rapid changes of P_{O_2}. The recessed electrode is not easy to make accurately and some workers have made the

---

[4] Davies and Brink (124) found a 4 electron reaction with a recessed electrode filled with saline, and a 2 electron reaction when the recess was filled with agar, Longmuir (102) found $n \sim 4$ and Hill (125) with the flow electrode found $n = 4$.

recess by dissolving away the metal from a completely metal filled glass capillary until the required depth of recess was obtained. Hill (*125*) gives the following instructions. A glass tube about 3 mm diameter and with very thin walls is drawn out to give a capillary extension 2 cm long, about 120 μ outside and 80 μ inside diameter. A 40 μ diameter platinum wire is flamed to white heat and is then inserted through the wide end until it emerges through the fine end of the tube. The glass at the tip is sealed around the platinum with a microflame. The resulting external diameter is 100 μ. The electrode is immersed in boiling aqua regia (80% HCl, 20% HNO_3) and the platinum recessed to depth of 120–150 μ, which takes about

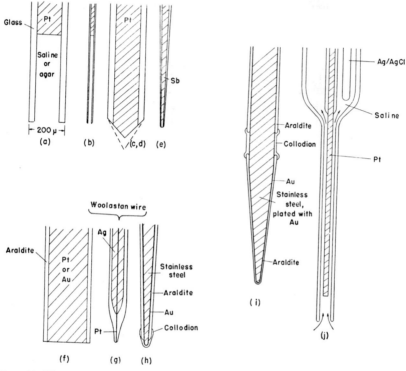

FIG. 11. Electrodes used for measurement of oxygen tension in tissues (drawn to scale). Electrodes a-e are contained in glass; others in materials as noted. (a) Recessed electrode, 200 μ dia; Davies and Brink (*124*); (b) recessed electrode, 25 μ dia; Davies and Brink (*124*); (c) open-ended electrode, 45° cone; Montgomery and Horwitz (*127*); (d) open-ended electrode, 60° cone (dotted); Inch (*121*); (e) open-ended electrode, antimony; Davies and Rémon (*93*); (f) gold in Araldite; Cater *et al.* (*136*); (g) Woolaston wire in glass, 10 μ dia, Pt electrode; Cater, Silver, and Wilson (*136*); (h) electropolished stainless steel, gold plated, and Araldite-insulated; Cater and Silver (*138a*); (i) for insertion into blood vessel (collodion, or polythene, or Teflon may be used), Silver (*138b*); (j) flow electrode; Hill (*125*).

3 hours. The recess is filled with water, dipped in 10% collodion in amyl acetate and allowed to dry in air for 3 minutes. The electrode is then immersed in water for the collodion to harden. This forms a membrane closing the recess. The technique used by Svaetichin (24) of drawing silver-solder in glass tubes could be used and the electrode surface-plated with gold or platinum. It is also easy to fuse antimony powder in glass and draw out fine tubes. The column of antimony sometimes breaks and at these breaks the tube can be cut to form recessed electrodes. Gold plating is necessary because the antimony dissolves in tissue fluids, unless a constant potential of -300 mv is applied. For use in blood, the recess can be filled with agar, or with distilled water, and then covered with a collodion membrane (124).

2. The Open-ended Electrode

Davies and Brink (124) used flush-ended electrodes for measuring rapid changes of oxygen tension, but found the plateau of the current–voltage curve poorly defined and the reproducibility of the calibration current was poor. However, they were measuring the current at an interval after applying the potential; in our experience the behavior of open-ended electrodes was more reproducible when a constant potential was applied and the steady state current was measured. Most investigations of oxygen tension in man and in animals have been made with open-ended electrodes using a potential difference of 0.6 volt between the oxygen cathode and the reference electrode — a silver–silver chloride or calomel half-cell (10, 43, 51, 67, 93, 126–137).

There are several techniques for making open-ended electrodes. Platinum wire fused into glass and the end ground off flush (124), or ground to a 45° pencil point (127) [Fig. 11(c)]. Inch (121) used 0.18 mm diameter platinum wire fused in glass, and ground to a 60° cone [Fig. 11(d)]. Urbach and Noell (135) used 90% Pt, 10% Ir alloy 0.2 mm diameter, insulated with Kel-F (35% type N suspension made by Kellogg Co.) and ground to an open conical tip 0.5 mm long. Cater and colleagues (10, 43, 51, 67, 138) used 0.315 mm diameter platinum or gold wire insulated with eight coats of Araldite 985E and sharpened to a pencil point with a glass knife for following changes of oxygen tension, and for quantitative measurements a flat end was ground, using a very soft hone stone after clamping the electrode in a "Tufnol" block (136, 137). This gives a clean electrode surface of reproducible size [Fig. 11(f)].

3. Microelectrodes

Davies and Rémond (93) made flexible electrodes of antimony in glass capillaries with tips of 14 μ for measuring oxygen tension on the surface of cat brain [Fig. 11(e)]. Cater *et al.* (*10*) used 25 μ diameter Pt 90%, Ir 10% alloy wire fused into a glass capillary. Cater and co-workers (*136*) used 100 μ diameter Woolaston wire[5] with a 10 μ core of platinum which was then threaded through a fine glass capillary leaving 1 or 2 mm exposed. The silver was stripped off this exposed tip with nitric acid and, after washing in distilled water, the Woolaston wire was drawn back so that the tip was flush with the capillary which was then fused round the 10 μ Pt leaving the end exposed [Fig. 11(g)]. The tip sometimes required careful grinding. Electrodes sufficiently rigid and robust to be inserted deeply into tissues such as brain, muscle, tumor, etc., have recently been made by Cater and Silver using the following technique. High quality stainless steel surgical needles are electropolished in a solution of 42 ml H_3PO_4 (syrupy), 24 ml H_2O, and 34 ml H_2SO_4 (Analar), using 6 volts dc, with the stainless steel forming the anode and a carbon rod the cathode. About 1 cm of the tip of the needle is slowly raised and lowered in the electropolishing solution without the tip breaking the surface. By adjusting the relative speeds of lowering and raising any degree of taper can be produced. If the point is too long and slender, dipping it through the surface will shorten or ampu- tate the point. The needle is rapidly transferred through sodium bicarbo- nate solution, then through dilute acetic acid, and washed in distilled water. If the tip is of suitable dimensions, it is degreased and electroplated with gold using potassium aurocyanide solution and a current density 1 ma/cm[2] for 5–10 seconds, with stirring. The electrode, except its tip, is then insulated with Araldite, by dipping into thin Araldite and 1 minute later the needle is lowered in a micromanipulator until the point just breaks the surface of some Araldite solvent (ethyl acetate 60%, toluene 34%, and diacetone alcohol 16% by weight) in a beaker. The Araldite is then cured for 10 minutes at 200°C and the process is repeated a number of times. Electrodes with points 10 to 50 μ [Fig. 11(h)] are suitable for tissues and are robust enough to be pushed through polythene or tissues without alteration of their calibration values. Electrodes with tips of 0.5 μ can be made for insertion into cells. These fine tips are damaged by the lightest touch.

4. Coated Electrodes

For measurements involving blood, Davies and Brink (*124*) filled their recessed electrodes with agar to prevent the entry of red blood corpuscles. They also found that a recessed electrode, filled with distilled water and then covered with a collodion film, functioned well in blood. Clark (*139*)

---

[5] Woolaston wire (*138c*) has a 10 μ diameter core of platinum surrounded by silver to form a wire of 100 μ outside diameter.

has designed an electrode for measuring oxygen tension in blood using a platinum cathode covered with polythene sheet 35 μ thick. The silver–silver chloride reference electrode is incorporated so that no current flows through blood, thus avoiding deposition of fibrin on the membrane. This electrode has been used by a number of investigators (82, 140, 141). The Clark electrode is large and would need to be modified for work *in vivo*. Electrodes suitable for measuring oxygen tension in the circulating blood and bone marrow of animals are described by Cater, Silver, and Wilson (136) (Figs. 12 and 13). Open-ended electrodes can be somewhat

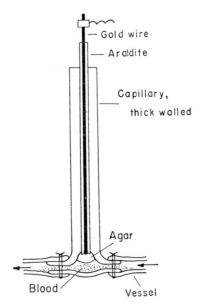

FIG. 12. Electrode for measuring oxygen tension in circulating blood (136).

improved by coating them with collodion, polythene, or polytetrafluoroethylene, which will prevent flow and movement artifacts and poisoning of the electrode by fibrin films *in vivo* (the speed of response to changes of P_{O_2} is, however, slower). Such coated electrodes can be inserted into veins or arteries to record P_{O_2} in flowing blood. A better type of electrode for insertion into vessels is illustrated in Fig. 11 (i); note that the electrode surface is a cylinder behind the sharp tip.

5. Flow Electrodes

Hill (125) used a "flow electrode" in which a 100 μ diameter capillary tube was immersed in Ringer's solution close to the muscle or tissue under investigation, and the fluid was drawn up the tube at a constant rate by suction. As the fluid passed the platinum cathode (60 μ diameter, 2 cm long), it gave up all its oxygen. The electrode shown in Fig. 11 (j) was made by drawing out a glass tube, with very thin walls and an internal diameter of 2 mm, in a microflame to obtain a capillary of diameter ∼100 μ. A 60 μ diameter platinum wire was insulated with glass to within 2 cm of its end and it was pushed down the capillary until stopped by the constriction. The anode was a 100 μ diameter silver wire coated with silver chloride by

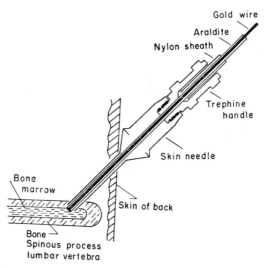

Fig. 13. Electrode for measuring oxygen tension in bone marrow (*136*).

electrolysis. Reeves, Rennie, and Pappenheimer (*142*) used a flow chamber oxygen electrode for measuring the P_{O_2} in urine *in vivo*.

B. QUANTITATIVE MEASUREMENTS AND PROBLEMS OF CALIBRATION

Absolute measurements of P_{O_2} can be made with recessed electrodes but with open-ended electrodes quantitative measurements depend upon accurate calibration under conditions which must be as close as possible to those obtaining in the particular site *in vivo* for which the electrode is to be used. Difficulties in calibration have been discussed by Inch (*121, 143*), Connelly (*144*), and Cater (*68*). There are three methods of measurement: (i) application of a constant potential and measurement of the current when the steady state obtains; (ii) measurement of the current at a precise interval after applying the potential; and (iii) applying a sweep potential and recording the polarographic curve (*191-193*). The last two methods introduce electrode capacity effects, and time constants of recording apparatus, and the last method in particular requires very complicated electronic apparatus. Method (i) is simple and gives a negligible zero current in control systems swept out with nitrogen.

Steady state measurements with open-ended electrodes approximate to the equation for spherical diffusion (136).

$$i_t = nFDC \cdot 4\pi r_0^2 \left[\frac{1}{r_0} + \frac{1}{(\pi Dt)^{1/2}} \right] \tag{42}$$

or

$$i_t = Kr_0 + \frac{Kr_0^2}{(\pi Dt)^{1/2}} \tag{43}$$

where r_0 is the radius of the electrode. If the two terms of Eq. 43 are evaluated using known values of C and D for air-saturated saline at 25°C, the value of the second term will fall off with time and its importance will depend on the size of the electrode. Thus, for a sphere 1 mm in diameter, the terms become equal after 100 sec and the second term is one-tenth of the first after 10,000 sec; for a sphere of 10 μ diameter, the second term is one-tenth of the first after 1 sec. It is clear that the steady state is rapidly attained if the electrode is small (68).

The following features of calibration merit attention.

1. A linear relationship between P_{O_2} and electrode current was found by Davies and Brink (124), Montgomery and Horwitz (127), Longmuir (102), Inch (121) and Cater, et al. (136). [Harris and Barclay (145) found the current $\propto \log P_{O_2}$ but this relationship was traced to the internal resistance of their circuit (146).]

2. The current rises with temperature; most observers are in close agreement with 2% per 1°C (102, 127, 136).

3. The current–voltage curves with open type electrodes do not show a plateau unless the electrode is larger than 500 μ diameter. This effect is not due to thermal convection currents because a similar type of curve is obtained if the electrode is in contact with compressed cotton wool or is in the tissues. Cater, Silver, and Wilson (136) suggested that the applied potential caused a flow of fluid past the end of the electrode, the effect of which would become the more obvious the smaller the electrode. This is supported by the finding that, after coating the end of the electrode with collodion, a plateau is obtained in the current–voltage curve even with small electrodes.

4. Electrodes with tips > 1 μ, when inserted into tissue, will be in extracellular fluid. Calibration in artificial extracellular fluid equilibrated with a 5% CO_2–air mixture gave values very similar to those obtained in phosphate buffer or Ringer's solution. Artificial extracellular fluid contains electrolytes, bicarbonate buffer, glucose, urea, amino acids, and 0.1%

serum protein (*136*). Adding protein until the concentration reached 2% had little effect, but 2.5% protein lowered the calibration current by 15% (3% due to lowered solubility of oxygen, 12% due to other causes, viscosity, etc.). If electrodes are to be used in blood or in other sites *in vivo* where high protein concentrations are encountered, they should be calibrated under these conditions. In blood, fibrin is deposited upon the electrode unless it is protected by a collodion, polythene, or PTFE coat.

5. Sulfur compounds: Gluthathione (GSH, 30 mg/100 ml), lowered the calibration current by 30%, but natural extracellular fluid contains no appreciable quantity of GSH which is present inside cells. A GSH concentration of 3 mg/100 ml was found to lower the calibration current after several hours, possibly by the formation of a complex with the metal of the electrode. The current–voltage curve, after deliberate poisoning of the electrode with ammonium sulfide, was little changed for gold, but platinum was more seriously affected. Stainless steel is not so badly affected as platinum, but gives only ⅓ the oxygen cathode current of a gold electrode of identical size. Platinum gives a current ∼1.4 times that of gold.

6. The validity of the extrapolation from the *in vitro* calibration conditions to the conditions *in vivo* has been questioned:

a. On the ground of oxygen utilization by the electrode. But Urbach and Noell (*135*) brought evidence to show that the oxygen consumption of their electrode was negligible compared with the flux of oxygen from the capillaries, and Cater *et al.* (*136*) showed that the oxygen consumption of a 0.3 mm diameter electrode was about 1.5% of the oxygen supply to a 1 mm^3 of tissue. In active tissues the consumption of the electrode would be relatively less.

b. On the ground that the diffusion constant for oxygen is less in tissues. In a "model tissue" of compressed cotton wool and artificial extracellular fluid (70% solid phase, 30% fluid phase, mean diameter of fibers 19.5 μ) electrodes 10 μ and 100 μ in diameter showed no change, 315 μ diameter electrodes gave 95%, and 500 μ and 1 mm diameter electrodes 90% of calibration values. This problem was also investigated by perfusion experiments which worked on the following principle (*136*): if the oxygen consumption by the tissues could be reduced to zero, by cooling, and the vessels were perfused with calibration fluid, then the oxygen tension in the tissue should rise to that in the calibration fluid; then if the electrodes gave the same reading in tissues and in calibration fluid the extrapolation from calibration conditions to those in the tissues would be valid. Unfortunately, even a temperature of 0°C and 0.001 M sodium cyanide did not completely abolish the oxygen utilization of the tissues, but if the perfusion was rapid, a number of the intramuscular electrodes reached calibration values, a clear indication that in spite of the nonattainment of ideal conditions the extrapolation from calibration to *in vivo* conditions was satisfactory. This experiment might suggest that the low values for the O_2 diffusion constant of tissues may be due to the fact that the oxygen utilization by the tissues had not been completely abolished.

Attempts to calibrate electrodes by embedding them in pieces of tissue are likely to give misleading results. Montgomery and Horwitz (*127*) inserted their electrodes into pieces of skin, placed in aerated saline, and these gave readings about ⅓ of the value in saline. Inch (*121*), however, found the electrode current varied from near zero, for freshly excised skin, *up to values obtained in saline when the skin was several days old.*

C. SPATIAL RESOLUTION OF ELECTRODES

Kety (*147*) has reviewed the complicated problem of the diffusion of oxygen from capillaries into tissue, in terms of blood flow, oxygen utilization by tissue, diffusion coefficient, distance between capillaries and distance along the capillary (of these variables the oxygen utilization by tissues has the greatest effect on P_{O_2} at any point). It is clear, both from theory and actual measurements, that the oxygen tension in tissues varies markedly from one place to another. We can either attempt to obtain a mean value for the whole tissue by using a large electrode (or several electrodes to get a statistical sample) or attempt to probe out the change of P_{O_2} with change of position in the tissues. In practice, both types of information are urgently required. Before making electrodes suitable for insertion into cells, the author made calculations of the spatial resolution which could be expected from electrodes of various sizes. The mathematical formula, for which we are indebted to Dr. E. R. Lapwood (*148*), is as follows. Assuming spherical diffusion, and making all the usual assumptions, the expression L_R/L_∞ for the amount of oxygen taken from a sphere of radius R, compared to the total oxygen used by the electrode (radius r_0), is

$$\frac{L_R}{L_\infty} = 1 - \left\{ \frac{\mu\ ierfc\ \lambda\mu + \frac{1}{2}\ erfc\ \lambda\mu - i^2erfc\ \lambda\mu}{\mu\ ierfc\ 0 + \frac{1}{2}\ erfc\ 0 - i^2erfc\ 0} \right\} \qquad (44)$$

where

$$\mu = r_0/2(Dt)^{\frac{1}{2}}$$

and

$$\lambda = (R - r_0)/r_0$$

and where the functions $erfc\ \lambda\mu$, $ierfc\ \lambda\mu$, and $i^2erfc\ \lambda\mu$ are the functions defined and tabulated in (*149*). This is shown graphically in Fig. 14.

We see that theory predicts that a 1 μ electrode would receive 95% of its O_2 from a sphere of radius 150 μ, a 10 μ radius electrode from a sphere of tissue with a radius of 1.5 mm, and a 160 μ radius electrode from a sphere with a radius of 2.5 cm. Now our practical experience indicated that in tissues our electrodes appear to have much better resolving power than this. Thus in brain, a 50 μ diameter electrode may show a tenfold increase of P_{O_2} when moved through a distance of 50 μ, and this would not happen if it were taking oxygen from a sphere 7.5 mm in diameter. When theory and experimental findings are at such variance, it is necessary to re-examine the assumptions which have been made. Examination of formula (44) indicates that for good resolution

$$\mu\lambda = (R - r_0)/2(Dt)^{\frac{1}{2}}$$

should be > 2. A poor choice of the value for the diffusion constant D will not alter the result because it will increase t, the time taken to reach the steady state. Increasing the size of the electrode, r_0, will also increase t. A flat-ended electrode would use one-fourth as much oxygen as the corresponding sphere, which would improve resolution, but the electrodes used in brain had cone shaped ends. Assumption (1) made in the theory of diffusion is that $P_{O_2} = 0$ at the electrode surface. In view of the complicated series of reactions in the electrolysis of oxygen (see Chapter 7), the time constant may not be negligible. Assumption (2) is that there shall be no stirring of the solution, but in the tissues the conditions will be anything but static. Pulsation of vessels and formation of tissue fluid at the arteriolar end of the capillary and its absorption at the venous end *will ensure* move-

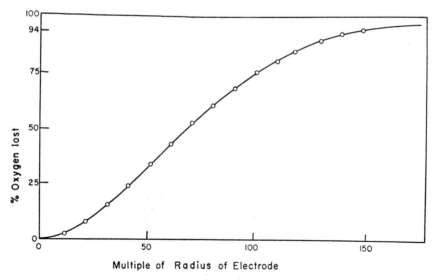

Fig. 14. Plot of spatial resolution of oxygen cathode derived from classical diffusion theory [refer Lapwood (*148*)]. The per cent oxygen lost to the electrode which came from within a sphere of radius R is shown. The units of R are multiples of the radius of the electrode (r_0).

ment. Assumption (3) is that the surface of the electrode is completely uniform, but it is probable that there are special areas of high reactivity on the electrode surface, so that it will behave, not as a uniform disc or sphere, but as though it were a number of much smaller areas. This would improve the resolution considerably. The net result of factors (1), (2), and (3) is to make the bare electrode behave as though it were covered by a thin membrane or a special diffusion zone, in contact with a stirred solution. This will greatly improve its resolving power compared with what theory would predict in an unstirred solution. A further improvement of resolving power would be expected if this natural diffusion layer of the bare electrode is replaced by an artificial barrier of collodion or polythene. This will stabilize the system and improve the resolving power by reducing the oxygen consumption of the electrode.

D. POISONING

Many observers have noted a fall of electrode current with time after insertion, and have attributed this to poisoning of the electrode. Our experiments have been remarkably free from this artifact, the causes of which are as follows.

1. Mechanical barriers of precipitates, extraneous organic matter, films of protein, fibrin from blood, and silicone.

2. Inactivation of the surface of the metal by oxide films. The authors always ground or plated a fresh surface on to the electrode for each experiment; this excluded any possibility of old films of dried protein, etc. A freshly abraded surface is activated in water and charged with H_2O_2 (see Chapter 7).

3. Sulfhydryl complexes formed on the electrode. This is the only cause of real poisoning we have identified. It is not normally seen in the body because the extracellular fluid contains such a low concentration of sulfur compounds. It can be avoided by coating the electrode with collodion.

4. Physiological changes. In our experiments it has been notable how well electrodes behave when inserted into brain. This tissue would be expected to poison an electrode because of its high protein and GSH content, but experience was the reverse of what was expected. This led us to believe that many of the so-called cases of poisoning were not due to a change of the electrode, but were the direct result of physiological reactions of the vascular supply to the conditions of the experiment. There may be local pressure on vessels, or spasm of vessels due to local injury by the electrode, which is likely to cause by its presence an inflammatory reaction. The vessels in the brain do not respond in these ways. The effects of long periods of anaesthesia in experimental animals are likely to give falling levels of P_{O_2} in tissues; even in unanaesthetized humans electrodes in leg

muscles show falling levels of P_{O_2} because the circulation in muscle falls if the muscle has a long period of forced inactivity. Activity puts up the P_{O_2} in muscle more quickly than breathing oxygen. Another important variable is metabolic rate, which increases with temperature. Much has been attributed to poisoning of the electrodes which should have been recognized as physiological change.

E. RESULTS

Much useful practical information has resulted from measurements of P_{O_2} *in vivo*. The effect of oxygen concentration on the rate of respiration of bacteria (*102*), on metabolism (*103, 105, 150*), and on liver cells (*104*) has been described. In tissue culture, the rate of fall of P_{O_2} enabled the respiration rate of the cells to be measured (*145, 146, 151*). The effect of P_{O_2} on the activity of the cells was noted. The arrest of the fall of P_{O_2} in tissue culture has been used to measure the cytotoxic action of drugs (*152*).

In animals and man, the P_{O_2} of the skin and subcutaneous tissue is fairly high and increases two- or three-fold when oxygen is breathed (*43, 51, 67, 126, 127, 133, 135, 137*). Urbach and Peirce (*128*) measured the oxygen consumption of the skin by cutting off its blood supply by pressure and noting the rate of fall of P_{O_2}. In cases of arterial embolism, the P_{O_2} level of the tissues of the limb has been measured to determine whether amputation was necessary (*127*).

The P_{O_2} of muscle tends to be rather low at rest, but increases with activity or when oxygen is breathed. Vasodilatory drugs increase the level (*137*).

The surface of the brain has been investigated (*93, 131, 134*) with special reference, (1) to the distribution of P_{O_2} in relation to the vessels and the interarteriolar distance, and (2) to the effects of convulsant drugs. In the brain, Cross and Silver (*154*) have shown that the P_{O_2} varies markedly within small distances. Breathing oxygen results in a very rapid rise of P_{O_2} in some parts of the brain. Drugs which increase the rate of cerebral blood flow also cause a marked rise of P_{O_2}.

In active tissues, such as lactating mammary gland, the P_{O_2} falls temporarily to zero after injections of adrenalin, vasopressin, etc., which constrict the vessels (*43*).

The P_{O_2} of bone marrow is normally low and responds poorly or not at all to the breathing of oxygen (*137*).

Tumors have a very variable P_{O_2}. It may be very low in tumors which have outstripped their blood supply. In cutaneous or ulcerated tumors the P_{O_2} is usually fairly high, and responds well to breathing oxygen (*132, 135, 137*). After treatment of tumors by radiation, the P_{O_2} when breathing air, and the response to breathing oxygen, are both significantly increased (*137*).

VIII. Bioelectric Potentials

No discussion of electrode potential studies *in vivo* would be complete without a mention of bioelectric potentials, if only to clarify the meaning of this term which has been used to describe several different phenomena.

A. Potential Differences Producing Electrical Currents which Control Growth

Lund (*155, 156*) found that when an electric current was passed through a piece of *Obelia*, the end facing the cathode would not develop a hydranth. He suggested that *Obelia* produced continuous electric currents sufficient to determine the orientation of cells during development and regeneration. Later (*157*), he found the potential difference between the outer cell surface of ectoderm and inner cell surface of endoderm was 0.2 to 9 mv. A cathode potential difference sufficient to neutralize this (1.88 to 10 mv) would prevent hydranth formation, but 0.5 mv sufficed to change orientation of growth. The source of potential, and energy of current, was the oxidation-reduction potential of the cell (*158*). The concentration of oxygen increased the potential difference (*159*) and cyanide reduced it (*160*). Burr and Northrop (*161*) added much philosophy but not much data to Lund's concept that living organisms produce currents which control growth and development. That potential gradient and the resulting electrodynamic fields may be the basis of the well known capacity of growing tissue to regulate itself would appeal to common sense as possibly important in repair, but if the electrical pattern of the organism determines development, what determines the electrical pattern?

B. Membrane Potentials

Lund (*159*), and Steinbach (*162*) measured the electrical potential difference across living frog skin. Amberson (*163*) and Meyer (*164*) discussed how this potential is produced. The former described how potassium tends to diffuse from the cell but is held by the nondiffusible protein anion and concluded that such potentials are not properly called diffusion potentials, but are membrane potentials in a very strict sense, depending on the very structure of the living cell itself. This polarization of cell membranes is universally recognized as an important biophysical phenomenon and should clearly be designated as membrane potential.

C. Potential Differences between different Parts of the Skin

These have been termed bioelectric potentials and described by Floyd and Keele (*165–167*), Snodgrass and Davis (*168*), and Barnes (*169*). They are small differences of potential between two finger tips or the palm and the back of forearm, etc., probably due to differences of temperature, diffusion through skin, and pH. Burr, Musselman, Barton, and Kelly (*170*) report one case of a sudden alteration of the potential of the vagina compared to abdominal skin at the time of ovulation. Rock *et al.* (*171*) reported another case and Rock, Reboul, and Snodgrass (*172*) report on 9 other women. This data was all carefully reviewed by Snodgrass, Rock and Menkin (*173*) who made direct measurements on ovaries *in situ* at laparotomy, with reference electrode against broad ligament, and failed to show any marked potential gradients within the estimated time of ovulation. The difficulty of maintaining the stability of a reference electrode on the skin surface was suggested as a rational explanation for the inconsistent results obtained in the "abdomino-vaginal sign" of ovulation. Finger-to-finger potential measurements also gave no indication of ovulation. They concluded that bioelectric phenomena related to ovulation were due primarily to cutaneous vascular conditions.

Langman and Burr (*174*) found that the normal uterine cervix was usually positive compared to abdominal skin, while uterine tumors were negative. Max, Mauss, Day, and Rhoads (*175*) failed to confirm this, but they used a less sensitive technique. However, Dalgaard and Thygesen (*176*), using a careful technique, could not confirm Langman and Burr's findings. In any case, the possibility that the observations could be due to differences of pH was not excluded. The normal vagina is very acid in reaction and might well be more acid than skin. After parturition, or when bleeding occurs from an ulcerated tumor, the vagina is less acid. Langman and Burr's controls, with a single exception, were all young and in the reproductive period of life; the tumor cases were mostly post-menopausal, when the acid reaction of the vagina is much reduced.

D. Potentials of Injury

Burr, Harvey, and Taffel (*177, 178*) and Burrows, Iball, and Roe (*179*) studied the potential difference between wounds and normal skin. The latter group used a vacuum tube microvoltmeter with an input impedance of 10^7 ohms and silver–silver chloride electrodes in 0.9% salt solution. When skin was cut, the injured spot was usually positive (in the external circuit) compared to intact skin, but injured muscle was negative compared to normal muscle. The pH difference between normal and injured skin would be expected to produce the opposite effect. One notes that silver–silver chloride electrodes were used with 0.9% saline, certainly isotonic, but not in equilibrium with the Cl^- concentration of the tissues. There would be a Cl^- diffusion gradient into the injured site but not into intact skin. In muscle, both reference electrode and the electrode on injured muscle would be expected to show a Cl^- diffusion gradient, but the injured muscle would have Na^+ and K^+ diffusion gradients as well, i.e., a loss of membrane potential. Barnes (*180–182*) used the rate of diminution of the potential of experimental abrasions as an index of wound healing. Burr, Smith, and Strong (*183*) investigated potential changes before and after the appearance of cancer in mice, and Burrows, Roe, and Schober (*184*) carefully compared and analyzed statistically the difference in skin potential on the backs of mice painted with 9,10-dimethyl-1,2-benzanthracene. During the hypertrophic thickening of the skin prior to tumor formation they noted the reverse effect to that produced by wounding.

That a potential difference exists between wound and skin there can be little doubt, but on the relative part played in the production of this potential by changes in pH, redox potential, and oxygen tension we can only speculate. It would be valuable to measure the potential of the wounded surface against a reference electrode placed subcutaneously (in controlled conditions of temperature and chloride concentration). The measuring apparatus could with advantage be of much higher impedance than that previously used and the electrode in the wound should be in artificial extracellular fluid and not in 0.9% saline. Is the wound potential an important factor in healing; will fibroblasts and epithelial cells migrate along the potential gradient; will there be electrophoresis of protein and other material? On these questions, until more data are available, we can only speculate.

Bioelectric potentials have been critically reviewed by Crane (*185*) who included under this heading the steady potentials developed by various plant and animal tissues, and the action potentials of muscles, nerves and the electric organs of fishes. The steady potentials may be due to diffusion potentials, membrane potentials, phase boundary potentials, oxidation-reduction potentials, or electrokinetic potentials. Conway (*186*) has suggested that in yeast both the mechanism of ion exchange and the source of energy may be supplied by an oxidation-reduction system. In anaerobic yeast cultures, redox dyes altered the steady state potential; those dyes which raised the potential increased the loss of H^+ and the gain of K^+, those which lowered the potential had the reverse effect (*187, 188*). Membrane potentials and electrokinetic potentials have been reviewed by Teorell (*189*). A microelectrophoresis apparatus for measuring the zeta potential on the surface of bacteria is described by James (*190*). He reviews the information electrokinetic potential measurements have given concerning the chemical composition of the cell surface of various bacteria and the effects of acids, immune sera, detergents, antibiotics, antiseptics, and enzymes.

REFERENCES

1. Hill, R., *in* "Modern Methods of Plant Analysis" (K. Paech and M. V. Tracey, eds.), Vol. 1, p. 393. Springer, Berlin, 1956.
2. Curtis, H. J., and Cole, K. S., *J. Cellular Comp. Physiol.* **19**, 135 (1942).
3. Hodgkin, A. L., and Huxley, A. F., *J. Physiol. (London)* **104**, 176 (1945).
4. Nastuk, W. L., and Hodgkin, A. L., *J. Cellular Comp. Physiol.* **35**, 39 (1950).
5. Ling, G., and Gerard, R. W., *J. Cellular Comp. Physiol.* **34**, 382 (1949).
6. Nastuk, W. L., *J. Cellular Comp. Physiol.* **42**, 249 (1953).
7. Del Castillo, J., and Katz, B., *J. Physiol. (London)* **128**, 396 (1955).
8. Adrian, R. H., *J. Physiol. (London)* **133**, 631 (1956).
9. Brock, L. G., Coombs, J. S., and Eccles, J. C., *J. Physiol. (London)* **117**, 431 (1952).
10. Cater, D. B., Phillips, A. F., and Silver, I. A., *Proc. Roy. Soc.* **B146**, 289 (1957).
11. Weale, R. A., *J. Physiol. (London)* **112**, 4 P. (1951).
12. Weale, R. A., *Nature* **167**, 529 (1951).
13. For information on the de Fonbrume microforge, see references 9 and 14.
14. Kennard, D. W., *in* "Electronic Apparatus for Biological Research" (P. E. K. Donaldson, ed.), p. 534. Butterworths, London, 1958.
15. Alexander, J. T., and Nastuk, W. L., *Rev. Sci. Instr.* **24**, 528 (1953).
16. Tasaki, I., Polley, E. H., and Orego, F., *J. Neurophysiol.* **17**, 454 (1954).
17. Caldwell, P. C., and Downing, A. C., *J. Physiol.* **128**, 31P. (1955).
18. Kao, C.-Y., *Science* **119**, 846 (1954).
19. Woodbury, J. W., *J. Cellular Comp. Physiol.* **39**, 323 (1952).
20. Tasaki, I., *Japan. J. Physiol.* **3**, 73 (1953).
21. Hodgkin, A. L., and Katz, B., *J. Physiol. (London)* **108**, 37 (1949).
22. Tomita, T., and Funaishi, A., *J. Neurophysiol.* **15**, 75 (1952).
23. Gray, J. A. B., and Svaetichin, G., *Acta Physiol. Scand.* **24**, 278 (1951).
24. Svaetichin, G., *Acta Physiol. Scand.* **24**, Suppl. **86**, 5 (1951).
25. Huxley, A. F., and Stämpfli, R., *J. Physiol. (London)* **108**, 315 (1949).
26. Fatt, P., and Katz, B., *J. Physiol. (London)* **115**, 320 (1951).
27. Marmont, G., *J. Cellular Comp. Physiol.* **34**, 351 (1949).
28. Frank, K., and Fuortes, M. G. F., *J. Physiol. (London)* **130**, 625 (1955).
29. McNichol, E. F., and Wagner, H. G., *Naval Med. Research Inst.* **12**, 97 (1954).
30. Solms, S. I., Nastuk, W. L., and Alexander, J. T., *Rev. Sci. Instr.* **24**, 960 (1953).
31. Haapanen, L., and Ottoson, D., *Acta Physiol. Scand.* **32**, 271 (1954).
32. Woodbury, J. W., *Federation Proc.* **12**, 159 (1953).
33. Burch, M. G., *Proc. Roy. Soc.* **48**, 89 (1890).
34. Lucas, K., *J. Physiol. (London)* **44**, 225 (1912).
35. Rushton, W. A. H., *Proc. Roy. Soc.* **B123**, 382 (1937).
36. Green, J. D., *Nature* **182**, 962 (1958).
37. Lorente de Nó, R., *Studies Rockefeller Inst. Med. Research* 132 (1947).
38. MacIlwain, H., *Biochem. J.* **49**, 382 (1951).
39. Silver, I. A., *in* "Electronic Apparatus for Biological Research" (P. E. K. Donaldson, ed.), p. 568. Butterworths, London, 1958.
40. Dixon, M., *Proc. Roy. Soc.* **B101**, 57 (1927).
40a. Clark, W. M., and Cohen, B., *Public Health Repts.* (*U.S.*) **38**, 933 (1923).
41. Hewitt, L. F., *in* "Oxidation-Reduction Potentials in Bacteriology and Biochemistry," 6th ed., p. 9. Livingstone, Edinburgh, 1950.
42. Dixon, M., *in* "Multi-enzyme Systems," p. 60 ff, Cambridge Univ. Press, London and New York, 1949.

43. Cater, D. B., Phillips, A. F., and Silver, I. A., *Proc. Roy. Soc.* **B146,** 400 (1957).

44. Okuyama, D., *J. Biochem. (Tokyo)* **14,** 69 (1931–32).

45. Boyd, E. M., and Reed, G. B., *Can. J. Research* **4,** 54 (1931).

46. Vlès, F., Reiss, P., and Deloyer, L., *Compt. rend. soc. biol.* **108,** 37 (1931).

47. Uchimura, Y., *J. Biochem. (Tokyo)* **25,** 207 (1937).

48. Seyderhelm, R., Mulli, K., and Thyssen, J. *Münch. med. Wochschr.* **84,** 620 (1937).

49. Cater, D. B., and Phillips, A. F., *Nature* **174,** 121 (1954).

50. DuBridge, L. A., and Brown, H., *Rev. Sci. Instr.* **4,** 532 (1933).

51. Cater, D. B., Phillips, A. F., and Silver, I. A., *Proc. Roy. Soc.* **B146,** 382 (1957).

52. Feates, F. S., *Trans. Faraday Soc.* **56,** 1671 (1960).

53. Gillespie, L. J., *Soil Science* **9,** 199 (1920).

54. Barnes, E. M., and Ingram, M., *J. Sci. Food Agr.* **6,** 448 (1955).

55. Knight, B., and Fildes, P., *Biochem. J.* **24,** 1496 (1930).

56. Broberg, G., *Nord. Veterinarmed.* **9,** 57 (1957).

57. Broberg, G., *Nord. Veterinarmed.* **9,** 918 (1957).

58. Needham, J., and Needham, D. M., *Proc. Roy. Soc.* **B98,** 259 (1925).

59. Brooks, M. M., *Am. J. Physiol.* **76,** 360 (1926).

60. Rapkine, L., and Wurmser, R., *Proc. Roy. Soc.* **B102,** 128 (1927).

61. Cohen, B., Chambers, R., and Reznikoff, P., *J. Gen. Physiol.* **11,** 585 (1928).

62. Redslob, E., and Reiss, P., *Arch. phys. biol.* **7,** 221 (1928–29).

63. Piha, S., *Särtryck Farmaceutiskt Notisblad* **11,** 213 (1951).

64. Jalavisto, E., and Piha, S., *Ann. Med. Exptl. et Biol. Fenniae (Helsinki)* **30,** 361 (1952).

65. Piha, S., *Ann. Acad. Sci. Fennicae Ser. A II No.* **80,** 18 (1956).

66. Harvard, R. E., and Kendal, L. P., *Biochem. J.* **28,** 1121 (1934).

67. Cater, D. B., Phillips, A. F., and Silver, I. A., *Giorn. ital. chemioterap.* **3,** 269 (1956).

68. Cater, D. B., *Progr. in Biophys. and Biophys. Chem.* **10,** 153 (1960).

69. Mitchell, J. S., *in* "Studies in Radiotherapeutics," pp. 128–136. Blackwell, Oxford, 1960.

70. Dixon, M., and Quastel, J. H., *J. Chem. Soc.* **123,** 2943 (1923).

71. Michaelis, L., *in* "Oxidation-Reduction Potentials," pp. 113–143. Lippincott, Philadelphia, Pennsylvania, 1930.

72. Michaelis, L., and Flexner, L. B., *J. Biol. Chem.* **79,** 689 (1928).

72a. Kolthoff, I. M., and Lingane, J. J., "Polarography," Vol. II, p. 849. Interscience, New York, 1952.

73. Williams, J. W., and Drissen, E. M., *J. Biol. Chem.* **87,** 441 (1930).

74. Preisler, P. W., and Berger, L., *J. Am. Chem. Soc.* **69,** 322 (1947).

75. Preisler, P. W., and Bateman, M. M., *J. Am. Chem. Soc.* **69,** 2632 (1947).

76. Freedman, L. D., and Corwin, A. H., *J. Biol. Chem.* **181,** 601 (1949).

77. Cecil, R., and McPhee, J. R., *Biochem. J.* **59,** 234 (1955).

78. Cecil, R., *Biochim. et Biophys. Acta* **18,** 154 (1955).

79. Voegtlin, C., Kahler, H., and Fitch, R. H., *Natl. Insts. Health Bull.* **164,** 15 (1935).

80. Stow, R. W., Baer, R. F., and Randall, B. F., *Arch. Phys. Med. Rehabil.* **38,** 646 (1957).

81. Gertz, K. H., and Loeschke, H. H., *Naturwissenschaften* **45,** 160 (1958).

82. Severinghaus, J. W., and Bradley, A. F., *J. Appl. Physiol.* **13,** 515 (1958).

83. Hertz, C. H., and Siesjö, B., *Acta Physiol. Scand.* **47,** 115 (1959).

84. Maxon, W. D., and Johnson, M. J., *Ann. Chem.* **24,** 1541 (1952).

85. Sonnenschein, R. R., Walker, R. M., and Stein, S. N., *Rev. Sci. Instr.* **24,** 702 (1953).

86. Caldwell, P. C., *J. Physiol. (London)* **126**, 169 (1954).

87. Harris, E. J., *Electronic Eng.* **23**, 109 (1951).

88. MacInnes, D. A., and Dole, M., *J. Am. Chem. Soc.* **52**, 29 (1930).

89. Ingvar, D. H., Siesjö, B., and Hertz, C. H., *Experientia* **15**, 306 (1959).

90. Severinghaus, J. W., *in* "Symposium on pH and Blood Gas Measurement" (R. F. Woolmer, ed.), p. 126. Churchill, London, 1959.

91. Wright, M. P., *in* "Symposium on pH and Blood Gas Measurement" (R. F. Woolmer, ed.), p. 5. Churchill, London, 1959.

92. Astrup, P., *in* "Symposium on pH and Blood Gas Measurement" (R. F. Woolmer, ed.), p. 81. Churchill, London, 1959.

93. Davies, P. W., and Rémond, A., *Research Publs. Assoc. Research Nervous Mental Disease* **26**, 205 (1947).

94. Kauko, Y., and Knappsberg, L., *Z. Elektrochem.* **45**, 760 (1939).

95. Gatty, O., and Spooner, E. C. R., "The Electrode Potential Behavior of Corroding Metals in Aqueous Solutions," p. 331, Oxford Univ. Press, London and New York, 1938.

96. Tourky, A. R., and Khairy, E. M., *J. Chem. Soc.* 2626 (1952).

97. Thompson, F. C., and Brudevold, F., *J. Dental Research* **33**, 849 (1954).

98. Charlton, C., *Australian Dental J.* **1**, 228 (1956).

99. Haggard, H. W., and Greenberg, L. A., *Science* **93**, 479 (1941).

100. Levin, I., *Chemist Analyst* **41**, 89 (1952).

101. Perley, G. A., and Godshalk, J. B., U.S. patent No. 2,416,949; British Patent No. 567,722 (June 10, 1942).

102. Longmuir, I. S., *Biochem. J.* **57**, 81 (1954).

103. Longmuir, I. S., and Clarke, B. J., *Biochem. J.* **63**, 57 (1956).

104. Longmuir, I. S., *Biochem. J.* **65**, 378 (1957).

105. Chance, B., *Federation Proc.* **16**, 671 (1957).

106. Gray, L. H., Conger, A. D., Ebert, M., Hornsey, S., and Scott, O. C. A., *Brit. J. Radiol.* **26**, 638 (1953).

107. Laser, H., *Nature* **174**, 753 (1954).

108. Krogh, A., *Skand. Arch. Physiol.* **20**, 259, 279 (1908).

109. Comroe, J. H., and Drippe, R. D., *Am. J. Physiol.* **142**, 700 (1944).

110. Gray, L. H., *in* "Progress in Radiobiology" (J. S. Mitchell, B. E. Holmes, and C. R. Smith, eds.), p. 267. Butterworths, London, 1956.

111. Rahn, H., *Federation Proc.* **16**, 685 (1957).

112. Kramer, K., *Z. Biol.* **96**, 61 (1935).

113. Kramer, K., and Sarre, H., *Z. Biol.* **96**, 76, 89, 101 (1935).

114. Matthes, K., *Arch. Exptl. Pathol. Pharmakol. Naunyn-Schmiedeberg's* **179**, 698 (1935).

115. Matthes, K., and Gross, F., *Arch. Exptl. Pathol. Pharmakol. Naunyn-Schmiedeberg's* **191**, 369, 381, 391, 523, 706 (1939).

116. Millikan, G. A., *Rev. Sci. Instr.* **13**, 434 (1942).

117. Goldie, E. A. G., *J. Sci. Instr.* **19**, 23 (1942).

118. Hartmann, F. W., Behrmann, V. G., and Chapman, F. W., *Am. J. Clin. Pathol.* **18**, 1 (1948).

119. Wood, E. H., and Geraci, J. E., *J. Lab. Clin. Med.* **34**, 387 (1949).

120. Sekelj, P., Johnson, H. L., Hoff, H. E., and Schuerch, M. P., *Am. Heart J.* **42**, 826 (1951).

121. Inch, W. R., *Can. J. Biochem. and Physiol.* **36**, 1009 (1958).

122. Danneel, H., *Z. Elektrochem.* **4**, 227 (1897–8).

123. Blinks, L. R., and Skow, R. K., *Proc. Natl. Acad. Sci. U.S.* **24,** 420 (1938).

124. Davies, P. W., and Brink, F., *Rev. Sci. Instr.* **13,** 524 (1942).

125. Hill, D. K., *J. Physiol. (London)* **107,** 479 (1948).

126. Tobias, J. M., and Holmes, R., *Federation Proc.* **6,** 215 (1947).

127. Montgomery, H., and Horwitz, O., *J. Clin. Invest.* **29,** 1120 (1950).

128. Urbach, F., and Peirce, G., *Science* **112,** 785 (1950).

129. Penneys, R., *J. Clin. Invest.* **31,** 204 (1952).

130. Penneys, R., and Montgomery, H., *J. Clin. Invest.* **31,** 1042 (1952).

131. Davis, E. W., McCulloch, W. S., and Roseman, E., *Am. J. Psychiat.* **100,** 825 (1944).

132. Urbach, F., *Proc. Soc. Expt. Biol. Med.* **92,** 644 (1956).

133. Montgomery, H., *Federation Proc.* **16,** 697 (1957).

134. Davies, P. W., and Bronk, D. W., *Federation Proc.* **16,** 689 (1957).

135. Urbach, F., and Noell, W. K., *J. Appl. Physiol.* **13,** 61 (1958).

136. Cater, D. B., Silver, I. A., and Wilson, G. M., *Proc. Roy. Soc.* **B151,** 256 (1959).

137. Cater, D. B., and Silver, I. A., *Acta Radiol.* **53,** 233 (1960).

138. Cater, D. B., *Ann. Rept. Brit. Empire Cancer Campaign* **32,** 448 (1954).

138a. Cater, D. B., and Silver, I. A., unpublished (1960).

138b. Silver, I. A., personal communication (1960).

138c. Walden, L., *in* "Further Laboratory and Workshop Notes" (R. Lang, ed.), p. 148. Edward Arnold, London, 1950.

139. Clark, L. C., Jr., *Trans. Am. Soc. Artificial Internal Organs* **2,** 44 (1956).

140. Sproule, B. J., Miller, W. F., Cushing, I. E., and Chapman, C. B., *J. Appl. Physiol.* **11,** 365 (1957).

141. Kreuzer, F., Watson, T. R., and Ball, J. M., *J. Appl. Physiol.* **12,** 65 (1958).

142. Reeves, R. B., Rennie, D. W., and Pappenheimer, J. R., *Federation Proc.* **16,** 693 (1957).

143. Inch, W. R., *Ann. Rept. Brit. Empire Cancer Campaign* **34,** 529 (1956).

144. Connelly, C. M., *Federation Proc.* **16,** 681 (1957).

145. Harris, H., and Barclay, W. R., *Brit. J. Exptl. Pathol.* **36,** 592 (1955).

146. Harris, H., *Brit. J. Exptl. Pathol.* **37,** 512 (1956).

147. Kety, S. S., *Federation Proc.* **16,** 666 (1957).

148. Lapwood, E. R., Emmanuel College, Cambridge, England. Personal communication (1959).

149. Carslaw, H. S., and Jaeger, J. C., *in* "Conduction of Heat in Solids," pp. 482–485. Oxford Univ. Press, London and New York, 1959.

150. Cruickshank, C. N. D., and Trotter, M. D., *Biochem. J.* **62,** 57 (1956).

151. Harris, H., *Brit. J. Exptl. Pathol.* **36,** 115 (1955).

152. Davis, J. M. G., and Woodliff, H. J., *Blood* **15,** 534 (1960).

153. Kay, R. H., and Coxon, R. U., *Nature* **177,** 45 (1956).

154. Cross, B. A., and Silver, I. A., personal communication (1960).

155. Lund, E. J., *J. Exptl. Zool.* **34,** 471 (1921).

156. Lund, E. J., *J. Exptl. Zool.* **36,** 477 (1922).

157. Lund, E. J., *J. Exptl. Zool.* **41,** 155 (1924–25).

158. Lund, E. J., *J. Exptl. Zool.* **51,** 265 (1928).

159. Lund, E. J., *J. Exptl. Zool.* **51,** 291 (1928).

160. Lund, E. J., *J. Exptl. Zool.* **51,** 327 (1928).

161. Burr, H. S., and Northrop, F. S., *Quart. Rev. Biol.* **10,** 322 (1935).

162. Steinbach, H. B., *J. Cellular Comp. Physiol.* **3,** 1 (1933).

163. Amberson, W. R., *Symposia on Quant. Biol.* **4,** 53 (1936).

164. Meyer, K. H., *Trans. Faraday Soc.* **33**, 1049 (1937).

165. Floyd, W. F., and Keele, C. A., *J. Physiol. (London)* **86**, 23 P., 25 P. (1936).

166. Floyd, W. F., and Keele, C. A., *J. Physiol. (London)* **87**, 24 P. (1936).

167. Floyd, W. F., and Keele, C. A., *Trans. Faraday Soc.* **33**, 1046 (1937).

168. Snodgrass, J. M., and Davis, H., *Am. J. Physiol.* **129**, 468 P. (1940).

169. Barnes, T. C., *Am. J. Med. Sci.* **207**, 550 (1944).

170. Burr, H. S., Musselman, L. K., Barton, D. S., and Kelly, N. B., *Science* **86**, 312 (1937).

171. Rock, J., Reboul, J., and Wiggers, H. C., *New Engl. J. Med.* **217**, 654 (1937).

172. Rock, J., Reboul, J., and Snodgrass, J. M., *Am. J. Obstet. Gynecol.* **36**, 733 (1938).

173. Snodgrass, J. M., Rock, J., and Menkin, M. F., *Am. J. Physiol.* **140**, 394 (1943–44).

174. Langman, L., and Burr, H. S., *Science* **105**, 209 (1947).

175. Max, L. W., Mauss, E. A., Day, E., and Rhoads, C. P., *Cancer* **6**, 77 (1953).

176. Dalgaard, S., and Thygesen, J. E., *Acta Radiol.* **34**, 488 (1950).

177. Burr, H. S., Harvey, S. C., and Taffel, M., *Yale J. Biol. Med.* **11**, 104 (1938).

178. Burr, H. S., Taffel, M., and Harvey, S. C., *Yale J. Biol. Med.* **12**, 483 (1939–40).

179. Burrows, H., Iball, J., and Roe, E. M. F., *Brit. J. Exptl. Pathol.* **23**, 253 (1942).

180. Barnes, T. C., *Am. J. Surgery* **69**, 1, 82 (1945).

181. Barnes, T. C., *Anat. Record* **94**, 379 (1946).

182. Barnes, T. C., *Anat. Record* **96**, 506 (1946).

183. Burr, H. S., Smith, G. M., and Strong, L. C., *Am. J. Cancer* **32**, 240 (1938).

184. Burrows, H., Roe, E. M. F., and Schober, B., *Cancer Research* **5**, 524 (1945).

185. Crane, E. E., *Progr. in Biophys. and Biophys. Chem.* **1**, 85 (1950).

186. Conway, E. J., *Science* **113**, 270 (1951).

187. Conway, E. J., Brady, T. G., and Carton, E., *Biochem. J.* **47**, 369 (1950).

188. Conway, E. J., and Kernan, R. P., *Biochem. J.* **61**, 32 (1955).

189. Teorell, T., *Progr. in Biophys. and Biophys. Chem.* **3**, 305 (1953).

190. James, A. M., *Progr. in Biophys. and Biophys. Chem.* **8**, 96 (1957).

191. Evans, N. T. S., and Naylor, P. F. D., *J. Polarographic Soc. No.* **2**, 26, 40 (1960).

192. Naylor, P. F. D., and Evans, N.T.S., *J. Polarographic Soc. No.* **2**, 33, 46 (1960).

193. Cowell, T. K., and Styles, P. R., *J. Polarographic Soc. No.* **2**, 49 (1960).

Chapter Twelve

Electrodes in Fused Salt Systems

R. W. Laity

I. Introduction

Although regarded by some as a novel class of electrolytes, molten salts have been employed as media in the measurement of electromotive force since well before 1900. Such a large body of literature on the subject has accumulated that it would be unwise in a book of this kind to attempt a critical survey of every electrode–electrolyte system that has been studied. It is nevertheless useful to the experimenter undertaking a particular study to know whether (and to what extent) his system has previously been explored. He may be assisted in this by the rather comprehensive tabulations of literature references to specific systems to be presented here. The principal objective in this chapter, however, will remain in keeping with the title of the book. That is, the emphasis will be on the experimental preparation and theoretical significance of reference electrodes in molten salt systems.

It is worth mentioning at the outset that the types of molten salt investigations for which reliable reference electrodes have been found necessary duplicate exactly the uses to which such electrodes have been put in aqueous electrolytes. Specifically, this includes: (i) thermodynamic studies, such as construction of "electromotive force series" from the potentials of various electrodes relative to a particular reference, or determination of thermodynamic data for molten salt mixtures from the change in potential with composition of an indicator electrode *vs.* a suitable reference; (ii) kinetic studies, such as measurement of overpotential at gaseous electrodes, or recording of polarograms for the deposition of various metals (which may, of course, be used also for purposes of chemical analysis); (iii) mass and energy transport studies, such as determination of transference numbers from emf measurements on concentration cells with liquid junctions, or measurement of thermoelectric power in pure or mixed electrolytes. In none of these areas have the studies on molten salts been nearly so extensive or thorough as their aqueous solution counterparts. As with the latter electrolytes, however, the largest amount of the molten salt work falls into the first category listed, while the least studied area has been that numbered (iii).

It is clear from the above listing that the types of studies for which molten salt reference electrodes have been employed involve both thermodynamic and extra-thermodynamic considerations. Of particular significance in most applications are the concepts of electrode potential, ion activity and junction potential. Although the discussion of these concepts in Chapter 1 had particular reference to aqueous electrolytes, many of the points presented there are clearly of general validity in electrochemical systems. Relative to molten salts, it is necessary, however, to recognize that the term electrolyte has a different meaning than in the conventional systems; in one case it is merely an ionized solute and in the other, the whole of the system. This brings in quite new considerations. The concept of mean ionic activity coefficient, for example, is of little value in molten salt electrolytes, while that of transference number loses its conventional significance entirely. In the present chapter it is therefore necessary to supplement the general and theoretical introduction of Chapter 1 with an attempt to supply a suitable basis for the interpretation and comparison of electromotive force measurements in pure and mixed salt systems. This will be found in Section II. The apparently disproportionate length of this section arises from the author's attempt at thoroughness in an area which has not been surveyed in any previous treatise.

Of necessity, the theoretical considerations to be presented here involve some recapitulation of the material in Chapter 1. The reader will probably not be surprised to discover that no fundamentally new *principles* are required to deal with molten salt electrolytes. Indeed some of the equations developed will be seen to take essentially the same form as their counterparts in the more conventional electrolytic solutions. By following the necessary derivations from first principles, however, it is hoped that the reader will appreciate their significance as applied to molten salts and thereby avoid the misunderstanding and misuse that have so frequently resulted when seemingly familiar concepts were extended to this class of electrolytes.

The theoretical section is followed by a practical consideration of the variety of systems available for study. Some general remarks on high temperature experimental methods and problems then precede the discussion of specific reference electrodes for use in particular types of systems. In conclusion, some experimental electromotive series are presented in the Appendix.

II. Theoretical Considerations

A. Thermodynamics of Electrochemical Cells

The methods of thermodynamics make it possible to relate the electromotive force of any reversible cell to thermodynamic properties of the chemical system involved. In making use of such relations it is sometimes convenient to employ the concepts of "electrode potential" and "ionic activity," even though these concepts can only be defined unambiguously in certain limiting cases. No matter how helpful such quasi-thermodynamic ideas may be, however, their use is unnecessary in discussing the fundamental thermodynamic relations. A similar statement can be made with regard to the term "liquid-junction potential" frequently employed in connection with cells with transference. (Here, of course, the emf is related to certain transport properties of the system, in addition to thermodynamic properties, since the "thermodynamic" treatment must take irreversible transport processes into account.) In view of their superfluity, therefore, a discussion of potentially useful quasi-thermodynamic concepts will be put off until after presentation of the essential thermodynamic relations upon which they are based. Thus, only the total emf will be dealt with for each type of cell under consideration in this section. Ionic activities, electrode potentials, and liquid-junction potentials will be taken up in Section II, B.

1. Cells Without Transference

a. Formation Cells in Electrolytes of One Component. Most of the cells of interest which fall under the general heading of cells without transference can be put into the category of "formation cells," i.e., those in which the cell reaction involves formation of a particular substance from its elements. In the simplest possible type of formation cell the electrolyte is a pure binary molten salt. The electrodes must then be reversible to each of the two ionic constituents of the salt, as in the cell

$$Ag \mid AgCl \mid Cl_2 \ (1 \ atm)$$

The reaction taking place in this cell is

$$Ag + \tfrac{1}{2}Cl_2 \rightarrow AgCl$$

for which the free energy change ΔG is the standard free energy of formation of silver chloride at the particular temperature employed when the elements are in their standard states. Now from the thermodynamic relation

$$\Delta G = -nFE$$

it follows that the emf of the cell is a direct measure of the standard free energy of the pure salt. A tabulation of the results to be expected theoretically from available thermodynamic data for a large number of formation cells containing pure molten chlorides has been given by Hamer et al. (1). Some of these values are reproduced in the Appendix (p. 600).

As in all such cells, it is necessary here that the salt in the neighborhood of the chlorine electrode be saturated with Cl_2. This chlorine could react irreversibly with the silver metal if the latter were dipping into the same salt. Separate electrode compartments meeting at a liquid junction must therefore be used, and it is clear that the thermodynamic equation used here neglects any effects resulting from this inhomogeneity. Such approximations can be justified whenever the solubility of electrode material is small, as is the case in most electrochemical systems. A peculiar property of molten salts, however, makes this an important problem in a number of formation cells. It is the ability of the salts to dissolve metals, particularly the metals whose ions they contain. Thus, it may require as much as 20 mole per cent cadmium to saturate molten $CdCl_2$ with the metal, while liquid alkali metals become infinitely miscible with their halides at sufficiently high temperatures. In such cases the salt can no longer be considered a one-component electrolyte, so that the simple thermodynamic treatment employed here for such systems is inadequate. Fortunately, metal solubility is usually much less than in these extreme examples, and its effect on the salt can safely be ignored provided adequate precautions are taken to prevent mixing of the electrode "solutions."

Designations of solid or liquid were omitted for both the Ag and the AgCl in the cell representation above, since the states of these substances depend on the temperature, while the thermodynamic interpretation does not. Even a solid salt might be employed to obtain thermodynamic information of this type, provided its conductivity were sufficient to prevent polarization of the cell. Indeed, the entire thermodynamic discussion to be presented here is equally applicable to reversible cells involving solid salt electrolytes.

b. *Multicomponent Cells and the Significance of Thermodynamic Activity.* In the next simplest type of formation cell the electrolyte is composed of two salts, one of which consists of ions to which the electrodes are reversible. The following examples will serve the purposes of this discussion:

$$\text{Ag} \mid \text{AgCl} (x_A), \text{NaCl} (1 - x_A) \mid \text{Cl}_2 (1 \text{ atm}) \tag{A}$$

$$\text{Ag} \mid \text{AgCl} (x_B), \text{NaF} (1 - x_B) \mid \text{Cl}_2 (1 \text{ atm}) \tag{B}$$

Here x_A and x_B refer to the mole fractions of silver chloride in the melts. In each case the cell reaction can be separated conceptually into two steps: (1) formation of pure AgCl from its elements; and (2) addition of pure AgCl to a solution whose composition is given by x_A or x_B. If the free energy change per mole of pure AgCl formed is designated $\Delta G°$, then the free energy change for the dilution step is given by $RT \ln a_{AgCl}$, where a_{AgCl} is the thermodynamic activity of AgCl in the mixture referred to pure AgCl as standard state. The emf of either cell is thus given by

$$E = -\frac{\Delta G°}{nF} - \frac{RT}{nF} \ln a_{AgCl} \tag{1}$$

The significance of the term a_{AgCl} in these mixtures warrants further elaboration. The thermodynamic activity a_i of any component i of a mixture is defined by the relation

$$a_i = f_i/f_i° \tag{2}$$

where f_i is the fugacity of i vapor and the superscript ° refers to the standard state. The fugacity is in turn defined by the relations

$$\mu_{i(g)} = \mu_{i(g)}° + RT \ln f_i$$

and

$$\lim_{P \to 0} (f_i/P_i) = 1$$

where $\mu_{i(g)}$ is the chemical potential (partial molar free energy) of component i in a gas whose total pressure is P. For vapors sufficiently dilute to approximate ideal behavior (as will always be the case at temperatures and pressures far from the critical conditions), fugacity may be replaced by pressure, or by partial pressure in a gas mixture. Thus $f_i°$ ($\approx P_i°$) represents in the examples under consideration the vapor pressure of pure AgCl at the temperature of the measurement, while f_i is its partial pressure over the solution of interest.

It is important to realize that the approximate equivalence of fugacity and partial pressure refers only to a single molecular species in the vapor phase. Recent demonstrations of the existence of associated species (dimers and even higher polymers) in the vapors over pure molten alkali halides reveal that it is necessary to distinguish the partial pressure exerted by the simple molecules of a given salt, such as P_{AgCl}, from the total pressure, e.g.,

$$P_{\Sigma AgCl} = P_{AgCl} + P_{Ag_2Cl_2} + P_{Ag_3Cl_3} + \cdots$$

due to all molecular species in equilibrium with the liquid. If such a gas mixture were simply called "AgCl vapor," it would no longer be correct to equate fugacity with pressure. This is due to the fact that isothermal pressure changes cause vapor phase equilibria of the type

$$2AgCl \rightleftharpoons Ag_2Cl_2 \tag{3}$$

to shift, so that the gas as a whole cannot behave ideally. The partial pressure of a given species in the mixture, such as AgCl monomer, must nevertheless very nearly conform to the familiar equation

$$P_{AgCl}V = n_{AgCl}RT$$

so that it is still correct to write

$$f_{AgCl} \approx P_{AgCl}$$

The relation of fugacity to partial pressure for the vapor taken as a whole is derived as follows. Consider the change in the partial molar free energy of AgCl monomer, $\Delta\mu_{AgCl}$, accompanying an isothermal pressure change. From the definition of fugacity:

$$\Delta\mu_{AgCl} = RT \ln f_{AgCl}/f'_{AgCl} \approx RT \ln P_{AgCl}/P'_{AgCl}$$

where the prime refers to the initial state. Now in measurements at equilibrium it must also be true that

$$\Delta\mu_{AgCl} = \tfrac{1}{2} \Delta\mu_{Ag_2Cl_2} = \tfrac{1}{3} \Delta\mu_{Ag_3Cl_3} = \ldots$$

so that the free energy change *per gram formula weight of AgCl* is the same for each of the polymeric species as for the monomer. It follows that

$$\Delta\mu_{AgCl} = \Delta\mu_{\Sigma AgCl} = RT \ln f_{\Sigma AgCl}/f'_{\Sigma AgCl}$$

and hence

$$\frac{f_{\Sigma AgCl}}{f'_{\Sigma AgCl}} = \frac{f_{AgCl}}{f'_{AgCl}} \approx \frac{P_{AgCl}}{P'_{AgCl}} \tag{4}$$

where $f_{\Sigma AgCl}$ is the fugacity of the gas composed of silver chloride in all its molecular forms and $\mu_{\Sigma AgCl}$ is the free energy of this gas per gram formula weight of AgCl. If the state designated by the primes in Eq. (4) is chosen to be that of the vapor in equilibrium with pure molten silver chloride, it is seen by comparison with Eq. (2) that the activity a_{AgCl} may be regarded as a measure of the change (accompanying dilution of molten AgCl) in the fugacity either of AgCl gas molecules alone, or of the entire AgCl gas mixture. But only from the former viewpoint will the fugacity ratio of Eq. (2) be equivalent to the corresponding ratio of partial pressures. The relation of $f_{\Sigma AgCl}$ to $P_{\Sigma AgCl}$ in the simple case where only monomers and dimers are present may be seen by comparison of Eq. (4) with the following:

$$\frac{P_{\Sigma AgCl}}{P'_{\Sigma AgCl}} = \frac{P_{AgCl} + P_{Ag_2Cl_2}}{P'_{AgCl} + P'_{Ag_2Cl_2}} = \frac{P_{AgCl}(1 + KP_{AgCl})}{P'_{AgCl}(1 + KP'_{AgCl})} \tag{5}$$

where K is the equilibrium constant for the reaction in Eq. (3). Only as this equilibrium constant or the value of P_{AgCl} approaches zero (negligible extent of dimerization) does the fugacity ratio for the gas mixture approximate the corresponding pressure ratio. Note also that the AgCl pressure that would be calculated from the amount of solid AgCl in a gas condensate if the gas phase polymerization were not taken into account is equal to

$$P_{\text{AgCl}} + 2\,P_{\text{Ag}_2\text{Cl}_2} + 3\,P_{\text{Ag}_3\text{Cl}_3} + \cdots$$

and is a similarly inappropriate measure of $f_{\Sigma\text{AgCl}}$.

The preceding discussion emphasizes the fact that the thermodynamics of association reactions occurring in the vapor phase must be considered when activity of a liquid phase component is to be defined in terms of measurable vapor pressures. This should not be construed to mean that such gas reactions give any particular significance to the corresponding reactions which may be written for the liquid phase. Although it is perfectly possible to define activities in the melt for each of the polymers in terms of its partial vapor pressure, the quantities so defined are of purely formal significance, as indeed is the activity of AgCl itself in an essentially ionic liquid. The usefulness of the neutral salt activity in permitting a correlation of emf with vapor pressure measurements has just been demonstrated, however, and it is clearly the simplest thermodynamically defined quantity that will serve the purpose. Its use will therefore be continued in comparing the electrolyte systems in the two cells selected for illustration at the beginning of this section.

If cells (A) and (B) were employed to compare the activities of AgCl in the two types of solution under the condition $x_A = x_B$, there is little reason to suppose that the results would be similar. In terms of neutral salt concentrations this may be ascribed to the fact that while the solution in cell (A) can be regarded as a simple mixture of two components, that in cell (B) must be classed as a chemically reacting system, the simplest form for the reaction being

$$\text{AgCl} + \text{NaF} \rightleftharpoons \text{AgF} + \text{NaCl} \tag{6}$$

Thus, even if the mixtures in both cells behaved "ideally" the lowering of activity of AgCl in cell (B) due to this reaction would give rise to a correspondingly larger emf. It is important at this point, however, to examine the concept of thermodynamic ideality as applied to molten salt mixtures.

A solution is usually considered ideal when the activity of each of its components is equal to its mole fraction, so that each activity coefficient $\gamma_i (= a_i/x_i)$ is unity. For the mixture in cell (A), a comparison of a_A with x_A could thus be considered a measure of the "ideality" of the system. Since each of the four salts in Eq. (6) will be present in the vapor over cell (B), however, each can be assigned an activity based on the fugacity of its vapor when it is in the pure state. Now if the mole fraction of silver chloride is taken as x_B and that of NaF as $(1 - x_B)$, the concentrations of AgF and NaCl must be taken as zero. Clearly the solution could not be ideal with this assignment of concentrations. How, then, can the equilibrium mole fractions of AgF and NaCl be specified? Their mode of formation requires that the concentrations of these salts be equal, but, beyond this restriction, the answer is that there is no unique way of assigning neutral salt concentrations in an ionic mixture of this type. The designation of the mole fractions of these two salts as zero is no more arbitrary than any other selection, in spite of the unorthodox consequence that the salts have infinite activity coefficients. It follows that while the concept of thermodynamic ideality has operational significance for the neutral salts in "nonreacting" systems, such as that in cell (A) where only one anionic species is present, it cannot be defined on the basis of salt concentrations for "reciprocal" systems, i.e., those containing more than one ionic species of each charge. It will be seen in Section B that this limitation can readily be removed by employing single ion activities, and only serves to point up the artificiality imposed by restricting the thermodynamic analysis to neutral components.

The emf of a one-component formation cell such as that discussed in subsection a may be regarded as a special case of Eq. (1). The relation is, in fact, perfectly general, applying not only to one- and two-component systems, but to formation cells with any number of components (putting in the activity of whatever salt is formed in the cell reaction). Thus, for a ternary reciprocal system (TRS) made up from the salts NaCl, AgF, and NaF, the emf of the formation cell

$$\text{Ag} \mid \text{TRS} \mid \text{Cl}_2$$

is correctly given by Eq. (1), even though AgCl was not one of the original components [but may be considered as having been formed by the reverse of the reaction in Eq. (6)]. This system provides another illustration of the impossibility of uniquely assigning concentrations to the neutral salts. The composition of *any* mixture of the four salts in Eq. (6) can be completely described in terms of the three salts of the TRS alone. Further, *any* three of the four salts can be chosen for this purpose, the "mole fraction" of any one salt depending upon which of the other three have been selected as components.

c. Concentration Cells Without Transference. To conclude this section, consider the arrangement:

$$\text{Ag} \mid \text{AgCl} \ (a_\text{I}), \text{NaCl} \mid \text{Cl}_2 \mid \text{AgCl} \ (a_\text{II}), \text{NaCl} \mid \text{Ag}$$

This cell is formed by connecting in series (with the positive poles opposing) two cells of type (A) having different electrolyte concentrations. It follows by subtraction that the emf is given by

$$E = -\frac{RT}{nF} \ln \frac{a_I}{a_{II}}$$

the "cell reaction" being the reversible transfer of AgCl from solution II to solution I. If a_{II} is made equal to unity by using the pure salt, the cell gives a direct measure of the activity of AgCl in solution I.

2. Cells with Transference

While the thermodynamic interpretation of electromotive force in cells without transference was seen in the preceding section to be simple and, on the whole, straightforward, the applicability of such cells is greatly limited by the requirement that two different reversible electrodes dip into the same melt. This means not only that two electrodes must be found that are reversible to different ions in the melt, but that these electrodes must be so chosen that they do not react irreversibly with any other species present. A sodium electrode, for example, could not have been employed in any of the cells used for illustration in that section, due to the irreversible displacement of silver ion by sodium metal. The same restriction prohibits the use of a fluorine electrode in any of the systems containing chloride.

Either of these limitations may be eliminated by the use of cells with transference. Here only one electrode reversible to one of the ions in a given system must be found to set up a concentration cell. In other cells electrodes may be isolated from ions with which they would react by the use of liquid junctions or ion-selective membranes between electrolytes of various compositions. The greater applicability of cells with transference, however, has been accompanied by greater misunderstanding of the factors controlling their emf's by some of those who have reported their use. The difficulty arises in attempting to write an expression which properly takes into account the irreversible diffusion process occurring in such cells, leading some workers to assert that potentials in cells of this type cannot be treated by thermodynamic methods.

The assertion is correct when the term "thermodynamic" is understood in its commonly restricted sense, i.e., pertaining only to systems at equilibrium. An unambiguous relation between emf and well-defined thermodynamic and transport properties of the systems involved can nevertheless be written for any cell with transference. An aqueous concentration cell with transference is a familiar example for which the correct expression is given in every elementary treatise on electrochemistry. The derivation usually presented of this expression, however, consists of a quasi-thermodynamic analysis of the "cell reaction" in which the irreversible nature of the process occurring at the junction of the two solutions is ignored. The same approach may be used in deriving the correct expression for the emf of *any* cell with transference, an example having been discussed elsewhere for a simple type of molten salt concentration cell (*2*).

A more satisfying and rigorous approach, however, is to employ the "thermodynamics of irreversible processes." This purely macroscopic discipline extends the applicability of conventional thermodynamics in the following manner: (*a*) the assumption is made that for a nonequilibrium system the laws of thermodynamics hold in any region small enough that any variations in the usual thermodynamic functions are negligible; (*b*) another law is added, known as the "Onsager reciprocal relations," governing the mutual effects of simultaneous transport processes upon one another. Assumption (*a*) is tacitly made in *all* thermodynamic measurements, since it is impossible to realize a condition of perfect equilibrium in the laboratory. As for the validity of (*b*), Onsager has given a theoretical justification of the reciprocal relations, which have also been subject to repeated experimental confirmations. In the interest of rigor and the promotion of a useful tool, therefore, use of the quasi-thermodynamic approach will be postponed here in order to present first this newer method of handling such problems. Since the fundamental basis of irreversible thermodynamics may now be found in a number of readily available treatises (*2a, b, c*), the present treatment will assume some familiarity with the principal points and terminology of this discipline.

a. Concentration Cells. Even the simplest example of a molten salt concentration cell requires at least two different salts, in contrast with aqueous or nonaqueous cells in which the concentration of a single salt may be varied relative to that of the inert solvent. The cell (*2*)

$$\text{Ag} \left| \underbrace{\text{AgNO}_3, \text{NaNO}_3}_{\text{A}} \vdots \underbrace{\text{AgNO}_3, \text{NaNO}_3}_{\text{B}} \right| \text{Ag}$$

serves as an example. For conceptual purposes this cell may be idealized as follows. Consider the electrode compartments to be two large well-stirred reservoirs, A and B, containing mixtures of silver nitrate and sodium nitrate in different proportions. These reservoirs are connected to one another through a small tube in which the concentration of each salt varies continuously from its value in A to that in B. With this arrangement the rate at which each concentration changes is slow, even though diffusion between compartments continuously takes place. Silver electrodes are immersed in each compartment, and are externally connected through a potentiometer. Attention is now focused upon a unit cross section of the connecting tube, through which it is possible to distinguish three fluxes: J_1, the flux of Ag^+; J_2, the flux of Na^+; and J_3, the flux of NO_3^-. Each J_i is a vector having the dimensions of moles $cm^{-2}sec^{-1}$, so that when current is allowed to flow, the current density in amps cm^{-2} is equal to $(J_1 + J_2 - J_3)F$. The "thermodynamic forces" corresponding to these fluxes must be chosen in such a way that the product of each force by its corresponding flux gives the contribution of that process to the total entropy production (in order to validate subsequent application of the Onsager relations). The quantities serving this purpose are the gradients of electrochemical potential $\nabla\bar{\mu}_i$, which can be dissected conceptually into the sums $\nabla\mu_i + z_iF\nabla\psi$. The change in electrochemical potential is a thermodynamically defined quantity, even though changes of chemical potential of a single ion $\Delta\mu_i$ taken separately, or changes of (Galvani) electrical potential $\Delta\psi$ between media of different composition are not (3). The present discussion being restricted to thermodynamic terminology, only electrochemical potentials will be used for single ions.

A variety of formulations for the phenomenological relations between forces and fluxes may now be set down. The following appears to have some advantage over earlier formalisms:

$$\nabla\bar{\mu}_i = \sum_{k=1}^{n} R_{ik}J_k \tag{7}$$

where the summation is taken over the total number of ions n. The phenomenological coefficients R_{ik}, defined in this way have been called "friction coefficients" (4). They are related for all i not identical with k by the reciprocal relations

$$R_{ik} = R_{ki} \tag{8a}$$

The number of independent coefficients is further reduced by employing the relations (5, 6):

$$\sum_{k=1}^{n} R_{ik}C_k = 0$$

Multiplication of the latter by v_i followed by subtraction of Eq. (7) eliminates the coefficients R_{ii}:

$$-\nabla\bar{\mu}_i = \sum_{k} R_{ik}C_k(v_i - v_k) \tag{8b}$$

where v_i is the velocity of the ion in a region where its concentration is C_i, in accord with the relation $J_i = C_iv_i$. For the three-ion system under consideration Eqs. (8) are written

$$-\nabla\bar{\mu}_1 = R_{12}C_2(v_1 - v_2) + R_{13}C_3(v_1 - v_3) \tag{9a}$$

$$-\nabla\bar{\mu}_2 = R_{12}C_1(v_2 - v_1) + R_{23}C_3(v_2 - v_3) \tag{9b}$$

$$-\nabla\bar{\mu}_3 = R_{13}C_1(v_3 - v_1) + R_{23}C_2(v_3 - v_2) \tag{9c}$$

Any two of these relations are sufficient to derive the third, so that the present formalism reduces the number of equations to two and the number of phenomenological coefficients to three.

Now the potentiometer measures the difference of potential $\Delta\psi$ between the two silver electrodes [thermodynamically defined, since they are of identical composition (3); cf. Chapter 1, Section II]. Considering the metal to be made up of Ag^+ ions and electrons, it readily follows that this is equal to the difference of electrochemical potential of silver ion divided by the charge on one mole. Reversibility of the electrodes requires that in each compartment silver ions in solution have the same electrochemical potential as in the metal, so that when the potentiometer is balanced

$$-\Delta\psi = \frac{\Delta\bar{\mu}_1}{F} \tag{10}$$

Equations (9) may now be employed to evaluate $\Delta\bar{\mu}_1$ in terms of the difference in *chemical* potential of silver *nitrate* between compartments A and B.

The chemical potential of a neutral salt μ_{ik} is related to the electrochemical potentials of its constituent ions by

$$\mu_{ik} = \nu_i\bar{\mu}_i + \nu_k\bar{\mu}_k$$

where ν_i is the number of moles of i resulting from complete dissociation of one mole of salt, and ν_k is similarly defined. In the system under discussion the ν's are each unity, and the subscripts 1, 2, and 3 are for Ag^+, Na^+, and NO_3^- respectively, so that the gradient of the chemical potential of silver nitrate, $\nabla\mu_{13}$, is obtained by adding (9a) and (9c). Using $C_1 + C_2 = C_3$, this gives

$$-\nabla\mu_{13} = (R_{12} + R_{13})C_2v_1 - (R_{12} + R_{23})C_2v_2 - (R_{13} - R_{23})C_2v_3 \tag{11}$$

Since the current flow is zero in an emf measurement, $C_2v_2 = C_3v_3 - C_1v_1$. Applying this condition to (11) gives

$$-\nabla\mu_{13} = (R_{12}C_3 + R_{13}C_2 + R_{23}C_1)(v_1 - v_3) \tag{12}$$

The same condition applied to (9a) gives

$$-\nabla\bar{\mu}_1 = (R_{12} + R_{13})C_3(v_1 - v_3) \tag{13}$$

Now dividing (13) by (12) yields

$$d\bar{\mu}_1 = \frac{(R_{12} + R_{13})C_3}{R_{12}C_3 + R_{13}C_2 + R_{23}C_1} d\mu_{13}$$

in which the ∇'s have been replaced by d's, since those on both sides of the equation refer to the same gradient. Integration of this expression and substitution into (10) gives the desired relation:

$$\Delta\psi = \frac{RT}{F} \int_A^B \frac{(R_{12} + R_{13})C_3}{R_{12}C_3 + R_{13}C_2 + R_{23}C_1} \, d \ln a_{13} \qquad (14)$$

Here $d\mu_{13}$ has been replaced by $RT \, d \ln a_{13}$ to show the relation of emf to thermodynamic activity of $AgNO_3$ in this concentration cell.

It remains to identify the integrand in Eq. (14) with more familiar properties of the system. We anticipate the answer, since the author has already presented it in an earlier publication (2). There the coefficient of $(RT/F) \, d \ln a_{13}$ was shown by a derivation based on a quasi-thermodynamic approach to take the form

$$(C_2 - C_2 t_1 + C_1 t_2)/C_2$$

where t_1 and t_2 are the "transference numbers" of Ag^+ and Na^+ respectively. These can in principle be measured for any given concentration with the same cell, by electrolyzing between the silver electrodes a mixture of uniform composition throughout both compartments. The t_i are then the fractions of the current carried through the connecting tube by each species i. Since all species involved here are univalent, the transference number of Ag^+ can be written

$$t_1 = \frac{C_1 v_1}{C_1 v_1 + C_2 v_2 - C_3 v_3}$$

with corresponding expressions applying to each of the other two ions. Substituting these relations into (11) and applying the new experimental condition that $\nabla\mu_{13} = 0$ gives an expression which can be written in the form

$$\frac{C_2 - C_2 t_1 + C_1 t_2}{C_2} = \frac{(R_{12} + R_{13})C_3}{R_{12}C_3 + R_{13}C_2 + R_{23}C_1} \qquad (15)$$

Comparison of (15) with (14), confirms the anticipated relation. The Onsager relations were assumed in this derivation [specifically, in writing Eqs. (9b) and (9c)], and it is their use that makes it possible to identify terms from the emf expression with transference numbers measured by dynamic methods.

The concept of "transference number" cannot have its usual significance in a molten salt. What makes the purely ionic melt unique in comparison with other electrolytes is the absence of an inert solvent reference frame against which to compare the relative velocities of the ions. In the experiment just described the connecting tube served as reference. A reference of this type has a rather arbitrary nature, since bulk flow of the electrolyte under a hydrostatic head creates a flux of each ion which is experimentally inseparable from that due to electrical migration. It is easy to show, in fact, that the "transference numbers" must have values which depend upon the dimensions of reservoirs A and B. It would thus appear that the expression for the emf in Eq. (14) contains an arbitrariness which can only be removed by carrying out the transference experiment with the particular cell to be employed in the emf measurement. This is not so, fortunately, for the t's in (15) occur in a combination which is unambiguous, even though the values of each separately are indeterminate. To see this, recall that in *any* experimental arrangement the "transference number" of each univalent cation is proportional to the product of its velocity by its concentration, so that

$$-C_2 t_1 + C_1 t_2 = k(-C_2 C_1 v_1) + k(C_1 C_2 v_2)$$
$$= k C_1 C_2 (v_2 - v_1)$$

The expression in Eq. (15) is thus seen to depend only on the velocity *difference* of the two ions, i.e., the velocity of one relative to the other, which is independent of the total rate at which the electrolyte happens to be moving through the tube (at least to a very good approximation). By expressing the results of transference experiments in a reference-independent form like that in Eq. (15), therefore, it is possible to report data which are not only of fundamental interest in themselves [see, for example, reference (7)], but which are of prime importance in interpreting the emf's of cells with transference. Klemm (8) has reported transference data in such a form for the system LiCl–KCl at one concentration, while Aziz and Wetmore (9) and Duke, Laity and Owens (10) have presented (conflicting) data for the system AgNO$_3$–NaNO$_3$ in this manner. The PbCl$_2$–KCl system was studied by Duke and Fleming (11). Such data are scarce for molten salt systems, but may be calculated in a few additional instances from data reported in other forms (7). To perform the integration of Eq. (14) it is, of course, necessary to know how the transference numbers vary with concentration, so that a whole series of experiments must be carried out on any one system. The equal mobilities of Ag$^+$ and Na$^+$ at all concentrations of the system AgNO$_3$–NaNO$_3$ have been shown elsewhere (2) to lead to a particularly simple and easily integrable form for the emf expression.

Substantially the same "thermodynamic" analysis as that presented above can be applied to any molten salt concentration cell with transference no matter how complex the electrolyte system. The treatment of cells with more than three different ionic species will not be given here, but general expressions for finding the emf of *any* cell with or without transference will be found at the beginning of Section B (p. 541).

b. Daniell Cells. Some of the earliest measurements of electromotive force in molten salt systems were carried out on cells of the type

$$\text{Ag} \mid \text{AgCl} \vdots \text{PbCl}_2 \mid \text{Pb} \qquad \text{(C)}$$

containing a liquid junction between two pure salts (*12*). Such cells have continued to be the subject of considerable interest, often being referred to as "Daniell Cells." The (irreversible) thermodynamic treatment parallels very closely that presented in subsection *a* for concentration cells with transference. In the present example reservoir A contains a silver electrode immersed in pure AgCl, reservoir B contains a lead electrode in pure PbCl$_2$, and the electrolyte in the connecting tube is a mixture of the two salts which varies continuously over the entire range of intermediate concentrations.

Since the two electrodes are of different metals, the measured potential difference must first be assigned to the two (copper) wires coming from the potentiometer in order to be thermodynamically defined. It will be designated $\Delta\psi^{Cu}$, which is equal to $-\Delta\bar{\mu}_e^{Cu}/F$, the difference of electrochemical potential per faraday of the electrons in the two wires. When no current is flowing, the electrons in each wire are in equilibrium with those in the electrode with which it is in contact. Thus,

$$\Delta\psi^{Cu} = (1/F)(\bar{\mu}_e^{Pb} - \bar{\mu}_e^{Ag})$$

The molar free energies of the metals themselves are given by

$$\mu_{Ag} = \bar{\mu}_{Ag^+}^{Ag} + \bar{\mu}_e^{Ag} = 0$$

$$\mu_{Pb} = \bar{\mu}_{Pb^{2+}}^{Pb} + 2\bar{\mu}_e^{Pb} = 0$$

where the phase to which the potential refers is represented as a superscript (cf. Chapter 1). The zero values are in accord with standard practice for the free energies of pure elements. Now the cation in each electrode is in equilibrium with the same ion in the melt, i.e., $\bar{\mu}_{Ag^+}^A = \bar{\mu}_{Ag^+}^{Ag}$ and $\bar{\mu}_{Pb^{2+}}^B = \bar{\mu}_{Pb^{2+}}^{Pb}$. It follows from the foregoing relations that

$$\Delta\psi^{Cu} = \frac{\bar{\mu}_{Pb^{2+}}^B}{2F} - \frac{\bar{\mu}_{Ag^+}^A}{F} \tag{16}$$

The standard free energies of the pure salts are sums of the electrochemical potentials of their ionic constituents:

$$\mu_{AgCl}^\circ = \bar{\mu}_{Ag^+}^{AgCl} + \bar{\mu}_{Cl^-}^{AgCl}$$

$$\mu_{PbCl_2}^\circ = \bar{\mu}_{Pb^{2+}}^{Pb} + 2\mu_{Cl^-}^{PbCl_2}$$

Substituting these relations into (16) gives

$$\Delta\psi^{Cu} = \frac{\mu_{PbCl_2}^\circ}{2F} - \frac{\mu_{AgCl}^\circ}{F} + \frac{1}{F}(\bar{\mu}_{Cl^-}^{AgCl} - \bar{\mu}_{Cl^-}^{PbCl_2})$$

$$= \frac{\mu_{PbCl_2}^\circ}{2F} - \frac{\mu_{AgCl}^\circ}{F} - \frac{1}{F}\int_{AgCl}^{PbCl_2} d\bar{\mu}_{Cl^-}$$

From this point the approach is exactly that used in the preceding section for cells with transference. The value of $d\bar{\mu}_{Cl^-}$ in terms of $d\mu_{AgCl}$ is found from Eqs. (9c) and (11) as $d\bar{\mu}_3$ and $d\mu_{13}$, respectively. This time the condition of no net current is $2C_2v_2 = C_3v_3 - C_1v_1$ and the electroneutrality condition is $C_1 + 2C_2 = C_3$, due to the double charge on the lead ion. The result is

$$d\bar{\mu}_3 = \frac{(R_{23} - 2R_{13})C_1}{R_{12}C_3 + 4\,R_{13}C_2 + R_{23}C_1}\,d\mu_{13}$$

Identification of the coefficient of $d\mu_{13}$ with the appropriate combination of transport numbers is again realized by setting $\nabla\mu_{13}$ equal to zero in Eq. (11), this time making use of the definitions

$$t_1 = \frac{C_1v_1}{C_1v_1 + 2C_2v_2 - C_3v_3}$$

$$t_2 = \frac{2C_2v_2}{C_1v_1 + 2C_2v_2 - C_3v_3}$$

The resulting expression can be written in the form

$$\frac{2C_2t_1 - C_1t_2}{2C_2} = \frac{(R_{23} - 2R_{13})C_1}{R_{12}C_3 + 4R_{13}C_2 + R_{23}C_1}$$

so that the final expression for the emf of this Daniell cell becomes

$$\Delta\psi^{Cu} = \frac{\mu^\circ_{PbCl_2}}{2F} - \frac{\mu^\circ_{AgCl}}{F} - \frac{RT}{2F}\int_{AgCl}^{PbCl_2}\frac{2\,C_2t_1 - C_1t_2}{C_2}\,d\ln a_{13} \qquad (17)$$

The same total emf is obtained by considering cell (C) to be made up from three simpler cells connected in series:

$$\text{Ag} \mid \text{AgCl} \mid \text{Cl}_2 \qquad \text{Cl}_2 \mid \text{AgCl} \vdots \text{PbCl}_2 \mid \text{Cl}_2 \qquad \text{Cl}_2 \mid \text{PbCl}_2 \mid \text{Pb}$$

c. *Cells with Salt Bridges.* In molten salt studies use is sometimes made of a pure or mixed salt bridge between compartments containing electrolytes of different composition. A simple cell involving this type of bridge is the following:

$$\text{Ag} \mid \text{AgCl} \vdots \text{KCl} \vdots \text{PbCl}_2 \mid \text{Pb} \qquad (D)$$

in which the salt bridge consists of pure molten potassium chloride. To relate the emf of such a cell to the appropriate thermodynamic and transport properties of the systems involved, note that exactly the same potential would be obtained by connecting the two cells

$$\text{Ag} \mid \text{AgCl} \vdots \text{KCl} \mid \text{Cl}_2$$

and

$$\text{Cl}_2 \mid \text{KCl} \vdots \text{PbCl}_2 \mid \text{Pb}$$

in series. The methods used for Daniell cells in the preceding section are clearly applicable to each of these cells. The same conceptual dissection can be performed on any cell with a salt bridge.

In contrast to the familiar case of the KCl salt bridge in an aqueous system, the emf of cell D is in no sense dependent on the "relative mobilities" of K^+ and Cl^- in the pure salt. Such quantities, if definable at all (4, 13), are entirely unnecessary in a thermodynamic discussion of cells with transference.

d. *Cells with Ion-Selective Membranes.* Porous partitions of various materials are frequently employed in the formation of junctions between electrolytes of different composition. Their use normally does not entail any modification in the treatments of cells with transference presented thus far. This is due to the experimental fact that such partitions have negligible effects on the thermodynamic and transport properties of the systems they enclose, provided the average diameters of the pores are large compared with molecular dimensions. Materials are sometimes employed, however, through which only certain ions may pass, so that a knowledge of the properties of the partition is also required. Consider, for example, the cell

$$Ag \mid AgCl \vdots glass \vdots PbCl_2 \mid Pb \qquad\qquad (E)$$

which has been studied by Tamman (14) and subsequently by Grube and Rau (15). The glass partitions used in these studies were thin, but not porous, so that most of the current is presumably carried through the membrane by the sodium ions of the glass. In such circumstances the membrane must be considered as a separate electrolyte system, so that the thermodynamic analysis is equivalent to that presented in the preceding section for cells with salt bridges. The breakdown of cell (E) into its series components consists of

$$Ag \mid AgCl \vdots Na\text{-glass} \mid Na \qquad and \qquad Na \mid Na\text{-glass} \vdots PbCl_2 \mid Pb$$

Now the analog of the connecting tube used in the discussions of cells with liquid junctions occurs here at the interface between the molten salt and the glass. Thus, within a very short distance the concentrations of silver and chloride ions drop from their pure salt values to essentially zero, while those of sodium ion and other constituents of glass build up from zero to their normal values in the partition. Even if these changes be regarded as continuous, it is apparent that the system defined by the region of intermediate composition must be prohibitively difficult to isolate for study of its thermodynamic and transport properties over the complete concentration range. Such junctions are even difficult to reproduce, due to the dependence of their properties on the initial surface condition of the glass.

Thus, the emf of a cell like (E) depends on the nature of the glass used, and upon quantities not readily determined. This was realized by Grube and Rau, who attributed the large discrepancies between their results and those of Tamman to the fact that different glasses were used in the two studies (15). It will be seen in the discussion of junction potentials (p. 548 and ff.) that in spite of these limitations, useful deductions can be made in some cases from the emf values of cells in which glass membranes have been employed.

B. Application of Quasi-thermodynamic Concepts

In Section A formally correct expressions for the emf of electrochemical cells employing molten salts were developed without making use of the quasi-thermodynamic concepts of ion activity, electrode potential, or junction potential. The purpose was not to discourage the use of such concepts, but rather to show that it is not necessary to make departures from rigorous thermodynamic formalism which might detract from the fundamental soundness of the treatment. It will, in fact, be the purpose of the present section to *encourage* the proper use of these concepts. For not only do they simplify the task of relating emf of electrochemical cells to appropriate thermodynamic variables, but they also provide valuable insight for interpreting the significance of experimental results.

Each of the following concepts will be discussed in detail in this section.

(1) Ion activity. The activity of a single ion i present in the same system with an oppositely charged ion k is defined in terms of the activity of the neutral salt formed by combination of the pair:

$$a_{ik} = a_i^{\nu_i} a_k^{\nu_k} \tag{18}$$

where the ν's are the numbers of moles of each species formed by complete dissociation of one mole of salt ik.

(2) Junction potential. At a junction of two electrolytic substances, A and B, involving a total of n different ionic species:

$$E_{\text{junction}} = -\frac{RT}{F} \int_A^B \sum_{i=1}^n \frac{t_i}{z_i} d \ln a_i \tag{19}$$

where z_i is the charge and t_i the transference number of ion i. The reference frame employed in defining the transference numbers is arbitrary, so long as it is the same for each ion.

(3) Electrode potential. The standard electrode potential E_i° for some arbitrarily selected electrode in a given system is designated zero. If the

ionic species i in equilibrium with this electrode is positive, then the standard potential E_k° of an electrode in equilibrium with a negatively charged species k is given by:

$$E_k^{\circ} = -\frac{\Delta G_{ik}^{\circ}}{n_{ik}F} \tag{20}$$

where ΔG_{ik}° is the free energy change and $n_{ik}F$ the total charge transferred from the oxidized form of k to the reduced form of i in the formation of one mole of salt ik in a suitably chosen standard state. For an electrode in equilibrium with a positive species j, the standard potential E_j° is

$$E_j^{\circ} = \frac{\Delta G_{jk}^{\circ}}{n_{jk}F} - E_k^{\circ} \tag{21}$$

where k is *any* negative species in the system. If i is a negative ion, then the same definitions apply, except that k now refers to a positive and j to a negative species. Taking concentrations other than the standard state into account, the general expression for the potential of any electrode is

$$E = E^{\circ} + (RT/nF) \ln a_{ox}/a_{red}$$

where n is the number of electrons required to convert the oxidized to the reduced form of the species to which the electrode is reversible.

Using the above definitions, the emf of any cell is found by adding (with appropriate signs) the separate potentials of its component parts. Thus, the electrode potential of silver is subtracted from that of chloride to obtain the emf of the formation cells discussed in subsections a and b of Section II,A,1:

$$E_{cell} = E_{Cl}^{\circ} - (RT/F) \ln a_{Cl^-} - E_{Ag}^{\circ} - (RT/F) \ln a_{Ag^+}$$

when the activities of silver metal and chlorine gas at one atmosphere are taken as unity. From the definitions (18), (20), and (21), the correct relation [Eq. (1), p. 528] is seen to follow immediately, regardless of the choice of reference standard. In the concentration cell with transference (Section II,A,2,a) the two standard electrode potentials cancel each other out leaving

$$E = (RT/F) \ln a_{1B}/a_{1A} - \frac{RT}{F} \int_A^B [t_1 \, d \ln a_1 + t_2 \, d \ln a_2 - t_3 \, d \ln a_3]$$

Putting the first term on the right inside the integral and making use of (18) along with the fact that $t_3 = 1 - t_1 - t_2$ and the Gibbs-Duhem relation $(C_1 \, d \ln a_{13} + C_2 \, d \ln a_{23} = 0)$ converts this expression to the form obtained by combining Eqs. (14) and (15) (p. 536). In a similar manner, Eq. (17) for the emf of a Daniell cell can readily be derived using Eqs. (18)–(21).

The usefulness of quasi-thermodynamic quantities in deriving purely thermodynamic relations is clearly demonstrated in these examples. Perhaps even more important is the qualitative advantage afforded by these concepts in providing a basis for predicting the approximate emf of any cell in terms of the behavior of an idealized prototype, as well as for identifying in a given system the factors responsible for deviations from predicted values. In the following discussion particular attention will be paid to the utility of quasi-thermodynamic quantities in this latter respect.

1. Ionic Activities

The definition of activity for a neutral salt in an electrolytic system was discussed in Section II,A,1,b (p. 527). There it was seen that the salt defined by each possible cation-anion pair ik in a molten salt mixture can be assigned an activity a_{ik} in terms of its partial vapor pressure over the melt. The quasi-thermodynamic individual ionic activities a_i and a_k are partially defined in terms of a_{ik} by

$$a_{ik} = a_i^{\nu_i} a_k^{\nu_k} \tag{22}$$

where ν_i and ν_k are the numbers of each type of ion arising from the dissociation of one molecule of ik. This equation has a completely thermodynamic counterpart in the case of molecules $i'k'$ which dissociate to give uncharged species, i' and k', the analogous relation being identical with Eq. (22) if the standard states of reactants and products are chosen in such a way as to give an equilibrium constant of unity for the dissociation reaction. The activities of the dissociation products cannot be measured separately when they are electrically charged ions, however, so that it is necessary to introduce either a nonthermodynamic argument or an arbitrary convention to complete the definition of ionic activity. The Debye-Hückel theory is an example of a nonthermodynamic argument which assigns ionic activity coefficients in dilute aqueous solutions of electrolytes, while the "mean ionic activity coefficient" is a conventional device which permits a complete definition of ionic activities in terms of neutral salt activities alone. The latter convention is particularly unsuitable for systems containing more than two ions, such as molten salt mixtures, since it does not define uniquely the activity of each of the ions. Thus, in a mixture like NaCl–KCl, the concentration of Cl$^-$ can be specified, but its activity is ambiguous, depending upon whether the mean coefficient employed in its calculation is that of KCl or of NaCl. Other conventions for completing the definition of ionic activity could undoubtedly be found which would avoid this difficulty, and, indeed, one was suggested many years ago by Guggenheim (16). It has already been demonstrated in the introduction to this section, however, that *no additional convention is needed* to employ ionic activities unambiguously in setting down the emf expression for a galvanic cell, since they occur only in combinations defined completely by Eq. (22). Before attempting to evaluate the suitability of any particular complement to Eq. (22), therefore, the use to which these quantities are to be put is worth examining to determine what sort of convention, if any at all, is required.

a. Thermodynamic Relations in "Ideal" Molten Salt Solutions. If the enthalpy change upon mixing n_i moles of a molecular substance i with n_k moles of k is found to be zero over a range of temperatures and pressures, while the corresponding entropy change is equal to $-n_i R \ln X_i - n_k R \ln X_k$, solutions of i and k are said to be "ideal" in this range. The change in the partial molar free energy μ_i in making up such solutions is given by

$$\mu_i - \mu_i{}^\circ = RT \ln X_i$$

from which it follows that $a_i = X_i$, or $\gamma_i = 1$, and similarly for component k. This result is consistent with that calculated from a statistical mechanical treatment based on the following microscopic model: (*a*) The energy of interaction of molecules of type i with those of type k, E_{ik}, is equal to the mean of the molecular interaction energies in the pure components, E_{ii} and E_{kk}, the latter quantities being assumed to remain unchanged upon mixing. This gives $\Delta \overline{H}_i = \Delta \overline{H}_k = 0$ for the partial molar enthalpies of solution. (*b*) The mixing is completely random, the total number of positions available for occupancy by molecules of either type in the mixture being equal to the sum of the number of such positions originally available in each of the pure substances. This gives $\Delta \overline{S}_i = -R \ln X_i$ and $\Delta \overline{S}_k = -R \ln X_k$ for the partial molar entropies of solution. Deviations of an experimental system from ideal behavior are frequently interpreted as a measure of the extent to which the molecular configurations and interactions in the real solution depart from those prescribed by the idealized model. In attempting to characterize an ideal model for a molten salt system, however, it is apparent that the microscopic units to be considered in evaluating entropy changes are ions, rather than molecules.

If ν_i moles of a hypothetical substance composed only of cations i were mixed with ν_k moles of a purely anionic substance, the assumption of random mixing employed above for molecular solutions leads to

$$\Delta \overline{S}_i = -R \ln [\nu_i/(\nu_i + \nu_k)]$$
$$\Delta \overline{S}_k = -R \ln [\nu_k/(\nu_i + \nu_k)]$$

(23)

for the partial molar entropies of the ions in the mixture. For the case $\nu_i = \nu_k$, $\Delta \overline{S}_i$ and $\Delta \overline{S}_k$ are equal, each having the value $R \ln 2$. A mixture containing several different ionic species j of each sign can similarly be imagined to have been made up from (hypothetical) pure ionic liquids, the partial molar entropy change of each on the assumption of completely random mixing being

$$\Delta \overline{S}_j = -R \ln X_j$$

where X_j is the "total-ion fraction" of the jth species, i.e., the number of j ions divided by the total number of ions. For the case in which all species have charges of the same magnitude (regardless of sign), this can also be written

$$\Delta \overline{S}_i = -R \ln N_i/2$$
$$\Delta \overline{S}_k = -R \ln N_k/2$$

$$(24)$$

where i is any cationic species and N_i its "cation fraction" (number of i ions divided by total number of cations) and N_k is the "anion fraction" of a negative species k.

Although the entropy changes in making up these ionic mixtures from their microscopic constituents have been assigned in exactly the same manner as the ideal entropy of mixing of molecules, it is clear that any model for the *enthalpy* change in mixing ions of opposite charge must predict an enormous energy release. Thus a more complex theoretical calculation than that which led to zero enthalpy change for the molecular model is needed to apply a corresponding model in attempting to evaluate the ideal partial molar free energy change of an ionic species (and hence its activity in the mixture). To characterize a molten salt analogue of the ideal molecular solution it is possible to avoid the problem of the tremendous coulombic effect on the ionic enthalpy of mixing by considering only uncharged groups of ions, i.e., the electrically neutral salts and mixtures with which one deals experimentally. Thus, the partial molar enthalpy change on dilution of a neutral salt can be taken as zero in the ideal model. Since the entropy of mixing is best calculated from a model involving mixing of individual ions, the ideal partial molar entropy of solution of a neutral salt is found by adding the values for its constituent ions. Applying the completely-random mixing model to a system in which all species have charges of equal magnitude is found from Eqs. (23) and (24) to give

$$\Delta \overline{S}_{ik} = \Delta \overline{S}_{i(\text{mixt})} + \Delta \overline{S}_{k(\text{mixt})} - \Delta \overline{S}_{i(ik)} - \Delta \overline{S}_{k(ik)}$$
$$= -R \ln N_i N_k$$

for the partial molar entropy of mixing of salt ik. The corresponding change in the partial molar free energy of the salt is then given by

$$\mu_{ik} - \mu_{ik}^{\circ} = \Delta \overline{H}_{ik} - T\Delta \overline{S}_{ik} = RT \ln N_i N_k \qquad (25)$$

Now the assumption that cations and anions may exchange places randomly in a molten salt ignores the tendency of the strong coulomb forces to make the nearest neighbors of any ion be those of the opposite charge. The extreme example of this effect is found in the solid ionic crystal, which may be described as consisting of two interpenetrating lattices. The points of each lattice are available to ions of only one charge. On the assumption that a molten salt system more nearly approximates this model, Temkin (17) calculated the partial molar free energy of a neutral salt ik in a molten salt mixture for the case where all ions have charges of equal magnitude and the enthalpy of mixing is negligible. The result was identical with Eq. (25). From the model on which the derivation presented here was based, it is apparent that Temkin's assertion that this equation depends on the assumption that cations cannot exchange places with anions is incorrect. The fundamental assumption which makes both models give the same entropy of mixing is that the number of positions available to a given type of ion in the mixture is equal to the sum of those available to ions of the same charge in the pure salt components. Thus, the predictions of the two models diverge for most cases where ions of more than one charge type are involved, as in the system AgCl–PbCl₂. The cation fraction of Ag^+ in these mixtures is not equal to twice its total-ion fraction, so that the substitutions made in deriving Eq. (24) are no longer valid. For the general case, the derivation based on completely random mixing of the ions gives

$$\mu_{ik} - \mu_{ik}^\circ = RT \ln \left[\frac{\nu_i + \nu_k}{\nu_i} X_i \right]^{\nu_i} \left[\frac{\nu_i + \nu_k}{\nu_k} X_k \right]^{\nu_k} \tag{26}$$

where X_i and X_k are the total-ion fractions. The Temkin model for separate mixing of cations and anions gives

$$\mu_{ik} - \mu_{ik}^\circ = RT \ln N_i^{\nu_i} N_k^{\nu_k} \tag{27}$$

where the cation and anion fractions, N_i and N_k are the units of concentration.

The present author would not dispute that the Temkin model is more reasonable for a molten salt than one involving completely random mixing. It seems worth pointing out, nevertheless, that the two models cannot be distinguished in the cases to which they are most likely to be applied. The applicability of either approach to more complex systems like AgCl–PbCl₂ is not so readily justified in terms of the analogy with solid crystals, since the number of available sites is expected to change with concentration. The predictions which follow from a variety of assumptions about possible changes in number of cation sites with composition in fused salt mixtures involving mixed-valence types have been calculated by Førland (18), who retained the concept of two separate ion lattices.

It is not in the province of this discussion to attempt a critical evaluation of the relative merits of different microscopic models. What should be apparent from the foregoing is that a number of different standards for "ideal" behavior might be employed depending upon the model selected in defining thermodynamic ideality for molten salts.

  b. Identification of Ion Activity with Concentration. In the discussion just concluded relations were derived between the partial molar free energy (chemical potential) of the salt defined by any electrically neutral combination of ions in a molten salt mixture and the concentrations of these ions in the melt. For some systems these expressions were seen to depend on the microscopic model chosen to represent an "ideal" system. To obtain the relation of ionic concentration to thermodynamic activity for the models considered, it is only necessary to compare Eqs. (26) and (27) with the thermodynamic equation

$$\mu_{ik} - \mu_{ik}^{\circ} = RT \ln a_{ik}$$

applicable to a neutral substance *ik* in any system. From Eq. (27) a particularly simple relation is seen to exist for the Temkin model (based on the postulates of negligible enthalpy change and random mixing of cations and of anions separately):

$$a_{ik} = N_i^{\nu_i} N_k^{\nu_k} \tag{28}$$

Here the concentrations of ions *i* and *k* are expressed as cationic and anionic fractions, respectively. Now Eq. (28) contains only quantities which are experimentally measurable. Its applicability to a given salt composed of ν_i cations and ν_k anions can be taken as a measure of conformity to the model, or, more correctly, conformity to that which is common to *all* idealized prototypes of the system predicting the same result. The concept of ionic activity is not required to make this comparison, nor, in fact, do any of the models proposed yield a simple expression for the activity of an ion.

  It is nevertheless useful to employ the convention

$$a_i \approx N_i$$
$$a_k \approx N_k \tag{29}$$

suggested by the formal similarity of Eq. (28) to Eq. (22) of the introductory portion of this section (p. 542). This convention is not a contradiction to the above arguments, but is actually justified by combining the principal points that have been made here with the commonly observed experimental behavior of molten salt systems.

  (1) In spite of their indeterminate nature the activities of individual ions can be employed in any thermodynamic application, because correctly used they will appear only in combinations uniquely defined by Eq. (22).

(2) Use of the approximation in Eq. (29) can thus give rise only to relations which are valid for the behavior of neutral salts conforming to a theoretically simple model.

(3) As a rough guide to the behavior of real molten salt systems, employment of equations deriving from this model has been amply justified by experiment.

(4) The particular virtue of an expression for ionic activity in the consideration of electrochemical cells is to give (approximate) operational significance to the equally indeterminate quasi-thermodynamic concepts of "junction potential" and "electrode potential."

Justification for employment of the last-named concepts is similarly founded on their usefulness in permitting predictions of the approximate emf's of galvanic cells to be based on convenient tabulations of data ("standard electrode potentials") in combination with a knowledge of appropriate transference numbers. It will be seen in the next section that the convention in Eq. (29) permits further useful approximations in the analysis of cells with transference.

2. Junction Potentials

The term "junction potential" refers to that part of the emf of a cell with transference which arises from the irreversible diffusion process taking place at an interface between electrolytes of different composition. It is given by

$$E_{\text{junction}} = -\frac{RT}{F} \int_A^B \sum_i \frac{t_i}{z_i} d \ln a_i \qquad (30)$$

in which the "transference number" t_i of each ion may be specified by the (arbitrary) choice of a particular velocity reference for all the ions. Any attempt to recombine the terms of Eq. (30) in such a way as to give an expression containing only thermodynamically defined neutral salt activities cannot succeed. For at least one ionic activity must remain that will be combined, after integration over the range of compositions between compartments A and B, with the ionic activities in the expressions for the "electrode potentials" in these two compartments. The junction potentials defined by Eq. (30) are therefore as indeterminate as the activities of individual ions. They cannot be predicted from any of the models thus far proposed for molten salts, nor from any other model which does not uniquely assign ionic activities.

In order to assign a numerical value to this quasi-thermodynamic potential it is necessary to adopt some convention for ionic activity. For solutions approximating ideal behavior a convenient choice was presented at the close of the preceding section, i.e., $a_i \approx N_i$. The use of this convention in evaluating both junction and electrode potentials results in the correct total emf for a cell containing an ideal electrolyte system. Any of the conventions that might be applied in assigning activities to the ions in *nonideal* solutions will normally involve multiplying the ionic concentrations, expressed either as cation (or anion) fractions or in some easily relatable form, by "ionic activity coefficients" defined in terms of neutral salt activities. The liquid-junction potentials that will be calculated in this section by setting $a_i = N_i$ will therefore serve as an approximate guide to the magnitudes to be expected for such potentials, more precise values depending on the convention employed for ion activities.

a. Liquid–Liquid Interfaces. It was pointed out earlier that in spite of the simplicity of the Hittorf-type transference experiment by which the quantities t_i in Eq. (30) can be determined for molten salt systems, very few results have been reported in the literature [these few having been summarized elsewhere (7)]. Since transport numbers in a molten salt must depend strongly on concentration, it is necessary for approximate evaluation of the integral to employ the less sensitive function u_i, the ionic mobility. The relation of a cation transference number to the latter quantity is

$$t_i = \frac{X_i z_i u_i}{\sum_{i=1}^{n} X_i z_i u_i + \sum_{k=n+1}^{m} X_k z_k u_k}$$

where ions 1 to n are cations, the remaining $m-n$ are anions, and X_i and X_k are total-ion fractions. Note that u_k and z_k are both taken to be negative for negative ions moving in their normal direction. A corresponding expression can be written for the transference numbers t_k of any anion. If the fraction of ions in the system that are cations is designated θ, the cation and anion fractions N_i and N_k can be used to express the transference number of a cation in the form

$$t_i = \frac{\theta N_i z_i u_i}{\theta \sum_{i=1}^{n} N_i z_i u_i + (1 - \theta) \sum_{k=n+1}^{m} N_k z_k u_k} \tag{31}$$

Substitution of (29) and (31) into (30) gives a general expression for the liquid-junction potential in an ideal system:

$$E_J = -\frac{RT}{F} \int_A^B \frac{\theta \sum_{i=1}^{n} u_i dN_i + (1 - \theta) \sum_{k=n+1}^{m} u_k dN_k}{\theta \sum_{i=1}^{n} N_i z_i u_i + (1 - \theta) \sum_{k=n+1}^{m} N_k z_k u_k} \tag{32}$$

Now if the ionic mobilities u_i and u_k are assumed to remain constant and of the same order of magnitude (so that the denominator of Eq. (32) is not a strong function of concentration), this equation shows that the contribution to the total liquid-junction potential of the integral with respect to N_i for each ion i is approximately proportional to the difference $(N_{iA} - N_{iB})$ of its concentrations in the two electrode compartments. Any system in which the ionic concentration differences across the liquid junction are small may thus be expected to have a small junction potential. This principle is frequently employed in molten salt studies by keeping the concentration of the ion of interest small compared with those of the "solvent" ions. In this way large relative differences (N_{iA}/N_{iB}) in the concentration of the former ion can be attained without significant absolute differences in the concentrations of any of the ions. This contrast with the large liquid-junction potentials that may be encountered in cells containing very dilute aqueous solutions of a binary electrolyte results from the fact that both ions of the latter must change concentration at the same rate, so that their transference numbers are almost independent of concentration. The integrated contribution of each ionic term to the liquid-junction potential then takes the form

$$(RT/F)\,(t_i/z_i)\,\ln\,(c_{iA}/c_{iB})$$

so that the relative concentrations become important.

The concentration of any one cation or anion in a molten salt system can only be increased at the expense of others of like charge. The contribution of each ion to the junction potential thus tends to be cancelled by those of others in Eq. (32). Even a cell with large variation of composition across the liquid interface may have a small junction potential. To illustrate this situation and the conditions under which it may be expected to occur it is worthwhile to consider an extreme example: the Daniell cell (C) (see p. 537). Here the composition varies all the way from pure AgCl in one compartment to pure $PbCl_2$ in the other. The emf of this cell was nevertheless found by Suchy (19) to be not far from that calculated by subtracting the emf values of the corresponding formation cells. Thus, using here for the formation cells the most recently available data (which should be accurate to within $\pm$ 3 mv), the emf's at two different temperatures are as follows:

For the cell (20, 21, 22)

$$Ag \mid AgCl \mid Cl_2, C$$

$$E_{525°C} = 0.891\ \text{volt},\ E_{580°C} = 0.876\ \text{volt}$$

For the cell (23, 24)

$$Pb \mid PbCl_2 \mid Cl_2, C$$

$$E_{525°C} = 1.255\ \text{volt},\ E_{580°C} = 1.223\ \text{volt}$$

These may be compared with the corresponding values for cell (C) obtained by Suchy (*19*):

$$\text{Ag} \mid \text{AgCl} \vdots \text{PbCl}_2 \mid \text{Pb}$$

$$E_{525°C} = -0.342 \text{ volt}, \ E_{580°C} = -0.327 \text{ volt}$$

The liquid-junction potential obtained by subtracting the emf values of the formation cells (assigning the same potential to the chlorine electrode in both pure salts and taking the emf of cell (C) as negative to be consistent with the sign conventions in force here) is equal to +22 mv at the lower temperature and 20 mv at the higher. Although clearly larger than experimental error, and therefore significant, these quantities make strikingly small contributions to the total emf values. This result can now be used to test the theoretical equation (32).

The integration of Eq. (32) becomes particularly simple for Daniell cells in which both pure salts have a common anion, provided the mobilities of the cations relative to the former ion are assumed independent of concentration. This assumption is not, in general, completely justified for molten salt systems, since the equivalent conductances of pure salts are usually not additive in mixtures. In the absence of the required experimental data for most real systems, however, it can be used to estimate the order-of-magnitude of junction potentials in ideal systems. Taking the negative ion as velocity reference ($u_3 = 0$) in a Daniell cell of this type, Eq. (32) becomes

$$E_J = -\frac{RT}{F} \int_{N_1=1}^{N_2=1} \frac{u_1 dN_1 + u_2 dN_2}{z_1 u_1 N_1 + z_2 u_2 N_2}$$

$$= -\frac{RT}{F} \int_{N_1=1}^{N_1=0} \frac{(u_1 - u_2) dN_1}{z_2 u_2 + (z_1 u_1 - z_2 u_2) N_1} \quad (33)$$

(noting that $N_2 = 1 - N_1$). Now the mobility of the cation (relative to the anion) in any *pure* salt is directly proportional to the equivalent conductance of the salt. The assumption of constant mobilities over the concentration range thus permits replacement of the cation mobilities in this equation by the equivalent conductivities of the corresponding pure salts. Upon integration this gives

$$E_J = \frac{RT}{F} \frac{\Lambda_{13} - \Lambda_{23}}{z_1 \Lambda_{13} - z_2 \Lambda_{23}} \ln \frac{z_1 \Lambda_{13}}{z_2 \Lambda_{23}} \quad (34)$$

Equation (34) expresses the liquid-junction potential in terms of quantities that are normally available for systems of interest, but suffers from an admittedly poor approximation. How badly the variation of ion mobility with concentration affects the results in a real cell can only be tested by comparison with experiment.

The Daniell cell (D) discussed above provides an excellent opportunity for such a test, since the system AgCl–PbCl$_2$ has been found to be ideal (*25*). Calculation of the required conductances from data tabulated by Conway (*26*) gives:

for AgCl: $\Lambda_{13(525)} = 129.3,$ $\Lambda_{13(580)} = 133.8;$

for PbCl$_2$: $\Lambda_{23(525)} = 44.1,$ $\Lambda_{23(580)} = 52.2.$

Substitution of these figures into Eq. (34) gives a junction potential of 54 mv at the lower temperature and 51 mv at the higher. Assuming Suchy's data to be correct, the corresponding experimental values of 22 and 20 mv, respectively, show that Eq. (34) predicts the correct sign and order of magnitude, but makes a poor quantitative guide to the liquid-junction potential in this system. The results indicate that the mobilities of the two cations are more nearly equal in mixtures of intermediate composition, as might have been expected from the usual negative deviation from additivity observed for conductivity isotherms (*4*). It is not unlikely that the tendency of cation mobilities to become more nearly equal is a rather general phenomenon in molten salt mixtures. If such is the case, Eq. (34) is seen to provide a *maximum* value for the junction potential in ideal systems. The unintegrated form [Eq. (33)] is always valid for such systems, and shows that small liquid-junction potentials may come about under two circumstances: (i) when the mobilities of the two cations are nearly the same in all mixtures; or (ii) when one cation is relatively more mobile than the other in one concentration region, but becomes relatively less so in another region, so that the integrand changes sign in the interval between the compartments.

From the foregoing discussion it is apparent that liquid-junction potentials in the type of molten salt cell considered are generally of smaller magnitude than those frequently encountered in systems containing an inert solvent. The well-known use of the salt bridge containing ions of equal mobility for minimizing such potentials in solutions of the latter type, on the other hand, has no counterpart in a molten salt Daniell cell. That neither KCl nor any other salt can serve this purpose in the same manner is made apparent by consideration of Eq. (34). Suppose, for example, the junction to be minimized is between two salts containing cations of the same valence type z. From Eq. (34) the junction potential calculated for a direct contact of the two salts is[1]

$$E_J = \frac{RT}{zF} \ln \frac{\Lambda_{13}}{\Lambda_{23}} \tag{35}$$

---

[1] An equation identical to (35) was given by G. N. Lewis and L. W. Sargent [*J. Am. Chem. Soc.* **31**, 355 (1909)] for the potential difference between equally concentrated solutions of two binary salts having one ion in common.

Now inserting a salt bridge containing a cation of the same valence type would replace this by two potentials, each given by expressions of exactly the same form as Eq. (35), and each involving the equivalent conductance of the salt in the bridge. Upon addition of these two equations, however, the latter quantity is cancelled out, leaving a relation for the net potential across the bridge which is identical to Eq. (35). Thus the introduction of a salt bridge with cations of the same valence type as those originally present at the junction has no effect whatever on the magnitude of the junction potential between electrode compartments, regardless of the mobilities of the bridge ions. (The quantitative accuracy of this statement depends, of course, on the reliability of the assumption that the cation mobilities are independent of concentration, as well as the assumption of ideality of the solutions formed by adjacent salts.)

Although the treatment of systems involving salts of different valence type or containing two or more different ionic species of each charge is more complex, two conclusions reached here are valid in general. (a) Junction potentials between molten salts or molten salt systems are generally smaller than those between aqueous or nonaqueous solutions in which the concentration of electrolyte relative to inert solvent varies across the junction. The former are particularly small, and may generally be neglected, when the only species changing concentration across the junction are dilute "solutes" in a "solvent" melt of nearly constant composition throughout the interface. (b) It is impractical to attempt to minimize junction potentials in molten salt systems by seeking suitable salt bridges. The potential of each salt system against the bridge depends upon the mobilities of *all* the ions in the interfacial region.

b. *Solid–Liquid Interfaces.* The complex nature of the junction between a molten salt and a glass was indicated in the discussion of the emf values of cells containing such junctions in Section II,A,2,d (p. 540). In the present section certain limiting cases will be shown, nevertheless, to give potentials between glass and salt which are either unambiguous or unnecessary to an understanding of the emf values of the cells involved. The junction between a liquid and a solid salt will also be considered.

An obvious example of a cell in which a knowledge of the junction potentials is superfluous has been studied by Grube and Rau (15):

$$\text{Ag} \mid \text{AgCl} \vdots \text{glass} \vdots \text{AgCl} \mid \text{Cl}_2 \qquad \text{(F)}$$

Here the salt–glass interfacial potentials are equal in magnitude but opposite in sign, so that the emf of the cell is independent of their values. An experimental arrangement of this type thus makes it possible to study formation cells like

$$\text{Ag} \mid \text{AgCl} \mid \text{Cl}_2 \qquad\qquad\qquad \text{(G)}$$

without interference from the irreversible reaction between the electrode materials. Having the AgCl in one electrode compartment saturated with Ag and that in the other with Cl_2 means, of course, that the two junctions will not be identical. Neither of the elements in its dissolved form can carry an appreciable fraction of the current through the junction, however, so that transport from this source need not be considered. Such transport could become a factor when the metal electrode is Cd, due to its large solubility with the (postulated) formation of Cd^+. And in their more concentrated solutions the alkali metals begin to conduct electronically, thereby becoming the dominant conductors in the melt. In these extreme cases, however, not only transport, but major changes in the thermodynamic properties of the salts are involved, so that cell emf's reflect also changes in the activities of the ions. That such is not the case in formation cell (F) is evidenced by the fact that the emf's reported by Grube and Rau are substantially identical with those reported elsewhere for cell (G) (20, 21, 22).

While the case just cited is perhaps a trivial one in itself, it illustrates an important principle: the magnitude of the sum of the potentials of two molten salt systems against opposite sides of a glass partition depends on the difference in composition of the two solutions. Since the contribution of each ion to the total depends on the *absolute* difference between its concentrations on the two sides (see preceding section), this contribution for a particular ion of interest can be made negligible by keeping its concentration small on one side of the glass and smaller, or even zero, on the other. This principle forms the basis of applicability of some "glass electrodes" in molten salt systems, permitting the ion reversible to the reference electrode to be kept separated from others with which it might react, while employing relatively much larger fractions of "solvent" electrolyte having essentially the same composition, e.g., NaCl–KCl eutectic, on both sides of the glass.

Even when the electrolyte on one side of a glass partition is very different from that on the other, the additivity of the two junction potentials employed in the discussion of cell (F) can be used to compare the emf's of cells involving the same junctions. Thus, Grube and Rau (15) showed that the sum of the emf's of the cells

$$\text{Pb} \mid \text{PbCl}_2 \;\vdots\; \text{glass} \;\vdots\; \text{AgCl} \mid \text{Cl}_2$$

and

$$\text{Ag} \mid \text{AgCl} \;\vdots\; \text{glass} \;\vdots\; \text{PbCl}_2 \mid \text{Pb}$$

was experimentally equal to that of cell (F) (and hence of cell (G)). This principle has also been employed in making use of a glass-enclosed salt bridge to connect solutions of nearly the same composition (27). The sum of the junction potentials is small, and independent of the composition of salt used in the bridge, whose function is simply to provide a better conducting path than could be attained with a bridge of pure glass.

The actual magnitude of a glass–salt junction potential could be calculated from Eq. (30) if the properties of the region of intermediate composition were known. Most of this region is inside the silicate network of the glass, the cations normally present in the glass presumably having been replaced to some degree by the cations of the melt. If the extent of this penetration by foreign ions could be minimized by appropriate choice of the glass and salt system employed, the significance of the potential would become more clearly defined. As an extreme case, consider a glass through which all current is carried by sodium ion in contact with a melt containing, in addition to sodium ion, only ions which are incapable of penetrating the glass. The boundary region here is reduced to a plane through which sodium ion only carries the current, so that its transference number relative to all the ions in the neighborhood of the junction (including the silicate network) is unity. The potential across such an interface is readily calculated by integration of Eq. (30):

$$E_J = -\frac{RT}{F} \ln \frac{a_{Na^+(melt)}}{a_{Na^+(glass)}} \tag{36}$$

The unknown activity of sodium ion in the glass would normally disappear in a practical application of Eq. (36), due to the corresponding transfer of this ion at the other side of the glass. The contact there would have to be with either a sodium electrode or another solution containing Na^+, since these are the only materials that will permit any current flow through this idealized system. The former case will be considered further in Section II,B,3,b (see p. 568). With the latter arrangement it is apparent that another expression of the same form as Eq. (36) with the sign reversed would describe the potential of melt II against the glass, so that the sum of the junction potentials across the glass would be given by

$$E_{net} = +\frac{RT}{F} \ln \frac{a_{Na^+(melt\ II)}}{a_{Na^+(melt\ I)}}$$

The system just described is closely analogous to the "glass electrode" commonly used for the determination of pH in aqueous solutions (see Chapter 5). Thus, even if the idealized glass permeable only to sodium ion were approximated in a real experiment, the familiar problem of the "asymmetry potential" encountered with the latter electrode could be a significant factor here.

The treatment of solid–liquid interfaces becomes more straightforward when the solid is a pure salt composed only of ions also present in the immediately adjacent melt. Consider the junction

$$KCl \text{ (s)} \; \vdots \; PbCl_2 \text{ (l)}$$

at a temperature above the melting point of any compounds like $KCl \cdot PbCl_2$, so that the only solid phase present at the interface is pure KCl. The irreversible process occurring here can be divided into two parts — the melting of solid KCl at its plane of contact with the liquid, followed by interdiffusion of the two molten salts. If the transport of KCl away from the solid by the latter process is slow compared with the melting rate, the liquid in contact with pure solid KCl will have the composition specified by the point corresponding to the temperature of the system on the liquidus line of the equilibrium phase diagram for the $PbCl_2$–KCl system. Hence there will be no free energy change for the melting process, and the "activity" of KCl in the solid relative to a hypothetical pure liquid KCl at the same temperature and pressure must equal its activity in the liquid referred to the same standard state. Now since the activity of a uni-univalent salt is equal to the product of the activities of its ions, it is convenient to choose the individual ionic activities in the solid equal to those in the liquid. From this convention it follows that if the liquids form nearly ideal solutions the activity of chloride ion in the solid is approximately unity, while that of potassium ion approximates its cation fraction in the adjacent melt, and may be far from unity, depending, of course, on the temperature of the measurement and shape of the liquidus line. (It will be recalled that in ideal systems this line is completely specified from pure salt to eutectic mixture by the melting point and heat of fusion of the salt.) Now the total solid–liquid junction potential can be treated as the sum of two potentials in series:

(1) *The interphase potential.* In a transference experiment all current would be carried across the interface by potassium and chloride ions, since the lead ion cannot penetrate the lattice. This follows from the fact that potassium and lead chlorides do not form solid solutions. A trace of lead ion might enter the lattice as an impurity, but the transference number of a trace would be negligibly small. Since the activities of the two current-carrying ions are the same in both phases, it is clear that the potential difference across this part of the junction must be *zero*.

(2) *The liquid–liquid-junction potential.* The region in which the composition of the liquid changes from its equilibrium value at the solid surface

to that of pure liquid PbCl$_2$ is treated by the methods described in the preceding section.

The total potential thus depends on the difference in mobility of the two cations in the liquid phase as a function of concentration. If this difference has the same sign in mixtures of all compositions, it follows that the solid–liquid junction potential here will be *less than* that of the hypothetical liquid–liquid interface:

$$KCl\ (l) \ \vdots \ PbCl_2\ (l)$$

at the same temperature. Assuming ideal behavior and constant cation mobilities, the latter potential is given by Eq. (34) of the preceding section, where Λ_{13} is the conductance of (hypothetical) pure liquid KCl. (This might be assigned by extrapolation of log Λ vs. $1/T$ plots from temperatures above the melting point to that under consideration.) To obtain the corresponding relation for the net potential of the solid–liquid junction under discussion here, the integration of Eq. (33) (p. 551) extends over the smaller concentration range indicated above, giving

$$E_{S-J} = \frac{RT}{F} \frac{\Lambda_{13} - \Lambda_{23}}{z_1\Lambda_{13} - z_2\Lambda_{23}} \ln \frac{z_2\Lambda_{23} + (z_1\Lambda_{13} - z_2\Lambda_{23})N_{1s}}{z_2\Lambda_{23}} \tag{37}$$

where N_{1s} is the cation fraction of potassium in the liquid adjoining the solid surface.

The preceding analysis may help to explain the rather surprising results of Pletenev and Rozov (*28*), who employed what seems to have been a salt bridge of solid KCl to connect electrode compartments containing molten salts. The experimental arrangement is shown in Fig. 1, where an asbestos cord is seen to be draped between small holes in each of two test tubes in such a way that each end is soaked with one of the melts contained therein. The authors explain that the cord itself has been soaked in KCl, presumably to provide electrical contact. Now the melting point of potassium chloride is 750°C, which is more than one hundred degrees higher than any of the temperatures employed in their measurements of emf. Since a vacuum tube voltmeter rather than a potentiometer was used for the latter purpose, it is not unlikely that the solid salt could provide an adequately conducting path. For the cell

$$Ag \ | \ AgCl \ \vdots \ KCl\ bridge \ \vdots \ PbCl_2 \ | \ Pb$$

at a series of temperatures from 525 to 600°C, Pletenev and Rozov reported emf's substantially identical (within 1 or 2 mv) to those reported by Suchy (*19*) for cell (C) (p. 537) in which the two pure salts were in direct contact. This agreement between the potentials of two such different junctions might be rationalized as follows. Application of Eq. (34) to each of the two junctions with a hypothetical liquid KCl gives at each temperature a sum which is somewhat greater than the potential calculated for the junction AgCl–PbCl$_2$ by the same equation. (This difference is due to the fact that cations of more than one valence type are involved.) At 525°K, for example, the former figure is 69 mv, compared with 54 mv for the latter.

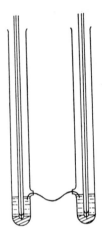

Fig. 1. Asbestos wick bridge between half-cells (28).

Now the reduction in each of the two KCl junction potentials due to the freezing of the salt might reasonably be just about enough to span the difference between the figures given. It is not worthwhile to attempt to make the comparison more quantitative by application of Eq. (37), however, in view of the discrepancies pointed out in the preceding section between the calculated and observed junction potentials of cell (C). The interesting conclusion to be drawn from both theoretical and experimental results presented here is that under certain simple and readily specified conditions the use of a solid salt bridge between molten salts can give a somewhat smaller total junction potential than that obtained with a bridge of liquid salt.

3. Electrode Potentials

The familiar table of standard electrode potentials is an invaluable guide for predicting approximate emf values of electrochemical cells, as well as a tool for studying thermodynamic properties of aqueous electrolytes. The possible utility of "electromotive force series" of this type for applications in molten media has stimulated considerable effort by workers in the molten salt field to construct analogous tables. In order to assign electrode potentials in any medium it is necessary to establish a clearly defined reference standard, such as the standard hydrogen electrode in aqueous solutions. The present discussion deals with the theoretical aspects of these problems, while Sections III, IV, and V will be concerned with experimental considerations and results.

a. Electromotive Force Series. The introduction of the quasi-thermo-dynamic concept of ionic activity made it possible to write expressions for the change in partial molar free energy of an ion accompanying a change in its concentration, i.e., a change in the composition of its environment. It was seen that in spite of the arbitrary nature of this quantity, its use entails no violation of thermodynamic principles, since in any application it must be combined with the activity of another ion in a form which is thermodynamically significant. (If such were not the case in a particular experiment, this experiment could be used to define ionic activity unam-biguously.) A similar situation prevails at the interface between a metallic electrode and a melt containing its ions, where the immediate environment of the metal ion is changed even more drastically in going from the electron cloud in the metal to the surrounding cluster of anions in a molten salt. Again it is impossible to assign thermodynamically the change in free energy for the transfer of the ion between media of different composition. Again it *is* possible to measure the free energy change in a process involving simultaneously the corresponding transfer of another ion — either another cation from salt to metal, or an anion from element to salt. This time, how-ever, the division of the free energy change into separate ionic contributions is even more arbitrary, since no simple model analogous to that for the ideal solution lends itself readily to such complex microscopic phenomena. Nor is an unique method of assignment particularly desirable, except, perhaps, as a means of coercing chemists into adopting a universal stand-ard. For while the equating of ion activity with concentration permits assessment of the approximate free energy changes of a great many processes (different changes of concentration), only one parameter is needed to describe the transfer of an ion between two uniquely specified media. So long as this parameter is chosen consistently with those for other ions, the designation of its absolute value is completely arbitrary.

The quasi-thermodynamic parameters of individual electrode reactions are conveniently tabulated for aqueous solutions at 25°C in the form of "standard electrode potentials," $E°$, taking that of the hydrogen electrode to be zero. The media between which the ion is transferred in specifying the potential of a given electrode are the electrode material in its standard state and an hypothetical, ideal, unimolal solution at the same temperature and pressure of an electrolyte containing the ion of interest (see Chapter 1,

Section V). The choosing of infinite dilution as the basis for defining this hypothetical standard state effectively assigns to the environment of each ion the chemical properties of pure water. That is, variations in free energy accompanying concentration changes are ascribed solely to the changes in entropy associated with expanding or contracting the volume of solution available to each ion; the corresponding values of ΔH, which would reflect ion-ion interactions as well as changes in the ion-water interaction energy, are taken to be *zero*. Thus, one of the two media between which the ion is transferred is taken to be essentially the same for all ions in assigning values of $E°$ in aqueous electrolytes.

By definition a molten salt system lacks the inert component that makes it possible to specify a common inert solvent medium in listing and comparing the standard potentials of all possible electrodes in aqueous solution. The nearest analogue to the water is the empty space that would remain upon complete removal of the ions comprising the salt system from their containing vessel. It is impossible to change the total ionic concentration relative to this "medium" at constant temperature and pressure, however, except by small changes in the molar volume of the system with composition. Extrapolations to "infinite dilution" relative to vacuum are therefore meaningless. In order to assign electrode potentials at all, it is necessary to select an *ionic* medium as a common reference "solvent." The principle employed for determining standard electrode potentials in a particular ionic solvent system at a specified temperature is then essentially the same as that used in aqueous solutions. In the establishment of molten salt electrode potentials, the reference *medium* for a solvent ion will not, of course, be a hypothetical one when the normal concentration of the ion in the solvent is unity. The standard potential of an electrode reversible to such an ion can thus be measured directly. For an electrode reversible to a solvent ion at any concentration other than unity, the standard potential $E°$ can be calculated from a single emf measurement in the pure solvent by the equation

$$E = E° + (RT/nF) \ln c_i$$

where E is the electrode potential relative to the reference standard and c_i is the concentration of the ion.[2] The procedure for obtaining the standard potentials of electrodes reversible to ions not common to the solvent system follows closely the analogous method for aqueous solutions described in Chapter 1. A series of measurements is made in solutions containing pro-

---

[2] This procedure, which has not been proposed elsewhere, is based on the customary practice of assigning an activity coefficient of unity to any ion in its reference medium. In solutions not far from the reference composition, it provides the simplest basis for predicting the emf values of cells.

gressively smaller concentrations of the ion of interest. Values for the function $E - (RT/nF) \ln c_i$ can then be tabulated as a function of c_i. No rule corresponding to the Debye-Hückel limiting law will normally be needed to complete the extrapolation to infinite dilution in molten salt systems, since ideal behavior is generally encountered at easily realized dilutions. The function then maintains during successive dilutions a constant value which is designated $E°$.

The choice of units for the concentration c_i was not specified in the preceding paragraph, since *any* of the conventional forms for expressing concentration will suffice in the construction of an electromotive force series. The values of $E°$ will depend on the particular form employed, however, as will all values of the function $E - (RT/nF) \ln c_i$. The relation between $E°$ values on different concentration scales is readily calculated. If c_i is taken, for example, to be the cation fraction N_i, it is apparent that values of $E - (RT/nF) \ln c_i$ will become constant as soon as the solution conforms to the Temkin standard for ideal behavior discussed in Section II,B,1,a. In *dilute* solutions, however, the concentration expressed in any other form c_i' is very nearly directly proportional to N_i. Representing the infinite dilution value of this proportionality constant by k, it is seen that the function $E - (RT/nF) \ln c_i'$ also approaches a constant value, $E°'$, such that $E°' = E° - (RT/nF) \ln k$. This relation for converting standard electrode potentials to other concentration scales shows that not only the absolute values of $E°$, but the relative positions in the electromotive force series, of electrodes at which different numbers n of electrons are transferred may be affected by such a conversion of scale. The series defined by taking $c_i = N_i$ has certain advantages for molten salt systems: (i) The potential of any electrode in an ideal molten salt system is given by

$$E = E° + (RT/nF) \ln N_i \tag{38}$$

over the entire range of composition. (ii) Since it may be desirable to determine the series at more than one temperature, it is convenient to employ units for a given composition which do not change with temperature, rather than volume-dependent quantities like *molarity* or *normality*. (iii) Much broader ranges of composition may be of interest in the molten salt system than are possible with aqueous electrolytes. As N_i approaches unity, the corresponding value of the *molality* approaches infinity. Further advantages of the convention $c_i = N_i$ will be evident in the following discussion.

Since any pure salt or salt mixture can serve as the solvent in making up a table of electrode potentials, it would be meaningless to talk about "*the* electromotive force series" in molten salts, even for a specified temperature, unless the entries in the table were independent of the solvent system employed. This could only come about if all salts formed ideal solutions with each other. If such were the case it would be unnecessary to specify a unique solvent, since the interaction of any ion with its environment would be independent of the composition of the medium. Experimental evidence of nonideality in many systems has, of course, ruled out this possibility. Such studies nevertheless indicate that the assumption of ideal behavior frequently provides a reasonable basis for making approximate estimates. Since the principal purpose in introducing quasi-thermodynamic concepts has been to facilitate such estimates, the possibility of a single electromotive force table for use as a general guide in molten salt studies merits further consideration here.

If an electromotive force series for the solvent NaCl at a specified temperature were established relative to the chlorine electrode, then taking the standard potential of the latter as zero would give an $E°$ for the sodium electrode (on the cation-fraction basis) equal to the emf calculated for the formation cell

$$\text{Na} \mid \text{NaCl} \mid \text{Cl}_2 \text{ (1 atm)} \tag{H}$$

from the standard free energy of the salt (Section II,A,1,a). Now suppose that KCl forms ideal solutions with NaCl. (Neither verification nor denial of this supposition is, to the author's knowledge, available in the literature.) Then the activity coefficient of potassium ion (as defined by any reasonable convention) is equal to unity at all concentrations from infinite dilution in the NaCl solvent to pure KCl. It follows that $E°$ for the potassium electrode in NaCl is equal to the emf of the formation cell

$$\text{K} \mid \text{KCl} \mid \text{Cl}_2 \text{ (1 atm)} \tag{I}$$

at the same temperature. If, on the other hand, the two salts do not form ideal solutions, the "standard potential" of the potassium electrode in NaCl differs from the emf of cell (I) by an amount which depends upon the magnitude of the deviation from ideality. A comparison of the two quantities, if available, would thus provide a convenient indication of the nature (positive or negative) and extent of the deviations. Both quantities would, in fact, be useful in predicting the approximate potentials of potassium electrodes in KCl–NaCl mixtures, the choice depending on the concentration region of interest. Distinguishing the two standard potentials by the subscripts i (infinite dilution basis) and p (pure salt basis), either $E_i°$ or $E_p°$ could be substituted into Eq. (38) to give the potential quite accurately near the corresponding end of the composition range. At concentrations nearer to a potassium ion fraction of 0.5, Eq. (38) would be less accurate using either standard potential, due to the deviation from ideality, but could be used to define upper and lower limits for the electrode potential.

The preceding discussion suggests two ways in which one might attempt to establish a single emf series for use in estimating electrode potentials in melts of all different compositions. (i) Taking advantage of the facts that almost all salts are at least partially miscible with one another and that deviations from ideality in such mixtures are often small, a single salt system like pure NaCl is established as "reference solvent." The standard potential of the chlorine electrode is taken to be zero in the reference solvent, while that of sodium equals the emf of the NaCl formation cell. Standard potentials of the type $E_i{}^\circ$ are assigned to all other electrodes. To the extent that salts of the foreign ions involved tend to form ideal solutions with NaCl, the table developed in this manner will have general utility, even for melts containing no sodium or chloride ions. That is, use of such standard potentials in Eq. (38) to calculate separate electrode potentials makes possible prediction of the approximate emf values of cells made up from any pair of electrodes in any melt. When standard potentials are assigned this way, however, it is clear that the approximation is likely to be best in melts containing mostly NaCl. (ii) A table of values of $E_p{}^\circ$ is made up, based on the free energies of formation of all the metal chlorides. Putting these quantities into Eq. (38) provides another guide to the approximate potentials to be expected for the corresponding metal electrodes relative to chlorine in molten salts systems generally. In this case, of course, the approximation is best in melts containing mostly the chloride of the metal of interest. Tables of both types, the former involving several different solvent systems, have been reported in the literature. A number of these are reproduced in the Appendix.

Employment of a table of emf values of pure metal chloride formation cells leaves unsettled the problem of assigning potentials to electrodes reversible to *anions* other than chloride. It will be recalled that there was no difficulty in defining $E_i{}^\circ$ for a bromine electrode in NaCl solvent, taking the activity coefficient of the bromide ion as unity at infinite dilution. Now if NaCl forms ideal solutions with NaBr, this standard potential can also be calculated by subtracting the emf of the formation cell

$$\text{Na} \mid \text{NaBr} \mid \text{Br}_2 \text{ (1 atm)} \tag{J}$$

from that of cell (H), i.e., $E_{\text{Na}}^\circ - E_{\text{Cl}}^\circ + E_{\text{Br}}^\circ - E_{\text{Na}}^\circ = E_{\text{Br}}^\circ - E_{\text{Cl}}^\circ = E_{\text{Br}}^\circ$. If the solutions are not ideal, this difference in the emf's of cells (H) and (J) can still be used to assign a value of $E_p{}^\circ$ to the bromine electrode relative to chlorine. As in the case of metals, the usefulness of this $E_p{}^\circ$ in NaCl–NaBr mixtures is more limited the greater the deviation of the solutions from ideality. Again thermodynamic data with which to test for ideality are not available. This time, however, it is possible to examine further the self-consistency of the manner in which $E_p{}^\circ$ was assigned to the bromine electrode. For, in designating potentials of the metal electrodes relative to chlorine, pure metal chlorides only were considered, each salt constituting its own well-defined "solvent." In the case of the bromine electrode two sodium salts were used to define the corresponding potential. Suppose, instead, that two potassium salts had been used, i.e., KCl and KBr. If these salts formed ideal solutions with the sodium salts, it would clearly make no difference which pair was used. They do not, however, as can be shown from available free energy data for the pure salts without making measurements on any of their mixtures. This is done as follows. Consider the reaction

$$\text{NaBr} + \text{KCl} - \text{NaCl} \rightarrow \text{KBr} \qquad (39)$$

in which, in addition to the product, each of the reactants is a pure liquid at the same temperature as the others. Since any mixture of these salts is actually a ternary system whose composition can be completely specified in terms of the three salts on the left, the product KBr can be regarded as a particular "mixture" made up from the other pure salts. For an ideal system the free energy change of this process would be zero. The actual free energy change at 1500°K can be calculated from the standard free energies reported for the pure salts by Brewer (29). It is found to equal 1.45 ± 0.50 kcal. From this it follows that the reversible emf of the cell

$$\text{Br}_2 \mid \text{NaBr} \mid \text{Na} \mid \text{NaCl} \mid \text{Cl}_2 \mid \text{KCl} \mid \text{K} \mid \text{KBr} \mid \text{Br}_2$$

[for which the cell reaction is given by Eq. (39)] is equal to 0.064 ± 0.022 volt at 1500°K. Expressing this emf as a sum of electrode potentials, $E_{\text{Br(Na)}}^\circ - E_{\text{Na}}^\circ - E_{\text{Cl}}^\circ - E_{\text{K}}^\circ + E_{\text{K}}^\circ - E_{\text{Br(K)}}^\circ = E_{\text{Br(Na)}}^\circ - E_{\text{Br(K)}}^\circ$, shows that it is equal to the discrepancy involved in assigning the bromine electrode potential by the two separate routes. The emf values of the alkali halide formation cells used in this calculation are all in the neighborhood of 2.5 to 3 volts, so that the error in using either quantity as the bromine electrode potential would be only a small percentage of the total emf of a formation cell in any composition of this ternary reciprocal system. The discrepancy is so small, in fact, that it is barely enough to be outside the limits of Brewer's estimated uncertainties. For this reason it is perhaps worthwhile to list the corresponding values for some other combinations at 1500°K:

$$E_{\text{Br(Na)}}^\circ - E_{\text{Br(Li)}}^\circ = -0.022 \pm 0.124 \text{ volt}$$
$$E_{\text{Br(Na)}}^\circ - E_{\text{Br(Rb)}}^\circ = +0.169 \pm 0.064 \text{ volt}$$
$$E_{\text{Br(Na)}}^\circ - E_{\text{Br(Cs)}}^\circ = +0.216 \pm 0.022 \text{ volt}$$

$$E^{\circ}_{F(Na)} - E^{\circ}_{F(K)} = -0.338 \pm 0.022 \text{ volt}$$
$$E^{\circ}_{I(Na)} - E^{\circ}_{I(K)} = +0.044 \pm 0.016 \text{ volt}$$

These calculations show that there most likely are genuine deviations from ideality in reciprocal alkali halide systems. In fact, the deviations seem to show definite trends which have interesting implications for the theory of solutions. In any case, it is apparent that none of the nonmetallic electrodes can be assigned an unambiguous potential relative to chlorine without introducing an additional convention. Such a convention might consist, for example, in choosing the sodium electrode as a secondary reference, and hence calculating potentials from the standard free energies of sodium salts. Inconsistencies of the type demonstrated here would be outweighed by the advantage of having an approximate basis upon which to compare the relative potentials of nonmetallic electrodes and to estimate approximate emf values for various cells.

This section should not be concluded without mention of a nonthermodynamic method often employed in the determination of electrode potentials. It is the measurement of decomposition voltages of electrolytic cells. The assumption is made that upon electrolysis of a molten ionic system the electrode reactions tend to produce elements comprising a particular salt of that system in their standard states, i.e., the normal states of these elements at the temperature and pressure of the measurement. The process thereby gives rise to a formation cell with an emf counter to the direction of the applied voltage. Appreciable currents should only be observed when the latter potential exceeds the former, so that a plot of the experimental dependence of current on applied potential may be used to locate the emf of the corresponding formation cell. Hamer and co-workers (1) have listed a number of factors, however, which may interfere with the success of this method in determining electrode potentials in molten salts. Included are chemical interaction of electrodes with electrolyte, production of electrodes in a nonstandard state, deviations from isothermal conditions (due to local heating caused by the passage of current), electrode polarization, and ohmic drop across the solution. In many cases these difficulties can either be minimized or accounted for quantitatively. This will be seen in the Appendix, where the reader may compare a number of potentials determined in this way with the corresponding reversibly determined quantities.

b. Reference Electrodes. It has been seen that any assignment of electrode potentials in molten salts requires the establishment of a standard reference electrode with its potential arbitrarily taken to be zero (or some other suitably designated value). As in other types of electrolytes, the ultimate standard may not always be the most convenient experimental electrode to work with. It will therefore be useful to consider also the types of electrodes most practical for reference purposes, and how their potentials may be related to the former.

The choice of any particular ultimate standard reference electrode for molten salt studies has not as yet received unanimous support by workers in the field. With the possible exception of a few unusual systems, such as those containing bisulfates, molten salts are not suitable media for the hydrogen electrode which, of course, forms the basis of the familiar series of potentials in aqueous solution. An attempt has nevertheless been made by some workers (30, 31) to relate the potentials of molten salt electrodes to that of a hypothetical hydrogen electrode, through the free energy change of the gas phase reaction

$$H_2 + X_2 \rightarrow 2HX$$

at the temperature of interest, where X is one of the halogens. This convention has been criticized by Delimarskii (32) for its lack of either conceptual or practical significance in liquid phase salts containing no hydrogen ions. Some support has been given to the chlorine electrode as a reference standard (1, 33), while other standards proposed include cesium (34) and sodium electrodes (32). The most common practice, however, has been simply to choose any conveniently reproducible electrode in the system under study and designate its potential as zero for the purposes of the investigation.

It was pointed out in the preceding section that any molten salt system can act as the "solvent" for which a series of electrode potentials is defined. In contrast with the behavior of other types of solvents, an electrode material reversible to its ions in one such salt solvent will generally be reversible to the same ions dissolved in most salt systems, provided it does not react irreversibly with other ions in the melt. The same electrode can thus be used experimentally as reference standard in many different solvents, the principal limitation of a particular material being the temperature range in which its use is practical. It is important to bear in mind, however, that in order to specify precisely the potential of a particular reference electrode, not only the ultimate standard but also the reference solvent system must be designated. For, as was shown in subsection a, above, unless only salt systems forming ideal solutions with one another are studied, or the reference electrode is itself the ultimate standard, its potential relative to the latter may be expected to vary from one melt to another. An attempt to avoid this difficulty by always immersing the electrode material in a melt of fixed composition, which in turn meets any solvent of interest at a liquid junction, simply has the effect of transplanting the source of potential variation to the junction. There the changes of potential connected with thermodynamic nonideality of the system formed by the adjacent melts may be further complicated by undetermined transport properties of the same system (Section II,B,2,a).

The complex nature of junction potentials suggests the desirability of avoiding them when choosing an ultimate standard electrode for molten salt systems. In practice, however, such junctions are often necessary to prevent reaction of the electrode material with ions present in the melt under investigation. This consideration would seem to favor the selection for ultimate standard of an electrode material not readily oxidized by most metal ions, such as chlorine gas. This particular substance has the additional advantage of occurring in the same phase at all temperatures of interest. Although perhaps most suitable as an ultimate standard, the chlorine electrode is not always the most convenient reference electrode for experimental studies. Thus, it is frequently desirable to make use of other reference electrodes, whose potentials can, if so desired, be related to that of chlorine.

The relative experimental merits of various types of reference electrode in current use will be brought out in Section IV. These electrodes involve the use of various techniques to separate the electrode material from ions with which it might react. In concluding this section, the way in which junctions introduced in the isolation of different reference electrodes affect their potentials (measured relative to electrodes on the other sides of such junctions) will be discussed in terms of the theoretical principles that have been elaborated here.

In many studies the specific potential of the reference electrode, including its junction with the melt under investigation, is of no concern, so long as it does not change appreciably during successive measurements. Thus even the relatively extreme junction potentials to be anticipated when a salt bridge of pure NaCl is used to connect an electrode compartment of pure AgCl with a fluoride melt (35) can be tolerated, provided the composition of the latter is not varied too greatly. It was shown in Section II,B,2,a that the magnitudes of the junction potentials at either end of such a bridge depend on the relative mobilities of the ions of like charge as well as on the thermodynamic properties of mixtures of the adjacent melts.

When only dilute solutions of various ions in a common solvent are under study the reference electrode might, for example, be (36)

$$\text{Ag} \mid \text{AgCl (dilute) in NaCl–KCl mixture} \vdots \text{junction} \vdots$$

with the liquid on the other side of the junction consisting principally of the same NaCl–KCl mixture. No silver ion need be present in the latter solution, which may instead contain small concentrations of ions that would have reacted with silver metal had direct contact with the electrode been permitted. The same principle would apply whether the junction here involved liquid–liquid contact of the two electrode solutions or an intermediate bridge. The use of a bridge, however, also prevents mixing of ions that might react with one another. Such a bridge might consist of the "pure" KCl–NaCl solvent, or, in fact, of any molten salt system, or even a glass. The range over which the concentration of Ag^+ or of foreign ions on the other side of the bridge can be varied without the introduction of a significant net junction potential is reduced, however, as the individual potentials at either end of the bridge are made more extreme by the use of materials differing greatly from the solvent.

The final method of isolating the reference electrode, and in principle the best for a number of applications, is to make use of an ion-selective membrane, i.e., a partition which permits the passage of only one ionic species. In practice such membranes are difficult to obtain. The theory can be illustrated by a glass in which only Na^+ has appreciable mobility. It was shown in Section II,B,2,b (p. 555) that the junction potential of such a glass against a melt containing the same ion is equal to (RT/F) ln $[a_{Na^+(glass)}/a_{Na^+(melt)}]$. Now if contact to the other side of the glass is made by a sodium electrode whose potential is $E° + (RT/F)$ ln $a_{Na^+(glass)}$ it follows that the net potential of the electrode system is given by

$$E = E° + (RT/F) \ln a_{Na^+(melt)}$$

Thus an electrode of this type permits a direct measure of the potential of the metal in mixtures of any composition, while preventing electrode material from reacting with the melt. For experimental purposes it may be convenient to amalgamate the sodium with mercury or alloy it with tin. The potential of the idealized electrode would then be

$$E = E° + (RT/F) \ln [a_{Na^+(melt)}/a_{Na(amalgam)}]$$

If any other ion, such as Li^+, carries an appreciable fraction of the current, these simple relations are no longer adequate. In such a case not only the relative mobilities of the two cations but also their activities in both salt and glass become important. Unless a glass is employed that very nearly approximates the idealized membrane, therefore, it would be difficult to estimate the magnitude of the resulting junction potential in an experimental application.

III. Electromotive Force Measurements at High Temperatures

Certain experimental considerations are common to most studies involving the use of reference electrodes in molten salt systems. The present section will attempt to supply some useful background before the discussion of specific reference electrodes in Section IV.

A. MATERIALS

1. Electrolytes

Some of the salts which have been employed as constituents of molten media in electrochemical measurements are listed in Table I. The term "constituent" could refer to any of four categories: (i) a pure salt, used in a formation cell or as a "solvent" for small quantities of other salts; (ii) a component of a solvent system, such as a eutectic mixture of two or three salts; (iii) a component of a solution whose thermodynamic properties are investigated over a broad range of compositions; (iv) a "solute," added only in small quantities as a source of the ions to which a particular electrode is reversible. The references to the literature given in Table I pertain to the first three of these categories. Convenient sources of information relative to (iv) are the references listed for electrodes in Section III,A,3 (pp. 577 and 578). Each of the salts in Table I has thus constituted a significant fraction of an experimentally investigated system.

Although the literature cited in the table is not intended to provide an exhaustive survey, the numbers of references given for different types of salts will give the reader some idea of where greatest interest has been centered. Thus, it is apparent that certain alkali halides have been employed more frequently than any other salts, and that halides generally have been studied more than other types. The selection of a particular salt for use in quantities such that its properties will be manifested to a significant extent in the properties of the system involves a number of factors worthy of brief consideration here.

a. *Temperature Range.* The melting and boiling points listed in Table I are taken from Lange's "Handbook of Chemistry" (*37*), as are the decomposition temperatures indicated by the letter *d*. In spite of the fact that some of these figures have been superseded by more accurate determinations they serve to indicate the approximate liquid ranges of the pure salts. These ranges can usually be greatly extended downward by the use of mixtures, however, due to the mutual depression of freezing point exerted by salts upon one another. A eutectic mixture of LiCl and KCl, for example, melts at 352°C (*38*), more than 250° below the lower melting of the two pure salts. Since none of the more common alkali halides melt in the normal working range of Pyrex glass (see Part 2 of this section), the LiCl–KCl eutectic has been frequently employed as a solvent (*33, 36, 39–43*). Other combinations, such as an equimolar mixture of KCl and NaCl (*44, 45*) and even ternary solutions have been popular, one of the lowest-melting of all molten salt media being the eutectic composed of 30 mole per cent $LiNO_3$, 16 mole per cent $NaNO_3$, and 53 mole per cent KNO_3. This mixture freezes

TABLE I

Molten Salt Electrolytes

Salt	m.p. (°C)	b.p. (°C)	References
		HALIDES	
AgBr	434	d700	(*12, 113, 118–121*)
AgCl	455	1550	(*12, 27, 28, 99, 113, 116, 119, 121*)
AgI	d552	—	(*12, 55, 113, 119*)
AlBr$_3$	97.5	268	(*112, 122–124*)
	5.2 atm	752 mm	
AlCl$_3$	194	182.7	(*47, 77, 90, 124, 125*)
AlF$_3$	1040	—	(*71, 88, 110*)
AlI$_3$	191	382	(*124*)
BaCl$_2$	962	1560	(*108*)
CaBr$_2$	760	810	(*116*)
CaCl$_2$	772	1600	(*28*)
CdCl$_2$	568	960	(*12, 28, 126, 127*)
CdI$_2$	385	713	(*55*)
CuCl	422	1366	(*79, 121*)
KBr	730	1380	(*118, 121, 122*)
KCl	790	1500	(*12, 28, 36, 39, 42–44, 49, 77, 79, 80, 96, 103, 116, 121, 127–133*)
KF	880	1500	(*35, 65, 72*)
KI	723	1330	(*55*)
LiBr	547	1265	(*118, 120*)
LiCl	614	1360	(*27, 28, 36, 39, 42, 49, 79, 80, 129–132*)
LiF	870	1670	(*35, 43, 72, 82*)
MgCl$_2$	712	1412	(*28, 77, 103, 131, 133*)
NaBr	755	1390	(*112, 113, 116, 118, 119, 123, 124, 128*)
NaCl	800	1413	(*28, 44, 77, 90, 96, 103, 116, 119, 124, 125, 127, 128, 130, 131*)
NaF	992	—	(*35, 65, 71, 72, 82, 88, 110*)
NaI	651	1300	(*55, 113, 116, 119, 124*)
PbBr$_2$	373	918	(*12, 89*)
PbCl$_2$	501	954	(*12, 28, 89, 108, 127, 130, 134*)
PbI$_2$	402	954	(*55, 116*)
RbBr$_2$	682	1340	(*118*)
RbCl	715	1390	(*130*)
SnI$_2$	320	720	(*55*)
SrCl$_2$	873	—	(*128*)
TlI	440	824	(*55*)
ZnBr$_2$	394	650	(*135*)
ZnCl$_2$	283	732	(*12, 127, 134*)
ZnI$_2$	446	624	(*55*)

TABLE I (cont'd)

Salt	m.p. (°C)	b.p. (°C)	References
		NITRATES	
$AgNO_3$	209	444d	(2, 97, 98, 136, 137)
KNO_3	333	400d	(46, 80, 81, 93, 104, 137, 138)
$LiNO_3$	261	—	(46, 47, 104, 138)
$NaNO_3$	308	380d	(2, 46, 81, 93, 104, 136–138)
NH_4NO_3	d210	—	(47)
		OTHERS	
$PbSiO_3$	766	—	(56)
Li_2SiO_3	860	—	(82, 139)
K_2SO_4	1076	—	(111, 139)
Na_2SO_4	884	—	(66, 82, 111)
$KHSO_4$	210	d	(80)
$NaOH$	318	1390	(64, 68, 86)
Na_2CO_3	851	d	(66, 118a)
K_2CrO_4	975	—	(66)
$K_2Cr_2O_7$	398	d	(66)

at 120° (46). By resorting to a reciprocal system and employing a weakly ionized aluminum halide, Nachtrieb and Steinberg (47) obtained a solvent mixture freezing at the still lower temperature of 86.2°. Its composition (in mole per cent) is NH_4NO_3, 66.65; $LiNO_3$, 25.76; $AlCl_3$, 7.59. Diluting a pure salt by addition of others does not always lower its freezing point, however, as is evident from the phase diagram of the system $AgNO_3$–$NaNO_3$. The liquidus curve reported by Hissink (48) for this system rises continuously from the melting point of pure $AgNO_3$ to that of $NaNO_3$, showing that the partial molar free energy of $AgNO_3$ is smaller in the liquid mixtures than in solid solutions of the same composition at the same temperature. Although such freezing point elevation can occur whenever isomorphic crystals form a single continuous series of solid solutions, its occurrence in molten salt systems is relatively rare. Melting point maxima at intermediate compositions are quite common, however, as a result of formation of stoichiometric compounds like $KCl \cdot PbCl_2$.

The upper limit of temperature can also be extended, either by increased pressure or by addition of less volatile salts, provided the salt of interest is thermally stable. This limitation is seldom of concern in the more ionic of the halides, but is a major problem in work with molten nitrates, which decompose to give oxygen and nitrites, as well as oxides. Systems requiring higher temperatures have not often been sought intentionally, most of the work referred to here having been carried out below 1000°. This temperature is sufficient to melt all ionic crystals except metallic oxides, whose study is considered to constitute a separate field of endeavor.

b. *Stability in Air*. The possibility of reaction with atmospheric oxygen should not be overlooked, either by substitution of oxide for the anion, or by oxidation of a cation to a higher valence state. A more frequently encountered problem in this category, however, is hydrolysis of the salt by reaction with atmospheric water vapor. The fact that the hydrogen halides are considerably more volatile than H_2O makes the molten halides particularly susceptible to this difficulty, a typical reaction being

$$LiCl + H_2O \rightarrow LiOH + HCl$$

When glass vessels are used, this reaction is followed by attack of the alkaline hydroxide on the container, so that even a slight extent of hydrolysis cannot be tolerated.

c. *Reactivity toward Container*. In addition to the example just cited, the reactivity of fluorides with glass or silica containers is well known. Further discussion of containing materials will be found in Part 2 of this section.

d. *Purity*. Requirements of purity usually depend upon the type of study being undertaken. Thus, as for other electrolytes, scrupulous purification is generally necessary in investigations of electrode kinetics (*49*). By far the most commonly troublesome impurity in molten salt studies is water. A number of the solid halides tend to be hygroscopic, the salts of lithium and zinc being extreme cases, so that as initially obtained they are never water-free. Thus, the hydrolysis problem mentioned above is not avoided by simply controlling the atmosphere above the melt. The water must first be expelled from the salts without driving off hydrogen halide. Elaborate procedures for accomplishing this have been evolved, particularly for melts containing LiCl (*49–51*). Laitinen and co-workers (*51*) have also described a criterion for purity to demonstrate the effectiveness of their method. It involves carrying out repeated polarograms until the absence of the hydrogen-reduction wave testifies to the complete removal of water.

e. *Volatility*. Even though a salt is kept well below its normal boiling point, it may exert a considerably higher vapor pressure than other components of the same melt. If kept in an open vessel, or a closed one continually flushed with gas, the more rapid evaporation of such a salt can result over a period of time in a significant change in the composition of the system. Relative volatilities of various salts are indicated by their boiling points, from which it will be seen that particular care must be taken with aluminum and zinc halides (except for the fluorides).

f. *Stability toward Electrode Materials*. In choosing a solvent for use with a number of different electrode systems, the relatively inert salts will clearly be most desirable. This generally means salts whose ions are not readily reduced by metals or oxidized by the corresponding metal ions, which explains the popularity of alkali halides as molten media. Not only reactivity must be considered, but also the peculiar ability of molten salts to physically dissolve metals, as when sodium dissolves in molten NaCl. The nature and explanation of this phenomenon have not as yet been well characterized, but it seems to be limited to metals whose cations are present in the melt (52).

Some of the considerations pertinent to the choice of electrolyte for any type of electrochemical study in a molten medium have been given above. Other factors, such as ionic character, ability to form complexes, simplicity of theoretical interpretation of results, etc., will in general depend upon the type of study undertaken and the specific purpose of the investigation.

2. Containing Materials

The choice of materials for the construction of cells, electrode housings, partitions, etc., depends upon the temperature range to be employed, the nature of the electrolyte, and the type of study undertaken. Substances capable of withstanding high temperatures without decomposition, structural deformation, or reaction with the melt are generally desirable. Materials meeting these specifications may still be ruled out for certain studies, however, because of difficulty of cell fabrication, inability to sustain a vacuum or controlled atmosphere, high electrical conductivity, or tendency to introduce intolerable impurities. Extensive tabulations of refractories, along with their relevant properties, have been given by Seybolt and Burke (53) and by Livey and Murray (54). (The books referred to are very useful sources of additional information about experimental methods of high temperature research.) In this brief section attention will be confined to containing materials which have actually been used in molten salt electrochemistry.

a. Glass. Because of its great versatility of form and the ease with which a given design can be fabricated, its chemical inertness, structural strength, optical transparency, high electrical resistivity, low vapor pressure, etc., glass has always been the material of choice whenever experimental conditions permit its use. Unfortunately, however, even the heat-resistant borosilicate glasses, such as Pyrex, cannot maintain structural rigidity at temperatures much in excess of 500°C, so that their prolonged use is limited to systems melting below this temperature. For experiments lasting a few hours or less, Pyrex may be used up to 600°, or even higher, provided cells are constructed to withstand some deformation and are considered expendable. Supremax glass has been used at 650°C, while some of the

Russian work conducted at 700° was apparently carried out in glass cells. The softening temperature of glass has probably been decisive in the selection of molten salt systems for study in a number of investigations carried out at lower temperatures, so strong is the inclination of experimenters to use glass cells. The low melting point of the LiCl–KCl eutectic (see Section III,A,1) has certainly been exploited with this feature in mind, as have a number of nitrate-, and silver-containing melts. Indeed, the list of electrochemical studies on molten salts carried out in glass containers is much too long to warrant reproduction here. It includes a major fraction of the references at the end of this chapter.

It has already been mentioned that glass is subject to chemical attack by alkaline oxides and hydroxides, as well as by molten fluorides. Containing materials for these substances will be discussed below. Sodium ions in the surface of glass are replaced by silver or cuprous ions from an adjacent melt, but the extent of contamination from this source is usually negligible. Other sources of difficulty may be introduced by the rapidly increasing electrical conductivity of glass at high temperatures, and by its large coefficient of thermal expansion. The former liability sometimes proves to be an asset, however (see Section IV,B), while the latter can often be circumvented by the use of specially formulated glasses or graded seals.

b. Porcelain. Although less easily fabricated than glass, porcelain or mullite ($3Al_2O_3 \cdot 2SiO_2$), can be used up to 1780°C. Porcelain beakers were used by Elkins and Forbes (*27*) to contain a nitrate melt at 490°, and by Delimarskii and Kolotii (*55*) for molten iodides in the range 500 to 700°. Didtschenko and Rochow (*56*) melted lead silicate at 850 to 900° in porous porcelain cups lined with platinum foil.

Porcelain, like glass, is unsuitable for fluoride melts.

c. Pure Oxides. The most frequently used material in this category is fused quartz, or silica, which melts about 1700°C. Its useful temperature limit is around 1000°, however, due to the devitrification to a structurally unsuitable crystalline form at higher temperatures. When it can be used, it is sometimes preferable to porcelain, due to its greater versatility for fabrication purposes — especially in the commercial form of Vycor or Vitreosil (96% SiO_2). Molten salt studies involving silica containers have been numerous. Examples are the use of a quartz tube by Coriou *et al.* (*35*) to contain molten AgCl over a large temperature range, and the recent series of emf measurements by Flengas and Ingraham (*57–61*) employing silica containers and electrode housings with NaCl–KCl melts at temperatures around 700°.

Alumina (Al_2O_3) and zirconia (ZrO_2) have the much higher useful temperature limits of 1900 and 2400°C, respectively. The latter was used by Malkin and co-workers (*62*) as a container for molten silicates and phosphates at 1550°, while the former has had a number of molten salt applications in cases where alkaline melts would have strongly attacked a siliceous material. Hill *et al.* (*63*) used an alumina crucible for Li_2SO_4–K_2SO_4 eutectic containing small quantities of metallic oxides at 580–708°, while Rose and co-workers (*64*) maintained molten NaOH in an alumina crucible at 730°. Attack on the container was reported in the latter case, however, at temperatures above 630°. A more satisfactory material for such melts is magnesia (MgO), which is still more basic and melts at 2800°C. The fabrication of transparent crucibles from MgO single crystals has been described (*64a*). Alumina has also been used to contain a molten aluminum electrode immersed in a fluoride melt (*65*).

d. Metals. Inert metals have frequently been made to serve the dual purpose of container and electrode. Platinum crucibles have been particularly popular for this purpose, especially due to the resistance of this metal to chemical attack. It was used by Flood and co-workers (*66*) to contain such reactive systems as Na_2CO_3–Na_2SO_4 and K_2CrO_4–$K_2Cr_2O_7$. Grjotheim (*65*) found it a suitable material for containing NaF–KF eutectic at 850°. Another metal often used for highly reactive fluoride melts is nickel (*67*), while crucibles of gold and gold–palladium alloy have been employed with such reactive systems as molten NaOH and carbonates (*68, 68a*).

e. Graphite. With a melting point of about 3500°C graphite is one of the most versatile materials available for high temperature work. It can be machined to produce desired forms (although the procedure is messy and loose bits of graphite in the system will be unavoidable). It is stable at high temperatures in the presence of most substances (but deteriorates in air due to the reaction with oxygen). The electrical conductivity of graphite is high (very much higher than that of molten salts). Thus, while useful for making electrical contact, it must be employed judiciously in measurements of emf. When porous graphite was used to help separate the electrode compartments in concentration cells containing molten chlorides, for example, its ability to transport current between the compartments much more effectively than the melt contained in its pores was apparently responsible for the absence of a measurable "liquid-junction potential" (*69*). A similar difficulty would have been encountered by Piontelli and Montanelli (*70*) had he not prevented short-circuiting of his electrodes through contact with a common graphite container by inserting a corundum (Al_2O_3) insulating sheath. The high conductivity of graphite is frequently taken advantage of, however, as in the work of Cuthbertson and Waddington (*71*) with cryolite–alumina cells. Here the carbon crucible served both as container and electrode. Graphite containers have been used for other fluoride melts at much higher temperatures, a number of examples having been reported by Delimarskii and Grigorenko (*72*).

f. Boron Nitride. Several containing materials for molten fluorides have been mentioned above, most of them electrical conductors. When a stable container of high resistivity was required, Yim and Feinleib (*73*) turned to a newly available material, hot-pressed boron nitride. It was found very satisfactory for work with molten fluorides.

In addition to the extensive surveys of refractory materials mentioned

TABLE II

METAL ELECTRODES

Electrode	m (°C)	b (°C)	References
Ag(I)	961	1950	*(1, 2, 12, 14, 15, 19, 21, 22, 27, 28, 33, 35, 36, 42, 44, 56, 63–66, 83, 84, 93, 96, 98, 99, 101, 102, 110, 111, 118, 119, 136, 137, 139–141, 143, 144)*
Al(III)	660	2057	*(33, 65, 70, 77, 90, 125, 143)*
Au(I)	1063	2600	*(33)*
Bi(III)	271	1450	*(33, 44, 143)*
Cd(II)	321	767	*(12, 28, 33, 58, 126, 127, 143)*
Co(II)	1480	2900	*(33, 44, 65)*
Cr(II)	1615	2200	*(33, 59)*
Cr(III)	1615	2200	*(59, 65)*
Cu(I)	1083	2300	*(33, 42, 44, 59, 65, 125, 143)*
Cu(II)	1083	2300	*(59)*
Fe(II)	1535	3000	*(33, 41, 42, 44, 60, 125)*
Fe(III)	1535	3000	*(65)*
Ga(III)	29.8	1700	*(33)*
Hg(I)	−38.9	357	*(46, 47, 104, 122, 138, 143)*
Hg(II)	−38.9	357	*(33)*
In(III)	155	1450	*(33)*
Li(I)	186	1336	*(33)*
Mg(II)	651	1110	*(33, 77, 131)*
Mn(II)	1260	1900	*(33, 60, 65, 125)*
Mo(III)	2620	3700	*(42)*
Na(I)	97.5	880	*(112–116, 119, 123, 124, 143, 145)*
Ni(II)	1452	2900	*(33, 44, 57, 65)*
Pb(II)	327.5	1620	*(12, 14, 15, 19, 28, 33, 44, 57, 64, 107, 108, 126, 127, 130, 134, 142, 143, 146)*
Pd(II)	1550	2200	*(33)*
Pt(II)	1755	4300	*(33, 85, 104, 147)*
Sb(III)	631	1380	*(33)*
Sn(II)	232	2260	*(33, 60, 143)*
Sn(IV)	232	2260	*(64)*
Tl(I)	303	1650	*(33, 59)*
V(II)	1710	3000	*(41)*
Zn(II)	419	907	*(12, 33, 42, 44, 57, 103, 125–127, 143)*

at the beginning of this discussion, the reader is referred to the excellent monograph *High Temperature Technology*, edited by Campbell (*74*), for a review of some of the newer materials, especially those suitable at temperatures around 2000°C and even very much higher.

3. Electrodes

The metals which have been reported reversible to their ions when used as electrodes in molten salt media are listed in Table II. Since many have been used both above and below their melting points, no distinction has been made as to liquid or solid state. None of the references pertains to gaseous metal electrodes, however, as none seem to have been reported. *Nonmetallic* gases reversible to their ions, on the other hand, have frequently been employed, a list being given in Table III. The latter table

TABLE III

GASEOUS AND REDOX ELECTRODES

Electrode	References
GAS	
Br$_2$, C	(*12, 41, 89, 118, 120*)
Cl$_2$, C	(*15, 21, 22, 28, 33, 41, 44, 101–103, 107–109, 127, 130, 134, 146, 148*)
I$_2$, C(m. 114°C, b. 185°C)	(*12, 41*)
O$_2$, Pt and others*	(*56, 63, 64* (Ag), 66, 83, 110* (C), 111* (Au), 139–141*)
CO$_2$ + O$_2$, Pt	(*66, 118a*)
REDOX	
Cr^{2+}, Cr^{3+}, Pt	(*33, 59*)
Cu^{1+}, Cu^{2+}, Pt	(*33, 59*)
Fe^{2+}, Fe^{3+}, Pt	(*33, 41, 42, 44, 60, 125*)
V^{2+}, V^{3+}, C	(*41*)

includes a list of "redox electrodes" in which the electrode reaction involves only constituents of the melt. An additional conducting material must always be used in such electrode systems, as well as with gaseous electrodes. This material not only makes electrical contact from the potentiometer to the reaction site, but also may act as a catalyst for the electron transfer. The conducting materials used in the literature cited are included in Table III, from which it will be noted that platinum and graphite are most commonly employed.

The length of the list of reversible electrode materials in Tables II and III is due partially to the fact that a great many different "solvent" systems are represented here, each salt or mixture constituting a distinct medium. It was pointed out earlier, however, that an electrode reversible to a given ion in one salt system is likely to be reversible to the same ion in most others, provided they do not contain ions with which it might react. This is borne out for many of the electrodes listed by the number of different electrolyte systems in the references cited. It is apparent that other factors favor the reversibility of electrodes in molten salts.

One of these undoubtedly arises from the higher temperatures of the measurements. For an electrode to be reversible it must be possible to pass current easily in either direction. The more slowly the forward and reverse electrochemical processes occur, the more nearly the electrode approximates the "ideal polarized electrode" which acts as a capacitor in adopting any potential applied to it (75). Thus the reversibility of an electrode depends upon the velocities of the oxidation and reduction reactions taking place even when no net current is being passed, i.e., the magnitude of the exchange current (see Chapter 1). Now the rates of all reactions are accelerated by increasing temperature, thus favoring reversibility in the molten salt. This fact has been strikingly demonstrated in recent measurements of exchange currents in molten LiCl–KCl mixtures at 450°C by Roe and Laitinen (76). These workers found values for molar exchange currents ranging from 8 amp cm^{-2} for Bi (liq)/Bi^{3+} to 210 amp cm^{-2} for Cd/Cd^{2+}.

The results just cited make it clear why significant overvoltages have not been observed in polarization studies at electrodes in molten salts (77). As long as the current densities employed in such studies are small compared with the exchange currents, the equilibrium between oxidized and reduced forms at the electrode is negligibly perturbed by the slight excess of current in one direction. Large exchange currents also account for the equality of decomposition potentials with reversible emf's in a large number of cases, and explain why "activation polarization," a major obstacle in the operation of successful fuel cells at ambient temperatures has not been a problem in those employing molten salt electrolytes.

Reversibility of electrodes in molten salts is not guaranteed by the rapidity of the redox reactions. It is also necessary that the cathodic and anodic currents be due entirely to the forward and reverse directions of a single electrochemical reaction. If some other reaction, such as oxygen reduction, occurs at the same electrode at a rate competitive with or greater than that of the process of interest, the electrode, although its potential may be under control, must be irreversible. It adopts the "mixed potential" at which total cathodic current (due to all processes) is equal to total anodic current (78). Such behavior is almost certain to be the rule when, for example, a platinum wire is immersed in a salt system with no effort to control the concentrations of the species determining its potential.

The high velocities of all reactions lead to the rapid establishment of a steady state, but one which involves the continual forward progress of some [irreversible] reaction at the electrode surface. An example in which the reactions are more clearly defined is the reported displacement of potassium metal from a KCl melt by silver electrodes (21). Mixed potentials may also arise from the presence of impurities at the electrode. An example is the difficulty caused by failure to remove HCl in the attempt to prepare a reversible chlorine (graphite) electrode (79).

For studies in electrode kinetics and other uses in which the thermodynamic significance of the total cell emf is irrelevant, stability and convenience are more important factors in the choice of a reference electrode than reversibility. Platinum wires of the type referred to above have frequently been employed (39), as well as platinum "needles" (80), disks (81), and even the platinum crucible (82) containing the melt. For the indicator electrodes in such studies not only platinum (83, 84), but also tungsten (84, 85), nickel, (86) and graphite (87, 88) have been employed as electrode materials.

B. APPARATUS

1. Measuring Equipment

No special measuring equipment is needed for emf determinations at high temperatures, since this part of the apparatus is always located outside the region of high temperature. Electrical contact with the cell must, of course, be established by wires passing through the thermal gradient. The problem of electrode contacts will be discussed in Section III,B,3.

The accuracy of emf measurements in molten salts frequently does not warrant the use of a high-precision potentiometer. Although a few workers have reported difficulty in reproducing potentials to the nearest 50 mv (32, 68, 86), figures are most commonly given to the nearest millivolt. Random fluctuations probably associated with temperature variation usually make greater accuracy than this difficult to attain. A precision of 0.2 mv was obtained by Salstrom and Hildebrand (89), however, while the present author felt confidence in reporting to the nearest 0.01 mv the emf values of concentration cells with transference (2). The fact that small potentials were being measured and that identical electrodes were employed in a cell with good temperature uniformity undoubtedly contributed to the precision of the latter measurements. In general, one may conclude that an ordinary potentiometer is more than adequate for molten salt emf measurements. For careful work it is sometimes useful to insert a resistor of 100 to 1000 ohms in series with the galvanometer. This compensates the very low resistance of the electrolyte, thus keeping the "measuring current" too small to introduce significant polarization effects.

For studies in electrode kinetics most of the measuring techniques developed for aqueous solutions have been carried over into molten salt work (49, 70). Polarography employing conventional instruments has been studied extensively (46), an important use for voltammetric curves being the criteria for melt purity described by Laitinen (51) and others (49).

2. Temperature Control

The method of maintaining and controlling temperature depends on the range which is of experimental interest. A bromobenzene vapor thermostat was employed by Verdieck and Yntema (90) to maintain mixtures of $AlCl_3$ with alkali chlorides at 156°. For studies at higher temperatures, however, conventional thermostats are of academic interest only. An electric furnace is the universal choice, although two principal types should be distinguished. A resistance furnace is usually employed in molten salt work, the upper limit of its operating range depending on the materials used as heating elements more than on the refractory "core." Induction heating is more common in metallurgical studies, but was used by Senderoff and Brenner (91) for molten salt studies around 900°C.

Automatic control is generally employed to maintain the temperature constant. A variety of arrangements have been described (56, 91–94). These consist of a temperature-sensing element connected into an electronic circuit which controls the supply of heating current to the furnace. Placing the sensing element near the regulated heat supply is important. It may be located at the windings of the furnace where the temperature is considerably different from that in the cavity. Good control can nevertheless be achieved with this arrangement by regulating total input power, provided significant changes in room temperature do not occur. Short-term stability is frequently more important than preventing slow temperature drifts during emf measurements. Instead of regulating the entire power supply it is frequently convenient to control only a small auxiliary heater. This may take the form of an additional winding on the furnace, or, like conventional knife heaters, may be inserted directly into a heat-exchange medium surrounding the cell. In the present author's laboratory, such heaters have even been immersed in the electrolyte itself, when employing large, well-stirred, volumes.

A large number of instruments for automatic temperature control are commercially available, many of them either designed for or readily adaptable to the types of work under consideration here. An alternative not without merits even in these days of automation is the use of manual temperature control. In very precise work an experienced human being making use of a reliable temperature indicator can anticipate small temperature changes and regulate power input accordingly with better judgment than most mechanical feed-back arrangements. Whatever type of control is used, stability is greatly assisted by the use of a constant-voltage power supply and by conducting experiments away from drafts in a thermostatted room.

The importance of maintaining temperature *uniformity* cannot be over-stated. Any control arrangement regulates only the immediate environment of the sensing element(s). Considering that the temperature drops hundreds of degrees in the few inches that separate the inside of the furnace from the outside, it is apparent that very large thermal gradients may exist within the furnace unless proper provisions are made for uniformity. Too often this factor seems to have been overlooked, and it appears likely to account for the poor reproducibility reported by a number of workers. Increasing the number of turns in the furnace windings near the ends helps to compensate for the greater heat leak there. For really effective control, however, a reservoir of high heat capacity and good thermal conductivity should be present to smooth out local temperature variations. A metal block completely enclosing the cell has been used for this purpose, although a well-stirred bath of liquid is likely to be more practical. Molten salts themselves make the best liquids for this purpose, provided corrosion of the heating elements or contamination of the cell contents is not caused by their vapors. Indeed, if a sufficient quantity of the electrolyte under study is employed, it may serve as its own "bath." Then it is only necessary to ensure that adequate stirring is provided. Some workers have been content with the agitation produced by gas bubbles, and have introduced inert gases like nitrogen or argon, or electrode gases like chlorine from a tube under the surface of the melt. This may be satisfactory provided care is taken that the incoming gas is preheated to the desired temperature. A motor-driven agitator is more effective, however, and does not have the disadvantage of greatly increasing the rate of evaporation of the melt. This consideration is especially important when it is desired that the composition of a melt containing salts of different volatilities remain constant.

A detailed discussion of experimental methods of attaining high temperatures and controlling them has been given by Motzfeldt (*94*).

3. Cell Design

The wide range of systems of electrochemical interest makes it impossible to formulate a general set of directions for cell design. A variety of shapes and sizes have been used successfully, so that to some extent the choice represents the personal taste of the investigator. Certain problems common to most emf work affect the design of the cell, however, and some experimental solutions to these problems will be discussed in this section.

a. Isolation of Electrode Solutions. Since it is usually desirable to control the composition of solution around each electrode separately (and frequently necessary due to possible reactions between them), a number of techniques have been devised for isolating portions of the melt. "Isolation" cannot be complete, of course, since electrical contact must be maintained. The goal is thus the formation of liquid–solid and liquid–liquid junctions at which mixing of adjacent solutions is negligibly slow.

It was pointed out in Section II,B,2 that the "junction potential" across an interface between two melts of known composition has a simple quasi-thermodynamic interpretation, and that its magnitude can be estimated from a knowledge of the transport properties of the system. A liquid–solid junction involves more complex considerations, but its potential can be opposed by one of equal magnitude and opposite sign, if a liquid of nearly identical composition adjoins the opposite side of the solid. A solid partition clearly affords more effective isolation.

Thin partitions of solid glass have been used by a number of workers to isolate electrode compartments. At molten-salt temperatures glass is a considerably better conductor than at room temperature, so that the amplification of the measuring current required with glass electrodes at room temperature is no longer necessary. Reference has already been made to the early experiments with glass partitions done by Tamman (14) and by Grube and Rau (15). More recently Bockris and co-workers (36) have developed an "all-glass" reference electrode employing the same "solvent" melt both inside and outside the thin glass partition. Further discussion of this electrode is given in Section IV.

Direct contact of the adjacent solutions within a small capillary tube gives a clearly defined liquid–liquid junction. It is difficult to prevent fairly rapid mixing with an ordinary glass capillary, however, without making it so small as to be almost nonconducting. Openings of appreciable size were used, nevertheless, to connect the electrode compartments in the cell of Verdieck and Yntema (90). These workers had an ingenious method of preventing the chlorine dissolved in one solution from reacting with the aluminum electrode in the other. The compartment containing the aluminum electrode was a vertical glass tube drawn out to a capillary at the bottom. Granules of aluminum metal dropped in at the top settled into the constricted part of this tube where they could react with any incoming chlorine and prevent it from reaching the metal electrode suspended above.

A *porous* material is the equivalent of a bundle of very fine capillaries and can prevent mixing while providing good electrical contact. A variety of materials in a wide range of porosities is available. If the pores are too fine, the thermodynamic and transport properties of the solutions inside may be altered by the large surface-to-volume ratio, so that the interpretation of the liquid-junction potential becomes more complex. Such would undoubtedly be the case for porous glass of the typedescribed by Carson and co-workers (95). It contains pores only slightly larger than molecular dimensions. More difficult to evaluate *a priori* is the use of an asbestos fiber sealed through glass. It apparently soaks up enough salt to make good electrical contact and has been used by a number of workers (58, 90, 93). The relatively large pores of a fritted glass disk introduce no surface problems (2). Other porous materials that have been used include asbestos plugs or diaphragms (35, 42, 84), porous porcelain cups (56), and bridges of porous magnesia or alumina (66). A rod of alumina wet with "solvent" on the outside was employed by Grjotheim (65). Finally, the arrangement involving an asbestos cord soaked in KCl and suspended between compartments has already been described in Section II,B,2,b, and illustrated in Fig. 1 (p. 558).

b. *Electrode Contacts.* When two wires of different composition make electrical contact at two points not at the same temperature, an electrical potential is produced. This is the well-known thermocouple effect which forms the basis for the most common method of temperature measurement in molten salt work. *Electrodes* made of different materials immersed in a cell at high temperature and in contact with a potentiometer outside the furnace can produce the same effect, thus superimposing an unwanted potential on the emf of the cell. Many workers have realized this, and have made separate measurements of the "thermocouple correction" to be applied to their emf readings. Unless the source of the thermocouple effect is fully realized, however, the arrangement of electrodes and contacts in the experiments designed to measure it may not adequately reproduce the situation that will obtain in the electrochemical cell. It would seem wiser to eliminate the effect completely, as can easily be done by appropriate location of the electrode contacts. The important guiding principle in planning a suitable design is that a thermal emf can only be generated when the materials within the thermal *gradient* are of different composition, the magnitude of the effect depending solely on the composition of these materials and the size of temperature drop. Thus, any pair of electrode materials can be used without the necessity of applying corrections, provided the two wires coming from the potentiometer are of the same composition and make contact to the electrodes within the isothermal region of the cell.

Even if identical electrodes and contact leads are used a thermal emf can arise in a cell not adequately maintained at uniform temperature. The magnitude of this effect for silver electrodes in a silver nitrate melt is 0.3 mv per degree difference in temperature of the electrodes (97, 98). Potentials of several tenths of a millivolt were observed by the present author (2) in this system when the bath containing the cell was not stirred. Effective agitation of the bath reduced this to less than a microvolt.

When an electrode is a metal which is solid at the temperatures of interest, it usually takes the form of a thin strip or a coiled wire. Micro-electrodes are used in kinetic studies, but for measuring reversible potentials it is desirable to have a large area in contact with electrolyte. Contact from a wire to a solid electrode of either form can be made by spot welding. The electrode can then be suspended from the top of the cell so that it is the only metal making contact with the electrolyte. If the electrode material is molten, however, it is usually more dense than the electrolyte, and hence takes the form of a submerged pool at the bottom of its compartment. Contact from above then requires that the wire be insulated from the melt. This is frequently accomplished with a sheath of glass or alundum surrounding the wire. In Fig. 1 (p.558) both wires have been protected in this manner. Another method of contact is to seal the wire through the wall of the cell at a point below the level of the electrode pool. For glass cells, tungsten or platinum wires are used, although platinum is more likely to be soluble in the electrode metal. It dissolves readily in molten lead or aluminum even at temperatures below 700°C. Therefore tungsten, which also has nearly the same expansion coefficient as Pyrex glass, is usually the metal of choice. Wires of other metals may in turn be joined to the tungsten outside the compartment, since the stiffness and brittleness of tungsten make it difficult to manipulate.

   c. *Other Considerations.* Accessibility of the cell contents is frequently an important consideration in cell design. When good temperature uniformity is important and access to the cell unnecessary, it is probably best to have the cell completely inside the furnace with insulating material such as firebrick and Transite above it. Openings to the inside need only be large enough to admit wires and such auxiliary equipment as is necessary (gas inlet and outlet tubes, stirring propeller, auxiliary heater, etc.). If access to the cell is important, on the other hand, a design which has been used by a number of workers employs a long vertical tube projecting from the top of the furnace. It is capped with a silicone rubber stopper (which withstands 150°C without decomposition) containing holes through which the smaller tubes which act as electrode compartment housings are inserted. The most complete description has been given by Laitinen and co-workers (*51*) who used a tube 30 cm in height to contain a melt at 450°C. The temperature at the stopper was about 150°, so that the temperature gradient above the melt must have been greater than 10° per cm. A 46 cm tube was used in the cell of Senderoff and Brenner (*91*), the temperature at the bottom being as high as 900°C. An arrangement of this type is very convenient, pro vided the temperature gradient does not interfere with the accuracy of the measurements.

   It is often necessary to control the atmosphere over the cell, or to provide inlets and outlets for electrode gases. In such cases at least a part of the cell must be gas-tight. Again a silicone rubber stopper like that referred to above may be adequate. Wires can be sealed through the glass and agitation of electrolyte effected by gas bubbles (Section III, B, 2). Stopcocks are difficult to operate at high temperatures, but Salstrom and Hildebrand (89) successfully used H_2SO_4 as a lubricant at 450°. A discussion of techniques of manipulating materials inside a gas-tight cell in a furnace at high temperature has been given by Hills, Inman, and Young (49). A considerable amount of other information useful in electrochemical studies in molten salts is presented in the same article.

IV. Survey of Reference Electrodes

During the long history of electromotive force measurements in molten salts a great many different electrodes have been designated "reference electrodes" in specific cells. It is only in recent years, however, that workers in the field have concentrated on the problem of developing reference electrodes of more general applicability. Considering the variety of systems and temperatures of interest, it is easy to see why no single all-purpose reference electrode for molten salt studies has been universally employed. Some of those that have been developed nevertheless have features that are of very general utility. These will be reviewed in the present section.

Specific reference electrodes that have been described in the literature are listed in Table IV. It will be noted that there are two different characteristics according to which the entries could be classified: electrode material, and nature of junction employed. There are variations of electrolyte and temperature, too, but these are normally determined by the solvent in which the electrode is to be used and/or the electrode material. Accordingly, the present discussion will be divided into two parts, the first dealing with the electrodes themselves, the second with their isolation.

A. ELECTRODE MATERIALS

1. Metals

a. Silver. Of the reversible metal electrodes, silver has been the material most frequently employed. Some of its advantages were pointed out by Senderoff and Brenner (42), who noted that above 300°C there is no danger of oxide formation, since Ag_2O is unstable, and that there is only one stable valence state of silver ion. The metal has no observable tendency to dissolve in molten silver salts and has generally been found highly reversible to its ions. Aten and co-workers (99) found, for example, that in pure AgCl overpotentials for either cathodic deposition or anodic dissolution of silver at 475°C were less than 0.5 mv at current densities of 1 amp dm^{-2}. An

TABLE IV

Reference Electrodes

	Electrode	Junction	Solvent (comp. in mole per cent)	Temp °C	Reference
(a)	Ag (wire) (1 mm) | AgNO$_3$ (0.1 m), solvent	asbestos fiber sealed through glass	KNO$_3$–NaNO$_3$ (50–50)	350	(93)
(b)	Ag (foil) | AgCl (1 m), solvent	asbestos fiber sealed through silica	KCl–NaCl	650–950	(96) (58)
(c)	Ag (wire) | AgCl (0.13 m), solvent	glass	LiCl–KCl (eutectic)	350–550	(36)
(d)	Ag (wire) | AgCl (40 mole %) NaCl (60 mole %)	porcelain conductive to Na$^+$	AgCl–NaCl–KCl (4.76–47.6–47.6)	650–900	(149)
(e)	Ag (wire) (1 mm) | AgCl (pure)	asbestos plug in silica tube sealed with ZrO$_2$	NaCl (pure) in graphite sheath	850	(35)
(f)	Ag (rod) (⅛ inch) | AgCl (pure)	asbestos plug in 1.5 mm silica capillary	LiCl–KCl (eutectic)	600–900	(42)
(g)	Ag (coated on Pt loop) | AgCl (.952 mole %) NaCl (.048 mole %)	glass | KNO$_3$ + NaNO$_3$ | glass	AgCl + Alk. Cl	500	(27)
(h)	Al (rod) (1.5 mm) | AlCl$_3$ (66 mole %) NaCl (20 mole %) KCl (14 mole %)	constricted tube containing Al granules	same as electrode solution	156	(90)
(i)	Al (liq) | AlF$_3$ (dil.), solvent	alumina rod wet with solvent	NaF–KF (40–60)	850	(65)

(j)	Zn (liq)	$ZnCl_2$ (0.2 to 6 mole %), solvent	Pyrex glass	$MgCl_2$–NaCl–KCl (58–24–18) (wt %)	420–500	(103)
(k)	Hg (liq)	Hg_2Cl_2 (solid)	(direct contact with solvent)	NH_4NO_3–$LiNO_3$–$AlCl_3$ (66.7–25.8–7.6)	125	(47)
(l)	Hg (liq)	Hg_2SO_4 + K_2SO_4 (solid)	(direct contact with solvent)	several, including mixtures of alkali bisulfates, nitrates, and perchlorates	140	(104)
(m)	Pt (foil)	$PtCl_2$ (dil), solvent	fritted-glass disk	LiCl–KCl (eutectic)	450	(105)
(n)	C, Cl_2 (1 atm)	LiCl + KCl (eutectic)	fritted glass disk	same as electrode solution	450	(41) (79)
(o)	C, Cl_2	AgCl	porous quartz disk	same as electrode solution	530–920	(22)
(p)	C, Br_2	KBr (0.7 M), solvent	porous glass disk	LiCl–KCl (eutectic)	450	(41) (79)
(q)	C, I_2	KI (0.07–0.7 M), solvent	porous glass disk	LiCl–KCl (eutectic)	450	(41) (79)
(r)	Pt, O_2	$PbO \cdot SiO_2$	porous porcelain	same as electrode solution	800–900	(56)
(s)	Pt, O_2	CaO (0.1 to 1%), solvent	(direct contact of soln. with solid metal oxide coating on other electrode)	Li_2SO_4–K_2SO_4 (71.6–28.4) (eutectic)	580–720	(63)

(Continued)

TABLE IV (*cont.*)

REFERENCE ELECTRODES

	Electrode	Junction	Solvent (comp. in mole per cent)	Temp	Reference
(t)	C, O₂ — Al₂O₃ in solvent	perforated corundum crucibles	3NaF·AlF₃ (cryolite)	1000	(110)
(u)	Pt, O₂ (5.98%) + CO₂ (36–95%) + N₂ (0.5–2%); Na₂CO₃ (0.5 to 10%) + Na₂SO₄ or K₂Cr₂O₇ (4–46%) + K₂CrO₄ (54–96%)	porous MgO / porous alumina	same as electrode solution	850–1050	(66)
(v)	Na in Hg	glass containing Na⁺	NaBr–AlBr₃	300–375	(112)
(w)	Na in Sn (31%) (69%)	glass containing Na⁺	NaX–MX$_m$ X = halide M = Ag, Pb	410–700	(113) (115) (116)

irreversible reaction was found by Stern (*21*), however, when he immersed silver electrodes into KCl melts containing mole fractions of AgCl less than 0.08. Stern attempted to explain his result by postulating that silver displaces potassium until an equilibrium concentration of Ag^+ is attained. This does not seem likely to be the source of difficulty, however, in view of the free energies of the two halides relative to their elements. Using Brewer's data (*100*) at 1500°K, for example, the equilibrium mole fraction of AgCl in KCl (assuming ideal solutions and potassium present as pure liquid) is 1.2×10^{-8}. Combined with the fact that other workers apparently have not encountered irreversibility with silver–silver chloride electrodes at the same dilutions of Ag^+ in LiCl (*101*), NaCl (*102*), or mixed-chloride solvents (*33, 43, 96*), this suggests that the reaction in Stern's cell may have involved interaction of silver with an impurity, such as H_2O, rather than displacement of the alkali metal.

Silver metal was employed in reference electrodes (a)–(g) of Table IV. The metal is usually in the form of wires, although the foil used by Flengas and Ingraham (*96*) in cell (b) is probably less likely to break off in prolonged use. In contact with a melt containing Ag^+, silver continuously recrystallizes, so that a wire of small diameter is eventually converted to a fragile string of loosely joined crystals. The rate of the process depends on temperature, of course, and may not be due solely to the high exchange current. Not only does the metal tend to dissolve at the hotter end of the wire, most of the new crystals forming at the colder end, but also a thin layer of silver is usually found on the walls of the containing vessel. This suggests transport from the electrode of some physically dissolved silver not otherwise detected in the melt, but perhaps could be due to reduction of the ion by adsorbed water, or even to photochemical reduction. The dissolution of silver also proceeds more rapidly at a kinked or otherwise strained point in the wire, increasing the likelihood of its breaking at that point. Wires that are too heavy, on the other hand, usually give rise to greater difficulty in obtaining stable emf readings. This may be due to more permanent strains in the metal, not annealed on standing in the melt. The fact that all the silver reference electrodes in Table IV employ either foil or wire of fairly small diameter supports the conclusion that heavier pieces of the metal are to be avoided. Silver is available in very pure form and no additional treatment is needed prior to its use as electrode material. It is important, of course, that the surface be clean. Flengas and Ingraham cleaned their silver foil with acetone. The experimental arrangements of some of the silver electrodes in Table IV will be illustrated in Section IV,B.

With the exception of electrode (d), the reference electrodes can be divided into those employing dilute solutions of silver ion in solvent melts, and those in which a pure silver salt was used. The former has generally been found more satisfactory. The junction potential of the pure salt against other melts is usually unknown, besides being less reproducible and subject to greater random fluctuations with time. When contained in glass, melts tend to exchange silver ion for sodium ions in the silicate network of the glass, thus changing the Ag^+ concentration and introducing an unwanted impurity. The rate of this process, like that of metal recrystallization, depends upon Ag^+ concentration, being greatest in pure silver salts. The former problem could nevertheless be more serious in dilute solutions, due to the logarithmic dependence of electrode potential on Ag^+ concentration. The obvious way to avoid this is to use silica containers, as was done in half-cell (b) by Flengas and Ingraham, and in half-cell (f) by Senderoff and Brenner (42). The latter workers were particularly partial to the use of pure AgCl, due to the long temperature range from its melting point at 455°C to its boiling point at 1550°C. Solvents composed of alkali halide eutectics usually share the advantage of a long liquid range, however. In general it would seem desirable to make the electrolyte in the reference electrode as nearly as possible like that in the system under study. This not only minimizes the junction potential, but reduces in systems with liquid–liquid junctions the problem of flow between compartments due to a hydrostatic head. To prevent flow out of the reference electrode, for example, some workers (35, 42) took care to keep the level of pure AgCl just below that of alkali halide in the adjacent compartment, apparently forgetting that the greater density of AgCl might still give rise to flow in the wrong direction if the level difference were not made sufficiently great. Any finite difference of levels would, of course, be adequate with solutions of nearly the same composition on both sides of the junction.

Although it is possible to seal silver through glass, it is usually easier to use platinum for this purpose. Platinum can be spot-welded to silver metal inside the electrode envelope. This presumes, of course, that the silver is being used below its melting point of 950°C. To this author's knowledge the use of liquid silver electrodes has not been reported in the literature. There is no reason to suppose that such electrodes would not be feasible, although the well-known dissolution of oxygen in molten silver might cause trouble if air were not excluded. Some liquid metals that have been employed in reference electrodes are considered in the discussion immediately following.

b. *Other Metals:*

Aluminum melts at 660°C. The solid metal was used at 156°C in reference electrode (h) by Verdieck and Yntema (90), while Grjotheim (65) used molten aluminum at 850°C in electrode (i). These extremes of temperature point up an interesting feature of the aluminum halides. The chloride, bromide, and iodide are volatile, nonionic substances, normally studied as fused salts only in low-melting mixtures with alkali halides or other ionic salts. The fluoride, on the other hand, melts at 1040°C and is of most interest in the mineral cryolite, $AlF_3 \cdot 3NaF$, which melts at 1000°C and is the solvent for Al_2O_3 in the electrolytic production of aluminum. Because of this, electrodes have been used at both ends of the temperature scale. As reference electrodes they appear to offer no particular advantage over silver, except that they can be used in melts containing aluminum ions without the necessity of introducing junctions between systems of different composition.

Zinc has the even lower melting point of 419°C. This enabled Marsland (*103*) in developing reference electrode (j) to use the liquid metal in a glass envelope, contact to the zinc pool being established with a tungsten wire sealed through the glass. It is important to keep zinc inside such an envelope, since it is volatile (boiling point 907°C) and capable of forming a stable oxide in air. Zinc salts, like those of lithium, tend to be deliquescent, which increases the difficulty in preventing hydrolysis. The halides are less ionized than most molten salts (*7*), the chloride being especially viscous and a poorer conductor by about two orders of magnitude than a typically ionic salt. Thus, the advantages of having a liquid electrode (cleaner, more reproducible interface with electrolyte, and absence of the recrystallization problem) may in the case of zinc be outweighed by other limitations. Marsland's electrode was successful, but its operation was confined to a temperature range of less than one hundred degrees — from the melting point of zinc to the softening temperature of Pyrex glass.

Mercury is a liquid metal whose use in the familiar calomel and related reference electrodes has already been described in Chapter 3. Nachtrieb and Steinberg (*47*) employed the "calomel" electrode (k) at 125°C in the low-melting solvent indicated in Table IV. Mercurous chloride, which melts at 302°C, apparently saturates the melt easily, so that excess solid lies atop the mercury pool just as in the conventional electrode. An electrode of this type operating reversibly has its potential controlled by chloride content of the melt. Sulfate played the same role in mercury reference electrode (l), which was employed by Randles and White (*104*). Again the temperatures were unusually low (140°) for molten salt systems. The boiling point of mercury is only 360°C, so that such electrodes are of very restricted utility. Another use of mercury, as well as other liquid metals, will be indicated in the discussion of "glass" electrodes, below.

Platinum has been used in both reversible and irreversible reference electrodes. It was pointed out on p. 579 that the irreversible electrode created by simply dipping a platinum wire into a melt of any composition is often the most convenient reference electrode available. It has frequently been used as such, in cases where the magnitude of the reference potential was irrelevant so long as it remained stable. The latter condition obtains when the reaction establishing the "mixed" potential of the electrode is slow enough that significant changes do not occur in the concentrations of the reacting species, and when other processes taking place in the cell do not interfere with the former reaction. A *reversible* platinum reference electrode requires more care in its construction. Electrode (m) is one of this type which has been used extensively by Laitinen and co-workers (*33, 105*). The platinum (II) chloride is generated coulometrically, its formation being the only anodic reaction occurring in the LiCl–KCl eutectic at low current densities. Thus, the concentration of the potential-determining ion can be carefully controlled and accurately known. At 450°C the operation of this electrode was very successful, but investigators have subsequently encountered difficulty above 500°C which may possibly be due to volatilization of the $PtCl_2$ (*106*). The usable range of this electrode would seem to be greatly restricted. Thus, it appears to offer no particular advantage over analogous electrodes employing silver metal, which remains the most practical material for general use.

2. Gases

Gaseous electrodes are generally more difficult than those employing metals to construct and operate satisfactorily. Thus they do not make convenient reference electrodes for general use. Like the hydrogen electrode in protonic solvents, however, gaseous electrodes reversible to ions of a solvent melt are frequently of interest, and provide a good basis for establishing an ultimate reference potential for a given system. They have been the subject of considerable research, which has resulted in an understanding of some important factors involved in successful use.

Some preliminary comments made in Section III apply to gaseous electrodes generally. It is worth reminding the reader, for example, that the necessity of maintaining a continual flow of gas through the system requires an arrangement that assures the incoming gas sufficient opportunity to reach the temperature of the melt before it becomes involved in the potential-determining redox reaction. The possibility of a volatile component of the melt being carried off with the exit gas was also considered in the earlier section, along with the general problem of controlling and maintaining atmospheres of specified composition. In mentioning the necessity of an inert conductor to establish electrical contact, reference was made to its role as catalyst for the electrode reaction. The catalytic effectiveness of the inert material is particularly important, even in molten salts, for it is with gaseous electrodes that irreversibility is most likely to be encountered.

a. Halogens. In Table IV electrodes (n)–(q) are representative of the many halogen–halide electrodes described in the literature. The examples cited are from relatively recent reports in which some of the problems encountered in past work were successfully overcome. A common feature of all halogen electrodes that have been studied in molten salts is the employment of graphite as the inert conductor. Since in every case the halogen gas must be flowed over the surface of the graphite in contact with the melt, the principal differences among the various models reported have been in the manner of effecting this three-phase contact.

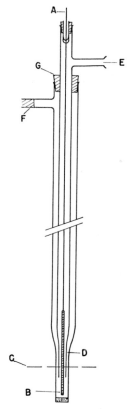

FIG. 2. Halogen reference electrode (79).

The design employed by Laitinen and Pankey (41) in cells (n), (p), and (q) is illustrated in Fig. 2. A platinum wire (A) sealed through Pyrex glass at the top provides contact from outside to the graphite electrode (B). The latter is a solid (but porous) rod of pure graphite, ⅛ inch in diameter and 6 inches long. Only this rod makes contact with the melt, the level of which is indicated by the dotted line (C). Halogen is admitted to the glass sheath (D) at delivery tube (E), flows over the graphite, and bubbles up through the melt at the bottom of the sheath, eventually passing out of the cell through exit tube (F). In this arrangement a one-holed silicone rubber stopper (G) holds the inner sheath in place concentric with the outer jacket, which is a 16 mm Pyrex tube. The diagonal cut through these tubes in the figure is to indicate that the over-all height (24 inches) is much greater relative to the diameter than in the segments shown. In some respects the setup illustrated here resembles that commonly used for a standard hydrogen gas electrode at ordinary temperatures.

Another method of delivering the halogen is to pass it down through the center of a hollow graphite tube immersed in the melt, allowing the gas to bubble out at the bottom. This technique has been used for chlorine electrodes by Stern (21), Smirnov et al. (107), Lantratov and Alabyshev (108), and others. Senderoff and Mellors (22) experienced difficulty in attaining stability and reproducibility, however, in any arrangement involving formation of fairly large chlorine bubbles in the region of three-phase contact. They therefore devised a chlorine electrode [reference electrode (o)] employing a very porous graphite cylinder, 15 mm in diameter, 4 inches high, and hollow inside, but open only at the top. Into the opening was fitted the gas delivery tube, a 2-ft length of high density graphite-base tubing of 10.5 mm od. This was cemented in place at the shoulder, so that gas could only escape by passing through the pores of the lower section. The arrangement appears most satisfactory, since it gives the gas maximum opportunity to come into equilibrium with the catalyst. Since the pressure of halogen at the point of contact with the melt determines the electrode potential, and this is presumably about 1 atm regardless of the pressure applied inside, the effective halogen pressure in an electrode of this type cannot be varied.

Besides over-all design, the other important consideration in the use of halogen–graphite electrodes is the preparation of the graphite required to establish reversible conditions. This includes both initial removal of impurities and establishment of equilibrium between adsorbed and gaseous halogen. The methods described by Pankey (79) proved satisfactory. In the case of the chlorine electrode, for example, the graphite was first washed alternately in concentrated hydrochloric acid and in deionized water. It was then dried at 140° before heating *in vacuo* to 500°C. After holding the electrode at this higher temperature for several hours, chlorine gas was let into the containing vessel. Then it was re-evacuated, and the cycle of venting to chlorine followed by evacuation was repeated several times, each phase lasting about 15 minutes. After cooling in an atmosphere of flowing chlorine, the electrode was ready for use in a halide melt. Senderoff and Mellors subjected their graphite to the much more extreme temperature of 2300°C in a chlorine atmosphere. Before stable emf readings could be obtained with such electrodes most workers, including those just mentioned, have found it necessary to anodize the electrode in the molten halide until a significant quantity of gaseous halogen has been produced electrolytically. Thus Pankey, as a routine procedure, passed a current of 1 amp for three minutes before attempting emf measurements, while Senderoff and Mellors reported that attainment of equilibrium, which usually took about two hours, was hastened by electrolysis at 1 amp for 30 seconds. The electrolytic charging of chlorine electrodes, as well as their stability and reversibility, has been studied extensively and discussed in detail by Drossbach (*109*).

Although basically the same techniques apply to bromine and iodine as those just described for chlorine (all three halogens being gases at the temperatures of most molten salt studies), Pankey found it advantageous to soak his graphite rod in liquid bromine as part of the preliminary equilibration. Salstrom and Hildebrand in the late twenties and early thirties made extensive use of bromine electrodes. They reported preparation procedures (*89*) which form the basis for much of the subsequent work on halogen electrodes, including those described above.

b. *Oxygen and Oxygen-containing Mixtures.* Electrodes (r)–(u) in Table IV are examples of reference electrodes that have been reported reversible to oxygen. The electrolytes listed indicate the variety of forms the reduced species may take. Thus, in electrode (r), which was studied by Didtschenko and Rochow (*56*), the reduced oxygen becomes part of the complex silicate anions in the lead glass. The behavior of electrode (s) reported by Hill and co-workers (*63*) corresponds to a simple oxygen–oxide couple, on the other hand, since the sulfur of the solvent anion already has its maximum coordination number. Another contrast with (s) is provided by electrode (t). In spite of the fact that Al_2O_3 is the only oxygen-containing species in the melt, the potential of the oxygen electrode was reported by Rempel, Anisheva, and Khodak (*110*) *not* to be directly dependent on the concentration of alumina. Finally, by adding CO_2 to oxygen in the electrode gas, Flood, Førland, and Motzfeld (*66*) succeeded in constructing a reference electrode reversible to carbonate ion.

With the exception of the graphite in electrode (t), metals have generally been used as inert conductors for oxygen electrodes. Although platinum has most frequently been employed, other metals including gold (*111*) and silver (*64*) have proved successful catalysts. In fact, silver would seem to be an especially good choice, since numerous studies on fuel cells have shown oxygen polarization to be negligible even at high current densities when silver is used at the cathode. The well-known Bacon cell employs nickel oxide rendered semiconducting by doping with Li_2O. It therefore seems likely that this material could also be used as inert conductor in reversible oxygen electrodes.

Reversible oxygen electrodes are generally easier to construct and use than the halogen electrodes described in subsection *a*, because the preparation of the metal and its equilibration with the gas requires much less painstaking procedures than the corresponding treatment 'of graphite. In the one instance already mentioned [electrode (t)] in which the latter material was employed, the failure of the potential to respond to changes in alumina concentration suggests that oxygen, like the halogens, does not readily equilibrate with graphite.

The electrode design illustrated in Fig. 2 (p. 593) can easily be modified to include any conducting material in place of the graphite rod (B). Gas electrodes can thus be constructed according to this plan, including oxygen and mixed-gas reference electrodes.

3. Metal–Glass Systems

Electrodes like (v) and (w) of Table IV have been placed in a special category here, because glass is the only part of the electrode system that makes contact with the molten salt. Any consideration of such systems must involve the questions of electrode material and isolation simultaneously, so that this brief discussion overlaps the two principal subdivisions of the section.

At the present writing sodium is the only metal that has been reported reversible to its ions upon direct contact with a glass containing them. This is a particularly fortunate circumstance, nevertheless. For sodium is one metal that could not be used in direct contact with most melts, due to its solubility in its own salts and its chemical reactivity in melts containing other ions. Reports on the development of sodium-glass electrodes have been extensive, even though confined exclusively to the Russian literature. Those most prominently identified with the work are Delimarskii and Kolotii, whose many papers on the subject consider such aspects as the use of pure sodium vs. sodium dissolved in mercury (*112*) or tin (*113*), temperature coefficient of the potential as a function of sodium concentration (*114*), electrode design (*115*), sensitivity to changes of Na^+ concentration in the melt (*116*), etc. The electrodes developed by these workers are described as rugged, and usable in any melt containing sodium ion. The materials employed nevertheless define temperature limits which cannot be exceeded. Thus, electrode (v) is limited by the boiling point of the amalgam to temperatures below 380°C, while the softening of sodium-containing glass restricts the serviceability of all such electrode systems above 600°. Use of the sodium-conductive porcelain developed by Labrie and Lamb (149) for electrode (v) in place of glass would, if successful, extend the upper limit to the boiling point of the metal (880°C at 1 atm).

B. Electrode Isolation

General methods of electrode isolation were discussed in Section III, B, 3, a. It is the purpose of the present section to illustrate specific designs of reference electrodes incorporating these techniques.

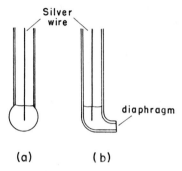

Fig. 3. All-glass reference electrode (36).

Electrodes employing fritted glass disks are particularly simple to construct. An example has already been shown in Fig. 2 (p. 593), which depicts electrode (n) of Table IV. In this particular case fritted Pyrex of medium porosity (maximum pore diameter about 15 microns) is the horizontal

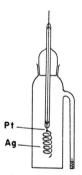

Fig. 4. Silver reference electrode for molten nitrates (93).

shaded area at the bottom of the outer jacket. Similar disks of porous silica are available, either loose or sealed into sealing tubes.

Two designs for the all-glass reference electrode (c) are illustrated in Fig. 3. In both cases the glass is very thin, having an electrical resistance

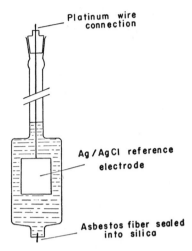

Fig. 5. Silver reference electrode for molten chlorides (*58*).

of 2000–5000 ohms in the range 350–550°C. The model shown on the right (Fig. 3b) is particularly suitable for electrode kinetic studies requiring a close approach to the working electrode.

Fig. 4 is an illustration of electrode (a), while Fig. 5 shows electrode (b). The former is made of Pyrex glass and has the asbestos fiber sealed into a side arm. An envelope of silica was used in the latter case, a much more difficult material with which to fabricate complicated designs. This accounts for its greater simplicity, the fiber being sealed through the bottom of the envelope. These examples, along with those of Figs. 3 and 6, show also various forms of silver electrodes.

The complicated design shown in Fig. 6 was used by Coriou and Dirian (*35*) in cell (e). Constructed as a reference electrode for fluoride melts, it has an outer sheath of pure graphite. The inner sheath is of silica, and contains a silver wire electrode in contact with pure AgCl. Contact from this salt to the NaCl in the outer sheath is made through an asbestos plug sealed with ZrO_2 cement. The latter salt in turn contacts the solvent by following the threads of the graphite screw-plug at the bottom of the outer sheath. The high conductivity of graphite would seem to provide a path of much lower resistance directly through the walls of the cell. Flow of current by this route, however, requires electrode reactions to occur on either side of the graphite wall, such that the total decomposition potential is about three volts. For example, if chloride were oxidized to chlorine on one side, some reduction such as sodium ion to sodium metal would have to occur at the other. This assumes, of course, that the graphite has not previously adsorbed chlorine or some other easily reducible substance.

When a *porous* graphite plug was used by Stern (*117*) to separate compartments of cells like

$$Cl_2 \mid NaCl \vdots KCl \mid Cl_2$$

it was easy for the graphite to pick up some chlorine (bubbles or dissolved gas) on each side, thus providing a conducting path with no back-emf. As mentioned in Section III,A,2, the potentials of these cells were invariably

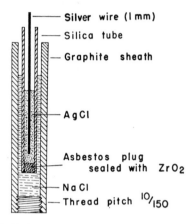

FIG. 6. Reference electrode for fluoride melts (*35*).

found to be zero, due to the much lower resistivity of the graphite path than the liquid–liquid junction in its pores. Thus the absence of any free halogen from electrode (e) undoubtedly accounts for its success.

V. Appendix: Tables of emf Values

The standard potentials listed in these tables are all taken from figures reported in the literature cited. Two ways of assigning standard potentials were explained in Section II,B,3,*a* (p. 559). Those in which the reference state is defined on the infinite dilution basis (and is therefore a hypothetical state) are designated $E_i{}^\circ$, when cation or anion fraction N_k is employed as concentration unit. The reference state in the other method is pure solvent. When this solvent is a single salt, standard potentials of electrodes reversible to its ions are designated $E_p{}^\circ$. When the solvent is a salt mixture, standard potentials of electrodes reversible to its constituent ions are designated $E_s{}^\circ$, and are calculated from

$$E = E_s{}^\circ + (RT/nF) \ln N_k$$

This equation has been used to calculate all the standard potentials designated $E_s{}^\circ$ in Table C, since for each ion measurements in a given solvent were made at only one composition. In order that the tabulated quantities might be called "standard potentials," this latter composition (solvent plus added salt) has been designated "solvent" in making the calculations for Table C. Thus, each entry refers, in principle, to a different "solvent" from all others. Actually, however, the values listed for E_s° are probably fair approximations to E_i° in the solvent at the head of each column.

TABLE A

E_p° IN PURE METAL CHLORIDES AT HIGH TEMPERATURES COMPARED WITH E_i° IN AQUEOUS SOLUTION AT 25° [a]

Order in aqueous solution	1. Aqueous	2. Molten or solid (s) metal chlorides	
	E_i° at 25° (volts)	a. E_p° at 500°C (volts)	b. E_p° at 1000°C (volts)
Li$^+$	−4.405	−3.646 (s)	−3.352
K$^+$	−4.285	−3.755 (s)	−3.155
Sr^{2+}	−4.25	−3.684 (s)	−3.333
Ca^{2+}	−4.230	−3.534 (s)	−3.208
Na$^+$	−4.074	−3.519 (s)	−3.019
Mg^{2+}	−3.73	−2.680 (s)	−2.346
Be^{2+}	−3.21	−2.144	—
Mn^{2+}	−2.54	−1.967 (s)	−1.725
Cr^{2+}	−2.27	−1.537 (s)	−1.262
Zn^{2+}	−2.123	−1.603	—
Cr^{3+}	−2.10	−1.376 (s)	−1.006
Fe^{2+}	−1.80	−1.267 (s)	−1.050
Cd^{2+}	−1.763	−1.403 (s)	−1.002
Tl$^+$	−1.696	−1.606	−1.470
Co^{2+}	−1.637	−1.140 (s)	−0.900
Ni^{2+}	−1.610	−1.070 (s)	−0.763
Sn^{2+}	−1.496	−1.320	—
Pb^{2+}	−1.486	−1.271	−1.039
Cu^{2+}	−1.023	−0.528 (s)	—
Cu^{1+}	−0.839	−1.024	−0.943
(Hg)$_2^{2+}$	−0.571	−0.597 (s)	—
Ag$^+$	−0.560	−0.896	−0.784
Pd^{2+}	−0.373	−0.457 (s)	—

[a] *Reference potentials:*   *Reference solvents:*
    1. E_i° (Cl$_2$, Cl$^-$) = 0.000   1. Water at 25°C.
    2. E_p° (Cl$_2$, Cl$^-$) = 0.000   2. Pure metal chlorides; a. at 500°C. b. at 1000°C.

Methods of determination:
    1. Galvanic cells and thermodynamic data as summarized in the literature.
    2. Calculated from thermodynamic data.
Source: Hamer, Malmberg, and Rubin (*1*).

The reference potentials for the bromine and iodine electrodes in Table C are based on the decomposition potentials of the pure sodium halides. In each case $E_p°$ for the sodium electrode was taken as -3.39 volt, the same as its value in pure sodium chloride when $E_p°$ for the chlorine electrode is taken as zero.

TABLE B

$E_i°$ IN ALKALI CHLORIDE SOLVENTS COMPARED WITH $E_p°$

Order in pure chlorides	1. Pure chlorides $E_p°$ at 800° (volts)	2. KCl–NaCl solvent a. $E_i°$ at 800° (volts)	b. $E_i°$ at 450° (volts)	3. KCl–LiCl solvent $E_i°$ at 450° (volts)
Mg^{2+}	-2.460	—	—	-2.796
Mn^{2+}	-1.807	-2.010	-2.135	-2.065
V^{2+}	-1.566	—	—	-1.749
Zn^{2+}	-1.476	-1.655	-1.835	-1.782
Tl^+	-1.473	—	—	-1.586
Cr^{2+}	-1.352 (s)	-1.560	-1.715	-1.641
Sn^{2+}	-1.259	-1.174	-1.315	-1.298
Cd^{2+}	-1.193	-1.400	-1.535	-1.532
Fe^{2+}	-1.118	-1.330	-1.465	-1.387
Cr^{3+}	-1.113	-1.205	-1.430	-1.376
Pb^{2+}	-1.112	-1.196	-1.352	-1.317
Co^{2+}	-0.977	-1.120	-1.277	-1.207
Cu^{1+}	-0.970	-1.076	-1.145	-1.067
Ni^{2+}	-0.875	—	—	-1.011
Ag^+	-0.826	-0.820	-0.905	-0.853
Pd^{2+}	-0.331	—	—	-0.430

Reference potentials:
1. $E_p°$ (Cl_2, Cl^-) = 0.000
2 & 3. $E_s°$ (Cl_2, Cl^-) = 0.000,
 where s refers to pure solvent.

Reference solvents:
1. Pure metal chlorides at 800°C.
2. KCl–NaCl equimolar mixture:
 a. At 800°C.; b. At 450°C.
3. KCl–LiCl eutectic at 450°C

Methods of determination:
1. Calculated from thermodynamic data.
2a. Measured against Ag^+, Ag reference electrode.
2b. Extrapolated from measurements between 650 and 900°C.
3. Measured against Pt^{2+}, Pt reference electrode.

Sources:
1. Hamer, Malmberg, and Rubin. (1).
2. Flengas and Ingraham (45).
3. Laitinen and Liu (33).

TABLE C

Standard Potentials in Bromides and Iodides Compared with Chlorides at 700°C

Order in pure chlorides	1. Chlorides			2. Bromides			3. Iodides		
	a. Pure chlorides $E_p°$ at 700° (volts)	b. NaCl-KCl-SrCl₂ $E_s°$ at 700° (volts)	c. NaCl-AlCl₃ $E_s°$ at 700° (volts)	a. Pure bromides $E_p°$ at 700° (volts)	b. NaBr-KBr $E_s°$ at 700° (volts)	c. NaBr-AlBr₃ $E_s°$ at 700° (volts)	a. Pure iodides $E_p°$ at 700° (volts)	b. NaI $E_s°$ at 700° (volts)	c. NaI-AlI₃ $E_s°$ at 700° (volts)
Na^+	−3.39	−3.39	—	−3.39	−3.39	—	−3.39	−3.39	—
Mn^{2+}	−1.88	−1.89	—	−1.87	−2.04	—	−2.02	−2.29	—
Al^{3+}	−1.61	−1.68	−1.79	−1.61	−1.67	−1.77	−1.67	−1.72	−1.75
Tl^+	−1.47	−1.49	−1.35	−1.73	−1.78	—	−1.99	−1.98	—
Zn^{2+}	−1.43	−1.47	−1.37	−1.54	−1.80	−1.54	−1.85	−1.91	—
Cd^{2+}	−1.28	−1.31	−1.26	−1.50	−1.60	−1.50	−1.77	−1.77	−1.64
Pb^{2+}	−1.12	−1.12	−1.10	−1.32	−1.34	−1.28	−1.57	−1.53	−1.49
Sn^{2+}	−1.08	−1.03	—	−1.17	−1.24	−1.20	−1.61	−1.57	−1.51
Co^{2+}	−0.97	−0.95	−0.85	−1.09	−1.30	−1.08	−1.15	−1.45	−1.17
Hg^{2+}	−0.86	−0.79	−0.78	−0.95	−0.96	−1.01	−1.21	−1.17	−1.19
Ag^+	−0.84	−0.73	−0.76	−1.14	−1.12	−1.00	−1.65	−1.46	−1.48
Cu^+	−0.74	−0.89	−0.73	−1.10	−1.04	−1.07	−1.41	−1.42	−1.32
Bi^{3+}	−0.64	−0.60	−0.68	−0.85	−0.81	−0.86	−1.25	−1.21	−1.33
Sb^{3+}	−0.49	—	−0.75	−0.83		−1.01	−1.09	−1.10	−1.15

Reference potentials:
  1a. $E_p°$ (Cl_2, Cl^-) = 0.000
  1b. and c. $E_s°$ (Cl_2, Cl^-) = 0.000
  2a. $E_p°$ (Br_2, Br^-) = −0.41
  2b. and c. $E_s°$ (Br_2, Br^-) = −0.41
  3a. $E_p°$ (I_2, I^-) = −0.97
  3b. and c. $E_s°$ (I_2, I^-) = −0.97

Reference solvents:
  1a, 2a, and 3a. Pure metal halides
  1b. NaCl-KCl-SrCl₂ + 10 mole % metal chloride
  1c, 2c, and 3c. NaX-AlX₃ + 5 mole per cent metal halide (X = Cl, Br, I)
  2b. NaBr-KBr + 10 mole per cent metal bromide
  3b. NaI + 5 mole per cent metal iodide

Method of determination: Decomposition potential of molten solvent at/or extrapolated to 700°C.
Source: Delimarskii (128).

REFERENCES

1. Hamer, W. H., Malmberg, M. S., and Rubin, B., *J. Electrochem. Soc.* **103**, 8 (1956).

2. Laity, R. W., *J. Am. Chem. Soc.* **79**, 1849 (1957).

2a. De Groot, S. R., "Thermodynamics of Irreversible Processes." North Holland Publ., Amsterdam, 1958; Interscience Publ. Inc., N. Y. (1958).

2b. Prigogine, I., and Defay, R., translated by Everett, D. H. "Chemical Thermodynamics," Longmans, Green, New York, 1954.

2c. Denbigh, K. G., "Thermodynamics of the Steady State." Wiley, New York, 1951.

3. Guggenheim, E. A., *J. Phys. Chem.* **33**, 842 (1929).

4. Laity, R. W., *J. Chem. Phys.* **30**, 682 (1959).

5. Onsager, L., *Ann N.Y. Acad. Sci.* **46**, 241 (1945).

6. Laity, R. W., *J. Phys. Chem.* **63**, 80 (1959).

7. Laity, R. W., *Ann. N.Y. Acad. Sci.* **79**, 997 (1960).

8. Klemm, A., Hintenberger, H., and Hoernes, P., *Z. Naturforsch.* **2a**, 245 (1947).

9. Aziz, P. M., and Wetmore, F. E. W., *Can. J. Chem.* **30**, 779 (1952).

10. Duke, F. R., Laity, R. W., and Owens, B., *J. Electrochem. Soc.* **104**, 299 (1957).

11. Duke, F. R., and Fleming, R. A., *J. Electrochem. Soc.* **106**, 130 (1959).

12. Lorenz, R., and Kaufler, F., Elektrochemie geschmolzener Salze, *in* "Handbuch der angewandten physikalischen Chemie" (G. Bredig, ed.) Vol. 11, Part I. Barth, Leipzig, 1909.

13. Sundheim, B. R., *J. Phys. Chem.* **60**, 1381 (1956).

14. Tamman, G., *Z. anorg. u. allgem. Chem.* **133**, 267 (1924).

15. Grube, G., and Rau, E. A., *Z. Elektrochem.* **40**, 352 (1934).

16. Guggenheim, E. A., *J. Phys. Chem.* **34**, 1758 (1930).

17. Temkin, M. I., *Zhur. Fiz. Khim.* **20**, 105 (1946).

18. Førland, T., "On the Properties of Some Mixtures of Fused Salts." Norges Tekniske Vitenskapsakademi, Oslo, Series 2, No. 4 (1957).

19. Suchy, R., *Z. anorg. Chem.* **27**, 152 (1901).

20. Salstrom, E. J., *J. Am. Chem. Soc.* **56**, 1272 (1934).

21. Stern, K. H., *J. Phys. Chem.* **60**, 679 (1956).

22. Senderoff, S., and Mellors, G. W., *Rev. Sci. Instr.* **29**, 151 (1958).

23. Wachter, A., and Hildebrand, J. H., *J. Am. Chem. Soc.* **52**, 4655 (1930).

24. Hildebrand, J. H., and Rühle, G. C., *J. Am. Chem. Soc.* **49**, 722 (1927).

25. Salstrom, E. J., *J. Am. Chem. Soc.* **56**, 1272 (1934).

26. Conway, B. E., "Electrochemical Data," pp. 269 and 279. Elsevier, Amsterdam, 1952.

27. Elkins, H. B., and Forbes, G. S., *J. Am. Chem. Soc.* **55**, 3250 (1933).

28. Pletenev, S. A., and Rozov, V. N., *Acta Physicochim. U.R.S.S.* **7**, 339 (1937).

29. Brewer, L., *in* "The Chemistry and Metallurgy of Miscellaneous Materials" (L. L. Quill, ed.). McGraw-Hill, New York, 1950.

30. Jellinek, K., *Lehrbuch phys. Chem.* **4**, 574 (1933).

31. Antipin, P. F., Alabyshev, A. F., Artamonov, B. P., Barzakovskii, N. A., and Belozerskii, V. B., "Electrokhimia rasplavlennykh solei," p. 187. O.N.T.I., 1937.

32. Delimarskii, Yu. K. *Zhur. Fiz. Khim.* **24**, 875 (1950).

33. Laitinen, H. A., and Liu, C. H., *J. Am. Chem. Soc.* **80**, 1015 (1958).

34. Pleskov, V. A., *Uspekhi Khim.* **16**, 254 (1947).

35. Coriou, H., Dirian, J., and Hure, J., *J. chim. phys.* **52**, 479 (1955).

36. Bockris, J. O'M., Hills, G. J., Inman, D., and Young, L., *J. Sci. Instr.* **33**, 438 (1956).

37. N. A. Lange, ed., "Handbook of Chemistry," 7th ed. Handbook Publ., Sandusky, Ohio, 1949.

38. Richards, T. W., and Meldrum, W. B., *J. Am. Chem. Soc.* **39**, 1816 (1917).

39. Black, E. D., and De Vries, T., *Anal. Chem.* **27**, 906 (1955).

40. Gruzensky, P. M., *J. Electrochem. Soc.* **103**, 171 (1956).

41. Laitinen, H. A., and Pankey, J. W., *J. Am. Chem. Soc.* **81**, 1053 (1959).

42. Senderoff, S., and Brenner, A., *J. Electrochem. Soc.* **101**, 31 (1954).

43. Yang, L., and Hudson, R. G., *Trans. AIME* **215**, 589 (1959).

44. Rempel, S. I., and Ozeryanya, D. N., *Zhur. Fiz. Khim.* **25**, 1181 (1951).

45. Flengas, S. N., and Ingraham, T. R., *J. Electrochem. Soc.* **106**, 714 (1959).

46. Steinberg, M., and Nachtrieb, N. H., *J. Am. Chem. Soc.* **72**, 3558 (1950).

47. Nachtrieb, N. H., and Steinberg, J., *J. Am. Chem. Soc.* **70**, 2613 (1948).

48. Hissink, D. J., *Z. phys. Chem.* **32**, 537 (1900).

49. Hills, G. J., Inman, D., and Young, L., "Techniques of Studying Electrode Processes in Fused Salts Below 1000°" (CITCE VIII). Madrid, 1956; Butterworths, London, 1958.

50. Pound, G. M., Fullmer, J., Roland, E., and Pocacha, J., U.S. Atomic Energy Comm. Rept. No. AECD-3700 (1954).

51. Laitinen, H. A., Osteryoung, R. A., and Ferguson, W. S., *J. Electrochem. Soc.* **104**, 516 (1957).

52. Bredig, M. A., Johnson, J. W., and Smith, W. T., Jr., *J. Am. Chem. Soc.* **77**, 307 (1955).

53. Seybolt, A. U., and Burke, J. E., "Procedures in Experimental Metallurgy." Wiley, New York, 1953.

54. Livey, D. T., and Murray, P., *in* "Physicochemical Measurements at High Temperatures" (J. O'M. Bockris, J. D. MacKenzie, and J. L. White, eds.) Academic Press, New York, 1959.

55. Delimarskii, Yu. K., and Kolotii, A. A., *Zhur. Fiz. Khim.* **23**, 90 (1949).

56. Didtschenko, R., and Rochow, E. C., *J. Am. Chem. Soc.* **76**, 3291 (1954).

57. Flengas, S. N., and Ingraham, T. R., *Can. J. Chem.* **35**, 1254 (1957).

58. Flengas, S. N., and Ingraham, T. R., *Can. J. Chem.* **36**, 780 (1958).

59. Flengas, S. N., and Ingraham, T. R., *Can. J. Chem.* **36**, 1103 (1958).

60. Flengas, S. N., and Ingraham, T. R., *Can. J. Chem.* **36**, 1662 (1958).

61. Flengas, S. N., and Ingraham, T. R., *Ann. N.Y. Acad. Sci.* **79**, 853 (1960).

62. Malkin, V. I., Khokhlov, S. F., and Shvartsman, L. A., *Intern. J. Appl. Radiation and Isotopes* **2**, 19 (1957).

63. Hill, D. G., Porter, B., and Gillespie, A. S., Jr., *J. Electrochem. Soc.* **105**, 408 (1958).

64. Rose, B., Davis, G., and Ellingham, H. J. T., *Discussions Faraday Soc.* **4**, 154 (1948).

64a. De Vries, R. C., General Electric Research Laboratory Report MD-31, Schenectady, New York, July, 1959.

65. Grjotheim, K., *Z. physik. Chem. (Frankfurt)* **11**, 150 (1957).

66. Flood, H., Førland, T., and Motzfeldt, K., *Acta Chem. Scand.* **6**, 257 (1952).

67. Grimes, W. R., *J. Phys. Chem.* **62**, 862 (1958).

68. Stern, K. H., and Carlton, J. K., *J. Phys. Chem.* **58**, 965 (1954).

68a. Janz, G. J., and Lorenz, M. R., *Rev. Sci. Instr.* **31**, 18 (1960).

69. Stern, K. H., *J. Phys. Chem.* **63**, 741 (1959).

70. Piontelli, R., and Montanelli, G., *J. Chem. Phys.* **22**, 1781 (1954).

71. Cuthbertson, J. W., and Waddington, J., *Trans. Faraday Soc.* **32**, 745 (1936).

72. Delimarskii, Yu. K., and Grigorenko, F. F., *Ukrain. Khim. Zhur.* **21**, 561 (1955).

73. Yim, E. W., and Feinleib, M., *J. Electrochem. Soc.* **104**, 622 (1957).

74. Campbell, I. E., "High Temperature Technology." Wiley, New York, 1956.

75. Grahame, D. C., *Chem. Revs.* 41, 441 (1947).

76. Roe, D. K., and Laitinen, H. A., Tech. Rept. No. 6 to OOR and Diamond Ordnance Fuze Lab. (D. K. Roe, Ph.D. Thesis, University of Illinois, Urbana, Illinois, 1959).

77. Piontelli, R., Sternheim, G., and Francini, M., *Compt. Rend. acad. sci.* 242, 1301 (1956).

78. Bockris, J. O'M., and Conway, B. E., *in* "Modern Aspects of Electrochemistry" (J. O'M. Bockris, ed.), p. 253. Academic Press, New York, 1954.

79. Pankey, J. W., Ph.D. Thesis, University of Illinois, 1958.

80. Lyalikov, Y. S., and Karmizin, K., *Zavodskaya Lab.* 14, 144 (1948).

81. Flengas, S. N., *J. Chem. Soc.*, p. 534 (1956).

82. Flood, H., and Førland, T., *Discussions Faraday Soc.* 1, 302 (1947).

83. Agar, J. N., and Bowden, F. P., *Proc. Roy. Soc.* A169, 206 (1939).

84. Chovnyk, N. G., *Zhur. Fiz. Khim.* 30, 277 (1956).

85. Laitinen, H. A., Liu, C. H., and Ferguson, W. S., *Anal. Chem.* 30, 1266 (1958).

86. Zosimovich, D. P., and Tsimmergakl, V. A., *Ukrain. Khim. Zhur.* 15, 351 (1949).

87. Delimarskii, Yu. K., *Uspekhi Khim.* 23, 766 (1954).

88. Antipin, L. N., and Tyurin, N. G., *Zhur. Fiz. Khim.* 32, 640 (1958).

89. Salstrom, E. J., and Hildebrand, J. H., *J. Am. Chem. Soc.* 52, 4641 (1930).

90. Verdieck, R. G., and Yntema, L. F., *J. Phys. Chem.* 46, 344 (1942).

91. Senderoff, S., and Brenner, A., *J. Electrochem. Soc.* 101, 16 (1954).

92. McFee, R. B., *Rev. Sci. Instr.* 23, 52 (1952).

93. Flengas, S. N., and Rideal, E., *Proc. Roy. Soc.* A233, 443 (1956).

94. Motzfeldt, K., *in* "Physicochemical Measurements at High Temperature" (J. O' M. Bockris, J. D. MacKenzie, and J. L. White, eds.), p. 47. Academic Press, New York, 1959.

95. Carson, W. N., Jr., Michelson, C. E., and Koyama, K., *Anal. Chem.* 27, 472 (1955).

96. Flengas, S. N., and Ingraham, T. R., *Can. J. Chem.* 35, 1139 (1957).

97. Holtan, H., *Tidsskr. Kjemi Bergvesen Met.* 12, 5 (1952).

98. Sundheim, B. R., and Rosenstreich, J., *J. Phys. Chem.* 63, 419 (1959).

99. Aten, A. H. W., den Hertog, H. J., and Westenberg, L., *Trans. Electrochem. Soc.* 47, 265 (1925).

100. Brewer, L., *in* "Chemistry and Metallurgy of Miscellaneous Materials" (L. L. Quill, ed.) McGraw-Hill, New York, 1950.

101. Panish, M. B., Newton, R. F., Grimes, W. R., and Blankenship, F. F., *J. Phys. Chem.* 63, 668 (1959).

102. Panish, M. B., Newton, R. F., Grimes, W. R., and Blankenship, F. F., *J. Phys. Chem.* 62, 1325 (1958).

103. Marsland, D. M., *Dissertation Abstr.* 19, 1222 (1958).

104. Randles, J. E. B., and White, W., *Z. Elektrochem.* 59, 666 (1958).

105. Laitinen, H. A., and Ferguson, W. S., *Anal. Chem.* 29, 4 (1957).

106. Bruckenstein, S., and Gruen, D., Private communication from H. A. Laitinen.

107. Smirnov, S., Palguyev, and Ivanovski, L. E., *Zhur. Fiz. Khim.* 29, 772 (1955).

108. Lantratov, M. F., and Alabyshev, A. F., *Zhur. Priklad. Khim.* 26, 263 (1953).

109. Drossbach, P., *J. Electrochem. Soc.* 103, 700 (1956).

110. Rempel, S. I., Anisheva, N. A., and Khodak, L. P., *Doklady Akad. Nauk.* S.S.S.R. 97, 859 (1954).

111. Lux, H., *Z. Elektrochem.* 52, 220 (1948).

112. Delimarskii, Yu. K., and Khaimovich, R. S., *Ukrain. Khim. Zhur.* 15, 77 (1949).

113. Delimarskii, Yu. K., and Kolotii, A. A., *Ukrain. Khim. Zhur.* 16, 438 (1950).

114. Delimarskii, Yu. K., and Kolotii, A. A., *Zhur. Fiz. Khim.* **28**, 1169 (1954).
115. Delimarskii, Yu. K., and Kolotii, A. A., *Zavodskaya Lab.* **22**, 25 (1956).
116. Kolotii, A. A., *Ukrain. Khim. Zhur.* **20**, 502 (1954).
117. Stern, K. H., *J. Phys. Chem.* **63**, 741 (1959).
118. Hildebrand, J. H., and Salstrom, E. J., *J. Am. Chem. Soc.* **54**, 4257 (1932).
118a. Janz, G. J., Colom, F., and Saegusa, F., *J. Electrochem. Soc.* **107**, 581 (1960).
119. Kolotii, A. A., *Zhur. Fiz. Khim.* **30**, 508 (1956).
120. Salstrom, E. J., and Hildebrand, J. H., *J. Am. Chem. Soc.* **25**, 4650 (1930).
121. Stern, K. H., *J. Phys. Chem.* **60**, 1443 (1956).
122. Delimarskii, Yu. K., and Izbekov, V. A., *Zapiski Inst. Khim. Akad. Nauk Ukr. R.S.R.* **3**, 541 (1936).
123. Delimarskii, Yu. K., and Khaimovich, R. S., *Ukrain. Khim. Zhur.* **15**, 340 (1949).
124. Delimarskii, Yu. K., and Kolotii, A. A., *Ukrain. Khim. Zhur.* **16**, 594 (1950).
125. Plotnikov, S. A., Kirichenko, V. A., and Fortunatov, E. I., *Zapiski Inst. Khim., Akad. Nauk Ukr. R.S.R.* **7**, 159 (1940).
126. Oppenheimer, F., *Z. anorg. u. allgem. Chem.* **161**, 183 (1927).
127. Lantratov, M. F., and Alabyshev, A. F., *Zhur. Priklad. Khim.* **26**, 353 (1953).
128. Delimarskii, Yu. K., *Zhur. Fiz. Khim.* **29**, 28 (1955).
129. Drossbach, P., and Petrick, P., *Z. Elektrochem.* **58**, 95 (1954).
130. Markov, B. F., Delimarskii, Yu. K., and Panchenko, P. D., *Zhur. Fiz. Khim.* **28**, 1987 (1954).
131. Markov, B. F., Delimarskii, Yu. K., and Panchenko, P. D., *Zhur. Fiz. Khim.* **29**, 51 (1955).
132. Parissakis, G., and Treadwell, W. D., *Helv. Chim. Acta* **38**, 1749 (1955).
133. Rempel, S. I., *Doklady Akad. Nauk S.S.S.R.* **74**, 331 (1950).
134. Wachter, A., and Hildebrand, J. H., *J. Am. Chem. Soc.* **52**, 4655 (1930).
135. Izbekov, V. A., *Ukrain. Khim. Zhur.* **20**, 14 (1954).
136. Goodwin, H. M., *Trans. Am. Electrochem. Soc.* **21**, 105 (1912).
137. Gordon, C. M., *Z. physik. Chem.* **28**, 302 (1899).
138. Karpatscheff, S., and Patzug, W., *Z. physik. Chem.* **173**, 383 (1935).
139. Hill, D. G., and Porter, B., *Abstr. 126th Meeting, Am. Chem. Soc., Paper No. 115* ,New York, 1954.
140. Csaki, P., and Ditzel, A., *Glastech. Ber.* **18**, 33, 65 (1940).
141. Lux, H., *Z. Elektrochem.* **45**, 303 (1939).
142. Piontelli, R., and Sternheim, G., *J. Chem. Phys.* **23**, 1358 (1955).
143. Skovets, E. M., and Kavetskii, N. S., *Zhur. Obshchei Khim.* **10**, 1858 (1940).
144. Salstrom, E. J., Kew, T. J., and Powel, T. M., *J. Am. Chem. Soc.* **58**, 1848 (1936).
145. Hauffe, K., and Vierk, A. L., *Z. Elektrochem.* **53**, 151 (1949).
146. Hildebrand, J. H., and Rühle, G. C., *J. Am. Chem. Soc.* **49**, 722 (1927).
147. Liu, C. H., Ph.D. Thesis, University of Illinois, Urbana, Illinois, 1957.
148. Lantratov, F. M., and Alabyshev, A. F., *Zhur. Priklad. Khim.* **27**, 722 (1954).
149. Labrie, R. J., and Lamb, V. A., *J. Electrochem. Soc.* **106**, 895 (1959).

Author Index

Numbers in parentheses are reference numbers and indicate that an author's work is referred to although his name is not cited in the text. Numbers in italics show the page on which the complete reference is listed.

A

Abel, E., 146 (62), *175*
Abichandani, C. T., 290 (115), *319*, 358, *388*
Ackerman, P., 335 (43), *385*
Acree, S. F., 55 (84), *70*, 108 (113, 114, 115), 110 (125), 111 (125), 120 (214, 215), *123, 124, 126*, 129, 159 (130), 160, *174, 177*, 210 (93), 211 (93), *228*, 398, 399 (36), *408*
Adams, R. N., 308 (165), *320*
Adamson, A. W., 147 (79), *176*
Adell, B., 307, *320*
Adrian, R. H., 469, *519*
Afanasiev, A. L., 207, 218 (87), *228*
Afans'ev, S. K., 349 (117), *387*
Agar, J. N., 75 (1), *121*, 162 (140), *177*, 576 (83), 577 (83), 579 (83), *605*
Akai, N., 119 (189), *125*, 324 (1), *384*
Akerlöf, G., 225 (151), *227, 229*, 404, *409*
Alabyshev, A. F., 566 (31), 570 (108, 127), 576 (108, 127), 577 (108, 127, 148), 594, *603, 605*
Aladjalova, N., 111 (142), *124*
Alder, B. J., 34 (15), *68*
Aleksandrova, A. M., 349 (115), *387*, 440 (13), 450 (13), *460*
Alexander, J. T., 471, 474 (30), *519*
Allen, D. S., 119 (202), *126*
Allen, P. L., 379, *391*
Allgood, R. W., 224 (139), *229*
Allmand, A. J., 335, *386*
Amberson, W. R., 516, *522*
Amis, E. S., 242 (43), *268*
Ammar, I. A., 76 (26), *121*
Anderegg, G., 146 (61), 147 (61), 148 (61), *175*
Anderson, E., 355 (150), 356 (150), *388*
Anderson, J. S., 282 (92), 283 (92), *318*

Anderson, P. A., 457, *462*
Anisheva, N. A., 570 (110), 576 (110), 577 (110), 588 (110), 595, *605*
Ansler, H., 219 (117), *229*
Anson, F. C., 111 (137), *124*
Anthanasiu, G., 219 (115), *229*
Antipin, L. N., 570 (88), 579 (88), *605*
Antipin, P. F., 566 (31), *603*
Archibald, E. H., 148 (82), *176*
Argersinger, W. J., 427 (82), *432*
Argo, W. L., 458 (106), *463*
Armstrong, A. M., 147 (80), *176*
Armstrong, G., 89 (63), 90 (68), 110 (129, 130), *122, 124*
Artamonov, B. P., 566 (31), *603*
Astrup, P., 501, *521*
Aten, A. H. W., 88 (60), 111 (141), *122, 124*, 570 (99), 576 (99), 585, *605*
Atkinson, R. H., 108 (118), *124*
Aubrey, J., 117 (175), *125*
Audubert, R., 83, *122*
Auerbach, Fr., 272, *317*
Austen, D. E. G., 369 (232), *391*
Austin, J. M., 196, 197, *227*
Avseevich, G. P., 338 (68), 348, 349 (99), 351, *386, 387*
Awad, S. A., 360 (176, 177), *389*
Ayers, A. D., 412 (20), *431*
Aziz, P. M., 537, *603*

B

Baars, E., 77 (35), 90 (35), *122*
Babcock, R. F., 429, *432*
Bacarella, A. L., 265, *269*
Baer, R. F., 495 (80), 497 (80), 499 (80), 500 (80), *520*
Baker, L. E., 281, 302, 307, 314, 315, *318*
Ball, J. M., 508 (141), *522*

H

Subject Index

A

Accuracy of measurement, 2
Acetate-reversible electrodes, 171–172, 497
Acetic acid-acetic anhydride, electrodes in, 451
Acetic acid, anhydrous, electrodes in,
  calomel, 449, 450
  chloranil, 448
  glass, 450, 451
  hydrogen, 447, 451
  lead-lead acetate, 449–450
  mercury-mercurous acetate, 449–450
    mercurous sulphate, 447
  quinhydrone, 448, 450
  silver-silver chloride, 448, 449, 450
  standard potentials of, 448
Acetone, anhydrous, electrodes in,
  cadmium amalgam, 444
  calomel, 443
  hydrogen, 442, 443
  mercury-mercurous iodide, 444
  quinhydrone, 442
  silver-silver chloride, 442, 443
  sodium amalgam-sodium iodide, 443
Acetonitrile, electrodes in, 445, 446
  calomel, 445
  glass, 446
  hydrogen, 446
  silver-silver chloride, 445, 446
  -silver nitrate, 446
  thallium amalgam, 445
Acidic organic solvents, electrodes in, 447–452
Action potentials, biological systems, 465, 472–476
Activation energy of electrode processes, 16, 75, 80–82, 276, 365, 378
Activity coefficients,
  correlation with emf data, 294
  discussion of interpretation of, 36–42
  mean ionic, definition of, 11, 12
  mole fractional, molal and molar, 195–196

quinone and hydroquinone, table, 294
  rational, 40
  single ionic, indeterminacy of, 11, 12
  equations for, and theoretical treat-
    ments of, 36–42
Activity,
  definition of, 9, 11, 527, 541
  ion fraction and, in fused salts, 543, 547
  of nonelectrolytic solute, 275, 293–296
    salting out effect, 275–276, 293–298
  of single ionic species, 11, 238, 531
  of water, 39, 72, 193, 194, 324, 400, 418
    in methanol-water mixtures, 324
  measurement with ion-selective mem-
    branes, 411, 428
  relation to fugacity, 528–531
  solubility product, *see also under* spe-
    cific substances, 7
Adsorption
  at surfaces of solids, general, 62
  of gases on solids, 83
  of hydrogen atoms, 24, 72, 73, 74, 77,
    79–84, 88
  of ions, 20
    on glass, 234
    on mercury, 20–23
    on quartz, 234
  of nonelectrolytic impurities, 24
  potentials, 234
  specific, 22, 23
  Volta, 20
Adsorption electrode, 234
Alkali metal halides,
  device for fusing, 202
  hydrolysis of, 202, 203, 572
  purification of, 201–203
  solvents in fused systems, 569–572, 601,
    602
  vapour state association of, 528
Amalgam concentration cells, 438
Amides, aliphatic, electrodes in, 452–454
Ammonia, electrodes in,
  cadmium amalgam, 456
  electron electrode, 456

L

Lead
  hydrogen overpotential at, 395
    dependence on purity, 395
  passivation in sulphuric acid solutions,
    399
  thermodynamic instability, 395
Lead accumulator cell, 403
Lead acetate, in platinizing solutions,
  107
Lead amalgam, 395, 396–397, 398
  chemical potential of lead, in, 396, 398
  dispensing, 397
  preparation, 397
Lead amalgam electrodes,
  -lead sulphate, 396–399
  -lead acetate, 450
Lead amalgam-mercurous sulphate standard cell, 396
Lead chloride (fused) formation cell, 550
Lead dioxide,
  α and β forms of, 402
  anodic formation of, 399, 402
  electrode potential discrepancies, 403
  non-stoichiometry of, 402
  preparation of, 399–400
Lead dioxide-lead sulphate electrode,
  395–396, 399–403, 407
Lead electrodes,
  -lead chloride(fused) 537–540, 550–552,
    554, 548, 576, 600–602
  -lead nitrate, 455
  -lead sulphate, 396–399
Lead sulphate,
  hydrolysis, 394
  preparation, 400
  solubility, 393
Lennard-Jones, theory of adsorption, 83
Lewis acids and bases, 286
Lewis and Sargent equation, 54, 552
Light, velocity of, 66
Lippmann equation, 20
Liquid junction potentials, 49, 50, 51, 53,
  439, 456
  calomel reference electrodes, 157–162
  discussion, biological studies, 467–468
  elimination by glass electrodes, 262
  fused salt systems, 532–537, 589, 540,

542, 548–553, 556–557, 567, 582–583,
  590, 597–599
  general equations for, 549–551
  tests of, 552–553
  Henderson equation, 54, 456
  indeterminacy of, 238, 548
  Lewis and Sargent equation for, 54,
    552
Liquid junctions, 157–162, 238, 239, 262,
  456, 467–468, 532–537, 539–540, 542,
  548–553, 556–557, 567, 582–583, 590,
  597–599
  dissimilar solvents, 439
  classification of, 53–55
  constrained, Planck integration of, 416
Lithium glass, for electrodes, 243, 247
Local action, 329

M

Magnesium electrodes,
  -magnesium bromide, 445
  -magnesium perchlorate, 445
Manganese dioxide electrodes, 330–331
Maximum electrical work, 6
Measurement of emf., 5, 14, 30, 57–59
Mechanical equivalent of heat, 66
Mediators in oxidations-reductions, 278,
  280
Membrane,
  ion-selective, 540, 541, 568
  collodion-based, 412, 423, 425
  montmorillonite, 429
  mounting, 422
  multilayer, 413, 430
  synthetic resins, 413, 423, 425, 426
Membrane electrodes,
  aims and definition of, 411, 412
  applications, 427–428
  concentration gradients, and, 423, 424
  development, 412–413, 424–425
  limits of performance, 428
  low resistivity, 422
  non-ideal, calibration, 418–422
  porosity and permeability, 424
  selectivity, cations and anions, 412, 428,
    429
  stirring of solutions, 423, 424
  time-dependence of potential, 424
  zeolitic, 412, 424, 425, 429